Symbol	Meaning	Page
d	domain	45
r	range	45
f	function	48
$f(x)$	value of a function	48
$[x]$	greatest integer $\leq x$	52
$f \circ g$	composite function	55
I_f	identity function	56
f^{-1}	inverse function of f	57
$\pm$	plus or minus	75
i or $\sqrt{-1}$	imaginary unit	79
k	constant of variation	88
$\doteq$	is approximately equal to	90
$\equiv$	is equivalent to	92
iff	if and only if	92
$\therefore$	therefore	93
$\begin{vmatrix} a_{11} & a_{12} \\ a_{21} & a_{22} \end{vmatrix}$	determinant	108
$s(n)$	sequence function	122
s_n	sequence	123
$\sum$	sigma notation for summation	124
∞	infinity	124
S_n	sum of first n terms	125
$\lim\limits_{n \to \infty} S_n$	sum of infinite geometric series	133
$n!$	product of all positive integers from 1 to n	136
π	$3.1415926\ldots$	141
sin	sine function over R	145
cos	cosine function over R	145
tan	tangent function over R	145
cot	cotangent function over R	145
sec	secant function over R	145
csc	cosecant function over R	145
$\overset{\frown}{AP}$	length of arc AP	160
C_A	corresponding arc	169

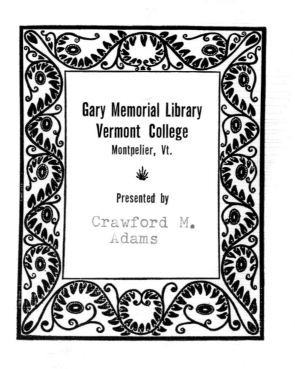

Contemporary College Algebra and Trigonometry

Contemporary College Algebra and Trigonometry

William A. Gager
PROFESSOR OF MATHEMATICS
UNIVERSITY OF FLORIDA

The Macmillan Company, New York
Collier-Macmillan Limited, London

First Printing

Library of Congress catalog card number: 68-10294

THE MACMILLAN COMPANY, NEW YORK
COLLIER-MACMILLAN CANADA, LTD., TORONTO, ONTARIO

Printed in the United States of America

Preface

Authors differ, of course, in what they think the content and the organization of a good course in modern algebra and trigonometry should be. This is a fortunate circumstance. It is an indication that improvements will continue to be forthcoming. In the integration of algebra and trigonometry there continues to exist a need for better continuity, for more clarity of content, and for improvements in the presentation of materials.

From the beginning to the end of this book the reader will find that I have given careful attention to the recommendations of the Commission of Mathematics of the College Entrance Board, the Committee on the Undergraduate Mathematical Program of the Mathematical Association of America, and to the content changes suggested by the School Mathematics Study Group.

My primary aim in *Contemporary College Algebra and Trigonometry* has been to present, in correct and mathematically sound fashion, those concepts, principles, and procedures of algebra and trigonometry that will guarantee a solid foundation for advanced work in mathematics. Rigor has been closely adhered to here because it is the very heart of mathematics; on the other hand, I believe that it has not been pushed to the point where it will drive any serious-minded student away from mathematics.

Another aim in writing this text has been to organize and arrange the material and format in ways that will encourage, motivate, and help students to gain the maximum possible insight into, and comprehension of, the basic concepts and principles of college algebra and trigonometry. The outcome of this aim is vitally important in this day when students are more and more expected to work out their destiny in mathematics primarily by their own efforts.

A special feature of this textbook is the Exercises, which, with minor exceptions, are of a dual nature: that is, an even-numbered problem that follows an odd-numbered problem in an Exercise involves the same principles. This means that an ample coverage of the text material can be obtained by assigning either the even-numbered or the odd-numbered problems in an Exercise.

However, this special provision has been incorporated for a far more important reason. It is well known that less advanced mathematics students too often experience complete frustration in their attempt to develop algebraic and trigonometric proofs and justify trigonometric identities. To make the maximum possible help available to such students when they are assigned even-numbered problems that call for the development of proofs and the justifying of identities, these same operations for odd-numbered problems are worked out in the answer section of the text.

Another feature of this book is the careful attention that has been given to keying by number each section, subsection, definition, axiom, principle, property, theorem, and example. The number keying makes possible a detailed and easy-to-read scheme for the entire book. The keying also enables the reader to refer back by number to each basic idea that has been used previously and to find it easily. For example, one can quickly learn that Definition 7.16-2 is the second definition in Chapter 7, Section 16. If Example 9.13-4 is to be accompanied by a graph, it will be labeled Figure 9.13-4a.

A third feature of this textbook is a detailed presentation showing how "computations with approximate data" should be made and recorded. Following the introduction of this material, all answers for problems in the text that involve measurements or other approximate data are altered to satisfy the approximate data rules. For example, if the answer for a problem whose data were expressed in three significant digits works out to be 376.472 sq. ft., the answer should be reported as 376 sq. ft. or, possibly to help motivate the idea, as $x \doteq (376.472)$ 376 sq. ft. The sign $\doteq$, which means "is approximately equal to," is used wherever it applies.

For ease of identification and reading, each statement that is basic to the structure of this course is set apart by extra spacing. Such statements along with many specific words and phrases are also emphasized by bold or italicized type.

The first chapter deals with the basic ideas of set theory, set operators, the algebra of sets, the principle of duality, and proofs of set theorems. The language and properties of set theory are used throughout the book.

Chapter 2 begins with the set of natural numbers and discusses the basic developments that lead to the set of integers, the set of rational numbers, the set of irrational numbers, and finally to the set of real numbers. The field properties, the equality properties, the order properties, and the completeness property, as applied to real numbers, are all presented and involved in problem situations. The importance of proof is stressed throughout the chapter.

Relations and the function concept, which is a special kind of relation, are dominant from Chapter 3 on. Chapters 3 and 4 deal with one-to-one correspondence; relations; linear, quadratic, composite, identity, and inverse functions; linear, quadratic, equivalent, and radical equations; inequalities; imaginary numbers; and graphs of all kinds.

Consultations with other mathematics professors and my own past experience led to the decision that it would be best not to include a discussion of the theory of matrices in this particular course. However, in Chapter 5 the theory of determinants is developed through Cramer's rule to enable students to solve systems of equations by determinants. This chapter deals primarily with the idea of the slope of a line and with systems of second order, third order, and homogeneous linear equations and methods of solving them. Chapter 6 covers sequence functions, arithmetic and geometric sequences, arithmetic, geometric and infinite geometric series, factorial numbers, and the binomial theorem with applications.

Chapter 7 treats trigonometry as a study of periodic functions in terms of real numbers. This is the analytical approach, and the modern approach, to the study of trigonometry. The circular functions are defined on a unit circle. In connection with the sinusoidal curves, amplitude, period, phase number, phase shift, and displacement are discussed. Special emphasis is given to the fact that in the graph of the function $x = \cos t$ the x-values represent abscissas. In the graphing of the inverse circular functions, the purpose served by the identity function is again demonstrated.

Theorems on exponents and logarithms, exponential and logarithmic functions and their inverses, hyperbolic functions, and compound amount by continuous interest are dealt with in Chapter 8. The trigonometric functions of angles are treated in Chapter 9, where radian measure is used to provide a smooth and easily understandable transition from the circular functions in terms of real numbers and the trigonometric functions in terms of angles. A complete development of the procedures involved in computing with approximate data and measurement is given, vectors are discussed in considerable detail, and the customary practical applications of angle trigonometry are made.

The complex number system is defined and developed, both from the standpoint of ordered pairs and the binomial form, in Chapter 10. Other developments in this chapter include the geometric interpretation of complex numbers, polar coordinates and the comparison of polar and rectangular coordinates, the polar form of a complex number, multiplication and division, integral powers of complex numbers, and De Moivre's theorem.

Chapter 11 presents the remainder and factor theorems, synthetic division, polynomial functions and equations of degree n, upper and lower bounds of real roots, and methods of finding rational, irrational, and complex roots of polynomial equations.

A rather extensive modern introduction to probability undergirded by the necessary basic work in permutations and combinations is presented in Chapter 12. Set language and set-theoretic ideas are used throughout the chapter. Also, the Cartesian product is used to count the elements of sets; the coefficients of the binomial formula are developed in terms of combinations; sample space, sample point, outcome, and event are discussed; the probability function is defined in terms of certain postulates; and the addition theorem, the multiplication theorems, and the repeated trial theorem are developed and applied.

The content of this textbook is suitable and ample for an algebra and trigonometry course in any college or university. It is especially suitable for such a course in any junior college. Even the advanced students in high school, who are definitely a select group in mathematics, would find the approach suitable and challenging.

I would like to express my deep appreciation to all those, many of them known and some of them unrecognized, who have influenced me in preparing this book. Particularly, I want to thank Dr. Walter P. Morse, who made a critical analysis of the manuscript and offered many valuable suggestions. I appreciate also the aid given by Mrs. Jo Ann Knight, Mrs. Janna Steed, Mrs. Nancy Burris, Mrs. Barbara Sumner, and Mr. Kenneth Levine in preparing the manuscript. And finally I am grateful to Mr. Sidney R. Crawford of The Macmillan Company, who encouraged me to get under way, and to Mr. Harry R. Conn, mathematics editor of The Macmillan Company, who has led me to the finish line.

Gainesville   W. A. G.

Acknowledgment of Tables

The author and The Macmillan Company wish to thank the following companies who have granted us special permission to reprint, with such minor changes as were necessary to fit our needs, the following tables:

I and **III**: Tables V and VI from *Integrated College Algebra and Trigonometry* by E. F. Beckenbach and I. Drooyan, copyrighted, 1964, 1965, and 1967 by Wadsworth Publishing Company, Inc., Belmont, California.

II and **VIII**: Table E and Table D from *Functional Mathematics*, Book 4, by William A. Gager, F. W. Kokomoor, C. N. Shuster, and L. J. Bowman, copyrighted 1956 by Charles Scribner's Sons, New York.

IV: Table IV from *Unified Algebra and Trigonometry* by D. W. Hall and L. O. Kattsoff, copyrighted, 1962 by John Wiley & Sons, Inc., New York.

V: Table 5 from *Modern Introductory Analysis* by Mary P. Dolciani, E. F. Beckenbach, R. C. Jurgensen, A. J. Donnelly, and W. Wooten, copyrighted 1964 by Houghton Mifflin Company, Boston.

VI: Table 6 from *Modern Trigonometry* by A. M. Welchon, W. R. Krickenberger, and Helen R. Pearson, copyrighted 1962 by Ginn and Company (Blaisdell Publishing Co.), Boston, Mass.

VII: *1958 Commissioners Standard Ordinary Mortality Tables* from Flitcraft, Inc., Morristown, N.J.

Contents

Chapter 1. Basic Ideas from Set Theory   1

    1.1 The Set Concept   1
    1.2 Subsets   2
    1.3 Finite and Infinite Sets   4
    1.4 Set Operations   6
        1.4-1 Complementation   7
        1.4-2 Intersection   8
        1.4-3 Union   10
    1.5 Applying Operations to Three Sets   12
    1.6 The Algebra of Sets   14
        1.6-1 Closure   14
        1.6-2 Commutative Law   15
        1.6-3 Associative Law   16
        1.6-4 Distributive Law   16
        1.6-5 Some Postulates of Set Theory   17
    1.7 The Principle of Duality   18
    1.8 Proofs of Theorems   18

Chapter 2. The Real Number System   21

    2.1   The Set of Natural Numbers   21
    2.2   The Subtraction Property   22
    2.3   The Set of Nonnegative Integers   23
    2.4   The Set of Integers   23
    2.5   The Division Operation   24
    2.6   The Set of Rational Numbers   24
    2.7   The Set of Irrational Numbers   25
    2.8   The Set of Real Numbers   26
    2.9   Number Field   27
    2.10 Field Postulates as Applied to Real Numbers   28
    2.11 Equality Postulates   29

2.12 Additional Properties and Theorems of Real Numbers   31
2.13 Order Properties of Real Numbers   35
2.14 Inequalities Applied to Theorems   35
2.15 Completeness   37

Chapter 3.   Relations, Functions, and Their Graphs   39

3.1 The Rectangular Coordinate System   39
3.2 Cartesian Product   40
3.3 Variable and Constant   42
3.4 Relations   43
     3.4-1 Equivalence Relations   45
     3.4-2 Graphs of Absolute Value and Inequalities   46
3.5 Functions   48
3.6 Graphs of Functions   51
3.7 Composite Functions   54
3.8 The Identity Function   56
3.9 Inverse Functions   57
     3.9-1 Properties of an Inverse Function   60

Chapter 4.   Equations, Functions, and Inequalities   63

4.1 Equations   63
4.2 Classification of Equations   64
4.3 Linear Equations and Functions   70
4.4 Quadratic Equations and Functions   73
     4.4-1 Proof and Application of the Quadratic Formula   74
4.5 Imaginary Numbers   79
4.6 Discriminant of the Quadratic Equation   80
     4.6-1 Properties of the Quadratic Discriminant   80
4.7 Sum and Product of the Roots   82
4.8 Radical Equations   83
4.9 Radical Equations of the Second Order   85
4.10 Variation   88
     4.10-1 How to Solve Variation Problems   89
4.11 Inequalities   92
     4.11-1 Basic Operations Used in Solving Inequalities   92
     4.11-2 Algebraic and Graphical Solutions of Linear and
            Quadratic Inequalities   93

Chapter 5.   Linear Systems of Equations   99

5.1 The Linear Equation   99
5.2 Slope of the Graph of a Linear Equation   100
     5.2-1 Some Properties of the Slope Concept   101
5.3 The General Form of a Linear Equation in Two Variables   102
5.4 Two Linear Equations in Two Variables   103
     5.4-1 Possible Solutions of Linear Equations in Two
            Variables   103
     5.4-2 Graphical Solutions of Linear Equations in Two
            Variables   104

5.4-3 Solution of Linear Equations in Two Variables by
Equivalent Equation Method   106
5.4-4 Solving Linear Equations in Two Variables by
Determinants   108
5.4-5 Second-Order Determinants That Are Zero   110
5.5 Three Linear Equations in Three Variables   112
5.5-1 Solutions of Linear Equations in Three Variables
by the Equivalent Equation Method   112
5.5-1a Algebraic Formulas for x, y, and z 114
5.5-2 Determinant Method of Solving Linear Equations
in Three Variables   114
5.5-2.1 Determinant Formulas for x, y, and z 117
5.5-2.2 Third-Order Determinants with Zeros   118
5.6 Two Linear Equations in Three Variables   118
5.7 Homogeneous Linear Equations   119

Chapter 6.   Sequences and Series   122

6.1 Sequences   122
6.2 Series   124
6.3 Arithmetic Sequences and Series   126
6.3-1 Arithmetic Means   127
6.3-2 Interest Rate Formula for Installment Buying   128
6.4 Geometric Sequences and Series   129
6.4-1 Geometric Means   131
6.5 Infinite Geometric Series   133
6.5-1 Repeating Decimals   134
6.6 Binomial Series   135
6.6-1 Binomial Theorem   136
6.6-2 Factorial Numbers   136
6.6-3 Binomial Formula   137

Chapter 7.   Trigonometry in Terms of Circular Functions   140

7.1 The Nature of Circular Functions   140
7.2 Winding Around a Unit Circle   142
7.3 Quadrantal Numbers   143
7.4 The Circular Functions Defined   144
7.5 Behavior of the Sine and the Cosine Functions   146
7.6 Functions of Negative Numbers   148
7.7 Graph of the Sine Function, $y = \sin t$ 150
7.8 The General Sine Function and Its Graph, $y = a \sin bt$ 152
7.9 Phase Shift   153
7.10 Displacement of a Sine Function   155
7.11 Graph of the Cosine Function, $x = \cos t$ 155
7.12 Extension of Sine and Cosine Functions   159
7.13 Exact Values of the Circular Functions of $\pi/6$, $\pi/4$, $\pi/3$,
and Their Multiples   159
7.13-1 Graphs of the Circular Functions from 0 to 2π 166
7.14 Values of Circular Functions for Any Real Number   168

7.14-1 How to Find the Corresponding Arc C_A for Any
Real Number   170
7.15 The Eight Fundamental Identities and Their Applications   177
7.16 Trigonometric Equations   183
7.17 Circular Function Identities Involving Combinations of
Numbers   189
7.17-1   Distance Formula Between Two Points   189
7.17-2   Cosine of the Difference of Two Numbers   190
7.17-3   Cosine of a Negative Number   192
7.17-4   Cosine of $(\pi/2 - t)$, t a Real Number   193
7.17-5   Sine of a Negative Number   193
7.17-6   Tangent of a Negative Number   193
7.17-7   Cotangent of a Negative Number   194
7.17-8   Sine of $(\pi/2 - t)$, t a Real Number   194
7.17-9   Tangent of $(\pi/2 - t)$, t a Real Number   194
7.17-10 Cotangent of $(\pi/2 - t)$, t a Real Number   194
7.17-11 Cosine of the Sum of Two Numbers   194
7.17-12 Sine of the Sum of Two Numbers   195
7.17-13 Sine of the Difference of Two Numbers   195
7.17-14 Tangent of the Sum of Two Numbers   195
7.17-15 Cotangent of the Sum of Two Numbers   195
7.17-16 Tangent of the Difference of Two Numbers   196
7.17-17 Cotangent of the Difference of Two Numbers   196
7.17-18 Sine of Twice a Number   196
7.17-19 Cosine of Twice a Number   196
7.17-20 Tangent of Twice a Number   196
7.17-21 Sine of Half a Number   197
7.17-22 Cosine of Half of a Number   197
7.17-23 Tangent of Half of a Number   197
7.17-24 Product of $\sin s \cos t$, s and t Real Numbers   198
7.17-25 Product of $\cos s \sin t$ 198
7.17-26 Product of $\cos s \cos t$ 198
7.17-27 Product of $\sin s \sin t$ 198
7.17-28 Sum of $\sin u + \sin v$, u and v Real Numbers   198
7.17-29 Difference of $\sin u - \sin v$ 199
7.17-30 Sum of $\cos u + \cos v$ 199
7.17-31 Difference of $\cos u - \cos v$ 199
7.18 Inverse Circular Functions   207
7.18-1   Basic Facts Concerning Inverse Functions   207
7.18-2   The Identity Function and Inverse Circular
Functions   210
7.18-3   Graph of the Inverse Sine Function   210
7.18-4   Graph of the Inverse Cosine Function   212
7.18-5   Graph of the Inverse Tangent Function   213

Chapter 8. Exponential and Logarithmic Functions   220

8.1 Exponential Functions   220
8.2 Exponents and the Laws of Exponents   222
8.3 Inverse of Exponential Functions   227

8.4 Logarithmic Functions 228
8.5 The Number *e* 230
8.6 Hyperbolic Functions 232
8.7 Compound Amount by Continuous Interest 232
8.8 Logarithms and the Laws of Logarithms 234
8.9 How to Find the Common Logarithm of a Number 237

Chapter 9. Trigonometry in Terms of Angles 244

9.1 Angles 244
9.2 Radian Measure of Angles 245
9.3 Use of Table I and Table II 248
9.4 Computing with Approximate Data 249
    9.4-1 Unit of Measurement 250
    9.4-2 Absolute Error of a Measurement 250
    9.4-3 Precision of a Measurement 250
    9.4-4 Rounding Numbers 251
    9.4-5 Addition and Subtraction of Approximate Data 251
    9.4-6 Significant Digits 252
    9.4-7 Relative Error 253
    9.4-8 Accuracy of a Measurement 253
    9.4-9 Multiplication of Approximate Numbers 254
    9.4-10 Division of Approximate Numbers 255
    9.4-11 Square Roots of Approximate Numbers 255
    9.4-12 Computing with Approximate Data in Trigonometry 256
9.5 The Trigonometric Functions Defined 258
9.6 Trigonometric Values for Angles of 0°, 30°, 45°, 60°, and 90° 260
9.7 Trigonometric Functions for Angles of Any Size 262
9.8 Trigonometric Functions of an Acute Angle 265
9.9 Cofunctions and Reciprocal Functions 268
9.10 Dependent Nature of Trigonometric Functions 270
9.11 Values of Trigonometric Functions—Table III 272
9.12 Vectors 275
    9.12-1 Vector Addition 277
    9.12-2 Vector Subtraction 278
    9.12-3 Multiplication of a Vector by a Scalar 279
    9.12-4 Some Properties of Vectors 280
    9.12-5 Fixed Vectors 281
    9.12-6 Algebraic Nature of Vectors from Component Viewpoint 282
9.13 Azimuth and Bearing Angles 283
9.14 Solutions of Right Triangles 288
    9.14-1 How to Solve a Right Triangle 288
    9.14-2 Angles of Elevation and Depression 288
9.15 Solutions of Oblique Triangles 293
    9.15-1 Law of Sines 293
    9.15-2 Area of Triangles 299
    9.15-3 Law of Cosines 301

Chapter 10.   The Complex Number System   307

    10.1 Some Algebra of Ordered Pairs 308
    10.2 A Complex Number Defined 308
        10.2-1 Complex Numbers of the Form $(r, 0)$ Where $r \in R$ ... 310
        10.2-2 The Complex Number $(0, 1)$ 312
    10.3 Binomial Form of Complex Numbers 313
    10.4 Geometric Interpretation of Complex Numbers 316
    10.5 Polar Coordinates 319
        10.5-1 Polar Coordinates of a Point in a Plane 319
        10.5-2 Relation of Polar Coordinates to Rectangular Coordinates ... 321
    10.6 Polar Form of a Complex Number 323
    10.7 Multiplication, Division, and Integral Powers of Complex Numbers ... 326

Chapter 11.   Polynomial Functions of Degree n 331

    11.1 The Generalized Polynomial Function 331
    11.2 Some Arithmetic of Polynomial Functions 332
    11.3 Remainder and Factor Theorems 334
    11.4 Synthetic Division 335
    11.5 Polynomial Functions and Equations 339
        11.5-1 Upper and Lower Bounds 341
        11.5-2 Zeros of Functions and Roots of Equations 342
    11.6 Graphing Polynomial Functions and Their Equations ... 342
    11.7 Complex Roots of Polynomial Equations 348
    11.8 Roots of Odd Degree Polynomials 349
    11.9 Rational Roots of a Polynomial Equation 350

Chapter 12.   Probability   355

    12.1 Permutations 355
        12.1-1 The Count of the Number of Elements in a Set ... 356
        12.1-2 Permutation Formulas 358
    12.2 Combinations 363
        12.2-1 The Special Combination $C(n, 0)$ 366
        12.2-2 Coefficients of the Binomial Formula in Terms of Combinations ... 366
        12.2-3 Total Combinations of a Set of n Elements 368
        12.2-4 Mutually Exclusive Events 368
    12.3 Elementary Theory of Probability 370
        12.3-1 Finite Sample Spaces and Events 370
        12.3-2 Probability Defined 371
        12.3-3 Mathematical Expectation 376
        12.3-4 Empirical Probability 377
        12.3-5 Odds in Favor of an Event 378
        12.3-6 General Addition Theorem of Probability 380
        12.3-7 General Multiplication Theorems of Probability ... 383
        12.3-8 Repeated Trials Theorem 386

Tables

I.	Four-Place Values of Circular Functions	390
II.	Four-Place Logarithms of Numbers	394
III.	Four-Place Values of Trigonometric Functions	396
IV.	Four-Place Logarithms of the Trigonometric Functions	402
V.	Values of the Exponential Function	409
VI.	Natural Logarithms of Numbers from 0 to 250	410
VII.	1958 Commissioners Standard Ordinary Mortality Table	411
VIII.	Powers and Roots of Numbers from 1 to 100	412

Answers to Odd-numbered Problems   413

Index   465

Contemporary College
Algebra and
Trigonometry

1

Basic Ideas from Set Theory

For many centuries the basic idea in mathematics has been that of *number*, as used in counting. But twentieth-century mathematicians have come forward with an even more basic mathematical notion, the concept of *set*. The idea of set is so fundamental that practically all other mathematical concepts can be expressed in terms of it. It is appropriate, therefore, that we begin this course in modern algebra and trigonometry with a brief study of the language and the fundamental principles of the algebra of sets.

1.1 THE SET CONCEPT

No attempt will be made to give an axiomatic development of the set concept; nor will we make an effort to define it. Rather we will try to give meaning to the idea by describing several sets, such as

D: A set of dominoes;
B: A set, or collection, of books;
S: A set, or flock, of sheep;
T: A set, or class, of students in trigonometry;
N: The set of **positive integers** $(1, 2, 3, 4, \ldots)$.

The set of positive integers may also be referred to as the set of **counting numbers** or the set of **natural numbers.**

Note particularly that when the set of natural numbers is **ordered** so that 2 follows 1, 3 follows 2, 4 follows 3, and so on, there can exist no number or numbers between any two consecutive numbers of the set. This means that the set of natural numbers is a **discrete set.**

Capital letters of our alphabet are commonly used to designate sets, and two braces $\{ \ \}$ are used to enclose the **elements** (or members, or objects) of a set. Thus we can symbolize the set of natural numbers in this manner:

$$N = \{1, 2, 3, 4, 5, \ldots\}.$$

1

The statement is read, "The set N represents the numbers 1, 2, 3, 4, 5, and so on." The three dots at the right end of set N mean that the count is to continue without end. Bear in mind, though, that the three dots mean something quite different when they appear as $\{1, 2, 3, \ldots, 9\}$. Here, they mean that the pattern of counting is to continue until 9 is reached.

In set theory **each element in a set must be unique,** that is, **single in kind.** While it is not strictly wrong, it is not permissible to write four twos like this: $\{2, 2, 2, 2\}$. Four twos must be written $\{2\}$, so that the element 2 is unique. Similarly, the letters in the word "seesaw" written as a set must be written in any one of 24 arrangements, such as $\{s, e, a, w\}$, so that each element is unique.

There seems to be little difficulty in deciding whether a certain element belongs to a well-defined set. Quite obviously, (a) the given object is an element of the set, or (b) the object is not an element of the set. For example, the symbol 2 is definitely an element of the set of natural numbers, but 2 is certainly not one of the elements in a flock of sheep. To summarize:

A set is a collection of *unique objects* of any kind.
Each object in a set is an *element* of that set.

The two best ways to describe a set are the so-called **roster method** and the **rule method.** Lower case letters are commonly used to represent the elements when sets are so described.

1. In the roster method the elements of a set are listed or tabulated, as

$A = \{u, e, i, o, a\}$.

2. In the rule method, words, symbols, or a combination of words and symbols may be used to describe the set.

For example, if "x" is permitted to represent any natural number, if the vertical line "$|$" is used to mean "*such that*," and if the symbol "$<$" is used to mean "*is less than*," then

$M = \{x \mid x < 6\}$.

The above statement reads: "the set M consists of all x *such that x is less than* 6." In other words, $M = \{5, 2, 1, 4, 3\}$.

To indicate membership in a set, the symbol "$\in$" is used. Thus "$a \in A$" means that "*the element a is a member of set A*," or *belongs to set A*, or *is contained in set A*. The symbol "$\notin$" means "is *not* contained in."

1.2 SUBSETS

In set theory one is continually discussing sets that are made up for collections of objects from a larger set. This larger set is usually designated by U and is called the **universal set.** It is important to recognize that the size of this universal

set U is relative. *U depends only on the totality of elements that are being considered in some one particular discussion.* For example, we could have thousands of universal sets involving the natural numbers, such as the odd natural numbers, the even natural numbers, the set of natural numbers itself, and so on, but only one of these sets is the universal set in a particular discussion.

Definition: 1.2-1. *The **universal set** is the totality of elements being considered in a discussion of a set.*

Let us select the set of natural numbers N for our universal set U. If you will assume that "n" represents any element of set N and associate each element "n" with an element "$2n$" you will obtain set E as a subset of set N. *Set E is the set of **even natural numbers*** and by the roster method is expressed as

$E = \{2, 4, 6, 8, \ldots\}$.

Again if you will associate each element n in Set N with an element $2n - 1$ you will obtain set D, which is another subset of set N. *Set D is the set of **odd natural numbers.***

$D = \{1, 3, 5, 7, \ldots\}$.

A careful study of sets N, E, and D should help to make the following definitions meaningful to you.

Definition: 1.2-2. *If each element of set A is an element of set B, then A is said to be a **subset** of set B. This is written $A \subseteq B$ and represents the **INCLUSION** idea.*

Definition: 1.2-3. *Set A is a **proper subset** of set B if set A is a subset of set B and set B has one or more elements not found in set A. This is written $A \subset B$.*

You should note that the two preceding definitions are sufficiently general to include the following very interesting extreme:
Each set has a subset equal to itself. It is called an **improper subset.**

Definition: 1.2-4. *An **empty or null set** has no elements in it. It is symbolized by $\emptyset$ or by $\{\ \}$.*

The empty or null set assumes a role in set theory much like the role played by "zero" in number theory.

If you will study the following subsets in U_1, U_2, and U_3, you will find that the first subset listed is the set itself and is called the improper subset. The last subset listed for each set does not contain an element and is the empty set. **Every set has an empty set.**

$U_1 = \{1\}$. The subsets are $\{1\}$ and $\emptyset$.
$U_2 = \{1, 2\}$. The subsets are $\{1, 2\}$, $\{1\}$, $\{2\}$, and $\emptyset$
$U_3 = \{1, 2, 3\}$. The subsets are $\{1, 2, 3\}$, $\{1, 2\}$, $\{1, 3\}$, $\{2, 3\}$, $\{1\}$, $\{2\}$, $\{3\}$, and $\emptyset$.

Definition: 1.2-5.   *P, the set of all subsets of U, is called the **power set** of U. This set is represented by $P = 2^n$, where n is a count of the elements in U.*

As has already been pointed out, *only two things can happen to an element n. It belongs to a certain set or it does not.* Letting 2 represent this either-or condition, it is interesting to discover that if this 2 is raised to a power equal to the number of elements in a given set, the count of the subsets in the power set is obtained.

$P_1 = \{1\}$ has 2^1 or 2 subsets.
$P_2 = \{1, 2\}$ has 2^2 or 4 subsets.
$P_3 = \{1, 2, 3\}$ has 2^3 or 8 subsets.
$P_n = \{1, 2, 3, \ldots, n\}$ has 2^n subsets.
$N = \{1, 2, 3, 4, \ldots\}$ has subsets that cannot be exhausted by counting.

Is it true that each time you add an element to a set you double the number of subsets? Check this out on P_1, P_2, P_3, etc.

1.3 FINITE AND INFINITE SETS

In the preceding sets P_1 through P_n there is no difficulty whatsoever in counting the elements in a set. We call the number of elements the **finite cardinal number** of the set. It is common practice to call a set whose finite cardinal number is one of the natural numbers, or zero, a **finite set.** Thus, intuitively, P_1 through P_n are finite sets. But we should never be totally satisfied with intuitive notions about finite and infinite sets. So it becomes necessary for us to introduce the concepts of **one-to-one correspondence, equivalency, cardinal number,** and **equality** at this point.

One-to-one correspondence exists if the elements in any two sets can be properly paired. For example, there is one-to-one correspondence between the numerals from 1 through 7 and the names of the days in a week.

Definition: 1.3-1.   *There exists a **one-to-one correspondence** between set A and set B when a pairing has been made between A and B such that each element in set A has been associated with one and only one element in set B, and each element in set B has been associated with one and only one element in set A.*

Definition: 1.3-2.   *Two sets are said to be **equivalent** (or are of the same size) if one-to-one correspondence exists between them.*

Definition: 1.3-3.   *The set of all sets equivalent to set A is called the **cardinal number** of set A.*

Since **equivalent sets** are the same in size, it follows that they have the same **cardinal number.** But being equivalent or having the same cardinal number does not mean that the sets are equal. The two sets $A = \{a, e, i, o, u\}$ and $B = \{\text{book}_1, \text{book}_2, \text{book}_3, \text{book}_4, \text{book}_5\}$ are equivalent sets because they have the same cardinal number 5, but they certainly are not equal sets. Set A is not equal to set B, because set A is not a subset of set B, nor is set B a subset of set A. In fact, the two sets are **disjoint,** which means that they do not have a single element in common. The only set common to set A and set B is the empty set $\varnothing$.

All **empty (or null) sets are equal** (see Definition 1.2-4).

Definition: 1.3-4.   *Given two sets A and B, $A = B$ if and only if $A \subseteq B$ and $B \subseteq A$.*

The following two sets are equal

$$A_1 = \{a, e, i, o, u\} = \{e, u, i, o, a\} = A_2,$$

because each set contains exactly the same elements. But these two sets are equal because $A_1 \subseteq A_2$ and $A_2 \subseteq A_1$.

Equal sets may be substituted for each other.

Now that we know how to determine when two sets are equal, let us refer back to the two sets which we used in discussing the uniqueness of an element, namely,

$$S_1 = \{s, e, e, s, a, w\} = \{s, e, a, w\} = S_2,$$

or $S_1 = \quad \{2, 2, 2, 2\} \quad = \quad \{2\} \quad = S_2.$

Each element in S_1 is found in S_2; so it follows that $S_1 \subseteq S_2$. Each element in S_2 is found in S_1 so $S_2 \subseteq S_1$. Because $S_1 \subseteq S_2$ and $S_2 \subseteq S_1$, it follows that $S_1 = S_2$ for both of the given sets.

To guarantee uniqueness of elements in sets S_1 and S_2, the shorter of the two possible forms, that is S_2, is the only acceptable one to use.

Turning again to the set of natural numbers whose size cannot be determined by ordinary counting, let us attempt to make a comparison of this set N with one of its subsets, such as the set of even numbers E.

$$N = \{1, 2, 3, 4, 5, \ldots, n, \ldots\},$$

$$E = \{2, 4, 6, 8, 10, \ldots, 2n, \ldots\}.$$

First, we note that the two sets are equivalent. Set N is equivalent to set E because there is one-to-one correspondence between them. Moreover, $E \subset N$ because N contains elements, such as $1, 3, 5, \ldots$, which are not in E. Therefore, *set N has been shown to be equivalent to a proper subset of itself.* When this happens set N is said to be an **infinite set.** Likewise, set E is an infinite set. This type of thinking leads us to a good mathematical way of defining infinite and finite sets.

Definition: 1.3-5.   *A set which is equivalent to one of its proper subsets is called an* **infinite set.**

Definition: 1.3-6. *A set which is not equivalent to one of its proper subsets is called a* **finite set.**

EXERCISE 1.A

1. Write out six examples of sets.

2. List as many different words as you can that imply the same meaning as the word set.

3. Use the roster method to write the following statements in set form:
  (a) The natural numbers from 1 through 7.
  (b) The three sisters: Mary, Martha, and Melissa.
  (c) $\{x \mid x = n;$ where $n \leq 10$ and a natural number$\}$.

4. Express the following sets in rule method form:
  (a) $\{9, 3, 5, 1, 7\}$.   (b) $\{16, 1, 9, 4, 25\}$.
  (c) The even natural numbers from 1 to 15, inclusive.

5. Write a set with unique elements equal to the set $\{2, 2, 2, 4, 4, 4\}$.

6. What set has unique elements and is equal to the set $\{t, r, i, g, o, n, o, m, e, t, r, y\}$?

7. How many subsets does the set $\{8, 1, 27\}$ have? Write them out.

8. Give the number of subsets for the set $\{a, l, g, e, b, r\}$. Write out its improper subset and its empty set.

9. State, in sentence form, the meaning of $a \in A$; $A \subseteq B$; $\{\ \}$; $A = B$; $\{x \mid x = 2\}$.

10. Put these symbolic statements in words: $A \subset B$; $A \neq B$; $\varnothing$; $A \subseteq B$ and $B \subseteq A$; $\{x \mid x$ is a natural number and $1 \leq x \leq 26\}$.

11. What is the cardinal number of $\{x \mid x$ a positive integer and $1 \leq x \leq 26\}$?

12. Is there one-to-one correspondence between the set in Problem 11 and the letters of the English alphabet? Are the two sets equivalent?

13. The set E of odd natural numbers is a proper subset of the set of natural numbers. Should set E be classified as a finite set or an infinite set? Explain.

14. Set $\{m, l, k\}$ is a proper subset of set $\{m, k, l, j\}$. Is the latter set a finite set or an infinite set? Why?

15. Write out a set that has the same cardinal number as does the set of fingers on a normal left hand. Are the two sets equivalent?

16. Name a set which is equal to the set of vowels in the English alphabet.

17. How many different ways can a one-to-one correspondence be set up between the two sets $\{1, 2, 3\}$ and the set $\{a, b, c\}$?

18. Prove that there is one-to-one correspondence between any two equal sets.

19. Is the set $\{1, 2, 3, \ldots, n\}$ a finite set or an infinite set? What is its cardinal number?

20. Is the set $\{1, 2, 3, \ldots, n, \ldots\}$ a finite or an infinite set? Is there one-to-one correspondence between this set and the set in Problem 19? What does this tell you?

1.4 SET OPERATIONS

In the *algebra of numbers* one operates on a *pair of numbers* with the operators $+, -, \times, \div$, and one extracts roots and raises to powers to get a *single number*. Similarly, in the *algebra of sets* one operates on a *pair of sets* with certain operators to get a *single set*. While there are many differences between the basic principles of the algebra of sets and the algebra of numbers, there are also many similarities. Some of these will be pointed out as they are encountered in this book.

1.4-1 Complementation

It has been stated that the universal set U is the original set in a particular discussion. This means that it is as large as its largest subset. With this in mind let us take a set which we will call U, and a subset of U which we will call A.

$$U = \{1, 8, 3, 6, 5, 2, 7, 4\} \quad \text{and} \quad A = \{2, 8, 7, 5\}.$$

Our problem is to form a set that contains all the elements in U that are not in set A. We will call this set the complement of A, or the not A set, and will symbolize it by $\sim A$.

$$\sim A = \{1, 3, 4, 6\}.$$

Definition: 1.4-1a. *The set that contains all the elements in U that are not found in A, a subset of U, is called the* **complement of A.** *Symbolized in set form it is*

$$\sim A = \{x \mid x \in U \text{ and } x \notin A\}.$$

Figure 1.4-1a is a **Venn diagram,** a pictorial device which shows in an intuitive and a very interesting way how relationships in finite sets behave. In the Venn diagrams which we will use *we will consider the universal set U to be all elements or points within a rectangle. The interior region of any enclosed figure within the rectangle U will represent a subset of U.* Thus Figure 1.4-1a shows that U encompasses the entire rectangle, set A is within the circle and set $\sim A$ is all of U that is not in set A.

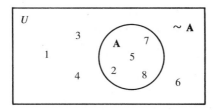

Figure 1.4-1a

To help you see in the easiest possible way how sets behave, numerals will be used in the first few Venn diagrams. Unless otherwise stated, each numeral used in the following diagrams will represent a distinct element of the set. That is, *the numeral 5 means the element 5. It does not mean 5 elements.*

The complement operator "$\sim$" is called a **unary operator,** because it operates on one given set A to produce a new set $\sim A$. The "intersection" and "union" operators that will be considered next are called **binary operators,** because they operate on two sets to form a new set.

Definition: 1.4-1b.   *A binary operation is a method of combining two elements to produce a unique third element.*

1.4-2 Intersection

Let us take $A = \{6, 3, 4, 1\}$ and $\sim A = \{2, 8, 7, 5\}$ and ask the question: Which elements are "common" to set A and set $\sim A$? In Figure 1.4-2a notice that the subsets are not enclosed in circles. Usually we will use circles, but any enclosed figure is acceptable. In this case we need to use two areas that appear to be equal to set U.

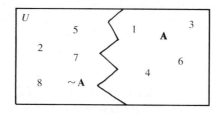

Figure 1.4-2a

From the Venn diagram in Figure 1.4-2a, it is evident that there is no element common to sets A and $\sim A$. So using the symbol "$\cap$" as the **intersection operator,** we conclude that $A \cap \sim A$ is the empty set $\varnothing$.

Definition: 1.4-2a.   *Two sets whose intersection has no element in common are called* **disjoint sets;** *the resulting set is empty.*

The set $A \cap \sim A$ is read "A intersection not A" or "the intersection of A and not A," or "A cap not A."

Just because the two sets A and $\sim A$ are disjoint does not mean that all pairs of sets under intersection are disjoint. Consider

$A = \{1, 8, 5, 7, 3\}$ and $B = \{4, 3, 2, 7, 9\}$.

For these two sets the elements 3 and 7 are "common" and therefore $A \cap B = \{3, 7\}$. Notice how the shaded portion of the Venn diagram in Figure 1.4-2b shows $\{3, 7\}$ to be common to the two sets.

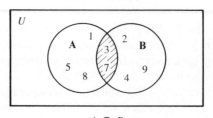

$A \cap B$

Figure 1.4-2b

Definition: 1.4-2b.   *The set A ∩ B contains all elements which are common to the* **intersection** *of sets A and B. That is,*

$A \cap B = \{x \mid x \in A \text{ and } x \in B\}$.

If for any sets A and B Figure 1.4-2c properly represents $A \cap B$, then $\sim(A \cap B)$ is represented by Figure 1.4-2d. Here the shaded part in the Venn diagram shows that every point that is not in $A \cap B$ is in $\sim(A \cap B)$. In Figure 1.4-2e the vertical shaded lines show that $\sim A$ includes all the points not in A and the horizontal shaded lines show that $\sim B$ includes all the points not in B. Therefore, $\sim A \cap \sim B$ contains all points common to $\sim A$ and $\sim B$. That is, $\sim A \cap \sim B$ contains all of U that has both vertical and horizontal shading.

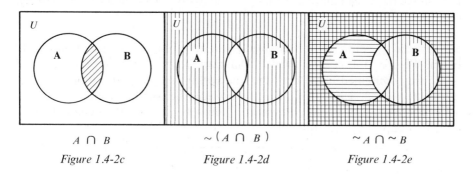

| $A \cap B$ | $\sim(A \cap B)$ | $\sim A \cap \sim B$ |

| *Figure 1.4-2c* | *Figure 1.4-2d* | *Figure 1.4-2e* |

Note that the preceding Venn diagrams clearly indicate that

$\sim(A \cap B) \neq \sim A \cap \sim B$.

Three other basic intersection facts are presented below, but they will be left for you to justify:

$A \cap A = A$,

$A \cap U = A$,

$A \cap \emptyset = \emptyset$.

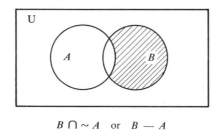

$B \cap \sim A$ or $B - A$

Figure 1.4-2f

Now that the "intersection" operator is available to us, let us reconsider the case of finding the complement of a subset of the universal set. It sometimes happens that we want only part of the complement. For example, let us assume that the universal set U contains two subsets, A and B, and we want only that part of the complement of A that is contained in set B. This we will call the **relative complement** and demonstrate it by the shaded portion in Figure 1.4-2f.

Definition: 1.4-2c. *The **relative complement** of subset A with respect to subset B in set U is $B \cap \sim A$, or $B - A$. ($B - A$ is the set of all elements in B that are not in A and is read "B minus A.")*

1.4-3 Union

Let us take the same pair of sets that we used in discussing intersection, namely,

$$\sim A = \{2, 8, 7, 5\} \quad \text{and} \quad A = \{1, 6, 4, 3\}$$

and ask the question: What set would you get if you combined A and $\sim A$? From Figure 1.4-3a the Venn Diagram shows that if sets A and $\sim A$ are combined we get the universal set U. In other words, $A \cup \sim A = \{1, 2, 3, 4, 5, 6, 7, 8\} = U$, where the symbol "$\cup$," called the **union operator,** is used to combine or join sets. $A \cup \sim A$ is read "A union $\sim A$," "A cup $\sim A$," or "the union of A and $\sim A$."

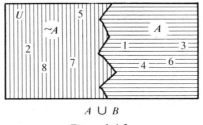

$$A \cup B$$

Figure 1.4-3a

Although it is true, as in the case of the two disjoint sets shown in Figure 1.4-3a, that the count of $A \cup \sim A$ is identical to the sum of the elements of A and the complement of A, do not be misled by this coincidence.

What happens if you combine two sets that are not disjoint, such as

$$A = \{1, 8, 5, 7, 3\} \quad \text{and} \quad B = \{4, 3, 2, 7, 9\}?$$

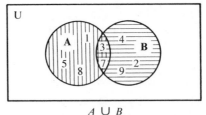

$$A \cup B$$

Figure 1.4-3b

According to the shaded portion of the Venn diagram in Figure 1.4-3b, $A \cup B = \{1, 2, 3, 4, 5, 6, 7, 8\}$. Can you explain why the cardinal number of the elements is 5 in each of set A and set B but the cardinal number of the elements in set $A \cup B$ is only 8?

Definition: 1.4-3a. *The set $A \cup B$ represents the* **union** *of set A and set B and contains all elements that belong either to A or to B or to both A and B. That is,*

$A \cup B = \{x \mid x \in A \text{ or } x \in B, \text{ or both}\}$.

For any two sets A and B the shaded part of Figure 1.4-3c represents the elements in $A \cup B$. Also $\sim(A \cup B)$ is represented by the shaded part in Figure 1.4-3d, and $\sim A \cup \sim B$ is represented by all of U that is in any way shaded in Figure 1.4-3e.

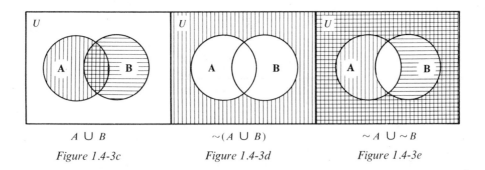

$A \cup B$	$\sim(A \cup B)$	$\sim A \cup \sim B$
Figure 1.4-3c	*Figure 1.4-3d*	*Figure 1.4-3e*

The Venn diagram for Figure 1.4-3d shows that $\sim(A \cup B)$ is not only the complement of $A \cup B$ but also contains exactly the same elements as does $\sim A \cap \sim B$ in Figure 1.4-2e. Therefore,

$$\sim(A \cup B) = \sim A \cap \sim B. \qquad (A)$$

Moreover, $\sim A \cup \sim B$ in Figure 1.4-3e contains exactly the same elements as does $\sim(A \cap B)$ in Figure 1.4-2d. Thus,

$$\sim(A \cap B) = \sim A \cup \sim B. \qquad (B)$$

(A) and (B) are known as De Morgan's laws.

Some other basic facts involving the union operator that you should investigate are

$A \cup A = A$,

$A \cup U = U$,

$A \cup \varnothing = A$.

1.5 APPLYING OPERATIONS TO THREE SETS

Once the concepts of *complement, intersection,* and *union* are understood, the ideas can be applied to three or more sets. A Venn diagram will be used to rationalize the following definition:

Definition: 1.5-1. *$A \cap B \cap C$ is the set of all elements x such that $x \in A$ and $x \in B$ and $x \in C$.*

In Figure 1.5-1 $A \cap B$ is first shaded with vertical lines. Then its intersection with set C is shaded with horizontal lines. That portion of set U which has both vertical and horizontal shading is the section that properly represents $A \cap B \cap C$.

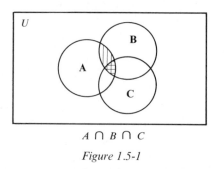

$$A \cap B \cap C$$

Figure 1.5-1

A slightly more difficult exercise is to show by Venn diagrams that $A \cap (B \cup C) = (A \cap B) \cup (A \cap C)$. Figure 1.5-2 shows the union of B and C by vertical lines and the intersection of A with $B \cup C$ by the horizontal lines. Therefore, $A \cap (B \cup C)$ is the double-hatched portion of U.

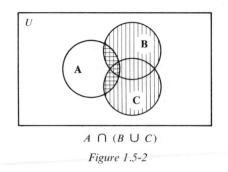

$$A \cap (B \cup C)$$

Figure 1.5-2

Figure 1.5-3 shows the intersection of A and B by vertical lines and the intersection of A and C by horizontal lines. Then the union (or the combining) of the two intersections includes all space shaded either by horizontal or vertical lines. This is identical to the double-hatched portion in Figure 1.5-2.

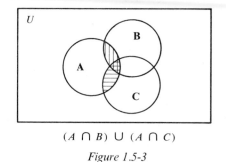

$$(A \cap B) \cup (A \cap C)$$

Figure 1.5-3

EXERCISE 1.B

Starred exercises (*) will later be stated either as postulates or theorems to be proved.

1. Find the complement of A if $U = \{a, b, c, d, e, f\}$ and $A = \{a, c, d\}$.

2. If $U = \{x \mid x$ is a vowel$\}$ and $A = \{e, u\}$ find $\sim A$.

3. Given that set A and set B are disjoint sets, how many elements are in the set $A \cap B$? Express your answer in symbolic form.

4. What must be true of sets A and B if the count of the elements of their union equals the sum of the elements of A and the complement of A?

5. The "intersection" and "union" operators are called binary operators. Why?

6. Name an unary operator. In what way does its operation differ from a binary operation?

7. Are the two sets $A = \{$John, Mary, Sue$\}$ and $B = \{$George, Jane, Mary$\}$ disjoint? Write the set $A \cup B$.

8. Use the two sets in Problem 7 to write $A \cap B$. Are the two sets equivalent? Are they equal?

9. What is meant by the statement $A \cap B = \varnothing$?

10. Give two possible explanations of the statement $A \cup B = \varnothing$.

11. If $A \subset B$ (A a proper subset of B), show by a Venn diagram the intersection of A and B.

12. Show by a Venn diagram the union of A and B, where $B \subset A$.

13. Are these statements true for all cases?

  (a) $A \cup B = U$. Explain.   (b) $(A \cup B) \cup (\sim A \cup B) = U$. Explain.

14. Is there one exception to the truth of these statements?

  (a) $A \cap B = \varnothing$.   (b) $(A \cap B) \cup [\sim(A \cap B)] = U$.

*15. Verify by Venn diagrams that $A \cap B = B \cap A$.

*16. Use Venn diagrams to show that $A \cup B = B \cup A$.

*17. Show by Venn diagrams that this statement is true:

$$A \cap (B \cap C) = (A \cap B) \cap C.$$

*18. By Venn diagrams verify the statement

$$A \cup (B \cup C) = (A \cup B) \cup C.$$

*19. Verify each of the following statements by a Venn diagram:

  (a) $A \cap A = A$.   (b) $A \cap U = A$.   (c) $A \cap \varnothing = \varnothing$.

*20. Show by a Venn diagram that each of the following statements is true:

(a) $A \cup A = A$.   (b) $A \cup U = U$.   (c) $A \cup \varnothing = A$.

*21. For the sets A, B, and C use Venn diagrams to show that

$$A \cup (B \cap C) = (A \cup B) \cap (A \cup C).$$

22. Use Venn diagrams to show that

$$A \cap B = A \quad \text{if and only if} \quad A \subset B.$$

23. If sets A, B, and C are disjoint, draw a Venn diagram to show $(A \cup B \cup C)$.

24. Given the sets A, B, and C to be disjoint, use a Venn diagram to show the set $\sim(A \cap B \cap C)$.

25. Use a Venn diagram to find a set equal to $U - A$ where set A is a subset of U.

26. Show by Venn diagram a set equal to $A - \varnothing$, where A is a subset of U.

27. From 40 students studying French, German, and Spanish, it was found that none of the 40 students was taking all three courses, but that 8 were studying French only, 2 were studying French and German, and 3 were studying French and Spanish. None of the 16 that were studying German were studying German only. (In contrast to our previous interpretation of numerals in Venn diagrams, the numeral 40 in this problem means 40 different elements and not the element 40, and the same is true of the other numerals.) Use a Venn diagram to find: (a) How many were studying German and Spanish? German or Spanish? (b) How many were studying Spanish only? French or Spanish?

1.6 THE ALGEBRA OF SETS

Every algebra of sets is a Boolean algebra, so named to honor a prominent English mathematician, George Boole (1815–1864). The power set as discussed in Section 1.2 and defined by Definition 1.2-5 is one example of a Boolean algebra.

It is definitely not the purpose of this text to delve deeply into the theory of the algebra of sets. It is the intent, however, to be sufficiently basic to provide adequate mathematical understanding to work out the necessary proofs of set relationships.

Because *a postulate is an assumption which is accepted without proof to provide a basis for argument* in mathematical situations, the set theory postulates that will be needed to complete the proofs of a selection of theorems are listed. Several of the statements appearing in the list of postulates in Section 1.6-5 have been discussed in detail in Sections 1.4 and 1.5. However, it does seem advisable to introduce at this point some brief remarks concerning closure, commutativity, associativity, and distributivity.

1.6-1 Closure

When the result of an operation on any two members of a set belongs to that set we say that the set has closure under that operation. The set of natural numbers has closure under the operation addition, because the sum of any two natural numbers is a natural number. The set of natural numbers also has closure under multiplication, because the product of any two natural numbers is a natural number. But the set of natural numbers does not have closure under the operation subtraction, because the difference of any two natural numbers is not necessarily a natural number.

Our list of postulates involves primarily the binary operations $\cup$ and $\cap$ (see Definition 1.4-1b), so we will define closure in this manner:

Definition: 1.6-1a.   *A set S is said to be* **closed** *with respect to a given binary operation if the result of operating on any two elements of S is unique and is an element of S.*

Altering the preceding definition to specifically involve the two set theory operations $\cup$ and $\cap$ we obtain:

Definition: 1.6-1b.   *The* **set of all subsets of** U **is closed** *under the binary operation* $\cup$ *(or* $\cap$*) if and only if the subset which results from the operation on any two subsets of U is also a subset of the set U.*

To illustrate what is involved in Definition 1.6-1b, let $U = \{1, 4, 2, 3\}$, $A = \{2, 1\}$, and $B = \{2, 4\}$. A and B are subsets of U. Then $A \cup B = \{1, 2, 4\}$ which is a subset of U. Likewise, $A \cap B = \{2\}$ which is a subset of U.

1.6-2 Commutative Law

In applying the binary operations " $+$ " or " $\cdot$ " to the real numbers, one soon makes these observations:

1. The sum of any two numbers is the same, regardless of the order in which the two addends are taken.
2. The product of any two numbers is the same, regardless of the order in which the two factors are taken.

When the order of adding (or multiplying) any two numbers has no effect on the result, we say that the operation is **commutative.** Thus, we can state that the binary operation " $+$ " (or " $\cdot$ ") on R is commutative if and only if $a + b = b + a$ (or $ab = ba$) whenever $a, b \in R$. Adapting the last statement to the set operations $\cup$ and $\cap$, we have:

Definition: 1.6-2a.   *The binary operation* $\cup$ *(or* $\cap$*) on a set U is* **commutative** *if and only if* $A \cup B = B \cup A$ *(or* $A \cap B = B \cap A$*) whenever A and B are subsets of U.*

If $U = \{1, 4, 3, 2\}$, $A = \{2, 1\}$, and $B = \{2, 4\}$, A and B are subsets of U. It can easily be determined that $A \cap B = \{2\}$ and $B \cap A = \{2\}$; hence, in this case, $A \cap B = B \cap A$. Also, $A \cup B = \{1, 2, 4\}$ and $B \cup A = \{2, 4, 1\}$, and hence, in this case, $A \cup B = B \cup A$.

1.6-3 Associative Law

Grouping the numbers 1, 4, and 7 with respect to the operation addition we see that $(1 + 4) + 7 = 12 = 1 + (4 + 7)$; and with respect to multiplication, $(1 \cdot 4) \cdot 7 = 1 \cdot (4 \cdot 7) = 28$. In evaluating any three numbers which have been grouped, either with respect to addition or with respect to multiplication, the two numbers inside the parentheses are evaluated first, then the result is paired with the third number and the final evaluation is made.

When a triple of numbers is considered under the operation of addition or multiplication, and the value remains the same under different groupings, the operation is said to be **associative.** Thus, the binary operation " $+$ " (" $\cdot$ ") on R is associative if and only if $(a + b) + c = a + (b + c)[(a \cdot b) \cdot c = a \cdot (b \cdot c)]$ whenever $a, b, c \in R$. This can be expressed in terms of the set operations $\cup$ and $\cap$ as follows:

Definition: 1.6-3a.   *The binary operation $\cup$ (or $\cap$) on the set U is* **associative** *if and only if $(A \cup B) \cup C = A \cup (B \cup C)$ [or $(A \cap B) \cap C = A \cap (B \cap C)$] whenever A, B and C are subsets of U.*

The preceding definition may be illustrated by letting $U = \{1, 3, 7, 2, 5, 8\}$, $A = \{2, 7\}$, $B = \{8, 2, 5\}$, $C = \{7, 3, 2\}$. A, B, and C are subsets of U. Then

$$(A \cup B) \cup C = \{2, 7, 8, 5\} \cup \{7, 3, 2\} = \{2, 7, 8, 5, 3\}$$

and $A \cup (B \cup C) = \{2, 7\} \cup \{8, 2, 5, 7, 3\} = \{8, 2, 5, 7, 3\}$,

thus $(A \cup B) \cup C = A \cup (B \cup C)$. Similarly, $(A \cap B) \cap C = \{2\} \cap \{7, 3, 2\} = \{2\}$ and $A \cap (B \cap C) = \{2, 7\} \cap \{2\} = \{2\}$, thus $(A \cap B) \cap C = A \cap (B \cap C)$.

1.6-4 Distributive Law

For $a, b, c \in R$ in the algebra of numbers, multiplication is distributive with respect to addition, as indicated by

$$a(b + c) = ab + ac. \tag{A}$$

This statement changes the product of two factors into the sum of two terms, and is called the **left-hand distributive law.** The **right-hand distributive law** is

$$(b + c)a = ba + ca = ab + ac. \tag{B}$$

From (A) and (B) it follows that

$$a(b + c) = (b + c)a.$$

Although it is true that the distributive law holds for multiplication distributed over addition as shown by $a(b + c) = ab + ac$, it is not true that a distributive law exists in the algebra of numbers if the binary operations " $\cdot$ " and " $+$ " are reversed. That is, $a + (b \cdot c) \neq (a + b)(a + c)$. The algebra of sets differs from the algebra of numbers in that the operations " $+$ " and " $\cdot$ " for numbers cannot be switched, but the operations $\cup$ and $\cap$ in sets can be interchanged. Thus, as indicated in the following definition, we have two distributive laws in the theory of sets.

Definition: 1.6-4a.   *The binary operations $\cup$ and $\cap$ on the set U are* **distributive** *if and only if A, B, and C are subsets of the set U and*

(1) $A \cap (B \cup C) = (A \cap B) \cup (B \cap C)$,

or (2) $A \cup (B \cap C) = (A \cup B) \cap (B \cup C)$.

Since $\cup$ and $\cap$ can be interchanged, as shown in (1) and (2), they can be considered as dual operations (see Section 1.7). A discussion that shows by Venn diagrams that

$$A \cap (B \cup C) = (A \cap B) \cup (B \cap C)$$

is given in connection with Figure 1.5-2 and Figure 1.5-3.

1.6-5 Some Postulates of Set Theory

Most of the postulates appearing in the following list have already been discussed in the preceding sections. Keep in mind as you work with these postulates that U is the universal set, P is the power set of the universal set, $\varnothing$ is the empty set, A, B, C, etc., are other sets, and $\sim$, $\cap$, and $\cup$ are set operators.

Closure Postulates

For any two subsets A and B in set U,
(1a): $A \cup B \in U$,   ($A \cup B$ unique);
(1b): $A \cap B \in U$,   ($A \cap B$ unique).

Commutative Postulates

For any two subsets A and B in set U,
(2a): $A \cup B = B \cup A$;
(2b): $A \cap B = B \cap A$.

Associative Postulates

For any subsets A, B and C in set U,
(3a): $(A \cup B) \cup C = A \cup (B \cup C)$;
(3b): $(A \cap B) \cap C = A \cap (B \cap C)$.

Identity Postulates

There exists in set U the identity sets $\varnothing$ and U such that for any set A in U
(4a): $A \cup \varnothing = \varnothing \cup A = A$;
(4b): $A \cap U = U \cap A = A$.

Idempotent Postulates

A set that remains unchanged when operated on by itself is idempotent. There exists in U a subset A such that
(5a): $A \cup A = A$;
(5b): $A \cap A = A$.

Complementation Postulates   If A is a subset of set U, then
(6a): $A \cup \sim A = U$;
(6b): $A \cap \sim A = \varnothing$;
(6c): $\sim(\sim A) = A$;
(6d): $A - \varnothing = A$;
(6e): $U - A = \sim A$.

Distributive Postulates	If A, B, and C are subsets of set U, then (7a): $A \cap (B \cup C) = (A \cap B) \cup (A \cap C)$; (7b): $A \cup (B \cap C) = (A \cup B) \cap (A \cup C)$.
DeMorgan's Postulates	If A and B are subsets in set U, then (8a): $\sim(A \cup B) = \sim A \cap \sim B$; (8b): $\sim(A \cap B) = \sim A \cup \sim B$.
Transitive Postulates	If A, B, and C are subsets of U and (9): If $A \subseteq B$ and $B \subseteq C$, then $A \subseteq C$.
Consistency Postulate	For any two sets A and B, if any one of the following statements is true, then the other two statements are also true. (10a): $A \subseteq B$; (10b): $A \cup B = A$; (10c): $A \cap B = A$.

Other properties could be postulated, but this list is sufficient to enable us to write the proofs of some theorems on sets that will be considered in this book.

1.7 THE PRINCIPLE OF DUALITY

In several branches of mathematics new theorem can be established from proven theorem by merely interchanging certain operators, words, or phrases and the new theorem is called the **dual theorem.**

Definition: 1.7-1.   *The* **principle of duality** *in set theory guarantees that if a set relationship is true, then the set relationship obtained from it by interchanging $\cup$ and $\cap$ is also true. Also, in sets where $\varnothing$ and U occur with $\cup$ and $\cap$ the principle of duality requires the interchange of $\varnothing$ and U.*

Referring back to the list of set theory postulates on page 17, you will see applications of this duality principle. For example in (3a) and (3b), every $\cup$ in (3a) is replaced by a $\cap$ in (3b), and every $\cap$ in (3a) is replaced by a $\cup$ in (3b). Likewise, each (a) statement is a dual of each corresponding (b) statement and vice versa in Postulates 2, 4, 5, 6, 7, and 8.

The beauty of the duality principle is that once a theorem has been proved, its dual can be accepted as true without further proof. Thus, this duality principle greatly reduces the number of theorems that have to be proved in set theory and in other branches of mathematics.

1.8 PROOFS OF THEOREMS

We will now proceed with some examples of proofs of set theorems. Keep in mind that only those advanced steps can be taken that can be fully justified by undefined terms, definitions, postulates, or previously proved theorems.

For "therefore" the symbol "$\therefore$" will be used.

Theorem: 1.8-1.   Prove that $A \cup U = U$.

PROOF: $A \cup U = A \cup (A \cup \sim A)$ Postulate (6a)
$\qquad\qquad = (A \cup A) \cup \sim A$ Postulate (3a)
$\qquad\qquad = A \cup \sim A$ Postulate (5a)
$\qquad\qquad = U;$ Postulate (6a)
$\therefore \qquad A \cup U = U.$ Postulate (9)

Theorem: 1.8-2.   Prove that $\sim U = \varnothing$.

PROOF: $\sim U = U \cap \sim U$ Postulate (4b)
$\qquad\qquad = \varnothing;$ Postulate (6b)
$\therefore \qquad \sim U = \varnothing.$ Postulate (9)

Theorem: 1.8-3.   Prove that $A \cap B \subseteq A$.

PROOF: $A \cap (A \cap B) = (A \cap A) \cap B,$ Postulate (3b)
$\qquad A \cap (A \cap B) = A \cap B,$ Postulate (5b)
$\qquad (A \cap B) \cap A = A \cap B.$ Postulate (2b)
By Postulate (10c), if $(A \cap B) \cap A = A \cap B,$

then $A \cap B \subseteq A.$ Postulate (10a)

Theorem: 1.8-4.   Prove that $B \cap \varnothing = \varnothing$.

PROOF: $B \cap \varnothing = (B \cap \varnothing) \cup \varnothing,$ Postulate (4a)
$\qquad\qquad = (B \cap \varnothing) \cup (B \cap \sim B),$ Postulate (6b)
$\qquad\qquad = B \cap (\varnothing \cup \sim B),$ Postulate (7a)
$\qquad\qquad = B \cap \sim B,$ Postulate (4a)
$\qquad\qquad = \varnothing;$ Postulate (6b)
$\therefore \qquad B \cap \varnothing = \varnothing.$ Postulate (9)

Theorem: 1.8-5.   Prove that $(A \cap B) - A = \varnothing$.

PROOF: $(A \cap B) \cap \sim A = \varnothing,$ Definition 1.4-2c
$\qquad \sim A \cap (A \cap B) = \varnothing,$ Postulate (2b)
$\qquad (\sim A \cap A) \cap B = \varnothing,$ Postulate (3b)
$\qquad\qquad \varnothing \cap B = \varnothing,$ Postulate (6b)
$\qquad\qquad\qquad \varnothing = \varnothing;$ Theorem 1.8-4
$\therefore \qquad (A \cap B) - A = \varnothing.$ Postulate (9)

Theorem: 1.8-6.   Prove that $A \cup (A \cap B) = A \cap (A \cup B) = A$.

PROOF: $A \cup (A \cap B) = (A \cup A) \cap (A \cup B),$ Postulate (7b)
$\qquad\qquad = A \cap (A \cup B);$ Postulate (5a)
$\therefore \qquad A \cup (A \cap B) = A \cap (A \cup B).$ Postulate (9)

The following statement has been proved:

$$A \cap B \subseteq A.$$ Theorem 1.8-3

Then $A \cap (B \cup A) = A \cap B = A,$ Postulate (10b)

and $A \cap (A \cup B) = A;$ Postulate (2a)

∴ $A \cup (A \cap B) = A \cap (A \cup B) = A.$ Postulate (9)

Theorem: 1.8-7.   For some set C if $A \cap C = B \cap C$ and $A \cup C = B \cup C,$ then $A = B.$

PROOF: $A = A \cap (A \cup C)$ Theorem 1.8-6

$\qquad = A \cap (B \cup C)$ (Equal sets, see Definition 1.3-4)

$\qquad = (A \cap B) \cup (A \cap C)$ Postulate (7a)

$\qquad = (A \cap B) \cup (B \cap C)$ Equal sets

$\qquad = (B \cap A) \cup (B \cap C)$ Postulate (2b)

$\qquad = B \cap (A \cup C)$ Postulate (7a)

$\qquad = B \cap (B \cup C)$ Equal sets

$\qquad = B;$ Theorem 1.8-6

∴ $A = B.$ Postulate (9)

Theorem 1.8-7 has proved that two sets are equal if and only if their intersections and their unions to the same set are equal.

Theorem: 1.8-8.   For any two sets A and B, if $A = B$, then $\sim A = \sim B.$

PROOF: $\sim A \cap A = \varnothing \qquad \sim B \cap B = \varnothing.$ Postulate (6b)

$\qquad \sim A \cap A = \sim B \cap B,$ Equal sets

$\qquad \sim A \cap A = \sim B \cap A.$ Given: $A = B$

∴ $\sim A = \sim B$ Theorem 1.8-7

Also, $\sim A \cup A = U \qquad \sim B \cup B = U,$ Postulate (6a)

$\qquad \sim A \cup A = \sim B \cup B,$ Equal sets

$\qquad \sim A \cup A = \sim B \cup A;$ Given: $A = B$

∴ $\sim A = \sim B.$ Theorem 1.8-7

EXERCISE 1.C

1. What is the dual of $A \cap \varnothing = \varnothing$? Of $A \cup B = (A \cup B) \cup A$?

2. Write a dual statement of $A \cup (B \cap C) = (A \cup B) \cap (A \cup C)$.

3. Using only the definitions and the postulates that have been given in this chapter, write out complete proofs for each of the following set relationships:

(a) $A \cup (\sim A \cap B) = A \cup B.$

(b) $A \cap B \cup \sim A = B.$

(c) $(A \cap \sim B) \cup (A \cap B) = A.$

(d) $\sim A = (\sim A \cap B) \cup \sim (A \cup B).$

(e) $(A \cap B) \cap (A \cap \sim B) = \varnothing.$

(f) $(A \cup \sim B) \cap (A \cup B) = A.$

(g) $U = (A \cup B) \cup \sim (A \cup B).$

(h) $(A \cap \varnothing) \cap U = \varnothing.$

(i) $(A \cup U) \cup \varnothing = U.$

(j) $\sim (A \cup U) \cap \varnothing = \varnothing.$

(k) $A \cup (A \cup B) \cup [(A \cup B) \cap (C \cup D)]$
$\qquad = (A \cup B) \cap (C \cup D).$

4. Write a dual relationship for Problem 3(e) and prove it.

5. Write a dual relationship for Problem 3(g) and prove it.

6. Which two statements in Problem 3 represent dual relationships?

The Real Number System

On the basis of a continuous demand for a more nearly complete number system over the centuries, several changes have taken place in regard to numbers. In the beginning the *natural numbers* were invented. Then came the *set of nonnegative integers*, the *set of integers*, the *set of rational numbers*, the *set of irrational numbers*, and a combination of the rational and irrational numbers which is called the *set of real numbers*.

A complete axiomatic approach to the preceding sets of numbers could be developed, but neither time, space, nor need justify such an approach in this course. Rather, a brief intuitive discussion of the basic developments that have brought the set of real numbers into existence will be presented in this chapter.

2.1 THE SET OF NATURAL NUMBERS

Peano, an Italian mathematician (1850–1932), stated this axiom: "*There is a natural number* 1." Peano went on to postulate that 1 has no predecessor. But it does have—in order—successors, the first successor being $1 + 1$, symbolized by 2; the next one being $1 + 1 + 1$, symbolized by 3; and so on without end. Thus, from Peano's axioms we have the following ordered set of natural numbers:

$$N = \{1, 2, 3, 4, 5, 6, \ldots\}.$$

Definition: 2.1-1. *A **mathematical system** consists of a set of elements with one or more operations, at least one relation, and some basic postulates.*

Definition: 2.1-2. *The **natural number system** consists of a set that has "1" as its first element, "2" as its second element, and so on, together with the operations addition "$+$" and multiplication "$\cdot$," an equivalence relationship,* *and the postulates of closure, commutativity, associativity, identity, and distributivity.*

Because it is not our stated purpose to develop the structure of the different number systems, we will use only the closure principle to show the inadequacy of each system as we come to it and the need for its extension.

Definition: 2.1-3.   *The* **closure postulate,** *as applied to a specific number system, declares that under an operation the result obtained by performing that operation belongs to that system.*

2.2 THE SUBTRACTION PROPERTY

There are four fundamental operations used in algebra: addition and multiplication which we will not define, and subtraction and division which will be defined later.

It is stated in Definitions 2.1-2 and 2.1-3 that the natural number system is closed under addition and multiplication. You will find that the result of adding or multiplying two natural numbers is always a natural number. Try it. We will proceed to show that *the natural number system is not closed under subtraction or under division.*

The subtraction principle applies to any number which can be added to another number to produce a given sum. For example, (what number?) $+ 7 = 13$. Actually, the subtraction operation is so closely related to the addition operation that it is not a necessary operation. However, we do make much use of it in mathematics in the form of: (what number?) $= 13 - 7$.

Definition: 2.2-1.   *If a is one of the numbers in a pair of numbers whose sum is c, then* **subtraction** *is the process of finding the other number b. Symbolically, $b = c - a$ if and only if $a + b = c$.*

No distinction has been or will be made between natural numbers and positive integers, although technically there is a distinction. Any natural number a can just as well be written as the positive integer $+ a$. In other words, $a = +a$. In contrast to "$+a$" we will define "0" and "$-a$" in the following manner:

Definition: 2.2-2.   **Zero** *is a number, denoted by the symbol* "0," *which can be added to any other number a without altering its value. That is, $a + 0 = a$.*

Definition: 2.2-3.   *For every positive integer* "$+a$" *there is a corresponding integer* "$-a$," *called a* **negative integer,** *which possesses the property that $a + (-a) = 0$.*

Later in this chapter you will notice that we will be calling the negative number $-a$ the **additive inverse.** Actually, "additive inverse" is a better name because it suggests that the addition of $-a$ has the opposite effect to that of the addition of $+a$. What is done by adding $+a$ to a given number is undone by adding $-a$. This can be easily demonstrated if for the moment we assume x to be any natural number and the associative postulate to be $(a + b) + c = a + (b + c)$. Then $(x + a) + (-a) = x + [a + (-a)] = x + 0 = x$.

Also, by emphasizing the fact that $-a$ has the opposite effect of $+a$, we can better understand that

If a is positive, $-a$ is negative. If $+a = 4$, then $-a = -4$.
If a is negative, $-a$ is positive. If $+a = -4$, then $-a = -(-4) = +4$.
If a is 0, then $-a$ is also 0.

Definition: 2.2-4. *For all* $a, c \in R$ *the* **difference of two numbers** *denoted by* $c - a$ *is given by*

$$c - a = c + (-a).$$

To show that the natural number system is not closed under subtraction, only one **counterexample** is necessary. Try subtracting 8 from 4. Is $4 - 8$ a natural number? The answer is no, and this one counterexample is sufficient to convince us that the natural number system is not closed under subtraction. It also implies that the natural number system must be extended if we hope to be able to solve problems involving subtraction.

2.3 THE SET OF NONNEGATIVE INTEGERS

With the number **zero** available to us, we will associate it with the elements of the set of natural numbers. Thus, our first extension of the natural number system will be the set of **nonnegative integers.** This set, containing zero and the natural numbers, is sometimes referred to as the **set of whole numbers.** The symbol N_n will be used to represent the nonnegative integers.

$$N_n = \{0, 1, 2, 3, 4, 5, 6, \ldots\}.$$

2.4 THE SET OF INTEGERS

According to Definition 2.2-3, for every positive integer a there exists a corresponding negative integer $-a$. Letting bar N, that is $\overline{N}$, represent the set of negative integers, we have

$$\overline{N} = \{-1, -2, -3, -4, \ldots\}.$$

Then $N_n \cup \overline{N}$ represents the set of integers. Like the natural numbers, the set of integers is a **discrete set.**

A very effective visualization of the set of integers can be obtained by using a **"one-dimensional coordinate system."** By representing a point "0" called **the origin** on an endless straight line, by choosing a suitable **unit of length** so that the discrete numbers can be properly spaced, by taking the direction to the right of the origin as positive and to the left as negative, a **number scale** is obtained. Figure 2.4-1, shows a number scale involving the integers.

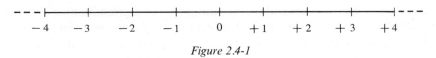

Figure 2.4-1

The set of integers is indicated by

$$I = \{ \ldots -3, -2, -1, 0, 1, 2, 3, \ldots \}.$$

Several questions need to be answered at this point. Is the set of integers closed to addition? To multiplication? To subtraction? To division? By postulation and examples you will quickly decide that the set of integers is closed to addition, multiplication, and subtraction. But what about division? In the set of integers can we find: (what number?) $\cdot$ 7 = 13?

2.5 THE DIVISION OPERATION

The division operator indicated by the symbol " $\div$ " is closely related to multiplication. It calls for a number which will multiply a given number to produce a given product; that is, (what number?) $\cdot$ 7 = 13.

Definition: 2.5-1.   *If b is a nonzero number and a is the product of two numbers, then* **division** *is the process of finding the quotient c such that* $b \cdot c = a$. *In symbols*

$$c = \frac{a}{b} \quad \text{if and only if} \quad b \cdot c = a.$$

If $c = \dfrac{a}{0}$, then $0 \cdot c = a$ but no integer c multiplied by 0 will give a. If $c = \dfrac{0}{0}$, then $0 \cdot c = 0$ and c is not unique; it can be any integer. Therefore,

Division by zero is not permissible.

To decide whether or not the set of integers is closed under division try dividing 13 by 7. Is the quotient an integer? Since one *counterexample* is necessary and sufficient to prove a statement false, the result of $\dfrac{13}{7}$ is sufficient to show that the set of integers is not closed under division. Thus, our number system needs to be extended beyond the set of integers.

2.6 THE SET OF RATIONAL NUMBERS

In our definition of division, and in checking closure under division in the set of integers, we encountered the form $\dfrac{a}{b}$. If a and b are integers, then $\dfrac{a}{b}$ represents the quotient of two integers and gives us a clue as to how we can define a set of numbers that will be sufficient to solve $b \cdot (?) = a$. We will call this new set the **set of rational numbers** and symbolize it by R_r.

Definition: 2.6-1. *A **rational number** is a number of the form* $\dfrac{a}{b}$ *or its equivalent form* $a \cdot \dfrac{1}{b}$, *where a and b are integers and* $b \neq 0$.

Since common fractions are also expressed in the form of $\dfrac{a}{b}$ where $b \neq 0$, the set of rational numbers consists of the set of integers and the set of all common fractions. In other words,

The set of rational numbers consists of
$\begin{cases} \text{1. The positive integers and} \\ \quad \text{fractions.} \\ \text{2. Zero.} \\ \text{3. The negative integers and} \\ \quad \text{fractions.} \end{cases}$

The rational number system R_r is closed under addition, subtraction, multiplication, and, with certain restrictions, under division. Although the set of rational numbers is sufficient to solve problems such as measurement, it is not sufficient for the solution of certain types of problems.

2.7 THE SET OF IRRATIONAL NUMBERS

Suppose our problem is to find the square roots of two. The correct values are $\sqrt{2}$ and $-\sqrt{2}$. But neither one of these values appears to be a rational number of the form $\dfrac{a}{b}$.

For the sake of argument let it be assumed that $\sqrt{2}$ is a rational number so that

$$\frac{a}{b} = \sqrt{2},$$

where $\dfrac{a}{b}$ is **relatively prime,** that is, it has no common factor other than 1. Then

$$a = \sqrt{2}b,$$

and $a^2 = 2b^2$.

Any number multiplied by 2 is an even integer, so $2b^2$ is an even integer. Also a^2, which equals $2b^2$, must be an even integer. Since it can be proved that if an even integer is a perfect square, then its square roots are also even, it follows that

If a^2 is even, then a has to be even.

It is easy to see if a were odd its square would be an odd number, which contradicts the fact that a^2 is an even number.

Let $a = 2w$,   (w is any other integer)

then $a^2 = 4w^2$.

We now have $a^2 = 4w^2$ and $a^2 = 2b^2$; therefore, by substitution

$$2b^2 = 4w^2$$

and $b^2 = 2w^2$.

Again, $2w^2$ is an even integer and so is b^2. It follows that b is an even integer. Since both a and b have been proved to be even integers, then $\dfrac{a}{b}$ has a common factor which contradicts the original assumption that $\dfrac{a}{b}$ does not have a common factor. Thus **$\sqrt{2}$ is not a rational number.**

Each number in a set of rational numbers can be expressed either as a **terminating decimal fraction,** such as $\frac{1}{8} = 0.125$, or as a **repeating decimal fraction** such as $\frac{1}{7} = 0.\overline{142857}$. The block of numbers under the horizontal bar is to be repeated indefinitely, that is $0.142857142857142857\ldots$.

The $\sqrt{2}$, and the square root of all other nonperfect square numbers, the cube root of all nonperfect cube numbers, the nth root of all nonperfect N-power numbers, and many other numbers, such as π and e, are not rational numbers. All of these are **nonrepeating decimal fractions.** They are classified as irrational numbers. R_i represents the set of irrational numbers.

Definition: 2.7-1.   *An **irrational number** is a number that cannot be expressed as a repeating decimal fraction. In other words, it cannot be expressed as $\dfrac{a}{b}$, where a and b are integers and $b \neq 0$.*

We will return to irrational numbers again when we discuss a *complete ordered field.*

2.8 THE SET OF REAL NUMBERS

Based upon the extensions that have been made to the set of natural numbers, the set of integers, and the set of rational numbers, we have finally discovered how the set of real numbers came about, and we are now ready to define the set of real numbers.

Definition: 2.8-1.   *The **set of real numbers** R is the set of all repeating or nonrepeating decimal fractions. In other words, the set $R = R_r \cup R_i$, where R_r is the set of rational numbers and R_i is the set of irrational numbers.*

Summary : **The Set of Real Numbers—R**

I. The Set of Rational Numbers—R_r:
    (a) Integers—I:
        (i) The Natural Numbers—N.
      (ii) Zero.
      (iii) The Negative Integers $\overline{N}$.

(b) The Fractions:
    (i) The Nonnegative Fractions.
    (ii) The Negative Fractions.
II. The Set of Irrational Numbers—R_i.

The **set inclusion principle** (see Definition 1.2-3) symbolizes the set of real numbers and its subsets as follows:

$$N \subset I \subset R_r \subset R$$

Again making use of the one-dimensional coordinate system to visualize the correspondence between the set of real numbers and the points on a straight line, we obtain the number line shown in Figure 2.8-1.

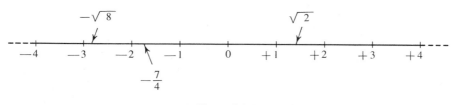

Figure 2.8-1

You realize, of course, that the set of real numbers and the set of points on the straight line are not equal sets. These two sets are equivalent. This means that **there is a one-to-one correspondence between the set of real numbers and the set of points on a straight line such that**

(a) **Each real number corresponds to a point on the straight line.**
(b) **Each point on the straight line corresponds to a real number.**

The preceding statements, when applied to the set of real numbers, will provide a number system which is complete. Thus, we have a **continuum,** a set of real numbers that corresponds to an infinite number of points.

Definition: 2.8-2.   *The set of all real numbers is called the* **continuum** *of real numbers.*

All the unused points (the spaces) left on the number line when the rational numbers were compared with the points on the number line have been used by comparing these points, one-to-one, with the irrational numbers. The completeness property which is involved here will be discussed in more detail later in this chapter.

2.9 NUMBER FIELD

The set of real numbers satisfies all the postulates of a **field.** This set forms a mathematical system called a **number field.** The field postulates which we will now present will enable us to prove number theorems and to justify many algebraic principles and procedures based upon the postulates and the theorems.

Definition 2.9-1.   *A mathematical system called a* **field** *consists of a set of elements together with two operations and an equivalence relation which satisfies postulates of closure, commutativity, associativity, identity, inverses, and distributivity.*

The **real number system** assumes the existence of the set of real numbers, the operations of addition and multiplication, and an equivalence relation, and satisfies these eleven field postulates

A_1: The system is closed under addition.

A_2: The system is commutative under addition.

A_3: The system is associative under addition.

A_4: The identity element under addition is 0 and is unique.

A_5: Each element a has a unique additive inverse $-a$.

M_1: The system is closed under multiplication.

M_2: The system is commutative under multiplication.

M_3: The system is associative under multiplication.

M_4: The identity element under multiplication is 1 and is unique.

M_5: The system has a unique multiplicative inverse $\dfrac{1}{a}$ for each nonzero a.

D: Multiplication distributes over addition.

2.10 FIELD POSTULATES AS APPLIED TO REAL NUMBERS

In our statements of the postulates, R will represent the set of real numbers; $a, b, c, d, \ldots$, will be elements in R; and the equality relation "$=$" will mean "the same as." A_1, A_2, A_3, A_4, and A_5 will represent the postulates under addition. M_1, M_2, M_3, M_4, and M_5 will represent the postulates under multiplication. D will represent the distributive postulate.

Operations under Addition

A_1: **Closure Postulate**
For each a and b in R, $a + b$ is in R and is unique.

A_2: **Commutative Postulate**
For each $a, b \in R$, $a + b = b + a$.

A_3: **Associative Postulate**
For each $a, b, c \in R$, $(a + b) + c = a + (b + c)$.

A_4: **Identity Postulate**
For each $a \in R$ there exists the additive identity element 0 such that $a + 0 = a$.

Operations under Multiplication

M_1: **Closure Postulate**
For each a and b in R, $a \cdot b$ is in R and is unique.

M_2: **Commutative Postulate**
For each $a, b \in R$, $a \cdot b = b \cdot a$.

M_3: **Associative Postulate**
For each $a, b, c \in R$, $(a \cdot b) \cdot c = a \cdot (b \cdot c)$.

M_4: **Identity Postulate**
For each $a \in R$ there exists the multiplicative identity element 1 such that $a \cdot 1 = a$.

A_5: **Inverse Postulate**

For each $a \in R$ there exists an additive inverse $-a$ such that $a + (-a) =$ the identity element 0.

M_5: **Inverse Postulate**

For each $a \in R$ and $a \neq 0$ there exists a multiplicative inverse $\dfrac{1}{a}$ such that

$$a \cdot \frac{1}{a} = \frac{a}{a} = 1, \text{ the identity element.}$$

The multiplicative inverse of a which is $\dfrac{1}{a}$ is also called the **reciprocal** of a. **An equivalent form of** $\dfrac{1}{a}$ **is** a^{-1} and it follows that

$$a \cdot a^{-1} = a \cdot \frac{1}{a} = \frac{a}{a} = 1.$$

D: **The Distributive Postulate** (distributes multiplication over addition)

For each $a, b, c \in R$:

Left-hand form: $a \cdot (b + c) = (a \cdot b) + (a \cdot c)$.

Right-hand form: $(b + c) \cdot a = (b \cdot a) + (c \cdot a)$.

2.11 EQUALITY POSTULATES

The concept of equality has not been defined, but we have been using it right along to mean "the same as." For example, we mean the sum of the left member of an equality, such as $(5 + 6 + 10 = 3 \cdot 7)$, "is the same as" the product of the right member. Expressions that are "the same as" involve the following very important principle:

Definition: 2.11-1.   *The* **principle of substitution** *asserts that any two expressions that are equal to each other may be substituted for each other.*

Along with the field postulates we will need the following **properties of equality** in our further study of the real number system.

For each $a, b, c, d, \ldots$ in the real number system R, we have

E_1: **The Reflexive Law**

$a = a$.

E_2: **The Symmetric Law**

If $a = b$, then $b = a$.

E_3: **The Transitive Law**

If $a = b$ and $b = c$, then $a = c$.

E_4: **The Addition Property**

If $a = b$ and $c = d$, then $a + c = b + d$.

E_5: **The Multiplicative Property**

If $a = b$ and $c = d$, then $a \cdot c = b \cdot d$.

As you work through Exercise 2.A you will discover that both **the set of rational numbers and the set of real numbers represent fields.** But, because there are certain deficiencies in the set of rational numbers, the real number system is by far the best mathematical system for our use in algebra and trigonometry.

You will also find as you work through the problems of Exercise 2.A that the set of natural numbers and the set of integers will satisfy some, but not all, of the field postulates. It should become evident to you as you answer the various questions in Exercise 2.A that the set of natural numbers N is a subset of the integers I, the set of integers I is a subset of the rational numbers R_r, and the set of rational numbers R_r is a subset of the set of real numbers R.

In the following examples, x represents any real number and $a, b, c, d, \ldots$ are elements of R. The letters to the right of the equations represent the field postulates that justify the steps taken in the proof (see Section 2.10).

Example: 2.11-1.   Prove that $c(a + b) + ab = a(c + b) + cb$.

$$
\begin{aligned}
\text{PROOF:} \quad c(a + b) + ab &= ca + cb + ab & (D) \\
&= ca + ab + cb & (A_2) \\
&= ac + ab + cb & (M_2) \\
&= a(c + b) + cb; & (D) \\
\therefore \qquad c(a + b) + ab &= a(c + b) + cb. & (E_3)
\end{aligned}
$$

Example: 2.11-2.   Prove that $(x + 2)(x + 3) = x^2 + 5x + 6$.

$$
\begin{aligned}
\text{PROOF:} \quad (x + 2)(x + 3) &= (x + 2)x + (x + 2)3 & (D) \\
&= x(x + 2) + 3(x + 2) & (M_2) \\
&= (x^2 + x \cdot 2) + (3x + 3 \cdot 2) & (D) \\
&= (x^2 + 2x) + (3x + 3 \cdot 2) & (M_2) \\
&= x^2 + (2x + 3x) + 3 \cdot 2 & (A_3) \\
&= x^2 + (2 + 3)x + 6 & (D \text{ and } M_1) \\
&= x^2 + 5x + 6; & (A_1) \\
\therefore \qquad (x + 2)(x + 3) &= x^2 + 5x + 6. & (E_3)
\end{aligned}
$$

EXERCISE 2.A

1. What is meant by the statement, "The real number system is closed under the operation addition"?

2. Is the real number system closed under multiplication? Explain.

3. Try to find one example that shows that the set of real numbers is not closed under subtraction.

4. Under what one condition does the set of real numbers fail to be closed under division?

5. In the algebra of sets $A \cup (B \cup C) = (A \cup B) \cup C$. If "$\cup$" is interpreted as "$+$" and a, b, c are assumed to be elements of the set of real numbers, what analogous statement could be written in the algebra of real numbers?

6. If $A \cap B = B \cap A$ in the algebra of sets and "$\cap$" is interpreted as "$\cdot$" and $a, b, \in R$, what analogous statement could be made in the algebra of real numbers?

7. Which of the following sets is (are) not closed under addition?

(a) $\{0\}$.   (b) $\{1, 2\}$.   (c) $\{x \mid x \text{ is a nonnegative integer}\}$.

8. Which of the following sets is (are) not closed under multiplication?

(a) $\{0\}$.   (b) $\{0, 1\}$.   (c) $\{x \mid x \text{ is a negative integer}\}$.

9. Under operations of addition and multiplication which of the field postulates are not satisfied by the set of rational numbers? Is the set of rational numbers a field?

10. Under operations of addition and multiplication, which field postulates are not satisfied by the set of integers? Is the set of integers a field?

11. Is the set of natural numbers closed under the operation of addition? subtraction? multiplication? division?

12. Given the set $D = \{x \mid x = 2n - 1, n$ a positive integer$\}$. Under which of the four fundamental operations is this set closed?

13. Does the set of natural numbers contain: (a) an additive identity element? If so, name it; (b) a multiplicative identity element? If so, name it.

14. For any element c in the set of integers: (a) What is its additive inverse? (b) What is its multiplicative inverse?

15. Which field postulate must be satisfied to guarantee closure under subtraction?

16. To guarantee closure under division, which field postulate must be satisfied?

17. How many integers are there less than 10? More than 10?

18. How many natural numbers are there less than 10? More than 10?

19. Is a natural number always an integer? an integer always a rational number? a rational number always a real number?

20. Is a real number always a rational number? a rational number always an integer? an integer always a natural number?

21. Is $0.\overline{4}$, (that is, 0.4444444...) a rational number? If so, express it in the form $\dfrac{a}{b}$.

22. Is 3.1415926... a rational number? If so, express it in the form $\dfrac{a}{b}$.

23. Why is it impossible for a number set which does not contain an additive identity to be closed under subtraction?

24. Does the set $\{0\}$ have a multiplicative inverse? If so, what is it?

25. What is the multiplicative inverse of a, if $a \cdot b = 1$?

26. What is the additive identity of a, if $a + b = 0$?

27. Prove that $(a + b)(c + d) = (ac + bd) + (ad + bc)$.

28. Prove that $(x + b)(x + a) = x^2 + (a + b)x + ab$.

29. Prove that $a(b + 1) + b + (-a) = b(a + 1)$.

30. Prove that $a[b(cd)] = d[c(ab)]$.

2.12 ADDITIONAL PROPERTIES AND THEOREMS OF REAL NUMBERS

There are several basic theorems which state properties of the real number system that are of utmost importance to us in the operations of algebra. We will demonstrate how the postulates of the real number system can be used to prove the truth of seven of these theorems.

One of the major things to notice in this section is how the field and other postulates are put to work to prove algebraic theorems, similar to the way you used basic postulates to prove theorems in geometry.

Some of the theorems which we will prove will no doubt seem self-evident to you. Even so, it is hoped that you will find it interesting and fascinating to prove these theorems strictly on the authority of the basic postulates and theorems that have been proved in this book.

Every theorem is composed of two parts. The part that gives information assumed to be true is called the **hypothesis** and will be indicated by **H** when used in the proofs. The part that follows logically from the hypothesis is called the **conclusion.**

In the following proofs each postulate that justified a particular forward step has been identified by an appropriate capital letter to the right of the equation (see Sections 2.10 and 2.11 for the postulates for these letters). You should follow this same practice in your proofs until you have thoroughly memorized all the postulates, definitions, and basic theorems.

Throughout the proofs a, b, c, and n are assumed to be real numbers.

Theorem: 2.12-1.   Prove that if $a + b = a + c$, then $b = c$.
(This is the additive cancellation law.)

PROOF:
$$(a + b) = (a + c), \qquad\qquad (H)$$
$$-a = -a, \qquad\qquad (E_1)$$
$$-a + (a + b) = -a + (a + c), \qquad\qquad (E_4)$$
$$(-a + a) + b = (-a + a) + c, \qquad\qquad (A_3)$$
$$0 + b = 0 + c; \qquad\qquad (A_5)$$
$$\boldsymbol{b = c.} \qquad\qquad (A_4)$$

Theorem 2.12-1a.   If $a \cdot b = a \cdot c$, then $b = c$. $(a \neq 0.)$
(This is the multiplicative cancellation law. The proof is left to the reader.)

Theorem 2.12-2.   If a and $0 \in R$, then 0 is the only real number such that $a + 0 = a$.

PROOF: Assume n to be any real number such that $a + n = a$. Then
$$a + n = a + 0; \qquad\qquad (E_3)$$
$$\therefore \qquad n = 0. \qquad\qquad \text{(Theorem 2.12-1)}$$

Since n was assumed to be any real number, and $n = 0$, it follows that the additive identity element "0" is unique.

Theorem 2.12-3.   Prove that the number $-a$ is the only real number such that
$$a + (-a) = 0.$$

PROOF: Assume n to be any real number such that $a + n = 0$. Then
$$a + n = a + (-a); \qquad\qquad (E_3)$$
$$\therefore \qquad n = -a. \qquad\qquad \text{(Theorem 2.12-1)}$$
No matter what n is assumed to be, it has been proved equal to $-a$. Therefore, the additive inverse $-a$ is unique.

It will be left for the reader to prove the uniqueness of the multiplicative identity "1," and the multiplicative inverse " $\dfrac{1}{a}$,"   where $a \neq 0$. Use a^{-1} for $\dfrac{1}{a}$ if you prefer it.

Theorem 2.12-4.   Prove that for all $a \in R$, $a \cdot 0 = 0$.

PROOF:
$$
\begin{array}{ll}
0 + 0 = 0, & (A_4) \\
a \cdot (0 + 0) = a \cdot 0, & (\text{Theorem 2.12-1a or } E_5) \\
a \cdot 0 + a \cdot 0 = a \cdot 0, & (D) \\
a \cdot 0 + a \cdot 0 = a \cdot 0 + 0; & (A_4) \\
\mathbf{a \cdot 0 = 0.} & (\text{Theorem 2.12-1})
\end{array}
$$

Theorem: 2.12-5.   For all $a, b \in R$, prove that $a(-b) = (-ab)$.

PROOF:
$$
\begin{array}{ll}
ab + a(-b) = a(b + (-b)) & (D) \\
\qquad\qquad = a \cdot 0 & (A_5) \\
\qquad\qquad = 0, & (\text{Theorem 2.12-4}) \\
-(ab) + ab + a(-b) = -(ab) + 0, & (E_4) \\
0 + a(-b) = -(ab) + 0; & (A_5) \\
\therefore \qquad \mathbf{a(-b) = -(ab).} & (A_4)
\end{array}
$$

Prove that $(-a)b = a(-b)$. Prove also that if $a \neq 0$, then $-(-a) = a$ and $(a^{-1})^{-1} = a$, where $a^{-1} = \dfrac{1}{a}$.

Theorem 2.12-6.   Prove that for all $a, b \in R$, $(-a)(-b) + ab$.

PROOF:
$$
\begin{array}{ll}
(-a)(-b) = (-a)(-b), & (E_1) \\
-(ab) = a(-b), & (\text{Theorem 2.12-5}) \\
(-a)(-b) + [-(ab)] = (-a)(-b) + a(-b) & (E_4) \\
\qquad\qquad = (-a + a)(-b) & (D) \\
\qquad\qquad = 0(-b) & (A_5) \\
\qquad\qquad = 0, & (\text{Theorem 2.12-4}) \\
(-a)(-b) + [-(ab)] = 0, & (E_3) \\
[(-a)(-b) + --(ab)] + ab = 0 + ab, & (E_4) \\
(-a)(-b) + [-(ab) + ab] = ab, & (A_3 \text{ and } A_4) \\
(-a)(-b) + 0 = ab; & (A_5) \\
\therefore \qquad \mathbf{(-a)(-b) = ab.} & (A_4)
\end{array}
$$

Theorem: 2.12-7.   Prove that if $ab = 0$, then both a and $b = 0$, or $a = 0$ or $b = 0$.

PROOF: If $a = 0$ and $b = 0$, then $\mathbf{ab = 0.}$ (Theorem 2.12-4)
If $a = 0$, then $0 \cdot b = 0$ and $\mathbf{0 = 0.}$ (Theorem 2.12-4)

If $a \neq 0$, then $\dfrac{1}{a}$, the multiplicative inverse or reciprocal of a, exists

and the following argument can be made:

$$ab = 0, \qquad\qquad\qquad (H)$$

$$\frac{1}{a} \cdot (ab) = \frac{1}{a}(0), \qquad\qquad (E_5)$$

$$\left(\frac{1}{a} \cdot a\right)b = 0, \qquad\qquad (M_3 \text{ and Theorem 2.12-4})$$

$$(1)b = 0; \qquad\qquad\qquad (M_5)$$

$$\therefore \qquad\qquad b = 0. \qquad\qquad\qquad (M_4)$$

If $b \neq 0$, then a proof similar to the preceding one shows that $a = 0$.

Theorem 2.12-7 will be used extensively later on in the solution of equations and in the derivation of formulas.

EXERCISE 2.B

For all $a, b, c, d, \ldots \in R$.
1. Prove that if $a = b$ and $c = d$, then $a + c = b + d$.
2. Prove that if $a = b$ and $c = d$, then $ac = bd$.
3. If $ab = ac$ and $a \neq 0$, prove that $b = c$.
4. Use a proof similar to the one used on Theorem 2.12-4 to prove $0 \cdot a = 0$.
5. Prove that $-(-a) = a$.
6. Prove that $(a^{-1})^{-1} = a$ for $a \neq 0$.
7. Prove that $-(ab) = (-a)b$.
8. Prove that $-1(a) = -a$.
9. If $a = b$, prove that $a - c = b - c$.
10. If $a = b$ and $c \neq 0$, prove that $\dfrac{a}{c} = \dfrac{b}{c}$.
11. Prove that $d(ab) + a(dc) = ad(b + c)$.
12. Prove that $(c + a) - (d + b) = (a - b) - (d - c)$.
13. Prove that $(a + b)(a - b) = a^2 - b^2$.
14. Prove that $(a + b)(a^2 - ab + b^2) = a^3 + b^3$.
15. If $a = b$, show that $-a = -b$.
16. If x is any real number such that $(x + a)(x + b)(x - c) = 0$, explain why it is true that $x = -a, x = -b$, and $x = c$.
17. If $ab = 1$ and $a \neq 0$, prove that $b = \dfrac{1}{a}$.
18. If $a + b = 0$, prove that $a = -b$.
19. Does the commutative postulate hold under subtraction of real numbers? Does the associative postulate hold?
20. Does the commutative postulate hold under division of real numbers? Does the associative postulate hold?

2.13 ORDER PROPERTIES OF REAL NUMBERS

The field and equality postulates permit us to find both sums and products of pairs of real numbers. Now, we propose to go a step further and find ways of determining which number comes first in a sequence. We have been assuming all along that the numbers 1, 2, 3, 4, . . . are in natural order, that the number 2 comes before 3, and that we can write it as $2 < 3$ because the **symbol "$<$"** **means "is less than."**

To make the concept "is less than" more precise the following definition is offered:

Definition: 2.13-1.   *If the set of real numbers, a, b, c, $d \in R$, satisfies the* **order** **postulates** O_1, O_2, O_3, *and* O_4, *then it is called an* **ordered field.**

O_1: The **Trichotomy Postulate**
   $a < b$ or $a = b$ or $b < a$.
O_2: The **Transitive Postulate**
   If $a < b$ and $b < c$, then $a < c$.
O_3: The **Addition Postulate**
   If $a < b$, then $a + c < b + c$.
O_4: The **Multiplicative Postulate**
   If $a < b$ and $0 < c$, then $ac < bc$.

In the trichotomy and transitive postulates O_1 and O_2, only the relation $<$ is involved, but in O_3 the relation $<$ is associated with addition, and in O_4 the relation $<$ is associated with multiplication. Also,

Axiom: 2.13-1.   *The relation $a < b$ asserts that a is less than b, and therefore $b - a$ is a positive number.*

2.14 INEQUALITIES APPLIED TO THEOREMS

In addition to the "is less than" relation, which we have used in stating the order postulates, there are three other relations with which we will be concerned. In order that we can have easy reference to them later, we will present these inequality relations in the form of a definition.

Definition: 2.14-1.   (a) *The symbol $<$ in $a < b$ means "is less than."*
   (b) *The symbol $\leq$ means "is less than or equal to."*
       $a \leq b$ if and only if either $a < b$ or $a = b$.
   (c) *The symbol $>$ in $a > b$ means "is greater than."*
       $a > b$ if and only if $b < a$.
   (d) *The symbol $\geq$ means "is greater than or equal to."*
       $a \geq b$ if and only if either $a > b$ or $a = b$.

Before we proceed to prove some basic inequality theorems, there are two definitions which we would like to present.

Definition: 2.14-2.   *For all $a \in R$, $a > 0$ is called a* **positive real number** *and $a < 0$ is called a* **negative real number**. *Zero is neither a positive nor a negative real number.*

Definition 2.14-3.   *The* **absolute value** *of a real number a, symbolized by $|a|$, is a nonnegative real number. Its value is determined as follows:*

If $a > 0$, then $|a| = a$.
If $a < 0$, then $|a| = -a$.
If $a = 0$, then $|a| = 0$.

Theorem 2.14-1.   Prove that if $a < 0$, then $-a > 0$.

PROOF:

$$a < 0, \qquad \text{(Hypothesis)}$$
$$a + (-a) < 0 + (-a), \qquad (O_3)$$
$$0 < -a. \qquad (A_4 \text{ and } A_5)$$
$$\therefore \qquad -a > 0. \qquad \text{(Definition 2.14-1c)}$$

Theorem 2.14-2.   Prove that $a < b$ is equivalent to $a - b < 0$.

PROOF:

$$a < b, \qquad (H)$$
$$a + (-b) < b + (-b); \qquad (O_3)$$
$$\therefore \qquad a - b < 0. \qquad \text{(Definition 2.2-4 and } A_5)$$

The converse: if $a - b < 0$, then $a < b$.

$$a - b < 0, \qquad (H)$$
$$a - b + b < 0 + b; \qquad (O_3)$$
$$\therefore \qquad a < b. \qquad (A_4 \text{ and } A_5)$$

Theorem: 2.14-3.   Prove that $a - b < 0$ is equivalent to $0 < b - a$.

PROOF:

$$a - b < 0, \qquad \text{(Hypothesis)}$$
$$-a + a - b + b < b - a; \qquad (O_3)$$
$$\therefore \qquad 0 < b - a. \qquad (A_5)$$

The proof of the converse is left to the reader.

The conclusion of Theorem 2.14-3 is interesting because it, along with Theorem 2.14-2, has justified the facts that $a < b$ is equivalent to $a - b < 0$, which is equivalent to $0 < b - a$, where $b - a$ is a positive number. See also Axiom 2.13-1.

Theorem: 2.14-4.   Prove that if $a < b$ and $c < 0$, then $ac > bc$.

From the preceding paragraph we know that $b - a$ is a positive number.

PROOF:

$$c < 0, \qquad (H)$$
$$(b - a)c < (b - a) \cdot 0, \qquad (O_4)$$
$$bc - ac < 0, \qquad (D \text{ and Theorem 2.12-4})$$

$$bc - ac + ac < 0 + ac, \qquad (O_3)$$
$$bc < ac; \qquad (A_4 \text{ and } A_5)$$
$$\therefore \qquad ac > bc. \qquad [\text{Definition 2.14-1(c)}]$$

2.15 COMPLETENESS

While it is true that the set of rational numbers and the set of real numbers are both ordered fields, the two sets differ in that the **set of real numbers is the only one that satisfies the postulate of completeness.**

Of the several ways of investigating the idea of completeness we will use the **least upper bound** procedure. To demonstrate this we will select any irrational number, such as $\sqrt{2}$, and attempt to approach its value by a sequence of rational numbers. Our list will include:

1.4, 1.41, 1.414, 1.4142, 1.41421, ...

Any one of these rational numbers, and others that could be annexed, will when squared come very close to but never quite equal the value 2. So we will say that the irrational number $\sqrt{2}$ is the *upper bound*, and more precisely the *least upper bound* of the above sequence of rational numbers.

Definition 2.15-1. *An **upper bound** of the real number system R is a number not exceeded by any other number in the system. A **least upper bound** of R is the "smallest number" in the set of upper bounds.*

If we attempted to approach $\sqrt{2}$ from the top side with the sequence

1.42, 1.415, 1.4143, 1.41422, . . .

we would find the square of any rational number in the sequence would slightly exceed 2. Therefore, $\sqrt{2}$ is the *lower bound* and more precisely the *greatest lower bound* of the preceding sequence of rational numbers.

Definition: 2.15-2. *The **greatest lower bound** of the real number system is a number that is lower than any other number in the system.*

Definition: 2.15-3. *The **completeness property** of real numbers asserts that every nonempty set of real numbers that is bounded from above has a least upper bound, and if bounded from below has a greatest lower bound.*

Just as the irrational member $\sqrt{2}$ is the least upper bound for some set of rational numbers, so every irrational number is the least upper bound for some set of rational numbers. Geometrically, this means that all points on the number line that were not matched with rational numbers are now matched with the irrational numbers. Thus, we say that the **real number system is a continuum formed by the union of the rational and the irrational numbers and is a complete ordered set.**

EXERCISE 2.C

For all problems it is assumed that $a, b, c, d \in R$.

1. If necessary, arrange each of these sets so that it will be properly ordered (smallest first):

(a) $\{2, -5\}$.   (b) $\{\frac{1}{2}, \frac{2}{3}, \frac{3}{4}\}$.   (c) $\{-\sqrt{2}, 0, |-4|\}$.

2. What is the correct order for each of these sets of numbers (smallest first)?

(a) $\{\sqrt{2}, 2, \sqrt{3}\}$.   (b) $\{|-20|, 4, 0.5\}$.   (c) $\{\frac{1}{8}, \frac{1}{12}, \frac{1}{10}\}$.

3. Prove that if $a > b$, then $a + c > b + c$.

4. Prove that if $a > b$, then $ac > bc$.   ($c > 0$.)

5. If $a \neq b$, prove that $a < b$ or $b < a$, but not both. Why?

6. Prove that when $a \neq 0$ either a is positive and $-a$ is negative or a is negative and $-a$ is positive.

7. If $a < 0$ and $b < 0$, prove that $ab < 0$.

8. If $a > 0$ and $b > 0$, and $a > b$, prove that $a^2 > b^2$.

9. Prove that the product of two positive numbers $0 < a$ and $0 < b$, is positive.

10. Prove that the product of two negative numbers is positive.

11. If $a > 0$, is it true that $a^2 > 0$?

12. If $a < 0$, is it true that $a^2 > 0$?

13. If $a \geq b$, show that $a^2 + b^2 \geq 2ab$.

14. If $a \leq b$, show that $a^2 + b^2 \geq 2ab$.

15. Prove that if $a > 0$, then $2 \leq a + a^{-1}$.

16. Prove that if $a > 0$ and $b < 0$, then $ab < 0$.

17. Find the absolute value of $a = -17$. Does your answer satisfy the definition for absolute value (Definition 2.14-3)?

18. If $a = -\sqrt{6}$, what is the value for $-a$? What is the absolute value of a?

19. Is the set $\{a | -\sqrt{10} \leq a \leq \sqrt{9}\}$ a bounded set? That is, is it bounded on both ends? If so, what is its least upper bound? What is its greatest lower bound?

20. From the set of natural numbers, the set of nonnegative numbers, the set of integers, the set of rational numbers, the set of irrational numbers, and the set of real numbers, list the set or sets that have: (a) a least upper bound, (b) a greatest lower bound, (c) fully satisfied the completeness property.

Relations, Functions, and Their Graphs

It would be unwise to attempt a study of relations and functions without making graphs of them. For this reason this chapter will begin with a brief review of a coordinate system.

3.1 THE RECTANGULAR COORDINATE SYSTEM

The **one-dimensional coordinate system** which was used in Chapter 2 to show the one-to-one relationship between real numbers and points on a line, consisted of an endless horizontal line, a point (called the origin) on the line, a unit of measurement, and a positive direction. We now propose to take a pair of one-dimensional coordinate systems and draw them so that their origins coincide and their lines are perpendicular. Then we have what is known as the **Cartesian or rectangular coordinate system.**

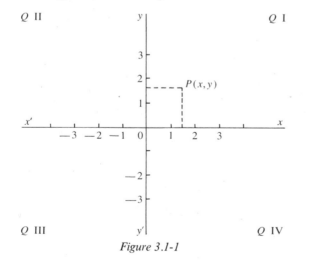

Figure 3.1-1

1. The horizontal line $x'0x$ is called the x *axis*, the vertical line $y'0y$ the y *axis*, and the point of intersection of the two lines is the *origin* 0.

2. The two axes determine the coordinate plane, called the xy plane, and divide it into these four quadrants, I, II, III, IV, located as shown in Figure 3.1-1.

3. An arbitrary unit of measurement is selected for each axis. These units of measurement may be the same, but they do not have to be. A distance measured horizontally to the right of the y axis is positive and to the left is negative. Such a distance is called the **abscissa** or the **x coordinate.** A distance measured vertically above the x axis is positive and below is negative. Such a distance is called the **ordinate** or the **y coordinate.**

4. Each point P in a plane, expressed as an ordered pair $P(x, y)$, determines a unique x coordinate and a unique y coordinate and, conversely, each pair of x and y coordinates determines a unique point P in a plane.

The idea of order is totally immaterial in the discussion of sets, as you may recall. For instance, it makes no difference whether we write the elements 2 and 5 as $\{2, 5\}$ or as $\{5, 2\}$. But the freedom which we have to change elements around within a set is not at all permissible within an ordered pair.

Definition: 3.1-1.   *An* **ordered pair,** *such as* (x, y) *is an arrangement of two objects that makes it evident which object is to be taken first and which object is to be taken second.*

In the ordered pair (x, y) the x to the left is always to be considered first. Then after x comes y.

You can readily see that the ordered pair $(2, 5)$, which represents a certain point in a plane, is quite different from $(5, 2)$ which represents an entirely different point.

Suppose that from any point P in Figure 3.1-1 perpendiculars are dropped to the x axis and to the y axis. Then measure the x coordinate as the distance from the origin 0 along the x axis to the foot of the perpendicular from P. Next, from the end of the x distance determine the distance vertically to the point P. This length is equal to the y coordinate. Thus, the x and y coordinates necessary to locate P have been determined by a procedure which suggests the following definition:

Each point P in a plane *is in one-to-one correspondence with an ordered pair of numbers* (x, y) *and, conversely,* **each ordered pair of numbers** (x, y) *is in one-to-one correspondence with a unique point P in a plane.*

3.2 CARTESIAN PRODUCT

In Section 3.1 we have been laying the groundwork for an additional method of forming a new set from two given sets. This new set is to contain all possible ordered pairs of (x, y). Assuming that the given sets are A and B, the new set called the **Cartesian product** of A and B, will be indicated by $A \times B$. It is read, A cross B.

Definition: 3.2-1.   *The* **Cartesian product** *of A × B is the set of all ordered pairs of (x, y) such that x ∈ A and y ∈ B.*

Given the two sets $A = \{1, 2, 3\}$ and $B = \{2, 4\}$, the Cartesian product for these two sets is the set

$A \times B = \{(1, 2), (1, 4), (2, 2), (2, 4), (3, 2), (3, 4)\}.$

The following statements which apply to the preceding Cartesian product should be carefully observed:

1. The elements for $A \times B$ are ordered pairs whose first coordinate x belongs only to set A and whose second coordinate y belongs only to set B.

2. Ordered pairs that have identical coordinates, such as $(2, 2)$ in $A \times B$, remain exactly as they are. Such ordered pairs represent a single element in the $A \times B$ set. Therefore, they do not in any way violate the demand that elements within a set should not be repeated.

Figure 3.2-1a is a graph of

$A \times B = \{(1, 2), (1, 4), (2, 2), (2, 4), (3, 2), (3, 4)\}.$

The elements of set A are represented along the x axis and the elements of set B are represented along or parallel to the y axis.

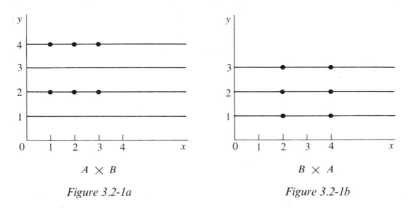

A × B	*B × A*
Figure 3.2-1a	Figure 3.2-1b

Figure 3.2-1b is a plot of the ordered pairs of the Cartesian set $B \times A$. It was obtained by taking the elements of set $B = \{2, 4\}$ as the first coordinates followed by the elements of set $A = \{1, 2, 3\}$ as the second coordinates.

$B \times A = \{(2, 1), (2, 2), (2, 3), (4, 1), (4, 2), (4, 3)\}.$

It is quite evident that the two graphs shown in Figures 3.2-1a and 3.2-1b are not the same. From this interchange of coordinates we can see that

$A \times B \neq B \times A.$

In other words, **Cartesian products obtained from distinct sets are not commutative.**

A special case of the Cartesian product $A \times B$ is obtained when $A = B = R$, R representing the set of real numbers. As you would suspect, **the graph of $R \times R$ is the set of all points in a plane.**

3.3 VARIABLE AND CONSTANT

Definition: 3.3-1.   *An **open sentence** is a statement that contains at least one symbol whose purpose is to serve as a place holder for the name of some object.*

An open sentence is neither true nor false. It becomes true or false depending upon the object that is substituted for the symbol. What is your reaction to this open sentence?

"Mr. x has been President of the United States."

Don't you immediately begin to substitute such names as Washington, Jefferson, Lincoln, Eisenhower, Kennedy, and so on, for x? And isn't the purpose of the x to serve as a place holder for each past president's name you can think of? Notice that as long as you call a past president's name the statement is true. But if you call names such as Benjamin Franklin, Thomas Edison, or Billy Graham, the statement is false.

The symbol x, which we have been using as a place holder, is called a **variable.** We have been using both variables and constants right along. But they are so fundamental in the study of mathematics that we want to define them at this point.

Definition: 3.3-2.   *A **variable** is a symbol which holds a place for each element in a specified set.*

A variable holds a place for certain constants, but not necessarily for all constants. For example, in $\{x \mid \frac{1}{x} = 4; x \in R\}$ the value $x = 0$ has to be ruled out. $\frac{1}{0} = 4$ is meaningless. As has been stated before, *division by zero is not permissible.* Therefore, for $\frac{1}{x} = 4$, $x = 0$ is not an admissible value.

Definition: 3.3-3.   *An **admissible value of a variable** is one that gives meaning to the statement.*

Definition: 3.3-4.   *The **scope** of a variable is the replacement set that contains all admissible values for the variable.*

If x represents all male citizens of the United States eligible to become President of the United States, the **scope** or replacement set for x would be $\{x \mid x$ is an eligible male citizen of the United States$\}$. The **solution set** $\{x \mid x$ has been President of the United States$\}$ would, of course, be a subset of the replacement set and would include only those males who have been President of the United States.

Let us now take our open sentence, "Mr. x has been President of the United States," and express it in present tense as follows:

"Mr. x is President of the United States."

It is quite clear that the variable x in this statement holds a place for exactly one name. This name is a fixed thing; it is a **constant.**

Definition: 3.3-5.   *A* **constant** *is a variable represented by a set that contains only one element.*

The x in the statement $x + 2 = 3$ is fixed. To make the statement true, x can be only the number 1. The **scope** of the set $\{x \mid x + 2 = 3; x \in R\}$ is any real number. But its **solution set** is the singleton $\{1\}$, a constant.

3.4 RELATIONS

The idea of **relation** permeates all mathematics. We have already been using the relation concept in expressions such as "the same as," "is less than," "is greater than," "is similar to," and "is equivalent to." We could go on with an almost endless number of relations such as "is the father of," "is the square root of," "is the divisor of," "is younger than," "$y = 2x + 1$," "$y = \pm\sqrt{x}$," and so on. Our purpose here is not to go deeply into the theory of relations, but to learn enough about the fundamental nature of relations so that we can study in considerable detail a relation called a **function.**

Definition: 3.4-a.   *In the mathematics of sets, a* **relation** *is a set of ordered pairs (x, y) such that for each admissible value for x there exists at least one value for y.*

As you proceed to study Figures 3.4-a and 3.4-b you will discover that a relation in the Cartesian set $R \times R$, where R represents the real numbers, is always a subset of $R \times R$. As a case in point look at Figure 3.4-a. Here, the graph of ordered pairs of the relation $y = 2x + 1$ includes only a small portion of the points in the plane which represents the graph of $R \times R$. Therefore, the graph of the relation $y = 2x + 1$ is definitely a subset of the graph of $R \times R$.

There is one special difference between the graphs in Figures 3.4-a and 3.4-b. In the graph of $y = 2x + 1$ for each assumed x coordinate there is a unique y coordinate, and vice versa. Thus, there is a one-to-one correspondence between the x coordinates, which we might call set A, and the y coordinates, which we might call set B. This is not the case for $y = \pm\sqrt{x}$ in Figure 3.4-b. Here, for each x coordinate there are two y values. This is sometimes called a **one-to-many correspondence,** but it still satisfies our definition for a relation. All Definition 3.4-a demands is that there be at least one y value for each x value. It does not say we cannot have as many as the specified relation produces.

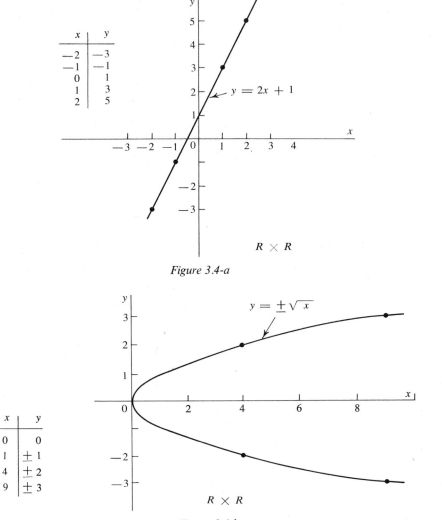

Figure 3.4-a

Figure 3.4-b

Figures 3.4-a and 3.4-b indicate that ordered pairs may be related by a formula. However, keep in mind that there is nothing in the definition of a relation (Definition 3.4-a) that demands the existence of a formula. If **formulas,** or **rules of correspondence** as they are sometimes called in connection with relations and functions, *are given they may be expressed either in the set-builder form or as a set of ordered pairs.* That is, for all x and y expressed as real numbers (or for objects of any kind):

$\{(x, y) \mid y = x^2 + 1\}$ may be written as $\{(x, x^2 + 1)\}$.

$\{(x, y) \mid y = x - 1\}$ may be written as $\{(x, x - 1)\}$.

$\left\{(x, y) \mid y = \dfrac{3}{x}\right\}$ may be written as $\left\{\left(x, \dfrac{3}{x}\right)\right\}$.

In our discussions of relations and functions we will use a lowercase r circled, $\circledP$, to represent the relation and a lowercase f to denote the function. The domain, range, independent variable, and dependent variable of a relation are defined as follows:

Definition 3.4-b.   *The* **domain d** *of a relation $\circledP$, or of a function f, is the set of all admissible values of the first coordinate of (x, y).*

Definition: 3.4-c.   *The first coordinate in an ordered pair is called the* **independent variable.**

Definition: 3.4-d.   *The* **range r** *of a relation $\circledP$, or of a function f, is the set of all possible second elements of the ordered pair (x, y).*

Definition: 3.4-e.   *The second coordinate in an ordered pair is called the* **dependent variable.**

Referring once more to Figures 3.4-a and 3.4-b, the following observations can be made:

1. Each of the relations shown is composed of three parts:
    (a) A domain which we will call set A.
    (b) A range which we will call set B.
    (c) A formula or a rule of correspondence which expresses the relationship between the two sets.

2. The x values are customarily given or assumed. Because the y values depend upon the values given to x, y is called the dependent variable.

3. Data for the graph of a few discrete points have been worked out and only the coordinates of these points are shown on the graph. However, *throughout this book we are assuming the availability of the real number system, and unless otherwise stated we are letting these few discrete points serve as the skeleton for the corresponding continuous curve.*

4. The domain and range for $y = 2x + 1$ include all the real numbers.

5. The domain for $y = \pm\sqrt{x}$ is limited to the positive real numbers and the range is all the real numbers.

6. Unless the domain and the rule of correspondence of a relation are stated one does not know how to proceed.

3.4-1 Equivalence Relations

Not all relations possess the reflexive, symmetric, and transitive properties which we have previously discussed in terms of equality. The relations that do possess these properties we call **equivalence relations,** and we define them in this manner:

Definition: 3.4-1a.   *An* **equivalence relation** *is*
1. **Reflexive:** $x \; \textcircled{r} \; x$.
2. **Symmetric:** *If* $x \; \textcircled{r} \; y$, *then* $y \; \textcircled{r} \; x$.
3. **Transitive:** *If* $x \; \textcircled{r} \; y$ *and* $y \; \textcircled{r} \; z$, *then* $x \; \textcircled{r} \; z$.

Below are examples of these three equivalence properties:
1. Every triangle is related to itself.
2. If x belongs to the same church as y, then y belongs to the same church as x.
3. If x owns fewer golf clubs than y and y owns fewer golf clubs than z, then x owns fewer golf clubs than z.

3.4-2 Graphs of Absolute Value and Inequalities

Below you will find the graphs of two relations which you may need to refer to from time to time. They involve **absolute value** and **inequality.**

$\textcircled{r} = \{(x, y) \mid x, y \in R \text{ and } y \geq |x + 1|\}$.

$\textcircled{r} = \{(x, y) \mid x, y \in R \text{ and } y \geq x\}$.

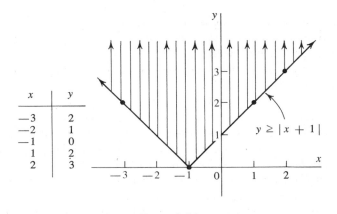

x	y
-3	2
-2	1
-1	0
1	2
2	3

Figure 3.4-2a

Notice in the data for Figure 3.4-2a that no matter what value is substituted for x the result of $|x + 1|$ is either a positive real number or zero since $y \geq |x + 1|$.

In Figure 3.4-2b all points on the graph of $y = x$ are shown and all points above the graph of $y = x$ represent the graph of $y > x$. Had the given problem been to graph only $y > x$, the graph of $y = x$ would still have been shown in the form of a broken line. Then $y = x$ would be merely serving as a guide line and its points would not belong to the graph of $y > x$.

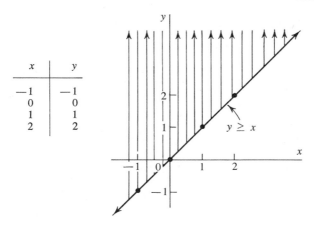

Figure 3.4-2b

EXERCISE 3.A

1. List all the ordered pairs of the Cartesian set $A \times B$ if $A = \{1, 2, 3\}$ and $B = \{a, b, c\}$. How many ordered pairs does the set have? How many elements?

2. If $A = \{3, 5\}$ and $B = \{2, 3, 4, 5\}$, list all the elements of the Cartesian set $A \times B$. How many elements does it have? How many ordered pairs?

3. If $A = \{5\}$, list all the ordered pairs of the Cartesian set $A \times A$.

4. Find all the elements of the Cartesian set $A \times A$ if $A = \{-1, 0, 1\}$.

5. If $(7, 9)$ is an ordered pair, is $(9, 7)$ the same ordered pair? Explain.

6. If $\{7, 9\}$ is a set, is $\{9, 7\}$ the same set? Is $\{9, 7, 0\}$ the same set as $\{9, 7\}$?

7. Is it correct to write the ordered pair $(2, 2)$ as (2)? Why?

8. Is it correct to write the set $\{2, 2\}$ as the set $\{2\}$? Why?

9. Make a list of ordered pairs that belong to the set $\{(x, y) \mid y = x + 2; x, y \in I\}$. Use the data to make a graph. Explain why this graph should not be drawn as a continuous curve.

10. Find six ordered pairs that belong to the set $\{(x, y) \mid y = x + 1, x, y \in R\}$. Make a graph of your data. If all possible values of x were used, would the graph be continuous?

11. Graph the relation $\{(x, \pm\sqrt{3 - x}) \mid x \in R\}$.

12. Graph the relation $\{(x, x \pm 4) \mid x < 6$ and a positive integer$\}$.

13. What kind of sentence is the statement "x is the name of an automobile manufactured by General Motors?" Is the statement true or false?

14. Change the statement in Problem 13 to make it true, to make it false.

15. Is the x in the statement "$x + 7 = 14$" a variable? a constant? What is the implied scope or replacement set for x?

16. In the statement "$x + 7 = 7 + x$" is the x a variable? a constant? What is the replacement set for x, if x is a real number?

17. For all $x \in R$ name one inadmissible value for x for the relation $y = \dfrac{x}{x - 2}$.

18. Can the scope of x include all the real numbers for $y = \dfrac{1}{x}$?

19. Determine the domain for the ordered pairs $(0, -1)$, $(1, 0)$, $(2, 3)$, $(3, 8)$, and $(4, 15)$. What is its range? Is this set of ordered pairs a relation?

20. For the ordered pairs $(-2, -21)$, $(-1, -16)$, $(0, -4)$, $(1, -6)$, $(2, -1)$, $(3, 4)$, find the domain and the range. Is the set of ordered pairs a function?

21. Given $x, y \in R$. Graph the relation $\{(x, y) \mid y < x - 2\}$.

22. Graph $\{(x, y) \mid y + 2 \geq x - 3 \text{ and } x, y \in R\}$.

23. Express in set form the set of all ordered pairs of numbers whose sum is zero.

24. Express in set form the set of ordered pairs whose second number is the square of the first one.

25. Make a graph of $\{(x, y) \mid |x - y| = 2\}$.

26. Make a graph of $\{(x, y) \mid |(x - 1) + y| = 2\}$.

27. Given the relation "live in the same city as." Is this an equivalence relation?

28. Is the relation "is the uncle of" an equivalence relation?

3.5 FUNCTIONS

A function is a special kind of relation. It is of extreme importance in all kinds of mathematics. *A function is sometimes defined as a relation consisting of set A and set B and a rule of correspondence such that for each x in set A there is a unique y corresponding to x in set B.* Actually, if set A along with a formula or rule of correspondence is known, set B can always be computed.

While the rule of correspondence of a function usually is given, it does not have to be. For this reason the following definition is preferred for a function:

Definition: 3.5-1.   *For any two nonempty sets A and B, a* **function** *f is any subset of A × B which has the property that no two distinct ordered pairs of the function have the same first element.*

Since the lowercase letter f is used to represent a function, the symbol $f(x)$, read: "f of x" or "f at x," will be used to represent the value of the function. In other words, $f(x)$ **stands for the same value as does** y **in the ordered pair** (x, y). Thus, we are free to use y and $f(x)$ interchangeably. This is why we can write either $f(x) = 2x + 1$ with ordered pairs of $[x, f(x)]$ or $y = 2x + 1$ with ordered pairs of (x, y). It is important, of course, for you to understand that $f(x)$ does not mean f multiplied by x.

By making a careful comparison of Definitions 3.5-1 and 3.4-a you will observe that

1. **All functions are relations** because they satisfy the relation definition.

2. **All relations are not functions,** because some relations have multiple y values corresponding to a given x value.

Definition: 3.5-2.   *If to each element x in set A there exists a unique element f(x) in set B, then there is said to be a* **mapping** *of set A into set B.*

In Figure 3.5-1a the Cartesian set is $A \times B$. Set A, the domain of the function, represents all x values; and set B, the range of the function, represents all y values. The graph of function f represents the set of ordered pairs and occupies only a small portion of the graph of the Cartesian set $A \times B$. Thus, f is a subset of $A \times B$.

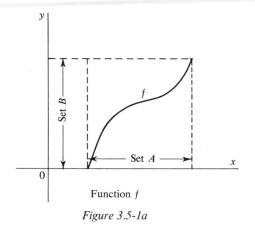

Function f

Figure 3.5-1a

Figure 3.5-1b shows each x in set A mapped into one and only one y in set B. The fact that the diagram shows two different x values mapped into the same y does not in any way overstep our definition of a function (see Definition 3.5-1). All that Definition 3.5-1 demands is that there be a unique y value for

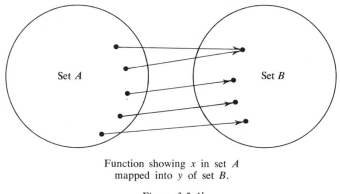

Function showing x in set A
mapped into y of set B.

Figure 3.5-1b

each x value. In other words, more than one y value cannot have the same x value. It does not say that several x values cannot have the same y value.

We have already learned that **if each element in set A maps into a unique element of set B and, conversely, if each element of set B maps into a unique element of set A, then there exists one-to-one correspondence between the two sets.** Figure 3.5-2 shows such a correspondence for the function $f(x) = \sqrt{9 - x}$. Notice that the arrows point both toward the x values shown in set A and the $f(x)$ values shown in set B.

A function such as $f(x) = \sqrt{9 - x}$, which possesses one-to-one correspondence, has an **inverse function** $x = \sqrt{9 - f(x)}$, *that is, a function in which the first and*

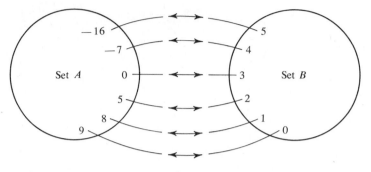

Figure 3.5-2. One-to-one correspondence for $f(x) = \sqrt{9-x}$.

second coordinates of the ordered pairs are interchanged. The ordered pair, $[x, f(x)]$ is changed to $[f(x), x]$. Inverse functions will be discussed in detail later.

We have previously mentioned that y and $f(x)$ are symbols that may be used to represent the same thing. While a statement such as $y = 2x + 1$ seems a little more friendly to some people than does the statement $f(x) = 2x + 1$, in either case the important part of the statement is $2x + 1$. From $2x + 1$ the ordered pairs $(x, 2x + 1)$ of the function can be obtained without any need whatsoever for either y or $f(x)$. Yet y and $f(x)$ are very convenient symbols to use to represent functions. Sometimes y is preferred and sometimes $f(x)$ is preferred. At the moment we feel that there is a real advantage in using the symbol $f(x)$ both to represent the function and to represent the vertical axis of the coordinate system used in graphing the function. Later we will feel perfectly free to use y if it appears to be more convenient for us to do so.

Let us use $[x, f(x)]$ to find a set of ordered pairs for the function f.

$f = \{[x, f(x)] \mid f(x) = 2x + 1\}$.

If $x = -2$, then $f(-2) = 2(-2) + 1 = -3$.
If $x = -1$, then $f(-1) = 2(-1) + 1 = -1$.
If $x = 0$, then $f(0) = 2(0) + 1 = 1$.
If $x = 1$, then $f(1) = 2(1) + 1 = 3$.
If $x = 2$, then $f(2) = 2(2) + 1 = 5$.

x	$f(x)$
-2	-3
-1	-1
0	1
1	3
2	5

Compare the preceding data with the data in Figure 3.4-a. The data and the graph in Figure 3.4-a have to do with a relation that is a function, because of the following two very fundamental reasons:

1. **If for every x in the domain of a relation there is a unique y in the range of the relation, then the relation is a function.**
2. **If a vertical line can be made to meet the graph of a relation at no more than one point, then the relation is a function.**

3.6 GRAPHS OF FUNCTIONS

To help us understand better how functions behave, several examples of graphs of functions will be presented. In these graphs, unless otherwise stated, the real numbers will be assumed and the Cartesian set, $R \times R$, will be assumed to occupy the entire plane even though only selected values will be used to construct the graphs.

Example: 3.6-1.   A graph of the function $f = \{[x, f(x)] \mid f(x) = x^2\}$ is shown in Figure 3.6-1. Because the domain of the function includes all the

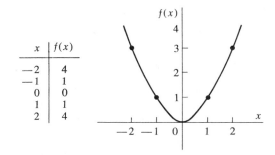

x	$f(x)$
-2	4
-1	1
0	0
1	1
2	4

Figure 3.6-1

real numbers, the graph is shown to be a continuous curve even though only a few convenient points have been used to determine it. The range, as you can see, includes only the nonnegative real numbers. *Since no vertical line can be made to meet the graph at more than one point, the graph represents a function.*

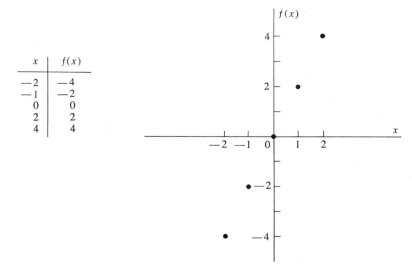

x	$f(x)$
-2	-4
-1	-2
0	0
2	2
4	4

Figure 3.6-2

Example: 3.6-2.   Figure 3.6-2 shows a graph of $f = \{[x, f(x)] \mid f(x) = 2x;$ x an integer$\}$. Since the domain of this function has been limited to integers, *only discrete points have been graphed on the plane*. The range involves even integers only. Why? Even though the graph is composed of scattered points, no vertical line can be made to meet the graph at more than one point. Thus, *again we have a function.*

Example: 3.6-3.   The graph of $f = \left\{ [x, f(x)] \mid f(x) = \dfrac{1}{x} \right\}$ is given in Figure 3.6-3. In this graph the domain includes all the real numbers except $x = 0$.

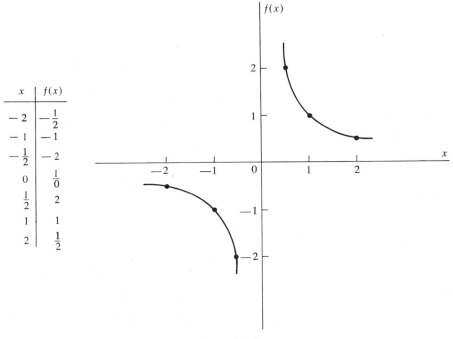

x	$f(x)$
-2	$-\frac{1}{2}$
-1	-1
$-\frac{1}{2}$	-2
0	$\frac{1}{0}$
$\frac{1}{2}$	2
1	1
2	$\frac{1}{2}$

Figure 3.6-3

Zero is not an admissible value. Why? The range includes all real numbers except $y = 0$. Again, no vertical line can be made to meet the graph in more than one point; therefore, *the relation is a function.*

Example: 3.6-4.   The symbol $[x]$ is used to represent an integer which is less than or equal to x. Figure 3.6-4 shows a graph of

$$\{[x, f(x)] \mid f(x) = [x]; \ x \in R, \ x \geq 0, \ [x] \in I, \ [x] \leq x\}.$$

Notice that when x is any fractional part of 1, $[x]$ has to be 0, because 0 is the only integer less than 1. Likewise when $1 < x \leq 2$ the value of $[x]$ is 1, and

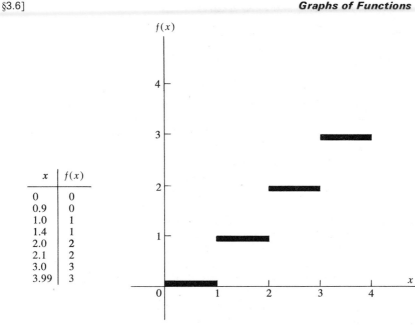

x	f(x)
0	0
0.9	0
1.0	1
1.4	1
2.0	2
2.1	2
3.0	3
3.99	3

Figure 3.6-4

so on. *The vertical line test shows this relation to be a function.* The domain of the function is the real nonnegative numbers and its range is the non-negative integers.

Example: 3.6-5.   Figure 3.6-5 shows a graph of $f = \{[x, f(x)] \mid f(x) = |x + 1|\}$. The *vertical-line test shows that this is a function* with its domain

x	f(x)
−3	2
−2	1
−1	0
0	1
1	2
2	3

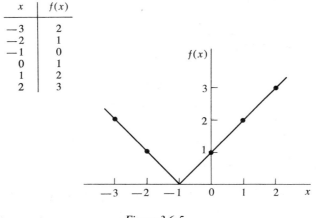

Figure 3.6-5

including the real numbers and the range including the nonnegative numbers. How does this set differ from the set graphed in Figure 3.4-2a?

EXERCISE 3.B

1. Does the set $\{(-2, 16), (-1, 1), (0, 0), (1, 1), (2, 16)\}$ represent a function? A relation? Explain.

2. Is the set of ordered pairs $\{(1, 3), (2, 4), (3, 5), (4, 4)\}$ a relation? A function? Why?

3. Why is the set $\{(1, 2), (2, 3), (3, 4), (3, 5)\}$ not a function? Is it a relation?

4. Determine whether or not the set $\{(0, 0), (0, 1), (0, 2), (0, 3)\}$ is a function.

5. For Problem 1 state the scope, the replacement set, and the domain for the set.

6. What is the range of the set in Problem 3? In Problem 4?

7. If $f(x) = |x^2 - 5|$, find $f(-4)$, $f(0)$, and $f(\sqrt{5})$.

8. If $f(x) = -|x^2 - 5x + 6|$, find $f(-2)$, $f(0)$, and $f(2)$.

9. Use the vertical-line test on the set $\{[x, f(x)] \mid f(x) = 4\}$ to determine whether or not it is a function.

10. Show why the set $\{(x, y) \mid y^2 = 2x\}$ does or does not represent a function.

11. Suppose the domain of a function is $\{0, 1, 2, 3\}$ and the rule of correspondence is $f(x) = |-(x + 2)|$, does this define the function? If so, what is its range?

12. If the domain of a function is $\{-2, -1, 0, 1\}$ and the rule of correspondence is $f(x) = x^2$, write the corresponding set of ordered pairs. Is there a one-to-one correspondence between the domain and the range?

13. Does the function $f = \{[x, f(x)] \mid f(x) = x + 7\}$ have an inverse function? If so, how does it differ from $f(x) = x + 7$?

14. What is the inverse function of $f(x) = 3x + 10$?

15. Write in symbolic form a relation that is a function and a relation that is not a function.

16. Is a function always a relation? Does a function always have an inverse? How do you test for an inverse function?

Plot a graph for each of the following functions and state its domain and range:

17. $\{[x, f(x)] \mid f(x) = x - 2\}$.

18. $\left\{[x, f(x)] \mid f(x) = \dfrac{x + 3}{x - 2}\right\}$.

19. $\{[x, f(x)] \mid f(x) = 3[x]\}$.

20. $\{[x, f(x)] \mid f(x) = x^2 - x - 3\}$.

3.7 COMPOSITE FUNCTIONS

There are all kinds of functions (as you will come to discover)—line functions, quadratic functions, exponential and logarithmic functions, trigonometric functions, inverse functions, and so on. The *two functions f and g are equal if and only if the domain of f is equal to the domain of g and $f(x) = g(x)$ for all x in this common domain.*

Functions can be added, subtracted, multiplied, and divided, just as real numbers. For example, two functions

1. f and g may be added to give $f + g$, where $(f + g)(x) = f(x) + g(x)$.
2. f and g may be subtracted to give $f - g$, where $(f - g)(x) = f(x) - g(x)$.
3. f and g may be multiplied to give $f \cdot g$ where $(f \cdot g)(x) = f(x) \cdot g(x)$.
4. f and g may be divided to give $\dfrac{f}{g}$, where $\dfrac{f}{g}(x) = \dfrac{f(x)}{g(x)}$ and $g(x) \neq 0$.

However, the operation that is of most concern to us at the moment is one that combines functions to form what are known as **composite functions.**

Definition: 3.7-1. *The* **composite of** *any* **two functions f and g,** *written as $f \circ g$, is a set of ordered pairs $(x, f[g(x)])$ such that x is an element of the domain of g and $g(x)$ is an element of the domain of f.*

In operating with the composite of f and g it is important for you to know that the symbol closest to the variable is the one that is applied first. So in $(f \circ g)x = f[g(x)]$, apply the g first and then f. Likewise for $(g \circ f)x = g[f(x)]$, apply the f first and then the g to their respective expressions. As you can see in Figure 3.7-1, one works from the inside out. The action for $f[g(x)]$ could be diagrammed in this manner:

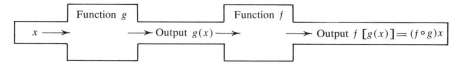

Figure 3.7-1

Even if $f \circ g$ is defined, $g \circ f$ may or may not be. Keep in mind also that $f \circ g$ may or may not be equal to $g \circ f$. **If $f \circ g$ and $g \circ f$ are not equal, they are not commutative. If $f \circ g$ and $g \circ f$ are equal, they are commutative,** and as we will show later they are inverse functions.

Example: 3.7-1.   Assume that $x \in R$ for the two functions f and g, and

$$f = \{[x, f(x)] \mid f(x) = x - 1\} \text{ so that } f(x) = x - 1,$$

$$g = \{[x, g(x)] \mid g(x) = x^2 - 1\} \text{ so that } g(x) = x^2 + 1.$$

Then $(f \circ g)x = f[g(x)] = f(x^2 + 1) = x^2 + 1 - 1 = x^2$,
and $(g \circ f)x = g[f(x)] = g(x - 1) = (x - 1)^2 + 1 = x^2 - 2x + 2.$

In order for x to be in the domain of $f \circ g$ it has to be in the domain of g, and $g(x)$ has to be in the domain of f. This requirement has been satisfied. The results of the composite function operations show that *the two composite functions are not commutative*. That is,

$$f \circ g \neq g \circ f.$$

Example: 3.7-2.   Assume that $x \in R$ and

$$f = \{[x, f(x)] \mid f(x) = 2x - 1\} \text{ so that } f(x) = 2x + 1,$$

$$g = \left\{ [x, g(x)] \mid g(x) = \frac{x - 1}{2} \right\} \text{ so that } g(x) = \frac{x - 1}{2}.$$

Then $(f \circ g)x = f[g(x)] = f\left(\dfrac{x-1}{2}\right) = 2\left(\dfrac{x-1}{2}\right) + 1 = x,$

and $(g \circ f)x = g[f(x)] = g(2x + 1) = \dfrac{2x + 1 - 1}{2} = x.$

This example shows *the composite of functions f and g are commutative,* so it follows that

$$f \circ g = g \circ f.$$

As will be discussed in the next section, **when $f \circ g$ is the same function as $g \circ f$, the f and g functions are inverses of each other.** So $g(x) = \dfrac{x-1}{2}$ is the inverse of $f(x) = 2x + 1$, and vice versa.

3.8 THE IDENTITY FUNCTION

Assume that $x \in R$ for the functions f and g, and

$f = \{[x, f(x)] \mid f(x) = x\}$ so that $f(x) = x,$
$g = \{[x, g(x)] \mid g(x) = x\}$ so that $g(x) = x.$
Then $(f \circ g)x = f[g(x)] = f(x) = x,$
and $(g \circ f)x = g[f(x)] = g(x) = x.$

This example differs from Example 3.7-2 in that the f and g functions used to obtain the composite functions are identical. Even so,

$$f \circ g = g \circ f.$$

This guarantees that f is the inverse of g and vice versa. Here is a case where a function is the inverse of itself.

The **identity function** *is a special case of a function and its inverse being identical.* It is expressed either as $I_f = \{(x, x)\}$ or as

$$I_f = \{[(x, f(x)] \mid f(x) = x; \ x \in R\}.$$

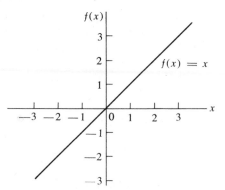

Figure 3.8-1. The identity function.

Figure 3.8-1 shows that the graph of this identity function exactly divides the first and third quadrants of the rectangular coordinate system.

Definition: 3.8-1.   *The **identity function** pairs every real number with itself over the field of real numbers.*

3.9 INVERSE FUNCTIONS

Assuming that it is fully understood that $y = f(x)$, from now on where it seems more convenient for us to do so we will use y in place of $f(x)$.

Function f has been defined as a set of ordered pairs (x, y) such that no two distinct pairs have the same first element x. If this same function possesses the property that no two distinct pairs have the same second element y, then **one-to-one correspondence** has been guaranteed and a second function called the **inverse function** exists.

The symbol f^{-1} will be used to represent the inverse function.

Definition: 3.9-a.   *An **inverse function** is a function obtained by interchanging the elements of every ordered pair of the function f. That is*

$(x, y) \in f$ if and only if $(y, x) \in f^{-1}$.

According to the demand of the preceding definition:

1. **The domain of f will become the range of f^{-1}.**
2. **The range of f will become the domain of f^{-1}.**

What actually takes place may be demonstrated by taking any function

$$f = \{(x,y) \mid y = 2x + 1; \ x, y \in R\} \tag{A}$$

and write its inverse function according to the demands of Definition 3.9-a; that is,

$$f^{-1} = \{(y, x) \mid y = 2x + 1; \ x, y \in R\}. \tag{B}$$

We object, however, to leaving the inverse function in form (B), because in this form we would not be able to graph the f and f^{-1} functions on the same x and y axes, and we would not be able to make any comparison between the two functions. Therefore, we rewrite the inverse function (B) so that its ordered pairs are in the same order as function f in (A). The inverse function then becomes

$$f^{-1} = \{(x, y) \mid x = 2y + 1; \ x, y \in R\}. \tag{C}$$

By replacing $x = 2y + 1$ by its equivalent value $y = \dfrac{x - 1}{2}$, we obtain the

ideal form of the inverse function

$$f^{-1} = \left\{ (x, y) \mid y = \frac{x-1}{2}; x, y \in R \right\}.$$ (D)

Example: 3.9-a. For the rule of correspondence $y = 2x + 1$, assume the domain to be limited to the set $\{-1, 0, 1, 2\}$. Then the range is $\{-1, 1, 3, 5\}$ and the function is

$$f = \{(-1, -1), (0, 1), (1, 3), (2, 5)\}.$$ (E)

Next, since the range of f is the domain of f^{-1}, the set $\{-1, 1, 3, 5\}$ is the domain of f^{-1}. This domain and the rule of correspondence $y = \frac{x-1}{2}$ determines the range of f^{-1} to be $\{-1, 0, 1, 2\}$. So the inverse function is

$$f^{-1} = \{(-1, -1), (1, 0), (3, 1), (5, 2)\}.$$ (F)

A study of the ordered pairs in (E) and (F) shows that the ordered pairs of f and f^{-1} are interchanged and satisfy the demand of Definition 3.9-a. Therefore, f in (E) and f^{-1} in (F) are inverse functions, and either is the inverse of the other. **A function and its inverse are always reversible.**

In Figure 3.9-a graphs are shown of function f represented by $f(x) = 2x + 1$,

$f(x) = 2x + 1 = y$				$f^{-1}(x) = \frac{x-1}{2} = y$	
x	y			x	y
-1	-1			-1	-1
0	1			1	0
1	3			3	1
2	5			5	2

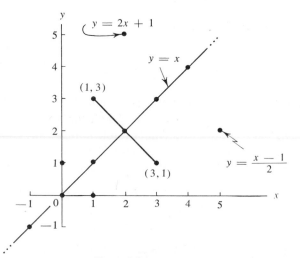

Figure 3.9-a

the inverse function f^{-1} represented by $f^{-1}(x) = \dfrac{x-1}{2}$, and I_f represented by $y = x$.

Definition: 3.9-b.   *Two points are said to be* **symmetric** *with respect to a line if that line is the perpendicular bisector of the line segment connecting the two points. Each point is said to be the reflection of the other in the line.*

The tables in Figure 3.9-a clearly show that the ordered pairs of f have been reversed to obtain the ordered pairs of f^{-1}. Figure 3.9-a also shows that the graph of the line $y = x$ is the perpendicular bisector of a line segment drawn from any two corresponding points of the two functions, such as from $(1, 3)$ to $(3, 1)$.

In Figure 3.8-1 we established the fact that $f(x) = y = x$ (or $I_f = \{(x, y) \mid y = x\}$) was the identity function. This identity function is vitally important to us at this point because across its graph the graph of any function f that has an inverse can be reflected to give the graph of its inverse function f^{-1}. This means that the graph of f^{-1} in Figure 3.9-a could just as well have been made by reflecting the graph of f across the graph of the identity function $I_f = \{(x, y) \mid y = x\}$.

Example: 3.9-b.   This is a graph of the inverse function f^{-1} obtained by reflecting the function $f = \{(x, y) \mid y = \sqrt{x}; 0 \le x \le 9\}$ across the graph of the identity function $I_f = \{(x, x)\}$.

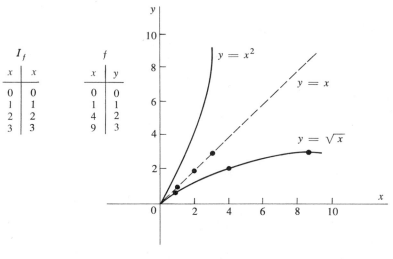

Figure 3.9-b

Now, let us check the f^{-1} graph by determining the f^{-1} function from function f and plotting its graph.

If $f = \{(x, y) \mid y = \sqrt{x}; 0 \leq x \leq 9\}$,

then $f^{-1} = \{(y, x) \mid y = \sqrt{x}\}$,

$f^{-1} = \{(x, y) \mid x = \sqrt{y}\}$,

and $f^{-1} = \{(x, y) \mid y = x^2; 0 \leq x \leq 3\}$.

$y = x^2$	
x	y
0	0
1	1
2	4
3	9

You can readily see that if the ordered pairs for $y = x^2$ are plotted in Figure 3.9-b, the graph is identical to the graph of the inverse function obtained by reflecting $y = \sqrt{x}$ about $y = x$.

3.9-1 Properties of an Inverse Function

We need to keep in mind that these procedures which have been devised to identify and graph an inverse function from a given function f may not·produce an inverse function at all. They may produce a **relation** instead. To obtain an inverse function from a function (or from a restricted function) several properties must be satisfied.

An inverse function exists if and only if

1. **the composites of f and f^{-1} are commutative,** *or*
2. **the function f completely satisfies one-to-one correspondence,** *or*
3. **a horizontal line can be made to meet the graph of f in no more than one point.**

Example: 3.9-1a. Let our first effort be to decide if $y = \sqrt[3]{x - 1}$ and its inverse $y = x^3 + 1$ are commutative. In checking out the composite functions it is obvious that it would be more convenient to use $f(x)$ and $f^{-1}(x)$ rather than y. So if

$$f = \{[x, f(x)] \mid f(x) = \sqrt[3]{x - 1}, \text{ where } x, f(x) \in R\},$$
$$f^{-1} = \{[x, f^{-1}(x)] \mid f^{-1}(x) = x^3 + 1, \text{ where } x, f^{-1}(x) \in R\}.$$
$$(f \circ f^{-1})x = f[f^{-1}(x)] = f(x^3 + 1) = \sqrt[3]{x^3 + 1 - 1} = x,$$
and $(f^{-1} \circ f)x = f^{-1}[f(x)] = f^{-1}\sqrt[3]{x - 1} = (\sqrt[3]{x - 1})^3 + 1 = x;$
$$\therefore \quad f \circ f^{-1} = f^{-1} \circ f.$$

The composites are commutative, and therefore the function f has an inverse f^{-1}.

Taking the function f as $f(x) = \sqrt[3]{x - 1}$, it seems quite obvious that no two of the first elements x have the same second element. This guarantees that *there is one-to-one correspondence between the elements of the two sets formed* by the ordered pairs.

Finally, if you will look at just the function f graph of Figure 3.9-1a you will see that *a horizontal line cannot possibly intersect the graph of function f in more than one point.*

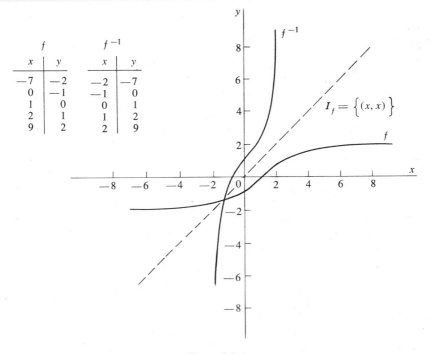

Figure 3.9-1a

Therefore, any one of the three tests which we have applied in Example 3.9-1a confirms the fact that function f does have an inverse function.

It is interesting to observe how the function f in Figure 3.9-1a, reflected across the identity function I_f, does produce the graph of the inverse function f^{-1}.

EXERCISE 3.C

Unless otherwise stated it will be assumed throughout this exercise that the domain of all functions, as well as $f(x)$, $g(x)$, or $f^{-1}(x)$, will be based upon the real numbers.

1. Determine $(f \circ g)x$ and $(g \circ f)x$ for the functions represented by $f(x) = 3x - 1$ and $g(x) = x + 4$. Are the composites of these two functions commutative?

2. What is the composite function of f and g for the functions represented by $f(x) = \sqrt{x - 4}$ and $g(x) = x^2 - 4$? Show that these two functions are not inverses.

3. Are the composites of the two functions represented by $f(x) = \sqrt{x - 4}$ and $g(x) = x^2 + 4$ commutative? If so, what is the relation between these two functions?

4. Test the two functions represented by $f(x) = \dfrac{1}{x + 1}$ and $g(x) = \dfrac{1 - x}{x}$ to determine if their composites are commutative. If they are, what does this tell you?

5. Make a graph of the identity function $I_f = \{(x, y) \mid y = x\}$. On the same set of coordinate axes make graphs of the two functions in Problem 3. What relation does the identity graph have in regard to the graphs of the other two functions?

6. Graph the function $I_f = \{(x, x)\}$. Make graphs of the two functions of Problem 4 on the same set of axes. What is the position of the identity graph with respect to the graphs of the other two functions?

7. Use the function $f = \{(x, y) \mid y = 2x + 7\}$ to write a comparable statement for its inverse in the form that will permit it to be plotted on the same axes as f.

8. For $f = \left\{(x, y) \mid y = \dfrac{x - 1}{3}\right\}$, write an inverse function in the form that will permit it and function f to be plotted in the same coordinate system.

9. Construct the graph for Problem 7. Does a horizontal line meet the graph of function f in more than one point? What is the significance of this fact?

10. Construct the graph for Problem 8. How many times can you make a horizontal line intersect the graph of function f? What does this tell you?

11. For $I_f = \{(x, y) \mid y = x\}$ show that $f \circ I_f = I_f \circ f = f$.

12. If $f = \{(x, y) \mid y = x^3\}$ and $I_f = \{(x, y) \mid y = x\}$ find the composite of f and I_f. In what way does the composite function differ from f?

13. Show that the function $f = \{(1, 2), (2, 1), (3, 4), (4, 3)\}$ is its own inverse. Plot both functions.

14. If $f = \left\{(x, y) \mid y = \dfrac{12}{x}\right\}$, how does its inverse differ from it? Plot both functions.

15. Does the function represented by $f(x) = x^2$ have an inverse? Explain.

16. Given $f = \{[x, f(x)] \mid f(x) = -x^2 \text{ and } -8 \leq x \leq 0\}$. Does this function have an inverse?

17. Name a geometrical test that guarantees: (a) a function, (b) an inverse function.

18. Name two nongeometrical tests which guarantee an inverse function.

19. State the domain of the inverse of a function in terms of its function.

20. State the range of an inverse function in terms of its function.

Equations, Functions, and Inequalities

The discussion in this chapter will be confined to first-degree equations and their corresponding linear functions, and to second-degree equations and their corresponding quadratic functions.

A first-degree equation means that the highest power of x used in the equation is *one*. The graph of a first-degree equation, or of its corresponding function, is always a straight line. Therefore, all **first-degree equations are linear (line) equations or linear functions.** Likewise, **second-degree equations are quadratic equations or quadratic functions.**

Before introducing linear equations and their functions let us consider some details which apply to equations in general.

4.1 EQUATIONS

An equation can be defined in several ways. One way is this:

Definition: 4.1-1. *An **equation** is an open sentence formed by two algebraic expressions and the equality relation, true for some values of the variable and false for others.*

About the simplest equation that can be written is

$$mx + b = 0,$$

where m and b are arbitrary constants. Let us take an equation which could easily be changed to the form $mx + b = 0$, but for discussion purposes we prefer to express it as

$$2x - 4 = x + 5,$$

Obviously, this open sentence is true for $x = 9$ but false for all other values of x in the real number system. Thus, it becomes evident that this particular equation is a **set selector.** That is, the equation

$$2x - 4 = x + 5$$

separates the real number system into two **disjoint sets:** the elements in one set make the equation true, and the elements in the other set make the equation false.

Definition: 4.1-2. *The set that contains all elements which satisfy a given equation is called a* **solution set** *or a* **truth set.**

Definition: 4.1-3. *The set that contains all admissible elements which do not satisfy the given equation is called the* **nonsolution set** *or the* **false set.**

Definition: 4.1-4. *Each element of a solution set is* **a solution** *or a* **root.**

Definition: 4.1-5. *To* **solve an equation** *is to find its roots or its solutions.*

The **solution set** for the equation $2x - 4 = x + 5$ $(x \in R)$, is the set $\{9\}$. The **nonsolution set** for $2x - 4 = x + 5$ is $\{x \mid x \neq 9 \text{ and } x \in R\}$.

In terms of functional notation, another definition for an equation is the following:

Definition: 4.1-6. *The statement* $f(x) = g(x)$ *is an equation having a domain of d, where d is the intersection of the domains of f and g.*

In order to show just what part d plays in the preceding definition, let us take the equation

$$\frac{2}{x - 3} = x - 2,$$

where $f(x) = \dfrac{2}{x - 3}$ and $g(x) = x - 2$. The domain of f represented by $f(x) = \dfrac{2}{x - 3}$ contains all the real numbers except $x = 3$. Why? The domain of g represented by $g(x) = x - 2$ contains all the real numbers. Therefore, the equation $\dfrac{2}{x - 3} = x - 2$ has a domain d which contains all the real numbers except $x = 3$.

The **solution set** *of* $\dfrac{2}{x - 3} = x - 2$ *is* $\{1, 4\}$. Check these roots by substituting each of them in the given equation.

4.2 CLASSIFICATION OF EQUATIONS

The classification of the equations in which we will be primarily interested in this course will include

(a) conditional equations;
(b) identical equations;
(c) equivalent equations.

Definition: 4.2-1.   *An equation that selects from its universal set only these values that make the equation true is called a* **conditional equation.**

The definition says that **a conditional equation is a set selector.**

1. $x + 5 = 6$ selects from $x \in R$ the solution set $\{1\}$.
2. $2x - 4 = x + 5$ selects from $x \in R$ the solution set $\{9\}$.
3. $\dfrac{2}{x - 3} = x - 2$ selects from all $x \in R$ the roots 1 and 4.
4. $x^3 - 5x^2 + 6x = 0$ selects from $x \in R$ the truth set $\{0, 2, 3\}$.
5. $x^3 - y = 0$ selects from $x, y \in R$ infinitely many solutions, even though some selections are not acceptable. One *counterexample* is $x = 4$ and $y = 0$.

Definition: 4.2-2.   *An equation that is true for all admissible values of the variables is called an* **identical equation.**

In contrast to a conditional equation, which is a set selector, an identical equation has no selective characteristics whatsoever. **An identical equation accepts all admissible values without question.** These are some samples of identical equations, true for all admissible values of x and y.

1. $x^2 - y^2 = (x - y)(x + y)$ 3. $x^2 - 5x + 6 = (x - 2)(x - 3)$.

2. $\dfrac{1}{x - 3} = \dfrac{x + 3}{x^2 - 9}$.   4. $x^3 - y^3 = (x - y)(x^2 + xy + y^2)$.

Definition 4.2-2 does not say that identical equations are true for all values. They are true only for all admissible values. You should notice that $x = 3$ in Example 2 above is not an admissible value, because it would make the denominator zero and division by zero is not permissible. Therefore, for $\dfrac{1}{x - 3} = \dfrac{x + 3}{x^2 - 9}$ the real number $x = 3$ has to be eliminated.

Now that we know something about conditional and identical equations, the following properties become of considerable interest to us:

Property: 4.2-1.   *If the solution set is empty, the equation is a* **null equation** *and the graphs of its two functions do not intersect.*

Property: 4.2-2.   *If the set containing the nonsolution elements is empty, the equation is an* **identical equation** *and the graphs of the two functions coincide.*

Property: 4.2-3.   *If neither the solution set nor the nonsolution set is empty, the equation is a* **conditional equation** *and the graphs of the two functions intersect at least once.*

A visualization of Property 4.2-1 is obtained by plotting on the same axes the functions $2x + 2 = 2x + 5$.

Example: 4.2-1. Given the equation $2x + 2 = 2x + 5$.
There is *no solution*; so this is a *null equation*. Plotting

$$f(x) = 2x + 2$$
$$\text{and } g(x) = 2x + 5,$$

we get

x	$f(x)$	x	$g(x)$
-2	-2	-2	1
0	2	0	5
2	6	2	9

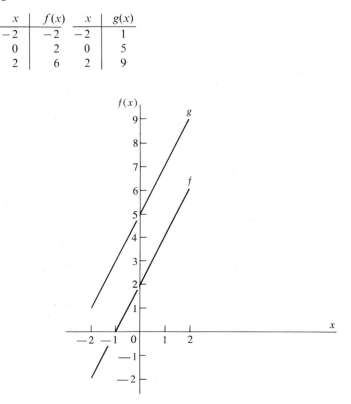

Figure 4.2-1

As predicted, Figure 4.2-1 shows that the graphs of the functions of the null equation $2x + 2 = 2x + 5$ do not intersect.

Example: 4.2-2. Given the equation $x^2 - x = (x - 1)x$.
Because the domain of the functions of this equation contains all the real numbers, the set of nonsolution elements is empty and *the equation is an identity.* Therefore, Figure 4.2-2 shows that the graphs of $f(x) = x^2 - x$ and $g(x) = (x - 1)x$ coincide and demonstrate Property 4.2-2.

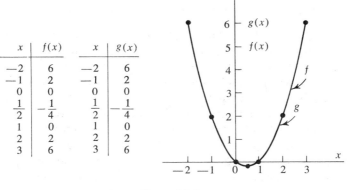

x	f(x)		x	g(x)
−2	6		−2	6
−1	2		−1	2
0	0		0	0
$\frac{1}{2}$	$-\frac{1}{4}$		$\frac{1}{2}$	$-\frac{1}{4}$
1	0		1	0
2	2		2	2
3	6		3	6

Figure 4.2-2

Example: 4.2-3.   Given the equation $\dfrac{2}{x-3} = x - 2$.

We have worked with this equation (see Definition 4.1-6) and know that its solution set is $\{1, 4\}$, and its nonsolution set is all the other real numbers except $x = 3$. Therefore, neither its solution set nor its nonsolution set is empty. So *the equation is conditional* and the graphs of its functions (Figure 4.2-3) intersect in at least one point.

$g(x) = x - 2$

x	g(x)
0	−2
1	−1
2	0
3	1
4	2
6	4

$f(x) = \dfrac{2}{x-3}$

x	g(x)
0	$-\dfrac{2}{3}$
1	−1
2	−2
2.5	−4
3	$\dfrac{2}{0}$
3.5	4
4	2
6	$\dfrac{2}{3}$

Figure 4.2-3

The graphs of the two functions of the equation $\dfrac{2}{x-3} = x - 2$ intersect in at least one point. They actually intersect in two points, at $(1, -1)$ and $(4, 2)$.

Once again notice that the total number of ordered pairs of either function f or g, or both of them, is only a small portion of the ordered pairs in $R \times R$. This is why the **functions f and g are subsets of the Cartesian product $R \times R$.**

Other than the identical equations which will be studied when we take up "identities" in circular and trigonometric functions, most of the work involving equations in this book will have to do with conditional equations.

For an equation that cannot be solved by just looking, the usual procedure is to replace it by a simpler equation that has the same solution set. Repeat the process as many times as is necessary to get the simplest possible equation. Each equation obtained in this manner is said to be equivalent to the equation from which it was derived.

Definition: 4.2-3.   *Equations that have the same solution set are called* **equivalent equations.**

Axiom: 4.2-1.   Equivalent equations *are obtained if and only if the same nonzero number is added to (or subtracted from) both members of the equation.*

Axiom: 4.2-2.   Equivalent equations *are obtained if and only if both members of the equation are multiplied (or divided) by the same nonzero number.*

Example: 4.2-4.   Find   the   solution   set   for   the   linear   equation

$$\left\{ x \,\middle|\, \frac{x}{2} = 1 + \frac{2x}{5};\ x \in R \right\}.$$

STEP 1.	$\dfrac{x}{2} = 1 + \dfrac{2x}{5},$	(Given)
STEP 2.	$5x = 10 + 4x,$	(Axiom 4.2-2)
STEP 3.	$5x - 4x = 10 + 4x - 4x,$	(Axiom 4.2-1)
STEP 4.	$(5 - 4)x = 10,$	(D and A_5)
STEP 5.	$1 \cdot x = 10,$	(A_1)
STEP 6.	$x = 10,$	(M_3)
STEP 7.	$\{10\}.$	(Solution set)

The equation $x = 10$ in Step 6 is the simplest equation we can get. You will find that the equation in each of the preceding steps is satisfied by the root 10. Therefore, each of the first six equations is equivalent to the other five and to the given equation.

Definition: 4.2-4.   *The numbers a and b in the product ab are called* **factors.**

Definition: 4.2-5. Factoring *is the process of finding the factors a and b which, if multiplied together, will produce the product ab.*

It is assumed that you already know how to factor numbers and algebraic expressions. If you do not, review factoring in an elementary algebra book.

Example: 4.2-5. Solve the equation $\dfrac{2x}{x-2} = \dfrac{x^2+7}{(x-3)(x-2)}$, $(x \neq 3,$ $x \neq 2)$.

STEP 1. $\dfrac{2x}{x-2} = \dfrac{x^2+7}{(x-3)(x-2)}$ (Given)

STEP 2. $2x(x-3) = x^2 + 7,$ (Mul. $(x-3)(x-2)$ and M_5)

STEP 3. $2x^2 - 6x = x^2 + 7,$ (D)

STEP 4. $-x^2 + 2x^2 - 6x - 7$
         $= -x^2 + x^2 + 7 - 7,$ (Axiom 4.2-1)

STEP 5. $x^2 - 6x - 7 = 0,$ (D, A_1, and A_5)

STEP 6. $(x-7)(x+1) = 0,$ (Definition 4.2-5)

STEP 7. $x - 7 = 0$ or $x + 1 = 0,$ (Product law, Theorem 2.12-7)

STEP 8. $x = 7$ or $x = -1,$ (Axiom 4.2-1)

STEP 9. $\{7, -1\}.$ (Solution set)

According to our definition of equivalent equations, what we are asserting is this:

If $\dfrac{2x}{x-2} = \dfrac{x^2+7}{(x-3)(x-2)},$ then $x = 7$ or $x = -1.$

Conversely, if $x = 7$ or $x = -1,$ then $\dfrac{2x}{x-2} = \dfrac{x^2+7}{(x-3)(x-2)}.$

Yet, not until we have substituted the 7 and -1 into the original equation and proved that they satisfy the equation, do we have the right to make such assertions. *Any time a given equation is multiplied by an expression which contains the variable, roots may appear that do not satisfy the given equation. Such roots are called* **extraneous roots.** We multiplied both sides of $\dfrac{2x}{x-2} = \dfrac{x^2+7}{(x-3)(x-2)}$ by $(x-3)(x-2)$; so we cannot be sure that 7 and -1 are not extraneous roots until we check them.

Definition: 4.2-6. Extraneous solutions *are solutions that do not satisfy the original equation but do satisfy equations derived from it.*

Fortunately, the roots 7 and -1 both satisfy the original equation. Therefore, we are now free to conclude that every equation from Step 8 back to Step 1 is satisfied by roots 7 and -1 and that all these equations are equivalent.

4.3 LINEAR EQUATIONS AND FUNCTIONS

A first-degree equation in one variable contains x to the first power. Thus:

Definition: 4.3-1.   *The equation $mx + b = 0$, where $m \neq 0$ and m and b are real numbers, is called a* **first-degree equation in one variable.**

Definition: 4.3-2.   *The equation $y = mx + b$, where m and b are real numbers, is called a* **first-degree equation in two variables.**

Since, as we learned in Section 3.5, Chapter 3, the symbols y and $f(x)$ serve the same purpose, the following two statements are equivalent in meaning.

1. $y = mx + b$ is a first-degree equation in the two variables x and y.
2. $f(x) = mx + b$ is a first-degree function in the variable x.

For the time being this fact will be assumed: *The graph of the linear function $f(x) = mx + b$, where m and b are real numbers, is a straight line.* Because the graph of $f(x) = mx + b$ is always a straight line, we are privileged to use interchangeably the expressions *linear function for a function of first-degree* and *linear equation for an equation of first degree.*

In graphing the function f as represented by $f(x) = mx + b$, all $f(x)$ values are ordinates. If a zero ordinate were selected such that $f(x) = 0$, and $mx + b = 0$ were solved for x, then the graph would cross the x axis at $-\dfrac{b}{m}$. This value $x = -\dfrac{b}{m}$ is the solution of the equation $mx + b = 0$, and $\left(-\dfrac{b}{m}, 0\right)$ is the point on the graph which falls on the x axis and is the root of the equation. The ordered pair $\left(-\dfrac{b}{m}, 0\right)$ is often referred to as the **zero value** of the function $f(x) = mx + b$.

Summarizing:

1. **To find the zero value of a function, let $f(x) = 0$ and solve for x.**
2. **To find the point where a linear equation in two variables crosses the x axis, let $y = 0$ and solve for x.**

Example: 4.3-1.   Given $\{(x, f(x)) \mid f(x) = 3x - 12; x \in R\}$. Find the zero of the function. Graph the function. Let $f(x) = 0$, then $3x - 12 = 0$. Solving for x, we get $x = 4$ so that the zero of the function is at $(4, 0)$ on the x axis (Figure 4.3-1). The root of the equation is $x = 4$.

The basic concepts of order, absolute value, and inequalities were presented in Chapter 2. There is a close relation between these concepts and those involving equations. For this reason you should expect to find problems that have to do with inequalities and absolute value in the Exercise sets in this chapter. They should cause you no difficulty, but if they do review the material in Chapter 2, particularly Sections 2.13 and 2.14.

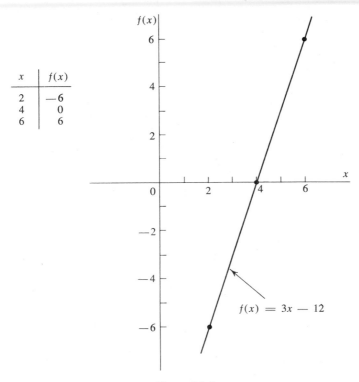

x	$f(x)$
2	-6
4	0
6	6

$f(x) = 3x - 12$

Figure 4.3-1

Example: 4.3-2. Find the solution set and the nonsolution set for $\{x \mid |x - 2| > 2, x$ an integer$\}$. Is the inequality a set selector?

We prefer at this point to use a trial-and-error approach to discover the answers to our questions.

If $x = 4$, then $|x - 2| > 2$ is $2 > 2$, which is false.
If $x = 5$, then $|x - 2| > 2$ is $3 > 2$, which is true.

All other integers greater than 5 will also satisfy the given inequality.

If $x = 0$, then $|x - 2| > 2$ is $2 > 2$, which is false.
If $x = -1$, then $|x - 2| > 2$ is $3 > 2$, which is true.

All other integers less than -1 will also satisfy the given inequality.

Thus, the **solution set** is $\{x \mid x \le -1$ and $x \ge 5; x$ **an integer**$\}$. The **nonsolution set** is $\{x \mid -1 < x < 5: x$ **an integer**$\}$.

The solution set and the nonsolution set are nonempty, so the inequality $|x - 2| > 2$ is *a conditional inequality and a set selector*.

EXERCISE 4.A

In the problems in this exercise the domain of the variable will, unless otherwise specifically stated, include all the real numbers.

1. Find the solution set for $\{x \mid x - 4 = 7\}$. If there is a nonsolution set, what numbers would it include?

2. What is the solution set for $\{x \mid 5x - 3 = x + 1$; if $x < 9$ and positive$\}$? List all elements of the nonsolution set.

3. If the domain of x is limited to $-9 < x < 0$, write the solution of $\dfrac{x}{2} - 6 = 3x - 2$ in set-builder notation (see Problems 1 and 2). What is its truth set? its root?

4. Express the solution of $\dfrac{x}{x - 2} = 3$ in set-builder notation (see Problem 3). List the inadmissible values of x. What is its root?

5. Given two functions represented by $f(x) = \dfrac{2}{x - 4}$ and $g(x) = \dfrac{3}{x}$. List the inadmissible values of x. State the domain D that is common to the two functions. Find the solution of $f(x) - g(x) = 0$.

6. If $f(x) = 3x + 4$ and $g(x) = \dfrac{x - 2}{3}$, determine the domain D common to the two functions. What is the solution for the equation $f(x) - g(x) = 0$?

7. State the reason for taking each step necessary to find the solution of the equation $\dfrac{4x}{x - 2} - 5 = \dfrac{10}{x}$. Check each root.

8. Solve the equation $\dfrac{4}{2y - 3} - \dfrac{2}{y + 2} = \dfrac{2}{3 - 2y}$ for y, stating the reason for each necessary step taken. Check each root.

9. Solve for w and check solution: $\dfrac{24}{w^2 - 4} = \dfrac{5w - 2}{w + 2} + \dfrac{3w}{2 - w}$.

10. Find the solution set and check it: $\dfrac{19}{t^2 - 3t + 2} = \dfrac{2t + 3}{t - 1} - \dfrac{1}{2 - t}$.

11. Find the value of F that will satisfy the equation $C = \frac{5}{9}(F - 32)$ and check.

12. Solve the equation $S = \dfrac{N(A + L)}{2}$ for L and check your answer.

Select from the following six equations correct answers for Problems 13 and 14.

(a) $2x^2 = 2 \cdot x \cdot x$.
(b) $2(x + x) = 16$.
(c) $2x^2 - 14x + 20 = 0$.

(d) $x^2 - 7x + 10 = (x - 5)(x - 2)$.
(e) $2x^2 - 1 = 2x^2 - 10x$.
(f) $3x = 3 - 27$.

13. Which of the preceding are conditional equations? What are the others?

14. Which of the preceding are identical equations? What are the others?

15. Explain why the equation $2x^2 = 18x$ is called a set selector. What is its solution set?

16. Is the equation $\dfrac{1}{x} = \dfrac{3}{2x + x}$ a set selector? How would you classify this equation?

17. Letting $f(x) = 2x^2$ and $g(x) = 18x$ in Problem 15, make graphs of the two functions. Do the graphs intersect? What does this tell you?

18. In the equation $\dfrac{1}{x} = \dfrac{3}{2x + x}$, let $f(x) = \dfrac{1}{x}$ and $g(x) = \dfrac{3}{3x}$ and make graphs of the two functions. What is peculiar about these two graphs? What does the behavior of the two graphs tell you?

19. State the solution for the set $\{x \mid x + 3 \le 5\}$. Express its nonsolution set in set-builder notation. Is this set a set selector?

20. Write the solution set for $\{x \mid |x - 3| < 2\}$ in set-builder notation. Is this set a set selector? If so, what is its nonsolution set?

4.4 QUADRATIC EQUATIONS AND FUNCTIONS

A quadratic equation is a second-degree equation in one variable where the highest power of the variable must be two.

Definition: 4.4-a. *The equation* $ax^2 + bx + c = 0$, *where a, b, c are real numbers and* $a \neq 0$, *is called the* **general quadratic equation.**

If a were not different from zero, that is, if $a = 0$, the equation $ax^2 + bx + c = 0$ would become $bx + c = 0$ which, according to Definition 4.3-1, is the most general linear equation. To be a quadratic equation, the x^2 must exist. The bx and c, either separately or together, do not necessarily have to be present. If both b and c are absent the solution is trivial, but if they both are present we have the most general quadratic equation.

Definition: 4.4-b. *A* **quadratic function** *is a quadratic equation expressed in* the form

$$f(x) = ax^2 + bx + c,$$

$a \neq 0$ *and a, b, c real numbers.*

One of the best ways to make mathematics meaningful and to make yourself a good mathematician is to attempt to discover methods of procedure that are all your own. There are many ways to solve a quadratic equation. So this is an excellent place to try out your mathematical initiative. For example, how would you solve $\{x \mid 5x^2 - 7x + 2 = 0; x \in R\}$? Here is one way:

STEP 1.	$5x^2 - 7x + 2 = 0$,	(Given)
STEP 2.	$(5x - 2)(x - 1) = 0$,	(Definition 4.2-5)
STEP 3.	$(x - 1) = 0$,	(Theorem 2.12-7)
STEP 4.	$x = 1$,	(Axiom 4.2-1, A_5 and A_4)
STEP 5.	$5x - 2 = 0$,	(Theorem 2.12-7)
STEP 6.	$x = \frac{2}{5}$,	(Axioms 4.2-1 and 4.2-2, A_5, A_3)
STEP 7.	$\{1, \frac{2}{5}\}$.	(Solution set)

The factors shown in Step 2 were obtained by inspection, which is just a nice way of saying "by guessing." You must, however, train yourself to guess intelligently.

You can move from Step 2 to Step 3 (also Step 5) only by the authority of Theorem 2.12-7 which declares that **"If** $ab = 0$, **then** $a = 0$ **or** $b = 0$, **or both."**

In solving $5x^2 - 7x + 2 = 0$ we have made use of the same equivalent equations idea used in solving linear equations. Either solution $x = 1$ or $x = \frac{2}{5}$ satisfies each of the equations in Steps 1, 2, 5, and 6, and these equations are all equivalent. Check to see if the solutions satisfy $5x^2 - 7x + 2 = 0$.

4.4-1 Proof and Application of the Quadratic Formula

The natural question to arise is this: "If $ax^2 + bx + c = 0$ is the most general quadratic equation, why not solve it for x and obtain a formula that will supply the roots for any quadratic equation?" A second question might be: "Could the values for x be obtained by the factoring process used in solving $5x^2 - 7x + 2 = 0$ in the preceding example?" The answer is "Yes." From several ways of solving the quadratic equation we therefore choose to proceed by the method of factoring. We will work toward our objective by forming equivalent equations until we arrange one that is in the form of the difference of two squares. Then we will separate the difference of two squares into two factors each of which, according to Theorem 2.12-7, will be equal to zero. From this point it will be relatively easy to solve for x. This will complete the proof. The steps in the proof are:

STEP 1. $ax^2 + bx + c = 0,$ (Given)

STEP 2. $x^2 + \dfrac{b}{a}x + \dfrac{c}{a} = 0,$ (Axiom 4.2-2)

STEP 3. $x^2 + \dfrac{b}{a}x + \left(\dfrac{b}{2a}\right)^2 - \left(\dfrac{b}{2a}\right)^2 + \dfrac{c}{a} = 0,$ (Axiom 4.2-1)

STEP 4. $\left(x + \dfrac{b}{2a}\right)^2 - \left(\dfrac{b^2 - 4ac}{4a^2}\right) = 0,$ (Factoring and combining terms)

STEP 5. $\left(x + \dfrac{b}{2a}\right)^2 - \left(\dfrac{\sqrt{b^2 - 4ac}}{2a}\right)^2 = 0,$ (Forming difference of two squares)

STEP 6. $\left(x + \dfrac{b}{2a} - \dfrac{\sqrt{b^2 - 4ac}}{2a}\right)$

$\times \left(x + \dfrac{b}{2a} + \dfrac{\sqrt{b^2 - 4ac}}{2a}\right) = 0,$ (Factoring)

STEP 7. $x = \dfrac{-b}{2a} + \dfrac{\sqrt{b^2 - 4ac}}{2a},$

$x = \dfrac{-b}{2a} - \dfrac{\sqrt{b^2 - 4ac}}{2a}.$ (Theorem 2.12-7)

The **quadratic formula** is obtained from Step 7 in this form:

$$x = \frac{-b \pm \sqrt{b^2 - 4ac}}{2a} \quad (a \neq 0)$$

Solutions obtained by the quadratic formula should be checked by substituting them back into the given quadratic equation. If you have any doubt about the solutions, $x = \dfrac{-b \pm \sqrt{b^2 - 4ac}}{2a}$, you should substitute these two values back into $ax^2 + bx + c = 0$ to determine if they actually do satisfy the equation. You will find that they do check. This means that each of the seven steps taken in the proof represents an equivalent equation and that taken together they constitute the proof of the following theorem.

Theorem: 4.4-1a.   *If* $ax^2 + bx + c = 0$, *then* $x = \dfrac{-b \pm \sqrt{b^2 - 4ac}}{2a}$.

Any quadratic equation in one variable can be readily solved by taking these three steps.

STEP **1.   Arrange the equation to be solved in standard position; that is, in the form $ax^2 + bx + c = 0$.**

STEP **2.   Match the coefficients and constant term of the given equation with those in $ax^2 + bx + c = 0$ to determine the values of a, b, and c.**

STEP **3.   Substitute the values for a, b, and c into the formula**

$$x = \dfrac{-b \pm \sqrt{b^2 - 4ac}}{2a},$$

and solve to get the roots for x.

Example: 4.1-4a.   Find $\{x \mid 5x^2 - 7x = -2; x \in R\}$.

STEP 1.   The equation $5x^2 - 7x = -2$ in standard position is $5x^2 - 7x + 2 = 0$.

STEP 2.   Comparing $\begin{bmatrix} 5x^2 - 7x + 2 = 0 \\ ax^2 + bx + c = 0 \end{bmatrix}$ $a = 5, b = -7, c = 2$.

STEP 3.   Substituting a, b, c into the quadratic formula, we obtained two roots:

For later reference we will let x_1 represent the first root and x_2 the second root.

$$x_1 = \frac{-b}{2a} + \frac{\sqrt{b^2 - 4ac}}{2a} \quad \text{and} \quad x_2 = \frac{-b}{2a} - \frac{\sqrt{b^2 - 4ac}}{2a}.$$

$$x_1 = \frac{-(-7)}{2(5)} + \frac{\sqrt{(-7)^2 - 4(5)(2)}}{2(5)},$$

$$x_2 = \frac{-(-7)}{2(5)} - \frac{\sqrt{(-7)^2 - 4(5)(2)}}{2(5)}.$$

$$x_1 = \frac{7}{10} + \frac{3}{10}, \qquad\qquad x_2 = \frac{7}{10} - \frac{3}{10}.$$

$$x_1 = 1, \qquad\qquad x_2 = \frac{2}{5}.$$

We have already solved this same equation by factoring and checked the roots; so we know that $x_1 = 1$ and $x_2 = \frac{2}{5}$ are correct solutions and satisfy $5x^2 - 7x = -2$.

A graph of the function represented by $f(x) = 5x^2 - 7x + 2$ is called a **parabola** (see Figure 4.4-1a). The graph shows that the curve crosses the x axis at two points: $(1, 0)$ and $(\frac{2}{5}, 0)$. These points are known as zeros of the function and can be obtained by letting $f(x) = 0$ and solving for x_1 and x_2, the abcissas at the points $(1, 0)$ and $(\frac{2}{5}, 0)$. **The zeros of a function are the roots of its equation.**

x	$f(x)$
-1	14
0	2
$\frac{2}{5}$	0
$\frac{7}{10}$	$-\frac{9}{10}$
1	0
2	8

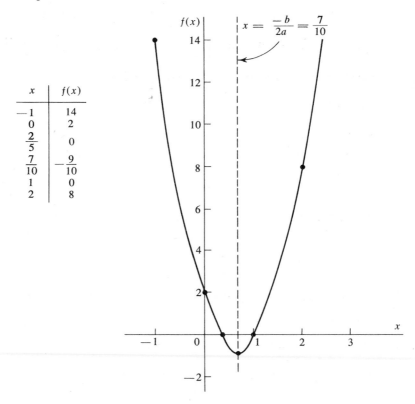

Figure 4.4-1a. Graph of $f(x) = 5x^2 - 7x + 2$.

A careful look at the quadratic formula shows that x_1 is obtained by adding $\dfrac{\sqrt{b^2 - 4ac}}{2a}$ to $\dfrac{-b}{2a}$, whereas x_2 is obtained by subtracting $\dfrac{\sqrt{b^2 - 4ac}}{2a}$ from

$\dfrac{-b}{2a}$. So, the graph of $x = \dfrac{-b}{2a}$, which is the equation of a straight line, is actually the bisector of the graph of the quadratic function and passes through its **vertex.** This is exactly what happens in Figure 4.4-1a, at $x = \dfrac{-b}{2a} = \dfrac{7}{10}$.

If the coefficient preceding x^2 in $ax^2 + bx + c = 0$ is positive, the lowest point on its graph is the vertex of the parabola and is called the **minimum point.** Note that the coordinates of the vertex, and the minimum point, of the graph of $f(x) = 5x^2 - 7x + 2$ in Figure 4.5-1 are $(\frac{7}{10}, -\frac{9}{10})$ and that the curve opens up.

If the coefficient preceding x^2 in $ax^2 + bx + c = 0$ is negative, the highest point on the graph is the vertex of the parabola and is called the **maximum point.** In Figure 4.4-1b you can see that the vertex of the parabola, and the maximum point of the curve, is at the point $(3, 0)$ and that the curve opens downward.

Example: 4.4-1b. Solve the quadratic equation $-x^2 + 6x - 9 = 0$ and graph its function.

$a = -1, \quad b = 6, \quad c = -9,$

$$x = \frac{-6 \pm \sqrt{36 - 4(-1)(-9)}}{2(-1)},$$

$$x = \frac{-6 \pm 0}{-2} = 3 \pm 0 = \textbf{3 or 3}.$$

Its roots are 3 or 3, and they are real and equal. The equation of the line that bisects the curve is $x = 3$. The vertex and maximum point of the parabola is at $(3, 0)$ and the parabola opens downward as shown in Figure 4.4-1b.

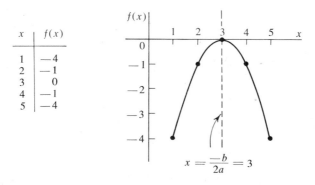

x	$f(x)$
1	-4
2	-1
3	0
4	-1
5	-4

$$x = \frac{-b}{2a} = 3$$

Figure 4.4-1b

Example: 4.4-1c. Solve the quadratic equation $x^2 - 2x + 2 = 0$ for its roots and graph its function.

$$a = 1, \quad b = -2, \quad c = 2.$$

Therefore, $x = \dfrac{-(-2) \pm \sqrt{(-2)^2 - 4(1)(2)}}{2(1)} = \dfrac{2 \pm \sqrt{-4}}{2}.$

The $\sqrt{-4}$ can be written correctly as $\sqrt{4(-1)} = (\sqrt{4})(\sqrt{-1}) = 2\sqrt{-1}$. So, for the time being, we will write the roots of the equation $x^2 - 2x + 2 = 0$ as $x = \dfrac{2 \pm 2\sqrt{-1}}{2}$ or $x = 1 \pm \sqrt{-1}$. An investigation of the meaning of $\sqrt{-1}$ will be made in the next section. We will show that one of the roots $x = 1 + \sqrt{-1}$ satisfies the equation $x^2 - 2x + 2 = 0$ and leave the other root $x = 1 - \sqrt{-1}$ for the reader to check.

Substituting $1 + \sqrt{-1}$ for x in

$$x^2 - 2x + 2 = 0$$

$$(1 + \sqrt{-1})^2 - 2(1 + \sqrt{-1}) + 2 = 0$$

$$1 + 2\sqrt{-1} - 1 - 2 - 2\sqrt{-1} + 2 = 0$$

$$0 = 0.$$

The peculiar thing about the graph of $f(x) = x^2 - 2x + 2$ in Figure 4.4-1c

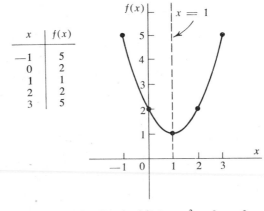

x	$f(x)$
-1	5
0	2
1	1
2	2
3	5

Figure 4.4-1c. Graph of $f(x) = x^2 - 2x + 2$.

is that it will never meet the x axis and therefore its corresponding equation $x^2 - 2x + 2 = 0$ can never have real roots. Its vertex or minimum point is located at $(1, 1)$.

4.5 IMAGINARY NUMBERS

The details of imaginary and complex numbers will appear in a later chapter. For the time being, just enough about them will be offered to answer the two questions implied by Example 4.4-1c. The questions are:

1. What kind of a number is $\sqrt{-1}$?
2. What kind of a number is $(a + b\sqrt{-1})$, where a and b are real numbers?

Let us assume that $\sqrt{-1}$ is a real number r such that $r^2 = -1$. Then,

If r is positive, r^2 is a positive real number.
If r is zero, r^2 is the number zero.
If r is negative, r^2 is a positive real number.

Thus, **if r is a real number, r^2 cannot be negative.** Therefore, our assumption that $r^2 = -1$ is a real number is false, and $\sqrt{-1}$ **is not a real number.**

As has happened so often in studying the development of the number system, we have uncovered a need for extending even the real number system.

Unfortunately, this new kind of number, $\sqrt{-1}$ has been called an **imaginary number.** It is, of course, no more imaginary than any other number you can name. Nevertheless, no one seems to have been brave enough to give it a better name. We will let this new number, $\sqrt{-1}$, be represented by i and define it as follows:

Definition: 4.5-1. *The **imaginary number** i is the square root of a negative number such that $i^2 = -1$. In general, if k is positive, $\sqrt{-k^2}$ is defined to be ki.*

Thus, the answer to our first question is that $\sqrt{-1}$ *is a new kind of number called an imaginary number and is represented by the letter i.*

The definition $i = \sqrt{-1}$ enables us to write an imaginary number, such as $\sqrt{-1}$, as follows:

$$\sqrt{-4} = \sqrt{(4)(-1)} = \sqrt{4} \cdot \sqrt{-1} = 2i.$$

It is customary to call a number such as $b\sqrt{m}$, where b is any real number and m is a negative number, a **pure imaginary number.** Then if some real number a is added to the pure imaginary number giving $a + bi$, we have what is called a **complex number.** For the time being we are going to define a complex number in this way:

Definition: 4.5-2. *A **complex number** is any number of the form $a + bi$, where a and b are real numbers and $i = \sqrt{-1}$.*

We now have the answer to our second question, namely, **a number of the form $a + bi$ or $a + b\sqrt{-1}$ is a complex number.** This enables us to conclude that the roots $x = 1 + \sqrt{-1}$ and $x = 1 - \sqrt{-1}$ which we obtained for the equation $x^2 - 2x + 2 = 0$ in Example 4.4-1c, and which now can be expressed as $x = 1 + i$ and $x = 1 - i$, were complex numbers.

4.6 DISCRIMINANT OF THE QUADRATIC EQUATION

The $b^2 - 4ac$ part of the quadratic equation may be used to determine the **nature of the roots** of a quadratic equation without first solving for the roots.

4.6-1 Properties of the Quadratic Discriminant

By careful analysis of the quadratic formula

$$x = \frac{-b \pm \sqrt{b^2 - 4ac}}{2a},$$

these three properties become evident:

1. *If $b^2 - 4ac > 0$* the result of $\dfrac{\sqrt{b^2 - 4ac}}{2a}$ in the formula would have to be added to $\dfrac{-b}{2a}$ to give one root and subtracted from $\dfrac{-b}{2a}$ to give the other root. Also, the result of $\sqrt{b^2 - 4ac}$ may be a rational number or it may be an irrational number. Therefore.

If $b^2 - 4ac > 0$, the roots are real, unequal, rational, or irrational.

For the case $b^2 - 4ac > 0$ study Example 4.4-1a and its graph.

2. *If $b^2 - 4ac = 0$*, the result of $\dfrac{\sqrt{b^2 - 4ac}}{2a}$ equals zero, and each of the roots will be equal to $\dfrac{-b}{2a}$. Thus,

If $b^2 - 4ac = 0$, the roots are real (numbers) and equal.

For the case $b^2 - 4ac = 0$, study Example 4.4-1b and its graph.

3. *If $b^2 - 4ac < 0$*, the number under the radical will be negative and the number will be imaginary. So,

If $b^2 - 4ac < 0$, the roots are complex numbers.

For the case $b^2 - 4ac < 0$, study Example 4.4-1c and its graph.

EXERCISE 4.B

1. If $a = 0$, what kind of an equation is $ax^2 + bx + c = 0$? What is its solution set?

2. Is $x^2 = 0$ a linear equation? Is it a quadratic equation? What is its solution set? How many roots does it have?

3. Solve, by factoring, the equation $6x^2 - 7x - 20 = 0$. Can all quadratic equations be solved by factoring? Explain.

4. By factoring procedure solve the equation $4x^2 - 17x - 42 = 0$. Is it possible to find the solution of $\{x \mid ax^2 + bx + c = 0\}$ by factoring?

5. Write a quadratic equation whose solution set is $\{4\}$.

6. The roots of a quadratic equation are 4 and 0. Write the equation.

7. By quadratic formula find solution sets for each of these quadratic equations:

(a) $2x^2 - 6x - 7 = 0$.
(b) $2x^2 - 17x + 8 = 0$.
(c) $64 + x^2 = 8x$.
(d) $4x^2 + 17x = 42$.

8. Solve these equations by the quadratic formula:

(a) $3x^2 - 10x - 7 = 0$.
(b) $2x^2 - 17 = 0$.
(c) $5x^2 + 45 = 30x$.
(d) $10x^2 + 14 = 0$.

9. The graph of $\{(x, y) \mid y = 3x^2 - 6x + 8\}$ is a parabola. Find the equation of the line that passes through the vertex of the parabola and bisects the curve.

10. Determine the equation of the graph that passes through the vertex of the parabola represented by $\{(x, y) \mid y = -5x^2 + 10x - 14\}$.

11. What are the coordinates of the point that is lower than any other point (minimum point) on the graph of the parabola in Problem 9?

12. Find the point that is higher than any other point (maximum point) on the graph of the parabola in Problem 10.

13. (a) Solve $x^2 - 1 = 0$. Are the roots real numbers?
(b) Solve $x^2 + 1 = 0$. Are the roots real numbers?

14. (a) Solve $4x^2 = 100$. Are the roots real numbers?
(b) Solve $x^2 + 16 = 0$. Are the roots real numbers?

Solve the following quadratic equations for x and check.

15. (a) $x^2 + x + 1 = 0$.
(b) $x^2 - 5 = 2x$.
(c) $6 - x^2 = 2x$.
(d) $4x - 5 = x^2$.

16. (a) $x^2 - 4x - 5 = 0$.
(b) $x^2 + 1 = x$.
(c) $x = x^2 + 3$.
(d) $x - 2 = 2x^2$.

17. Use $b^2 - 4ac$ to determine the nature of the roots of the equation $2x^2 - 6x + 4 = 0$. How many times will the graph of $2x^2 - 6x + 4 = 0$ cross the x axis? Check your conclusions by making a graph. From the graph approximate the values of the roots of the equation.

18. Determine the nature of the roots of $3x^2 - 30x + 75 = 0$ by use of the discriminant. Does this graph fail to meet the x axis, does it meet it in one point, or does it cross it in two points? Check your conclusions by drawing the graph. From the graph approximate the values of the roots of the equation.

19. Find the discriminant of the equation $x^2 - \dfrac{2x}{3} + 4 = 0$. What does the discriminant tell you about the roots of this particular equation? How many times will the graph of the equation cross the x axis? How many real roots are there? Check your conclusions by graphing the equation.

20. In the equation $4x^2 - 20x + 25 = 0$, the value of $b^2 - 4ac$ is zero. (a) Alter the given equation so that $b^2 - 4ac > 0$. Under this change what is the nature of the roots? Does this curve cross the x axis? (b) Alter the given equation so that $b^2 - 4ac < 0$. Under this change what is the nature of the roots? Does this curve cross the x axis?

4.7 SUM AND PRODUCT OF THE ROOTS

When we were developing the quadratic formula (in Section 4.4), we purposely labeled one root as x_1 and the other as x_2. This was done so that we could discuss the addition and multiplication of roots.

The sum of $x_1 + x_2$ is

$$x_1 + x_2 = \frac{-b}{2a} + \frac{\sqrt{b^2 - 4ac}}{2a} + \frac{-b}{2a} - \frac{\sqrt{b^2 - 4ac}}{2a},$$

$$= \frac{2(-b)}{2a};$$

$$\therefore \quad \boldsymbol{x_1 + x_2 = \frac{-b}{a}} \qquad \text{(sum of the roots of a quadratic equation).}$$

The product of $x_1 x_2$ is

$$x_1 x_2 = \left(-\frac{b}{2a} + \frac{\sqrt{b^2 - 4ac}}{2a}\right)\left(-\frac{b}{2a} - \frac{\sqrt{b^2 - 4ac}}{2a}\right)$$

$$= \frac{b^2}{4a^2} + \frac{b}{2a}\cdot\frac{\sqrt{b^2 - 4ac}}{2a} - \frac{b}{2a}\cdot\frac{\sqrt{b^2 - 4ac}}{2a} - \frac{(b^2 - 4ac)}{4a^2}$$

$$= \frac{b^2}{4a^2} - \frac{b^2}{4a^2} + \frac{4ac}{4aa};$$

$$\therefore \quad \boldsymbol{x_1 x_2 = \frac{c}{a}} \qquad \text{(product of the roots of a quadratic equation).}$$

Letting x_1 be one root and x_2 be the other, we could write *the most general quadratic equation, in terms of its root,* in this manner:

$$ax^2 + bx + c = 0,$$

$$x^2 + \frac{b}{a}x + \frac{c}{a} = 0$$

$$x^2 - \left(-\frac{b}{a}\right)x + \frac{c}{a} = 0.$$

By substitution, $\boldsymbol{x^2 - (x_1 + x_2)x + x_1 x_2 = 0}$. (General quadratic equation)

Example: 4.7-1. Given the equation $2x^2 - 5x + 8 = 0$, where $a = 2$,

$b = -5$, and $c = 8$. Determine (a) the nature of its roots, (b) the sum of the roots, and (c) the product of the roots.

(a) $b^2 - 4ac = 25 - 4(2)(8) = -39$. The roots are complex numbers.

(b) $x_1 + x_2 = \dfrac{-b}{a} = \dfrac{-(-5)}{2} = \dfrac{5}{2}$, the sum of the roots.

(c) $x_1 x_2 = \dfrac{c}{a} = \dfrac{8}{2} = 4$, the product of the roots.

Example: 4.7-2. Write a quadratic equation where the sum of its roots is $\frac{5}{2}$ and the product of its roots is 4. Use the general quadratic equation in terms of roots:

$$x^2 - (x_1 + x_2)x + x_1 x_2 = 0.$$

Substituting, $x^2 - \frac{5}{2}x + 4 = 0.$
Multiplying by 2, $2x^2 - 5x + 8 = 0.$

Note that this is the equation we started with in Example 4.7-1.

Example: 4.7-3. Determine (a) the nature of the roots, (b) the sum of the roots, and (c) the product of the roots for the equation $x^2 + 7x + 8 = 0$.

(a) $b^2 - 4ac = 49 - 4(1)(8) = 17$. So the roots are real, unequal, and irrational.

(b) The sum of the roots is $x_1 + x_2 = \dfrac{-b}{a} = \dfrac{-7}{1} = -7.$

(c) The product of the roots is $x_1 x_2 = \dfrac{c}{a} = \dfrac{8}{1} = 8.$

Example: 4.7-4. Find the quadratic equation whose sum of roots is -7 and whose product of roots is 8. Using the quadratic formula in terms of roots:

$$x^2 - (x_1 + x_2)x + x_1 x_2 = 0.$$

Substituting, $x^2 - (-7)x + 8 = 0.$

$$x^2 + 7x + 8 = 0.$$

Note that this is the same equation we started with in Example 4.7-3.

4.8 RADICAL EQUATIONS

We have already been using polynomial equations. We will have a great deal to say about polynomial equations later, but for our immediate use we will need this definition:

Definition: 4.8-1.   *An equation of the form*

$$a_0x^n + a_1x^{n-1} + a_2x^{n-2} + \cdots + a_{n-2}x^2 + a_{n-1}x + a_n = 0,$$

where n is a nonnegative integer and $a(i = 0, 1, 2, \ldots, n) \in R$, is called a **polynomial equation.**

If we separate from the general polynomial equation as defined in (4.8-1)

$$a_{n-1}x + a_n = 0,$$

we obtain a **general linear equation** equivalent to

$$mx + b = 0.$$

Or, if we separate from the general polynomial equation as defined in (4.8-1)

$$a_{n-2}x^2 + a_{n-1}x + a_n = 0,$$

we obtain a **general quadratic equation** equivalent to

$$ax^2 + bx + c = 0.$$

We could keep on writing many polynomial equations of higher degree, but our immediate concern is with these two questions:

1. What kind of an equation is $\sqrt{x-1} + \sqrt{x+2} = 3$?
2. How can $\sqrt{x-1} + \sqrt{x+2} = 3$ be solved for x?

It is apparent that $\sqrt{x-1} + \sqrt{x+2} = 3$, or its equivalent $(x-1)^{1/2} + (x+2)^{1/2} = 3$, is not a polynomial equation because Definition 4.8-1 demands that n be a nonnegative integer, not a fractional exponent. Thus, this kind of an equation must have a new name. Since its peculiarity is that it involves the variable under the radical sign, it has become classified as a **radical equation,** or sometimes as an **irrational equation.**

Definition: 4.8-2.   *A* **radical equation** *is an equation that contains the variable either under a radical sign or with a fractional exponent.*

The principle which makes it possible for us to solve radical equations is based upon the following theorem which will be stated but not proved.

Theorem: 4.8-1.   The equation obtained by squaring the members of a given equation always contains the roots of the given equation. The converse is not necessarily true.

The reason that the converse of the preceding theorem is not necessarily true is easily shown by referring to Definition 4.1-6, where we defined the linear equation as

$$f(x) = g(x). \tag{A}$$

Squaring, we get $[f(x)]^2 = [g(x)]^2.$ $\hfill (B)$

Equation (B) not only contains the roots of $f(x) = g(x)$, but it also contains the roots of

$$f(x) = -g(x),$$

which is an entirely different equation from $f(x) = g(x)$ and is not equivalent to it.

As we have pointed out before, **any time an equation is multiplied by a number containing the variable of that equation, extraneous roots may be introduced.** To identify extraneous roots, the solutions must always be checked back into the original equation.

In our work with radical equations our efforts will be confined to **second-order radicals** (those containing the square root symbol), where the number under each radical sign will be positive and only the **principal root** is used.

While it is recognized that every positive number has at least two roots, in the solution of radical and other equations,

the $\sqrt{16}$ cannot mean ± 4.
The $\sqrt{16}$ has to mean just $+ 4$,
and $-\sqrt{16}$ has to mean just -4.

Definition: 4.8-3.   *The **principal root** of $\sqrt[n]{b}$ is p if and only if $p > 0$ and $p^n = b$, where b is a nonnegative integer and n is a positive integer.*

This definition guarantees that when b is a nonnegative number the square root of b is nonnegative. In solving radical equations, if b is positive and the radical sign is preceded by a minus sign, this sign is the controlling sign and must always be retained.

4.9 RADICAL EQUATIONS OF THE SECOND ORDER

To solve radical equations of the second order:

STEP 1.   Rearrange, if necessary, the given radical equation so that one of its members has in it only one radical.
STEP 2.   Square the member on each side of the equality mark, and simplify.
STEP 3.   If a radical expression still remains, rearrange again according to Step 1, and square both members of the equation.
STEP 4.   When all radicals have been eliminated, solve the equation for its roots.
STEP 5.   Check to determine if the roots obtained satisfy the original equation. Those roots that do not satisfy the given equation are extraneous roots.

Example: 4.9-1.   Find $\{x \mid \sqrt{x - 1} + \sqrt{x + 2} = 3; x \in R\}$.

STEP 1. $\sqrt{x - 1} = 3 - \sqrt{x + 2},$

STEP 2. $x - 1 = 9 - 6\sqrt{x + 2} + x + 2,$

STEP 3. $6\sqrt{x + 2} = 12$ or $\sqrt{x + 2} = 2,$

STEP 2. $x + 2 = 4,$

STEP 4. $x = 2.$ (Possible root)

STEP 5. $\sqrt{2 - 1} + \sqrt{2 + 2} = 3,$ (Substituting 2 for x in given equation)

$$1 + 2 = 3.$$

The right and the left member match; so $x = 2$ **is a real root.**

Example: 4.9-2.   Find $\{x \mid \sqrt{x - 1} = \sqrt{2x - 1} - \sqrt{x - 4}; x \in R\}.$

STEP 1.   The equation is arranged as well as it can be.

STEP 2. $x - 1 = 2x - 1 - 2\sqrt{(2x - 1)(x - 4)} + x - 4,$

STEP 3. $2\sqrt{(2x - 1)(x - 4)} = 2x - 4; \sqrt{(2x - 1)(x - 4)} = x - 2,$

STEP 2. $2x^2 - 9x + 4 = x^2 - 4x + 4,$

STEP 4. $x^2 - 5x = 0,$

$$x(x - 5) = 0,$$

$$x = 0 \text{ or } x = 5.$$ (Possible roots)

STEP 5a.   Substituting 0 for x in $\sqrt{x - 1} = \sqrt{2x - 1} - \sqrt{x - 4}$, we get

$$\sqrt{0 - 1} = \sqrt{2(0) - 1} - \sqrt{0 - 4}$$

$$\sqrt{-1} \neq \sqrt{-1} - \sqrt{-4}.$$

Therefore, $x = 0$ **is not a root of the given equation,** and not all the equations from Step 1 through Step 4 are equivalent equations.

If you would like to play with the resulting equation on the basis of $i = \sqrt{-1}$ you would get

$$i \neq i - 2i,$$
or $i \neq -i,$

which also indicates that $x = 0$ is not a root of the original equation.

STEP 5b.   Checking $x = 5$ in the original equation, we get

$$\sqrt{5 - 1} = \sqrt{2(5) - 1} - \sqrt{5 - 4},$$

$$2 = 3 - 1,$$

$$2 = 2.$$

$\therefore$ $x = 5$ **is a root of the given equation,** and the equations from Step 1 through Step 4 are equivalent.

EXERCISE 4.C

For Problems 1 and 2 given that $x^2 - (x_1 + x_2)x + x_1 x_2 = 0$, $ax^2 + bx + c = 0$, and $x \in R$.

1. Express the sum of the roots in terms of a and b.

2. Express the product of the roots in terms of a and c.

For Problems 3 and 4 find the sum and the product of each of the following:

3. (a) $\{x \mid x^2 + 7x + 10 = 0\}$.   (c) $x^2 = 9$.
    (b) $\{x \mid -3x^2 - 5x - 4 = 0\}$.   (d) $4x - 7x = x^2$.

4. (a) $\{x \mid x^2 - 3 = 0\}$.   (c) $2x^2 - 7x + 4 = 0$.
    (b) $\{x \mid -x^2 + 5x = 0\}$.   (d) $-5x^2 = 4x + 1$.

5. Use the sum and the product formulas to write a quadratic equation which has a solution set $\{4, -2\}$.

6. Make use of the sum and product formulas to write the quadratic equation whose solution set is $\{-3, 7\}$.

7. Form a quadratic equation having the complex roots $1 - i$ and $1 + i$. Then check the discriminant $b^2 - 4ac$ to see if it is less than zero.

8. The roots of a quadratic equation are i and $-i$. Write the equation. What is the value of b? Find the value of the discriminant.

9. Is it true that $\{\frac{3}{4}, \frac{1}{2}\}$ is the solution set for the equation $8x^2 - 10x - 3 = 0$?

10. Are the roots $1 - \sqrt{3}$ and $1 + \sqrt{3}$ the roots for the equation $x^2 - 2x - 3 = 0$?

11. Write a polynomial of first degree. Graph its function. Find the value for x at the point where the graph crosses the x axis. Does this value satisfy the equation?

12. Make up a polynomial equation of second degree and determine the sum and the product of its roots.

13. Which of these two equations is a radical equation?

(a) $\sqrt{2x^2} + \frac{5}{2}x + \sqrt{-9} = 0$.   (b) $\sqrt{x - 1} = 4$.

Solve the radical equation and check your results.

14. From these two equations select the radical equation:

(a) $\dfrac{\sqrt{x + 2}}{\sqrt{5 - x}} = 3$.   (b) $\dfrac{1}{x} + \sqrt{5x} = \sqrt{13}$.

Solve the radical equation and check your answers.

Solve Problems 15 and 16 below and check each solution.

15. (a) $\{x \mid 5 - \sqrt{2x + 1} = 0\}$.   (c) $\sqrt{3x + \sqrt{2x - 1}} = 5$.
    (b) $\{x \mid \sqrt{2x + 3} - \sqrt{1 - 4x} = 0\}$.   (d) $\sqrt{x - 3} + \sqrt{2x - 1} = \sqrt{4x + 5}$.

16. (a) $\{x \mid \sqrt{5x - 4} = 6\}$.   (c) $\sqrt{\sqrt{x - 5} - 1} = 10$.
    (b) $\{x \mid \sqrt{2x + 3} + \sqrt{4x - 1} = 0\}$.   (d) $\sqrt{x^2 + 4x + 4} - \sqrt{x^2 - 5x + 6} = 3$.

17. Is $\sqrt{x} = -1$ an equation? If so, solve it for x and check the solution.

18. What value of x satisfies $\sqrt{2x + 3} - \sqrt{2x + 5} = 0$? Does your solution make the equation true or false?

19. Find the solution set for $\sqrt{x^4 - 6x^2 + 9} + 2 = 0$. (Hint: let $w = x^2$ and solve the equation for w. Then revert back to x.

20. Determine the solution set for $\sqrt{16x^4 - 10x^2 + 2} = 1$. (See hint in Problem 19.)

4.10 VARIATION

There are numerous functional relations in engineering, physics, chemistry, and other disciplines that are represented by ratios and proportions. Under the heading of variation we will study four different forms of these dependencies.

Definition: 4.10-a.   *A* **ratio** *is the quotient obtained by dividing number a by number b, where b $\neq$ 0. The equality of two ratios is a* **proportion.**

The functional relations of the different types of variation do not have to be linear or quadratic, but most of the ones we will consider will be one or the other.

Definition: 4.10-b.   *If two variables x and y are so related that the ratio of y to x is either*

$$\frac{y}{x} = k \quad \text{or} \quad y = kx \qquad (k \neq 0)$$

where k is the constant of variation, then **y** *is said to* **vary directly as** *x.*

The set of multiplication tables is a familiar example of **direct variation,** as expressed by the formula $y = kx$. If 2 is taken as the **constant of variation,** making the variation formula $y = 2x$, we obtain the following table of twos:

x	1	2	3	4	5	6	7	$\cdots$	to n natural numbers
y	2	4	6	8	10	12	14	$\cdots$	table of twos

If 3 is used as the constant of variation, using $y = 3x$, we get the *table of threes*, and so on.

The ratio of the reading on a centigrade thermometer to the reading on a Fahrenheit thermometer can be set up as the following direct proportion:

$$\frac{c}{F - 32} = \frac{5}{9} \qquad (F \neq 32°),$$

where $\frac{5}{9}$ is the fixed ratio.

Definition: 4.10-c.   *If two variables x and y are so related that their product is either*

$$xy = k \quad \text{or} \quad y = \frac{k}{x} \qquad (k \neq 0),$$

where k is the constant of variation, then **y** *is said to* **vary inversely as** *x.*

You will notice as you work with **inverse variation** that when $k > 0$ the formula $y = \dfrac{k}{x}$ possesses a "teeter-totter" type of relationship. As the values of one variable are increased, the corresponding values of the other variable decrease, and vice versa. For example, the volume of a gas in a closed container gets smaller the greater the pressure, and vice versa.

Definition: 4.10-d.   *If the variable y varies directly as x and z so that*

$$y = kxz \qquad (k \neq 0),$$

where k is the constant of variation, then y **is said to vary jointly as x and z.**

The formula for the area of a rectangle, where $k = 1$, could be used to demonstrate **joint variation.** Symbolically,

$$A = kxy$$

or with $k = 1$ we have

$$A = xy.$$

A increases either as x or y, or both, increase.

Joint variation and combined variation, which will be discussed next, can be expressed in as many variables as a problem demands.

Definition: 4.10-e.   *A combination of joint variation and inverse variation is called* **combined variation.**

Newton's Law of Gravitation furnishes us with a very interesting example of **combined variation.** It states that the gravitational force F between two masses M_1 and M_2 varies directly as the product of the masses and inversely as the square of the distance between them. Thus, the rule of correspondence is

$$F = k\frac{M_1 M_2}{d^2},$$

where $k = 6.66 \ldots (10^{-8})$ is the constant of variation in centimeter-gram-second units.

It is of utmost importance to note that **each variation formula contains a constant of variation k.** When you are writing a variation formula you must always insert this k. No problem can be solved by variation formulas unless sufficient data are given to enable you to determine the value of k for that problem. So you must be alert to the fact that the k can prove a real troublemaker for you unless you adhere to a procedure such as the one demonstrated in the following examples.

4.10-1 How to Solve Variation Problems

STEP 1.   To each quantity in the problem assign a letter symbol. Then write a rule of correspondence (a formula) that includes all these letter symbols **and the constant k.**

STEP 2.   The given data, which must have a number for each symbol, should then be substituted into the formula to enable you to solve for k.

STEP 3.   Substitute into the formula the k value and the given data in order to obtain a solution.

Example: 4.10-1a. If the distance required to stop an automobile varies directly as the square of the speed at the time the brakes are applied, a car going 35 miles per hour can be stopped in 65 feet. If the same car were going 70 miles per hour, how far would it travel before it could be stopped?

STEP 1.   The rule of correspondence is $d = kv^2$.

STEP 2. $k = \dfrac{d}{v^2} \doteq \dfrac{65}{(35)^2} \doteq \dfrac{13}{245}$,

STEP 3. $d \doteq \dfrac{13}{245}(70)^2 \doteq \dfrac{13(4900)}{245} \doteq$ **260 feet**.

The symbol $\doteq$ means "is approximately equal to." As will be explained in Chapter 9, Section 9.4, all measurements, logarithmic tables, trigonometric tables, and the numbers in other tables that have been rounded to a certain place value accuracy are only approximately correct. It follows, of course, that the results obtained by computing with such numbers can be only approximately correct.

Example: 4.10-1b.   The electrical resistance of a copper wire varies directly as the length (in feet) of the wire and inversely as the square of the diameter (in inches). If the resistance of a wire 0.01 inch in diameter and 32 feet long is 3.2 ohms, what would be the resistance of a copper wire 0.05 inch in diameter and 500 feet long?

STEP 1. $R = \dfrac{kL}{D^2}$,

STEP 2. $k = \dfrac{RD^2}{L} \doteq \dfrac{3.2(0.01)^2}{(32)} \doteq 0.00001$,

STEP 3. $R \doteq \dfrac{0.00001(500)}{(0.05)^2} \doteq$ **2 ohms**.

EXERCISE 4.D

1. Write a variation formula which shows that one variable varies directly as three times the other. If $y = 2$ when $x = 5$, what is y when x is 15?

2. If y varies directly as the square of x, what is its rule of correspondence? If $y = 16$ when $x = 2$, what is y when $x = \frac{1}{2}$.

3. It is known that y varies inversely as the square of x and that $y = \frac{1}{4}$ when $x = \frac{1}{2}$. Find y when $x = \frac{1}{3}$.

4. Write a variation formula for y which varies inversely as the cube of x. If $y = 1$ when $x = 2$, what value is y when $x = 4$?

5. The variable r varies jointly as s and t and inversely as the square root of u. Write the rule of correspondence and state at least one limitation that must be placed on u.

6. If m varies jointly as n and the cube root of p and inversely as the square root of q, write its rule of correspondence. Does q have to be limited in any way? Solve for k.

7. In a direct variation it is assumed that $x = 3$ and $k = 10$. (a) What is y when x is halved? (b) What is y when x is doubled? (c) What is y when x is made four times as large?

8. If it is assumed that $x = 3$ and $k = 10$ in an inverse variation, (a) what is y when x is halved? (b) what is y when x is doubled? (c) what is y when x is made four times as large?

9. Graph on the same set of coordinate axes the functions represented by $f(x) = kx$ if:

(a) $k = \frac{1}{2}$.   (b) $k = 2$.   (c) $k = 4$.

10. For the set of positive real numbers, graph on the same coordinate axes the functions represented by $f(x) = kx^2$ if:

(a) $k = \frac{1}{2}$.   (b) $k = 2$.   (c) $k = 4$.

11. The pitch of a violin string varies directly as the square root of its tension. (a) Express the functional relation in equation form. (b) If the pitch is 45 times per second when the tension is 9 pounds, what is the pitch when the tension is 16 pounds?

12. In an electrical circuit the current c in amperes varies inversely as the resistance r of the wire. (a) Write the rule of correspondence. (b) If $c = 40$ when $r = 20$, what is c when $r = 4$?

13. Above the earth's surface the weight of an object varies inversely as the square of the distance from the center of the earth. Take radius of the earth to be 3959 miles. (a) Write the variation formula. (b) How much would an astronaut who weighs 185 pounds on the earth's surface weigh 84 miles above the earth's surface?

14. The acceleration of gravity on the earth's surface varies inversely as the square of the distance from the center of the earth. (Use 3959 miles as the radius of the earth.) (a) Write the formula that expresses the relationship. (b) If the acceleration of gravity on the earth is 32.2 feet per second per second, what would be the acceleration of gravity of a space capsule 114 miles above the earth's surface?

15. The volume of a right circular cylinder varies jointly as the square of the radius and its height. (a) Write the equation. (b) Find the value for k. (c) Is k a variable or a constant? Why?

16. The volume of a right circular cone varies jointly as the square of its radius and its height. (a) Write the rule of correspondence. (b) What is the value of k? (c) Can k be a fraction? Can k be zero?

17. The distance traveled by an object varies directly as the time and the average speed. Determine the value of the constant of variation. Could this value be negative? Explain?

18. The amount of simple interest earned in one year depends upon the principal and the rate of interest. What is the value of k? If the time factor had not been fixed, what would be the value of k?

19. The strength of a rectangular beam varies directly as its width and the square of its depth. If a beam 6 inches wide and 15 inches deep has a strength of 24,500 pounds, what is the strength of a beam 2 inches wide and 6 inches deep?

20. The safe load of a rectangular beam varies jointly as the width and the square of its depth and inversely as its distance between its supports. If a 3-inch by 10-inch beam 12-foot long can support 1400 pounds, what would be the safe load for a 2-inch by 6-inch beam 6-foot long?

4.11 INEQUALITIES

Inequalities have taken on such importance in the theory and practice of present-day mathematics that their properties and application should be carefully studied.

Up to this point in this chapter we have confined ourselves to open sentences of the equation type. Let us now consider **open sentences** such as $mx + b \neq 0$ or $ax^2 + bx + c \neq 0$, which are called **inequalities.**

Before proceeding it is essential that you study again Sections 2.13 and 2.14 in Chapter 2 and Section 3.4-2 in Chapter 3, to refresh your thinking on "is less than," the most basic concept of inequalities.

Definition: 4.11-a.   *An* **inequality** *is an open sentence such that* $a \neq b, a < b,$ $a \leq b, a > b,$ *or* $a \geq b$ *for any* $a, b \in R.$

As with equations, the **domain** of the function for which an inequality is true is called a **solution,** and the **set of all possible solutions** is known as the **solution set** of the inequality.

Definition: 4.11-b.   *An* **absolute inequality** *is true for every admissible value of the replacement set of the independent variable.*

For $x, y \in R, x^2 + x + y^2 + y + 1 > 0$ is an absolute inequality.

Definition: 4.11-c.   *A* **conditional inequality** *is not true for every admissible value of the replacement set of the independent variable.*

$2x + 3 < 0$ is a conditional inequality.

The solution set of an inequality is found by generating a series of equivalent inequalities as was done in solving equations. The operations used to change from one inequality to another equivalent one are as follows:

4.11-1 Basic Operations Used in Solving Inequalities

The symbol "$\equiv$" will be used to mean "is equivalent to," and the symbol "iff" means "if and only if."

Definition: 4.11-1a.   *Two inequalities whose symbols point in the same direction are said to have the* **same sense.** *Otherwise, they are said to have* **opposite sense.**

Case I.   For all admissible values of x in the expressions $f(x), g(x), h(x),$

$$f(x) < g(x) \equiv f(x) + h(x) < g(x) + h(x).$$

This open sentence means that if any real number is added to (or subtracted from) both members of an inequality, another inequality in the same sense is obtained.

If $3 < 4$, then $3 - 2 < 4 - 2$ and $1 < 2$.

Case II.   For all admissible values of x, and $h(x) > 0$,

$$f(x) < g(x) \equiv f(x) \cdot h(x) < g(x) \cdot h(x).$$

That is, *if both members of an inequality are multiplied (or divided) by the same positive real number, the sense of the inequality remains unchanged.*

If $3 < 4$, then $3 \cdot 5 < 4 \cdot 5$ and $15 < 20$.
If $3 < 4$, then $3 \div 2 < 4 \div 2$ and $1.5 < 2$.

Case III.   For all admissible values of x, and $h(x) < 0$,

$$f(x) < g(x) \equiv f(x) \cdot h(x) > g(x) \cdot h(x).$$

This statement says that, *if both members of an inequality are multiplied (or divided) by the same negative real number, the sense of the inequality is reversed.*

If $3 < 4$, then $3 \cdot (-5) > 4 \cdot (-5)$ and $-15 > -20$.
If $3 < 4$, then $3 \div (-5) > 4 \div (-5)$ and $-\frac{3}{5} > -\frac{4}{5}$.

Using Case III, it can be observed geometrically that when any real number on the number line is multiplied (or divided) by a negative number, the position of the resulting product changes to the opposite side of the origin. In other words, the smaller number on the positive side of the number lines becomes the larger number of the negative side, and the larger number on the positive side becomes the smaller number on the negative side, and vice versa.

4.11-2 Algebraic and Graphical Solutions of Linear and Quadratic Inequalities

Example: 4.11-2a.   Solve $x + 4 > 11$.

SOLUTION: $x + 4 > 11$,   (Given)
$x + 4 - 4 > 11 - 4$,   (4.11-1, Case I)
and $x > 7$.   (*A₅* and *A₁*)
Therefore, $x + 4 > 11$ is true if and only if $x > 7$ (*E₃*)

Example: 4.11-2b.   Solve and show by a graph the values of x that will satisfy $5x - 8 < 3x + 10$.

SOLUTION: $5x - 8 < 3x + 10$,   (Given)
$-3x + 5x - 8 + 8 < -3x + 3x + 10 + 8$,   (4.11-1, Case I)
$2x < 18$,   (*A₅* and *A₁*)
and $x < 9$.   (4.11-1, Case II)
∴ **$5x - 8 < 3x + 10$ is true iff $x < 9$** (see Figure 4.11-2b):   (*E₃*)

Example: 4.11-2c.   Solve and make a graph of the values of x that satisfy the inequality $x^2 + x - 6 > 0$.

SOLUTION: $x^2 + x - 6 > 0$ factors into $(x + 3)(x - 2) > 0$. For the

$$x < 9$$

(Case II)

Figure 4.11-2b. The small open circle○ at 9 means that x = 9 is not a solution.

product of the two factors $(x + 3)(x - 2)$ to be greater than zero either both factors must be positive or both factors must be negative. Therefore, two possibilities must be investigated:

1st Possibility	*2nd Possibility*
If $x + 3 > 0$ and $x - 2 > 0$,	If $x + 3 < 0$ and $x - 2 < 0$,
then $x > -3$ and $x > 2$.	then $x < -3$ and $x < 2$.
Only $x > 2$ satisfies the given inequality.	Only $x < -3$ satisfies the given inequality.

$\therefore$ $x^2 + x - 6 > 0$ **is true iff** $x > 2$ **or** $x < -3$.

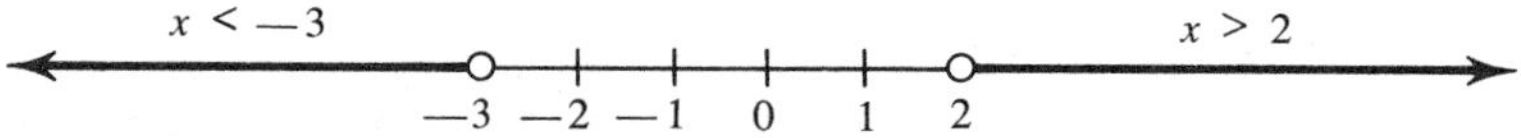

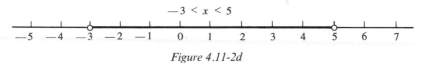

Figure 4.11-2c. The small circles at x = 2 and x = -3 in Figure 4.11-2c mean that these two numbers are not included in the set solution for $x^2 + x - 6 > 0$.

Example: 4.11-2d.   For what values of x is $x^2 - 2x - 15 < 0$?

SOLUTION: In factored form the inequality is $(x - 5)(x + 3) < 0$ and, since the product of two factors can be negative if and only if the two factors have opposite signs, the two possibilities are

1st Possibility	*2nd Possibility*
If $x - 5 > 0$ and $x + 3 < 0$,	If $x - 5 < 0$ and $x + 3 > 0$,
then $x > 5$ and $x < -3$.	then $x < 5$ and $x > -3$.
It is impossible for x to be greater than 5 and less than -3 at the same time.	All values of x greater than -3 and less than 5 satisfy the inequality.

$\therefore$ $\{x \mid -3 < x < 5\}$ **is the solution set for** $\{x \mid x^2 - 2x - 15 < 0\}$.

$$-3 < x < 5$$

Figure 4.11-2d

Example: 4.11-2e.   Make a graph of the inequality

$\{(x, y) \mid 3x + 2y \le 12; x, y \in R\}$.

The domain of x is unlimited, but only the values shown in the table are necessary to indicate the nature of the graph

The **equation part** of the given problem, that is, $3x + 2y = 12$, is satisfied by all the points on the straight line. The **inequality part** of the given statement, which is $3x + 2y < 12$, is satisfied by all the points that fall below the graph of $3x + 2y = 12$ (see Figure 4.11-2e).

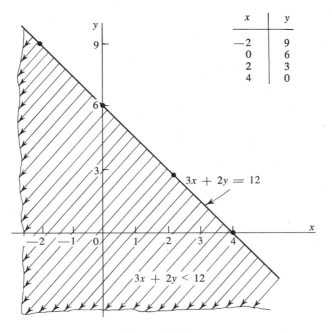

x	y
-2	9
0	6
2	3
4	0

Figure 4.11-2e

Example: 4.11-2f.   Make a graph of $\{(x, y) \mid y + x + 6 - x^2 \geq 0\}$.

Here again the equation part of the statement, namely, $y + x + 6 - x^2 = 0$, is satisfied by the coordinates of all the points on the parabola. The inequality part, $y + x + 6 - x^2 > 0$, is satisfied by the coordinates of all the points that fall above the parabola.

If the inequality had been a "less than" instead of a "more than" statement, its graph would have included all the points below the parabola instead of those shown in Figure 4.11-2f.

Example: 4.11-2g.   Make a graph of the inequality $\{(x, y) \mid y \leq |2x - 5|\}$.

According to Definition 2.14-3 in Chapter 2 and Section 3.4-2 in Chapter 3, the results of the absolute value function $|2x - 5|$ must be a positive real number or zero. The function can, of course, be written without the absolute value signs, that is,

$$y \leq |2x - 5| \equiv y \leq (2x - 5) \leq (-y),$$

and the graph plotted by using the two inequalities shown in Figure 4.11-2g.

x	y
−3	6
−2	0
−1	−4
0	−6
1	−6
2	−4
3	0
4	6

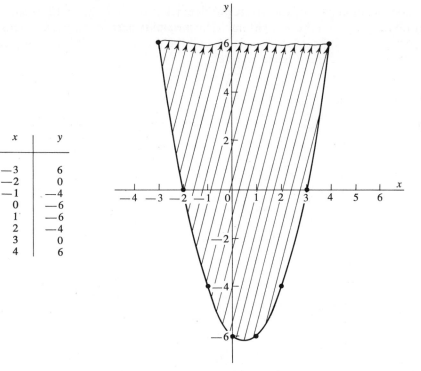

Figure 4.11-2f

Case 1		Case 2	
$y \leq 2x - 5$		$y \leq -(2x - 5)$	
x	y	x	y
2.5	0	0	5
3	1	1	3
4	3	2	1
5	5	2.5	0

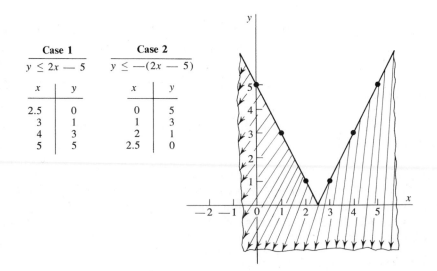

Figure 4.11-2g

EXERCISE 4.E

Solve the following inequalities.

1. $7x > 14$.

5. $\dfrac{2x + 5}{2} \geq 3$.

9. $x^2 - 5x + 6 < 0$.

2. $2x < 6$.

6. $\dfrac{3x - 2}{3} \leq 4$.

10. $x^2 + 4x + 3 > 0$.

3. $-3x < 5$.

7. $4x + 1 \leq x - 2$.

11. $y^2 < 2y + 24$.

4. $\dfrac{-5w}{2} > 4$.

8. $5x - 3 \geq x + 4$.

12. $r^2 + 10r + 25 > 0$.

Make a graph of each of the following inequalities.

13. $3x + 7 > 5$.
14. $6x + 2 < 3$.
15. $4x^2 < 2 - 7x$.
16. $3x - 2 + 2x^2 > 0$.
21. What is the solution set for $|x - 8| < 0$?

17. $\{(x, y)\,|\, y \geq x^2 + 3x + 2\}$.
18. $\{(x, y)\,|\, y \leq x^2 + x - 20\}$.
19. $|2x + 1| \leq 3$.
20. $|3x + 5| \geq 4$.

22. Find the solution set for $\dfrac{6 - 5x}{5} < -x$.

23. If $a, b \in R$ and $a \neq b$, show that $a^2 + b^2 > 2ab$.

24. Use Problem 23 to show that $\dfrac{a}{b} + \dfrac{b}{a} > 2$.

25. Find k for $\left\{ k \,\middle|\, \dfrac{1}{k^2} > 64 \,;\, k \in R \right\}$.

26. Find $\left\{ k \,\middle|\, \dfrac{1}{6k} < 5 \,;\, k \in R \right\}$.

Solve and graph each of the following inequalities:

27. $\{x \,|\, x^2 < 0\}$.
28. $\{x \,|\, x^2 > 0\}$.
29. $\{x \,|\, x^3 - x < 0\}$.
30. $\{x \,|\, x^3 - 4x > 0\}$.

31. $\{x \,|\, x^2 + 9 > 6x\}$.
32. $\{x \,|\, x^2 + 9 < -6x\}$.
33. $|7x - 1| \geq 2 + 4x$.
34. $2 + \dfrac{r}{3} \leq |r + 4|$.

Solve the following inequalities algebraically:

35. $-0.1 < x - 6 < 0.1$.
36. $-0.01 \leq x + 8 \leq 0.01$.

37. $-0.002 \leq 2x - 4 \leq 0.002$.
38. $0.01x - 4.64 \geq 0$.

Rewrite without absolute value signs and solve:

39. $\left| \dfrac{2x + 5}{6} \right| \geq 5$.

40. $\left| \dfrac{3x - 1}{5} \right| \leq 4$.

Solve for x in terms of the constants m and n.

41. $\dfrac{2}{3}m + 3nx + \dfrac{3}{2}n \leq mx$.

42. $m - 5nx \leq \dfrac{n}{4} + 2mx$.

Shade the portions of the xy plane which simultaneously satisfy the following inequalities.

43. $x \geq 0$, $y \leq 0$, and $2x - 3y \leq 6$.

44. $x \geq 0$, $y \geq 0$, and $2x + 3y \geq 6$.

45. $x + 2y \leq 4$, $x - 2y \leq 4$, and $x > 0$.

46. $x + 2y \geq 4$, $x - 2y \geq 4$, and $x \leq 8$.

Linear Systems of Equations

Sets of equations that are satisfied by a common solution, or many common solutions, are called **simultaneous equations.** Only sets of linear equations will be discussed in the following pages. As an example of a set of linear equations, consider

$$\{(x, y) \mid x + y = 7 \cap x - y = 11\},$$

and suppose as a first trial we take $x = 4$ and $y = 3$. The ordered pair $(4, 3)$ satisfies the first equation but not the second. As another trial take $x = 13$ and $y = 2$. This ordered pair satisfies the second equation but not the first. However, should you happen to stumble onto the values $x = 9$ and $y = -2$, you would have discovered an ordered pair of values that satisfies both equations. That is, in terms of sets the following is a true statement:

$$\{(x, y) \mid x + y = 7\} \cap \{(x, y) \mid x - y = 11\} = \{(9, -2)\}.$$

5.1 THE LINEAR EQUATION

If one ever hopes to be able to work with m linear equations in n variables one must first thoroughly learn about a linear equation in two variables.

In Chapter 4, Section 4.3, we learned that the linear function $f(x) = mx + b$ always plotted a straight line. We also learned in Section 4.3 that the linear function, $f(x) = mx + b$, and the linear equation in two variables, $y = mx + b$, were equivalent expressions. Thus, it is true that the graph of $y = mx + b$ will always be a straight line.

Linear equations may or may not be specifically solved in terms of y.

Definition: 5.1-1. *If an equation is in the form $y = f(x)$, that is, if it has been solved for y such as $y = mx + b$, then y is called an **explicit function** of x.*

Definition: 5.1-2.   *An equation in which y is not isolated on one side of the equality sign, such as Ax + By + C = 0, is called an* **implicit function** *of x.*

5.2 SLOPE OF THE GRAPH OF A LINEAR EQUATION

A straight line may be determined by means of two distinct points. But a line can also be plotted by using any one point on the line and its slope. A brief discussion of slope will be given at this point to show how this is done and to make the method available in the further study of simultaneous equations.

The equation $y = mx + b$ is known as the slope-intercept form of a linear equation, where m is a measure of the slope of the graph and b locates the point $(0, b)$ where the line intercepts the y axis.

The **concept of slope** has to do with the slant or the steepness of a line and is measured in this manner:

Definition: 5.2-a.   *The* **slope of a straight line** *is the ratio of the change between any two values of y to the change between the corresponding values of x.*

The slope of a straight line means the slope of any line segment of the line.

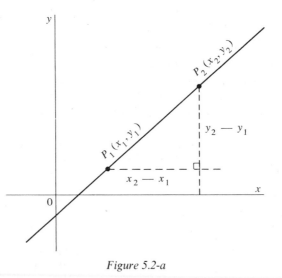

Figure 5.2-a

Denoting the slope of a line by m and selecting points $P_1(x_1, y_1)$ and $P_2(x_2, y_2)$ on the line, as shown in Figure 5.2-a, the **slope relation is**

$$m = \frac{y_2 - y_1}{x_2 - x_1},$$

provided this number exists.

5.2-1 Some Properties of the Slope Concept

1. The slope of a horizontal line is zero.
2. The slope of a line that moves up and to the right is positive.
3. The slope of a line that moves up and to the left is negative.
4. Any two nonvertical parallel lines have the same slope.
5. Two nonvertical lines are perpendicular if and only if the product of their slopes equals -1, that is, $m_1m_2 = -1$.
6. Two nonvertical coincident lines have the same slope.
7. The slope of a vertical line does not exist and $m = \dfrac{y_2 - y_1}{x_2 - x_1}$ does not apply.

Example: 5.2-1a. Use the slope idea to make a graph of $y = 3x + 4$, and check the graph with sets of ordered pairs.

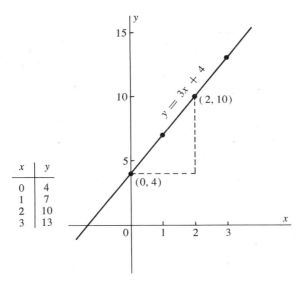

x	y
0	4
1	7
2	10
3	13

Figure 5.2-1a

1. Comparing $y = 3x + 4$ with $y = mx + b$ it is evident that $b = 4$ and that one point on the line is at $(0, 4)$.
2. The slope of the line is $m = 3$, which means for each one unit horizontally to the right of $(0, 4)$ one must move vertically 3 units to get back on the line. This tells us that other points on the line are at $(1, 7)$, $(2, 10)$, $(3, 13)$, and so on.
3. Check the graph in Figure 5.2-1a by using the ordered pairs given in the table.

5.3 THE GENERAL FORM OF A LINEAR EQUATION IN TWO VARIABLES

The most general form of a first-degree equation in two variables (see Definition 4.3-2) is

$$Ax + By + C = 0.$$

Theorem: 5.3-1.   The graph of the equation $Ax + By + C = 0$, where A, B, and C are real numbers and A and B are not both zero, is a straight line. Conversely, any straight line is the graph of $Ax + By + C = 0$.

If $A = 0$ and $B \neq 0$, then $Ax + By + C = 0$ becomes $By = -C$ and $y = \dfrac{-C}{B}$. The graph of $y = \dfrac{-C}{B}$ is a straight line parallel to the x axis and a distance of $\dfrac{-C}{B}$ from it. Conversely, **a straight line parallel to the x axis is expressed by the equation $y = \dfrac{-C}{B}$** or $By + C = 0$.

If $B = 0$ and $A \neq 0$, $Ax + By + C = 0$ becomes $Ax + C = 0$ and $x = \dfrac{-C}{A}$. The graph of $x = \dfrac{-C}{A}$ is a straight line parallel to the y axis and a distance of $\dfrac{-C}{A}$ from it. Conversely, **a straight line parallel to the y axis is expressed by the equation $x = \dfrac{-C}{A}$** or $Ax + C = 0$.

If both A and B are different from zero, then $Ax + By + C = 0$ becomes, in explicit form,

$$y = -\frac{A}{B}x - \frac{C}{B},$$

which is in the same form as the first-degree (and linear) function,

$$y = mx + b,$$

whose graph we know to be a straight line. Conversely, **any nonvertical straight line is represented by the equation $Ax + By + C = 0$.** Therefore, **the graph of the most general first-degree equation in two variables is a straight line.**

We have already made graphs of several linear equations of the form

$$Ax + By + C = 0,$$

and in each case we found that for each value assumed for x a unique value of y was obtained. Moreover, we found that an indefinitely large number of ordered pairs were possible. So we conclude that **the solution set for each linear equation is an infinite solution set.** This situation leads us to this very interesting and challenging question: How would one go about solving or graphing two linear equations in two variables?

5.4 TWO LINEAR EQUATIONS IN TWO VARIABLES

If we followed the notation in the preceding section our problem would be to solve two linear equations in two variables of the type

$$A_1x + B_1y + C_1 = 0,$$

$$A_2x + B_2y + C_2 = 0.$$

However, with no intention of making a simple notation complicated but with the foreknowledge that the following notation, and the form, will have many advantages in more advanced mathematics, the double subscript notation will be used in this text:

$$a_{11}x + a_{12}y = b_1$$

$$a_{21}x + a_{22}y = b_2.$$

The *first subscript* attached to a coefficient tells you *which row* the coefficient is in and the *second subscript* tells you *which column* the coefficient is in. For example, a_{11} is in the first row and the first column, a_{12} is in the first row and the second column, a_{21} is in the second row and the first column, and a_{22} is in the second row and the second column.

There are many methods of solving simultaneous equations, *such as the method of substitution, the comparison method, solution by graphs, the addition and subtraction method—which we will use extensively to obtain what we call the equivalent equation method, and solution by determinants. We will discuss the* **graph,** *the* **equivalent equation,** *and the* **determinant methods.**

5.4-1 Possible Solutions of Linear Equations in Two Variables

In a plane one of three things must happen to the graphs of two linear equations in two variables.

1. If the slopes of lines L_1 and L_2 are different, then $L_1 \cap L_2$ is a single ordered pair, that is, **the two lines intersect in a point,** and the coordinates of this point is the common solution of the set of simultaneous equations. This set is said to be a **consistent and independent simultaneous system.**

2. If the slopes of L_1 and L_2 are the same and $L_1 \cap L_2$, then $L_1 \equiv L_2$ and **the two lines are coincident,** that is, one line is plotted exactly on top of the other. Each of the infinite number of ordered pairs that satisfies one equation satisfies the other equation. This simultaneous set of equations is a **consistent and dependent system.**

3. If the slopes of L_1 and L_2 are the same and $L_1 \cap L_2 = \emptyset$, then **the two lines are parallel.** No common solution for this set of linear equations exists. A set of equations of this type is called an **inconsistent system of equations.**

Definition: 5.4-1a.   *The solution, or the solutions as the case might be, that satisfies both equations in a set of two linear equations in two variables is called a* **simultaneous solution.**

Definition: 5.4-1b.   *Any two systems of equations that have the same solution set are said to be* **equivalent systems** (see also Definition 4.2-3).

5.4-2 Graphical Solutions of Linear Equations in Two Variables

Example: 5.4-2a.   Find $\{(x, y) \mid 4x + y = 8 \cap x - y = 7\}$.

The equation $4x + y = 8$, arranged in **slope-intercept form,** is $y = -4x + 8$. Then $m = -4$ is its slope, and $b_1 = 8$ is its **y intercept.** Likewise, the slope-intercept form of $x - y = 7$ is $y = x - 7$. Its slope is $m = 1$ and its y intercept is $b_2 = -7$.

Since the slopes of the two equations are different, one being -4 and the other 1, Section 5.4-1(1) tells us that the graphs of the two lines intersect in a point and that the coordinates of that point is the common solution of the two equations (see Figure 5.4-2a). Thus, this particular set represents a **consistent and independent system of equations.**

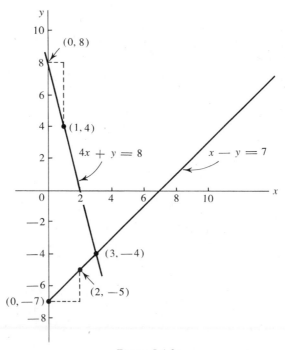

Figure 5.4-2a

Drawing the graph of the first equation by using the point at $(0, 8)$ and the slope $m = -4$, and drawing the graph of the second equation by using the point at $(0, -7)$ and $m = 1$, we observe that the two lines intersect at $x = 3$ and $y = -4$. Therefore, the **solution set is $\{(3, -4)\}$.**

Example: 5.4-2b.   Find the simultaneous solution for the equations

$$4x + y = 8,$$

$$12x + 3y = 24.$$

From the previous example we know that the slope of the first equation is $m = -4$ and its y intercept is $b_1 = 8$. Arranging $12x + 3y = 24$ in slope-intercept form and dividing both sides of the resulting equation by 3, we get $y = -4x + 8$, which also has a slope of $m = -4$ and a y intercept of $b_2 = 8$.

Since both of the given equations have the y intercept point (0, 8) in common and have identical slopes, their graphs are certain to be coincident (see Figure 5.4-2b). This assures us that any one of the infinitely large number of solutions

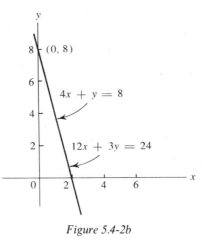

Figure 5.4-2b

of one equation is also a solution of the other, and the equations are equivalent (see Definition 4.2-3). According to Section 5.4-1(2), this set is an example of a **consistent and dependent system of simultaneous equations.**

Example: 5.4-2c.   Find the solution of the set

$$\{(x, y) \,|\, 4x + y = 8 \cap 12x + 3y = 24\}.$$

Here again we know from the two previous examples that the slope of the first equation is $m = -4$ and its y intercept is $b_1 = 8$. Expressing $12x + 3y = 15$ in slope-intercept form we get $y = -4x + 5$, which has a slope of -4 and a y intercept of $b_2 = 5$. Since both equations have the same slope $m = -4$, but different y intercepts, namely, $b_1 = 8$ and $b_2 = 5$, their graphs will be two parallel lines [see Section 5.4-1(3) and Figure 5.4-2c]. No solution exists. Therefore,

$$\{(x, y) \,|\, 4x + y = 8\} \cap \{(x, y) \,|\, 12x + 3y = 15\} = \emptyset.$$

This set is an example of an **inconsistent system of equations.**

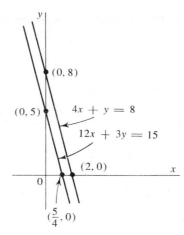

Figure 5.4-2c

5.4-3 Solution of Linear Equations in Two Variables by Equivalent Equation Method

As you will soon observe, the *equivalent equation method* of solving simultaneous equations involves the *addition-subtraction method*, the equivalency definitions from Section 4.2 in Chapter 4, and the following theorem:

Theorem: 5.4-3a. If equations $A(1)$ and $A(2)$ are any two linear equations in two unknowns, $A(1)$ may be replaced by $A(1) + kA(2)$, where k is any nonzero real number.

If equation $A(1) = a_{11}x + a_{12}y - b_1 = 0$ and equation $A(2) = a_{21}x$ and $a_{22}y - b_2 = 0$, then $A(1) + kA(2) = a_{11}x + a_{12}y - b_1 + k(a_{21}x + a_{22}y - b_2) = 0$, and it becomes immediately apparent that any solution of $A(1)$ and $A(2)$ is also a solution of $A(1) + kA(2) = 0$.

Conversely, if any ordered pair of numbers of x and y satisfy $A(1) + kA(2) = 0$ and $A(2) = 0$ they will also satisfy $A(1) = 0$ and $A(2) = 0$. Thus the systems

$$\left. \begin{array}{l} A(1) = 0 \\ A(2) = 0 \end{array} \right\} \quad \text{and} \quad \left\{ \begin{array}{ll} A(1) + kA(2) = 0 \\ A(2) \quad\quad\;\; = 0 \end{array} \right.$$

are equivalent.

No one would claim that the equivalent equation method is the most direct or easiest method of solving a system of simultaneous equations. However, it is a method that clears the way for greater mathematical maturity.

As the following example will show, **the basic principle of the equivalent equation method is to eliminate one variable at a time to produce systems of equivalent equations.** The process is continued until the values of the variable are obtained.

Example: 5.4-3a.   Find the values for x and y that satisfy

$\{(x, y) \mid 2x - 5y = 16 \cap 3x + 2y = 5\}$.

$A \quad \begin{array}{ll} (1) & 2x - 5y = 16, \\ (2) & 3x + 2y = 5. \end{array}$

To obtain the next equivalent system multiply $A(1)$ by 2 and $A(2)$ by 5 and add. Thus

$B \quad \begin{array}{ll} (1) & 2x - 5y = 16, \\ (2) & 19x = 57. \end{array}$

Equivalent system C is obtained by multiplying $B(1)$ by $\frac{1}{2}$ and $B(2)$ by $\frac{1}{19}$.

$C \quad \begin{array}{ll} (1) & x - \dfrac{5}{2}y = 8, \\ (2) & x = 3. \end{array}$

Substituting $C(2)$ in $C(1)$ and solving for y gives D, the final system of equivalent equations, to be

$D \quad \begin{array}{ll} (1) & y = -2, \\ (2) & x = 3. \end{array}$

Since systems A, B, C, and D are equivalent systems, it follows that the solution for system D is the *one and only solution* for system A. Therefore, A is a **consistent, independent system** of simultaneous equations, and

$\{(x, y) \mid 2x - 5y = 16\} \cap \{(x, y) \mid 3x + 2y = 5\} = \{(3, -2)\}$.

Example: 5.4-3b.   Consider the two linear equations:

$A \quad \begin{array}{ll} (1) & 2x - 5y = 16, \\ (2) & 4x - 10y = 32. \end{array}$

It becomes very evident that if you multiply $A(1)$ by 2 you get exactly equation $A(2)$. If you then attempted to eliminate one of the variables by subtraction you would lose both variables. As a matter of fact you would get

$0 + 0 = 0$.

So no equivalent system B can be obtained.

Since it has already been established that any linear equation in two variables has an infinite number of solutions and it has just been shown that equations $A(1)$ and $A(2)$ are equivalent, therefore, system A has an *infinite number of solutions*, and is a **consistent, dependent system** of simultaneous equations.

Example: 5.4-3c.   Find $\{(x, y) \mid 2x - 5y = 10 \cap 4x - 10y = 32\}$.

$$A \quad \begin{array}{ll} (1) & 2x - 5y = 10, \\ (2) & 4x - 10y = 32. \end{array}$$

Again if equation $A(1)$ is multiplied by 2 the left members of the two equations are alike but the right members differ. Since $4x$ and $10y$ each represent some numerical quantity, their sum could not be 20 in one case and 32 in another. Moreover, if you multiply $A(1)$ by 2 and subtract the two equations you get

$$0 + 0 = 12$$

which is false. Therefore, *no solution exists* for the given set. **System** A is said to be an **inconsistent system. Its graph consists of two parallel lines.**

5.4-4 Solving Linear Equations in Two Variables by Determinants

In this chapter only those properties of determinants needed to solve linear equations in two variables will be presented.

Consider the set of simultaneous equations

$$A \quad \begin{array}{ll} (1) & a_{11}x + a_{12}y = b_1, \\ (2) & a_{21}x + a_{22}y = b_2. \end{array}$$

If equation $A(1)$ is multiplied by a_{22} and $A(2)$ is multiplied by $-a_{12}$ and added, we get

$$(a_{11}a_{22} - a_{21}a_{12})x = a_{22}b_1 - a_{12}b_2.$$

Then $x = \dfrac{a_{22}b_1 - a_{12}b_2}{a_{11}a_{22} - a_{21}a_{12}}, \qquad (a_{11}a_{22} - a_{21}a_{12} \neq 0).$ (A)

To get y, multiply $A(1)$ by $-a_{21}$ and $A(2)$ by a_{11} and add.

$$(-a_{21}a_{12} + a_{11}a_{22})y = -a_{21}b_1 + a_{11}b_2.$$

Then $y = \dfrac{a_{11}b_2 - a_{21}b_1}{a_{11}a_{22} - a_{21}a_{12}}, \qquad (a_{11}a_{22} - a_{21}a_{12} \neq 0).$ (B)

Definition: 5.4-4a.   *A square array of numbers of the form*

$$\begin{vmatrix} a_{11} & a_{12} \\ a_{21} & a_{22} \end{vmatrix} = a_{11}a_{22} - a_{21}a_{12}$$

is a number and is called **a determinant of the second order.**

A second-order or a 2×2 determinant has two rows and two columns, with the elements a_{11} and a_{22} forming the **principal diagonal** and the elements a_{21} and a_{12} forming the **secondary diagonal.**

To determine the number value of a second-order determinant, the product of the elements of the secondary diagonal is subtracted from the product of the elements of the principal diagonal. As indicated by Definition 5.4-4a, this gives

$$\begin{vmatrix} a_{11} & a_{12} \\ a_{21} & a_{22} \end{vmatrix} = a_{11}a_{22} - a_{21}a_{12}.$$

Of particular importance to us is the fact that the expression $a_{11}a_{22} - a_{21}a_{12}$ of the preceding expansion, is identical to the denominators we obtained when we solved

$$a_{11}x + a_{12}y = b_1,$$

$$a_{21}x + a_{22}y = b_2.$$

for x and y in formulas (A) and (B), Section 5.4-4.

We propose, therefore, to write the equivalent of the formulas for x and y, for two linear equations in two variables, in determinant form.

Formulas	*Formulas in Determinant Form*
$$x = \frac{a_{22}b_1 - a_{12}b_2}{a_{11}a_{22} - a_{21}a_{12}}. \quad (A)$$	$$x = \frac{\begin{vmatrix} b_1 & a_{12} \\ b_2 & a_{22} \end{vmatrix}}{\begin{vmatrix} a_{11} & a_{12} \\ a_{21} & a_{22} \end{vmatrix}}.$$
$$y = \frac{a_{11}b_2 - a_{21}b_1}{a_{11}a_{22} - a_{21}a_{12}}. \quad (B)$$	$$y = \frac{\begin{vmatrix} a_{11} & b_1 \\ a_{21} & b_2 \end{vmatrix}}{\begin{vmatrix} a_{11} & a_{12} \\ a_{21} & a_{22} \end{vmatrix}}.$$

The determinant formulas are actually formed by what is known as **Cramer's rule.** That is, the a_{11} and a_{21} in the denominator determinant, which were the coefficients for x in the original equations, are replaced by the constant terms of the original equations. This produces $\begin{vmatrix} b_1 & a_{12} \\ b_2 & a_{22} \end{vmatrix}$ as the numerator determinant for the x formula. Likewise, the a_{12} and a_{22} in the denominator determinant, which were the coefficients for y in the given equations, are replaced by the constant terms to produce $\begin{vmatrix} a_{11} & b_1 \\ a_{21} & b_2 \end{vmatrix}$ as the numerator determinant of the y formula.

Before you proceed further, you should expand the preceding determinant formulas to be sure that they are equivalent to formulas (A) and (B).

Never attempt to solve a set of simultaneous equations in two variables "by determinants" until you have arranged the given equations in this form:

$$a_{11}x + a_{12}y = b_1,$$

$$a_{21}x + a_{22}y = b_2.$$

This has to be done because it was the preceding form that was used to produce the determinant formulas.

Example: 5.4-4a.   Find $\{(x, y)\,|\,3x + 10y = 3 \cap 6x - 5y = 16\}$.

Since A
$$\begin{aligned} (1) & \quad 3x + 10y = 3 \\ (2) & \quad 6x - 5y = 16, \end{aligned}$$

then

$$x = \frac{\begin{vmatrix} 3 & 10 \\ 16 & -5 \end{vmatrix}}{\begin{vmatrix} 3 & 10 \\ 6 & -5 \end{vmatrix}} = \frac{-15 - 160}{-15 - 60} = \frac{-175}{-75} = \frac{7}{3};$$

$$y = \frac{\begin{vmatrix} 3 & 3 \\ 6 & 16 \end{vmatrix}}{-75} = \frac{48 - 18}{-75} = \frac{30}{-75} = -\frac{2}{5}.$$

Check the ordered pair $(\frac{7}{3}, -\frac{2}{5})$ to see if it satisfies equations $A(1)$ and $A(2)$.

5.4-5 Second-Order Determinants That Are Zero

In regard to the determinant formulas, note these facts:

1. If the denominator of the determinant formula is not zero, as in Example 5.4-4a, there is a unique solution and **the system is consistent and independent.**

2. If the denominator of each determinant formula is zero, and the determinants in the numerators of the formulas for both x and y are zero, then any solution that satisfies one equation will satisfy the other and **the system is consistent and dependent.**

3. If the denominator of each determinant formula is zero, and any one of the determinants in the numerators of the formulas for x and y is not zero, then there is no common solution and **the system is inconsistent.**

EXERCISE 5.A

1. Write out a system of simultaneous equations in two variables.
2. How many solutions does a linear equation in two unknowns have?

3. Arrange $y = \dfrac{2x}{3} - 4$ to form an implicit equation.

4. Arrange $2x + 5y = 11$ to form an explicit equation.

5. Find the slope of the line $2x - 3y = 7$.

6. What is the distance from the origin to the point where the line $3x + 4y = 5$ crosses the y axis?

7. What is the numerical value of the product of the slopes of two perpendicular lines?

8. Discuss the two possibilities that exist if all you know is that the two lines have the same slopes.

9. Make a graph of the line that passes through the point $(2, 5)$ and has a slope of 3.

10. Write the equation for Problem 9.

11. Use the slope idea to determine if the graphs of these two equations,

$$5x - 2y = 7,$$

$$2x + 3y = 4$$

intersect.

12. Apply the slope concept to determine whether the set of equations

$$3x - y = 4$$

$$15x - 5y = 20$$

form an independent, a dependent, or an inconsistent system of linear equations.

Make graphs by the slope-intercept method and find the solution, or solutions, for each of the following sets of simultaneous equations:

13. $\{(x, y) \mid 2x - 3y = 4 \cap x + 2y = 6\}$.

14. $\{(x, y) \mid 5x - 3y = 1 \cap 10x - 6y = 2\}$.

15. $\{(x, y) \mid 6x - 3y = 2 \cap 6y + 9 = 12x\}$.

16. $\{(x, y) \mid x + 8y = 7 \cap 5x - 3y = 2\}$.

17. $\{(x, y) \mid 6y = 15 \cap 4x + 7y = 9\}$.

18. $\left\{(x, y) \mid x + 4 = 0 \cap \dfrac{x}{2} + \dfrac{y}{3} = 3\right\}$.

Use the equivalent equation method to find the solution or solutions for each of the following sets of simultaneous equations:

19. $5x - 3y = 20$,
$\quad 2x + 5y = 4$.

20. $x - 4y = 5$,
$\quad 2x - 8y = 2$.

21. $7x - 11y = 0$,
$\quad 13x + 6y = 0$.

22. $3y - 2x + 4 = 0$,
$\quad 8 - 4x + 6y = 0$.

23. $7x - 3y = 6$,
$\quad 2x + 5y = 3$.

24. $1.4x - 2.3y = 9.6$,
$\quad 2.1x + 3.9y = 2.4$.

Use determinants of second order to find the solution or solutions for each of the following sets of simultaneous equations:

25. $12x - y = 4$,
$\quad 3x + 4y = 1$.

26. $5x + 6y = 7$,
$\quad 2x - 7y - 13 = 0$.

27. $3y + 4x = 2$,
$\quad 8x + 6y = 4$.

28. $8x - 7y = 3$,
$\quad 24x - 21y = 6$.

29. $0.5x - 2.5y = 0$,
$\quad 1.3x + 2.6y = 0$.

30. $4y - 13x + 4 = 0$,
$\quad 9y - 2x - 3 = 0$.

Are the following statements true?

31. $\{(x, y) \mid x - 5y = 6\} \cap \{(x, y) \mid 2x - y = 3\} = \{(1, -1)\}$.

32. $\{(x, y) \mid 2x - 3y = 4\} \cap \{(x, y) \mid 6y - 4x = -9\} = \emptyset$.

33. Find the amount of money invested at each rate if a woman invests part of $40,000 at $4\frac{1}{2}$ per cent annually and the remainder at 6 per cent annually. The annual income from earned interest is $2,000.

34. A man worked 72 hours and received $254 for painting a building. At his usual pay of $3.00 an hour and $4.50 for each hour overtime, how many hours of overtime did he work?

35. If cashew nuts cost $1.25 a pound and peanuts $0.55 a pound, how many pounds of each should be mixed to get 20 pounds of mixture to sell at $0.70 a pound?

5.5 THREE LINEAR EQUATIONS IN THREE VARIABLES

A linear equation in three variables, such as $x + 6y + 4z = 14$, is the equation of a plane which passes through the points:

$$(4, 3, -2), \qquad (6, -2, 5), \qquad \text{and} \qquad (-4, 1, 3).$$

These **triples** are the x, y, z values of the given equation, and each one satisfies the equation.

If three planes pass through the same point, the ordered triple of that point will satisfy each equation for each plane. Of course, **if the three planes coincide, there will be an infinite number of solutions** that will satisfy their equations. **If the three planes are parallel, the solution set of their respective equations will be empty.**

The most elementary way of expressing *three linear equations in three variables* is:

$$a_1 x + b_1 y + c_1 z = d_1,$$

$$a_2 x + b_2 y + c_2 z = d_2,$$

$$a_3 x + b_3 y + c_3 z = d_3.$$

However, as explained in Section 5.4, the double-subscript method is preferred and will be used in this text.

$$a_{11} x + a_{12} y + a_{13} z = b_1,$$

$$a_{21} x + a_{22} y + a_{23} z = b_2,$$

$$a_{31} x + a_{32} y + a_{33} z = b_3.$$

5.5-1 Solution of Linear Equations in Three Variables by the Equivalent Equation Method

Find $\{(x, y, z) \mid 3x - y + 4z = 3 \cap 2x + y - z = 0 \cap x + 3y + z = 4\}$.

$$
\begin{array}{rl}
(1) & 3x - y + 4z = 3, \\
A \quad (2) & 2x + y - z = 0, \\
(3) & x + 3y + z = 4.
\end{array}
$$

It is not absolutely necessary, but it is helpful if possible, to have a system of equivalent equations that begins with a unit x. We will, therefore, rewrite system A to get the following equivalent system:

$$
\begin{array}{lll}
& (1) & x + 3y + z = 4, \\
B & (2) & 2x + y - z = 0, \\
& (3) & 3x - y + 4z = 3.
\end{array}
$$

Equivalent system C is obtained by substituting the sum of $-2B(1)$ and $B(2)$ for $B(2)$, and the sum of $-3B(1)$ and $B(3)$ for $B(3)$.

$$
\begin{array}{lll}
& (1) & x + 3y + z = 4, \\
C & (2) & - 5y - 3z = 8, \\
& (3) & - 10y + z = -9.
\end{array}
$$

To get equivalent system D substitute $-1/5C(2)$ for $C(2)$ and the sum of $-2C(2)$ and $C(3)$ for $C(3)$

$$
\begin{array}{lll}
& (1) & x + 3y + z = 4, \\
D & (2) & y + \tfrac{3}{5}z = \tfrac{8}{5}, \\
& (3) & 7z = 7.
\end{array}
$$

Equivalent system E is obtained by substituting $\tfrac{1}{7}D(3)$ for $D(3)$

$$
\begin{array}{lll}
& (1) & x + 3y + z = 4, \\
E & (2) & y + \tfrac{3}{5}z = \tfrac{8}{5}, \\
& (3) & z = 1.
\end{array}
$$

The final equivalent system F is obtained by substituting $E(3)$ in $E(2)$, and the results of $E(3)$ and $E(2)$ into $E(1)$, to get

$$
\begin{array}{lll}
& (1) & \mathbf{x = 0,} \\
F & (2) & \mathbf{y = 1,} \qquad\qquad\qquad\qquad \text{Solution set} = \{(0, 1, 1)\}. \\
& (3) & \mathbf{z = 1.}
\end{array}
$$

Because Definition 4.2-3 and Theorem 5.4-3a assure us that A, B, C, D, E, and F are equivalent systems, and because Definition 5.4-1b assures us that equivalent systems have the same solution set, we conclude that the **ordered triple $(0, 1, 1)$** of system F is the solution of system A. Check to be certain that the solution set $\{(0, 1, 1)\}$ satisfies each of the given equations.

By the equivalent equation method of the preceding section you can verify, if you are willing to do the work involved, the following formulas for x, y, and z in these three equations:

(1) $a_{11}x + a_{12}y + a_{13}z = b_1$,

(2) $a_{21}x + a_{22}y + a_{23}z = b_2$,

(3) $a_{31}x + a_{32}y + a_{33}z = b_3$.

5.5-1a Formulas for x, y, and z

$$x = \frac{b_1 a_{22} a_{33} + b_2 a_{32} a_{13} + b_3 a_{12} a_{23} - b_1 a_{32} a_{23} - b_3 a_{22} a_{13} - b_2 a_{12} a_{33}}{a_{11} a_{22} a_{33} + a_{21} a_{32} a_{13} + a_{31} a_{12} a_{23} - a_{11} a_{32} a_{23} - a_{31} a_{22} a_{13} - a_{21} a_{12} a_{33}};$$

$$y = \frac{a_{11} b_2 a_{33} + a_{31} b_1 a_{23} + a_{21} b_3 a_{13} - a_{31} b_2 a_{13} - a_{11} b_3 a_{23} - a_{21} b_1 a_{33}}{\textbf{(Denominator same as for } x\textbf{)}};$$

$$z = \frac{a_{11} a_{22} b_3 + a_{31} a_{12} b_2 + a_{21} a_{32} b_1 - a_{31} a_{22} b_1 - a_{11} a_{32} b_2 - a_{21} a_{12} b_3}{\textbf{(Denominator same as for } x\textbf{)}}.$$

The denominator in each of these formulas for x, y, and z must, of course, be different from zero to obtain a unique solution.

5.5-2 Determinant Method of Solving Linear Equations in Three Variables

Even though solutions for systems of linear equations may be just as easily obtained by the equivalent equation method as by any other approach, yet solving systems of linear equations by determinants is, from a mathematician's viewpoint, a very interesting and satisfying procedure.

Definition: 5.5-2a.   *A number expressed by a square array of numbers of the form*

$$\begin{vmatrix} a_{11} & a_{12} & a_{13} \\ a_{21} & a_{22} & a_{23} \\ a_{31} & a_{32} & a_{33} \end{vmatrix} = a_{11} A_{11} + a_{12} A_{12} + a_{13} A_{13} = D$$

is called **a determinant of the third order** *or a* 3×3 *determinant.*

As you can see a 3×3 determinant has three rows and three columns, with the elements a_{11}, a_{22}, and a_{33} forming the **principal diagonal,** and a_{31}, a_{22}, and a_{13} forming the **secondary diagonal.** *There exists a method of expanding and evaluating determinants by use of diagonals.* However, such a procedure does not apply to determinants beyond the third order, and therefore will not be presented here. Instead, a general method involving **minors** and **cofactors** will be used.

Definition: 5.5-2b.   *If in a determinant the row and column of any selected element is deleted, the determinant of the remaining rows and columns is called* *a* **minor** *of that element.*

In the determinant $\begin{vmatrix} a_{11} & a_{12} & a_{13} \\ a_{21} & a_{22} & a_{23} \\ a_{31} & a_{32} & a_{33} \end{vmatrix}$

the **minor** of the element a_{11} is $\begin{vmatrix} a_{22} & a_{23} \\ a_{32} & a_{33} \end{vmatrix}$

and, the **minor** of a_{21} is $\begin{vmatrix} a_{12} & a_{13} \\ a_{32} & a_{33} \end{vmatrix}$.

If the *sum of the row and column number* of an element in a determinant is an *even number*, the element is said to be in **even position** and is represented by a **plus sign.** If the *sum of the row and column number* of an element is an *odd number*, the element is in an **odd position** and is represented by a **minus sign.** Thus, the proper sign to be associated with the minor of any element to represent properly its corresponding cofactor is indicated by referring to the following third-order determinant. The pattern of signs follows the same general form for a determinant of any order.

Third-Order Determinant   *Cofactor Signs*

$\begin{vmatrix} a_{11} & a_{12} & a_{13} \\ a_{21} & a_{22} & a_{23} \\ a_{31} & a_{32} & a_{33} \end{vmatrix}$ $\begin{vmatrix} + & - & + \\ - & + & - \\ + & - & + \end{vmatrix}$

Definition: 5.5-2c. *The* **cofactor** *of an element of a determinant is either plus or minus the minor of that element, depending on whether the element is in even or odd position.*

Theorem: 5.5-2a. If each element of a row (or column) of a square array of numbers is multiplied by its cofactor, the sum of the products is equal to the value of the determinant.

If D represents the number value of a determinant, A_{11} the cofactor of the element a_{11}, A_{21} the cofactor of a_{21}, and so on; then the value of D may be expressed in one of several ways. For example, three of the six possible ways of expanding

$$\begin{vmatrix} a_{11} & a_{12} & a_{13} \\ a_{21} & a_{22} & a_{23} \\ a_{31} & a_{32} & a_{33} \end{vmatrix} = D$$

are

$$D = a_{11}A_{11} + a_{21}A_{21} + a_{31}A_{31};$$

$$D_1 = a_{31}A_{31} + a_{32}A_{32} + a_{33}A_{33};$$

$$D_2 = a_{13}A_{13} + a_{23}A_{23} + a_{33}A_{33}.$$

Using D, and writing the equivalent of the cofactors A_{11}, A_{21}, and A_{31}, gives

$$D = a_{11}\begin{vmatrix} a_{22} & a_{23} \\ a_{32} & a_{33} \end{vmatrix} - a_{21}\begin{vmatrix} a_{12} & a_{13} \\ a_{32} & a_{33} \end{vmatrix} + a_{31}\begin{vmatrix} a_{12} & a_{13} \\ a_{22} & a_{23} \end{vmatrix}.$$

Then expanding the second-order determinants and doing the necessary multiplications gives

$$D = a_{11}a_{22}a_{33} - a_{11}a_{32}a_{23} - a_{21}a_{12}a_{33} + a_{21}a_{32}a_{13} + a_{31}a_{12}a_{23}$$

$$- a_{31}a_{22}a_{13}.$$

At this point we should become very excited over the fact that by rearranging the preceding expression so that when all positive terms are placed to the left of the negative terms we get

$$D = a_{11}a_{22}a_{33} + a_{21}a_{32}a_{13} + a_{31}a_{12}a_{23} - a_{11}a_{32}a_{23} - a_{31}a_{22}a_{13}$$

$$- a_{21}a_{12}a_{33}.$$

This is identically the denominator for each of the variables x, y, and z in the formulas in Section 5.5-1a. That is, by letting D_x represent the numerator of the x formula, D_y represent the numerator of the y formula, and D_z the numerator of the z formula, the algebraic formulas of Section 5.5-1a can be expressed as $x = \dfrac{D_x}{D}$, $y = \dfrac{D_y}{D}$, and $z = \dfrac{D_z}{D}$. Then applying Cramer's rule (Section 5.4-4) to

$$a_{11}x + a_{12}y + a_{13}z = b_1,$$

$$a_{12}x + a_{22}y + a_{23}z = b_2,$$

$$a_{13}x + a_{23}y + a_{33}z = b_3,$$

we can write the third-order determinants for three linear equations in three variables.

　　1. To get D_x, the numerator for the x-determinant formula, replace a_{11}, a_{21}, and a_{31}, the coefficients for x in the original equations, by b_1, b_2, and b_3, the constant terms of the original equations.
　　2. To get D_y, the numerator for the y-determinant formula, replace a_{12}, a_{22}, and a_{32} by the constant terms of the original equations.
　　3. To get D_z, the numerator of the z-determinant formula, replace a_{13}, a_{23}, and a_{33} by the constant terms of the given equations.

　　Thus for any three linear equations in three variables we have the determinant formulas shown in Section 5.5-2.1.

5.5-2.1 Determinant Formulas for x, y, and z

$$x = \frac{\begin{vmatrix} b_1 & a_{12} & a_{13} \\ b_2 & a_{22} & a_{23} \\ b_3 & a_{32} & a_{33} \\ a_{11} & a_{12} & a_{13} \\ a_{21} & a_{22} & a_{23} \\ a_{31} & a_{32} & a_{33} \end{vmatrix}}{}, \quad y = \frac{\begin{vmatrix} a_{11} & b_1 & a_{13} \\ a_{21} & b_2 & a_{23} \\ a_{31} & b_3 & a_{33} \\ a_{11} & a_{12} & a_{13} \\ a_{21} & a_{22} & a_{23} \\ a_{31} & a_{32} & a_{33} \end{vmatrix}}{}, \quad z = \frac{\begin{vmatrix} a_{11} & a_{21} & b_1 \\ a_{21} & a_{22} & b_2 \\ a_{31} & a_{32} & b_3 \\ a_{11} & a_{12} & a_{13} \\ a_{21} & a_{22} & a_{23} \\ a_{31} & a_{32} & a_{33} \end{vmatrix}}{}.$$

Again, if there should be any doubt in your mind about these 3×3 or third-order determinant formulas being equivalent to the formulas given in Section 5.5-1a you should check them out by expanding each determinant formulas and comparing the results.

We are now prepared to solve three linear equations in three variables by determinants of the third order.

Example : 5.5-2.1a. By the method of determinants, find

$$\{(x, y, z) \mid 3x - y + 4z = 3 \cap 2x + y - z = 0 \cap x + 3y + z = 4\}$$

The first thing to do is to arrange the three equations so that the coefficients of the variables form a third-order array of numbers, namely,

$$3x - y + 4z = 3,$$
$$2x + y - z = 0,$$
$$x + 3y + z = 4.$$

From preceding instructions we can now substitute the data of our problem into the three determinant formulas to obtain:

$$x = \frac{\begin{vmatrix} 3 & -1 & 4 \\ 0 & 1 & -1 \\ 4 & 3 & 1 \end{vmatrix}}{\begin{vmatrix} 3 & -1 & 4 \\ 2 & 1 & -1 \\ 1 & 3 & 1 \end{vmatrix}}; \quad y = \frac{\begin{vmatrix} 3 & 3 & 4 \\ 2 & 0 & -1 \\ 1 & 4 & 1 \end{vmatrix}}{\begin{vmatrix} 3 & -1 & 4 \\ 2 & 1 & -1 \\ 1 & 3 & 1 \end{vmatrix}}; \quad z = \frac{\begin{vmatrix} 3 & -1 & 3 \\ 2 & 1 & 0 \\ 1 & 3 & 4 \end{vmatrix}}{\begin{vmatrix} 3 & -1 & 4 \\ 2 & 1 & -1 \\ 1 & 3 & 1 \end{vmatrix}}.$$

Expanding the determinants:

$$x = \frac{3\begin{vmatrix} 1 & -1 \\ 3 & 1 \end{vmatrix} - 0\begin{vmatrix} -1 & 4 \\ 3 & 1 \end{vmatrix} + 4\begin{vmatrix} -1 & 4 \\ 1 & -1 \end{vmatrix}}{3\begin{vmatrix} 1 & -1 \\ 3 & 1 \end{vmatrix} - 2\begin{vmatrix} -1 & 4 \\ 3 & 1 \end{vmatrix} + 1\begin{vmatrix} -1 & 4 \\ 1 & -1 \end{vmatrix}} = \frac{12 + 0 - 12}{12 + 26 - 3} = \frac{0}{35} = 0;$$

$$y = \frac{-3\begin{vmatrix} 2 & 1 \\ 1 & 1 \end{vmatrix} + 0\begin{vmatrix} 3 & 4 \\ 1 & 1 \end{vmatrix} - 4\begin{vmatrix} 3 & 4 \\ 2 & -1 \end{vmatrix}}{35} = \frac{-9 + 0 + 44}{35} = \frac{35}{35} = 1;$$

$$z = \frac{3\begin{vmatrix} 2 & 1 \\ 1 & 3 \end{vmatrix} - 0\begin{vmatrix} 3 & -1 \\ 1 & 3 \end{vmatrix} + 4\begin{vmatrix} 3 & -1 \\ 2 & 1 \end{vmatrix}}{35} = \frac{15 + 0 + 20}{35} = \frac{35}{35} = 1.$$

This is the same problem that we solved by the equivalent equation method in Section 5.5-1 so there is no point in checking the solution set, $\{(0, 1, 1)\}$, in the original equations.

5.5-2.2 Third-Order Determinants with Zeros

1. **If $D \neq 0$,** for the third-order determinant formulas

$$x = \frac{D_x}{D}, \qquad y = \frac{D_y}{D}, \qquad \text{and} \qquad z = \frac{D_z}{D};$$

then the three linear equations in three variables **are consistent and possess a unique solution.**

2. **If $D = D_x = D_y = D_z = 0$,** then the three linear equations are either **dependent or inconsistent.** Other than to state that the system will be dependent if the three planes are not parallel but meet in a common line, and inconsistent if the three planes are parallel, these possibilities will not be studied further in this text.

3. **If $D = 0$ and any one of D_x, D_y, or D_z is not zero,** then the system of equations is **inconsistent.**

5.6 TWO LINEAR EQUATIONS IN THREE VARIABLES

How would one solve a system of equations of this type?

$$A \quad \begin{array}{ll} (1) & x - 3y + z = 1, \\ (2) & 2x + 2y + z = 3. \end{array}$$

By the equivalent equation method one could multiply $A(1)$ by -2 and add to $A(2)$ to get

$$B \quad \begin{array}{ll} (1) & x - 3y + z = 1, \\ (2) & 8y - z = 1. \end{array}$$

Because there is no feasible way of writing another equivalent system to obtain an equation in one variable, we are compelled to assign a value to the z in $B(2)$ and compute y, and then substitute z and y in $B(1)$ to get x. Therefore, let us assume a few of the many possible assumptions for z.

If $z = 0$, $y = \frac{1}{8}$, and $x = \frac{11}{8}$.

If $z = 7$, $y = 1$, and $x = -3$.

If $z = k$, $y = \dfrac{1 + k}{8}$, and $x = \dfrac{11 - 5k}{8}$.

This shows that the system $A(1)$ and $A(2)$ in two linear equations in three variables is a **consistent and dependent system of** simultaneous equations having an unlimited number of solutions, as indicated by its solution set

$$\left\{ \left(\frac{11 - 5k}{8}, \frac{1 + k}{8}, k \right) \right\}.$$

5.7 HOMOGENEOUS LINEAR EQUATIONS

Homogeneous linear equations are linear equations whose terms are all of the first degree such as $x + 5y = 0$ or $4x - 2y + 3z = 0$. Note that the constant terms are zeros.

Definition: 5.7-1. *A system of equations in which the constant terms are all zero is called a* **homogeneous** *system of simultaneous equations.*

The following is a system of homogeneous linear equations of the third order:

$$a_{11}x + a_{12}y + a_{13}z = 0,$$
$$A \qquad a_{21}x + a_{22}y + a_{23}z = 0,$$
$$a_{31}x + a_{32}y + a_{33}z = 0.$$

Writing the determinant formula for x for system A gives

$$x = \frac{D_x}{D} = \frac{\begin{vmatrix} 0 & a_{12} & a_{13} \\ 0 & a_{22} & a_{23} \\ 0 & a_{32} & a_{33} \end{vmatrix}}{\begin{vmatrix} a_{11} & a_{12} & a_{13} \\ a_{21} & a_{22} & a_{23} \\ a_{31} & a_{32} & a_{33} \end{vmatrix}} = \frac{0}{D} = 0.$$

Since **any determinant having all zeros in either a row or a column is zero,** the value of x is zero. Likewise, the numerator portion of the formulas for y and z each have a column of zeros. Therefore,

$$y = \frac{D_y}{D} = \frac{0}{D} = 0 \quad \text{and} \quad z = \frac{D_z}{D} = \frac{0}{D} = 0.$$

and the given set of homogeneous equations has **the trivial solution, (0, 0, 0).**

A system of homogeneous linear equations always has the trivial solution and may or may not have nontrivial solutions.

If $D \neq 0$, and the number of equations is equal to the number of variables as in system A, **the trivial solution is the only solution.** Geometrically, this condition happens when the three planes which represent the three equations in system A intersect at the origin only.

If $D = 0$, and the number of equations equals the number of variables, the set of homogeneous equations is a **dependent system and nontrivial solutions exist.** For example, the homogeneous system

$$5x + 7y + 9z = 0,$$

$B \qquad 3x + 4y + 5z = 0,$

$$2x + 3y + 4z = 0$$

has at least one nontrivial solution because

$$D = \begin{vmatrix} 5 & 7 & 9 \\ 3 & 4 & 5 \\ 2 & 3 & 4 \end{vmatrix} = 5\begin{vmatrix} 4 & 5 \\ 3 & 4 \end{vmatrix} - 3\begin{vmatrix} 7 & 9 \\ 3 & 4 \end{vmatrix} + 2\begin{vmatrix} 7 & 9 \\ 4 & 5 \end{vmatrix} = 5 - 3 - 2 = 0.$$

It will be left to the reader to apply the equivalent equation method to system B to see if the solution set $\{(1, -2, 1)\}$ is a nontrivial solution. Does the solution set $\{(k, -2k, k)\}$ also hold?

When $D = 0$ all the planes that represent the equations in system A intersect in a line which passes through the origin.

EXERCISE 5.B

Use the equivalent equation method to find the solutions of the following systems of linear equations. Check the solutions.

1. $x - 5y + 3z = 1,$
    $2x + 3y - 4z = 3,$
    $3x - y + z = 0.$

2. $2x + y + 5z = 3,$
    $3x + 6y + 4z = 18,$
    $5x - 2y + 3z = -6.$

3. $x - 2y + z = 4,$
    $3y + 2z = -2,$
    $4x - y = 1.$

4. $x - 5y + 4z = 7,$
    $3x + y - 2z = -3,$
    $x + 6y - 5z = 0.$

5. $x - 3y - z = 3,$
    $2x + y + 3z = 2.$

6. $3x - y + 4z = 0,$
    $x + 6y - 2z = 0.$

Evaluate the following determinants:

7. $\begin{vmatrix} 4 & -5 \\ 2 & 6 \end{vmatrix}.$

8. $-2\begin{vmatrix} 3 & -1 \\ -3 & 6 \end{vmatrix}.$

9. $\begin{vmatrix} a_{22} & a_{23} \\ a_{31} & a_{33} \end{vmatrix}.$

10. $\begin{vmatrix} 1 & -2 & 4 \\ 5 & 0 & 6 \\ 3 & 7 & -3 \end{vmatrix}.$

11. $\begin{vmatrix} 6 & 0 & -3 \\ 4 & 0 & 7 \\ 9 & 0 & -1 \end{vmatrix}.$

12. $\begin{vmatrix} 5 & -3 & 0 \\ 2 & 4 & 1 \\ 0 & 0 & 0 \end{vmatrix}.$

13. $\begin{vmatrix} 0 & -5 & 2 \\ 7 & 0 & -1 \\ 3 & -6 & 0 \end{vmatrix}.$

14. $\begin{vmatrix} 2 & 0 \\ 7 & 0 \end{vmatrix}.$

15. $\begin{vmatrix} x & -y & 0 \\ 0 & 3y & 1 \\ 3x & 0 & -4 \end{vmatrix}.$

Use the method of determinants to find the solution sets of the following systems of linear equations, and check each solution.

16. $x - 2y + 4z = 7,$
$\quad 3x + y + 2z = -1,$
$\quad 2x - y + 3z = 4.$

17. $x + y + z = 2,$
$\quad x + 2y - 3z = 4,$
$\quad 3x - 5y + 4z = 1.$

18. $x + 5y - 4z = 10,$
$\quad 3x + y + 2z = 2,$
$\quad 2x + 3y - z = 6.$

19. $3x + y + 2z = 0,$
$\quad x - y + 4z = 0,$
$\quad 5x - 3y - 2z = 0.$

20. $2x - y + 4z = 0,$
$\quad 4x - 2y + 8z = 0,$
$\quad 10x - 5y + 20z = 0.$

21. $x - 2y = 7,$
$\quad 3y - 2z = 0,$
$\quad 5x - 4y + 10z = 6.$

Sequences and Series

When we studied the ordered set of natural numbers, namely,

$$N = 1, 2, 3, 4, 5, 6, 7, 8, \ldots, n, \ldots,$$

in Section 2.1 of Chapter 2, we emphasized the facts that

1. the first element of the set N was 1 and that
2. each element in set N had an immediate successor.

As we proceed we will learn that a **sequence** is also an ordered set that possesses similar characteristics. That is, we must in some way know how to express or how to find the first element of the sequence, and then we must have some rule or directive to construct, term-by-term, every succeeding term.

6.1 SEQUENCES

In order to demonstrate that **a sequence is a set of numbers which is in one-to-one correspondence with the natural numbers,** let us take the sequence function

$$s(n) = 3n - 2, \qquad n \in N,$$

and, using the set of natural numbers as its domain, evaluate it as follows:

N	1	2	3	4	5	6	$\cdots$	n		$\cdots$	(Natural numbers)
$s(n)$	1	4	7	10	13	16	$\cdots$	$3n - 2$		$\cdots$	(Sequence function)

Likewise, for the sequence function defined by $s(n) = (-3)^n$, the range values for $s(n)$ are

N	1	2	3	4	5	$\cdots$	n	$\cdots$	(Natural numbers)
$s(n)$	-3	9	-27	81	-243	$\cdots$	$(-3)^n$	$\cdots$	(Sequence function)

In each of the two preceding examples *the range values obtained, when the natural numbers are used as the domain of the function, form a sequence.*

122

Definition: 6.1-1.   *An* **infinite sequence function** *is a set of numbers*

$$\{[1, s(1)], [2, s(2)], [3, s(3)], \ldots, [n, s(n)], \ldots\}$$

having the ordered set of natural numbers N as its domain.

Definition: 6.1-2.   *A* **finite sequence function** *has a one-to-one correspondence between the elements of the range of the function and the first n elements of the ordered set of natural numbers.*

Notice particularly in the preceding examples, and the definitions, that **the range values $s(1)$, $s(2)$, $s(3)$, ... in the sequence function depend upon and cannot exist separately from the natural numbers properly ordered.**

In working with sequences it is customary to refer to the range values of the sequence function, denoted by $s(n)$, simply as "the sequence," denoted by s_n. We will use both $s(n)$ and s_n to represent sequences.

As the following cases indicate, it is relatively easy to generate sequences because all you need to know is a first term and a rule.

	First Term	*Rule*	*Sequence*
(1)	1	Fixed addend is 3	$1, 4, 7, 10, 13, 16, \ldots$
(2)	7	Fixed addend is -2	$7, 5, 3, 1, -1, -3, \ldots$
(3)	2	Fixed multiplier is $\frac{1}{2}$	$2, 1, \frac{1}{2}, \frac{1}{4}, \ldots$
(4)	5	Fixed multiplier is -1	$5, -5, 5, -5, 5, \ldots$

Statements (1) and (2) are called **arithmetic sequences,** and statements (3) and (4) are called **geometric sequences.** Sequences of these types will be examined in detail later in this chapter.

Let us next study some examples of sequences to find out how the general term of a sequence behaves.

Example: 6.1-1.   Generate the sequence defined by the sequence function

$$s(n) = 2n - 9 \quad \text{and} \quad n \in \{1, 2, 3, 4, 5, \ldots\}.$$

Because the elements in the range of the sequence function are

$$s(1), s(2), s(3), \ldots, s(n), \ldots,$$

the specific terms of the sequence are

$$-7, -5, -3, -1, \ldots, (2n - 9), \ldots.$$

The nth term of the sequence, $2n - 9$, is called the **general term** of the sequence. Thus, this example shows that **the sequence function** is not only the general term of the sequence, but it **is the rule which makes it possible for one to generate the sequence.**

Suppose one were to write the general term of a sequence when only a few of the beginning terms of the sequence are given. For example, if the given sequence were $1, 2, 3, \ldots$ it certainly would seem that the general term of the sequence would be n. But, what is wrong in claiming that the general term of this sequence is $[n + (n - 1)(n - 2)(n - 3)]$? The point is, that either enough information must be given to establish a unique general term or the possibility of more than one general term for the given sequence must be considered. **For any specific general term all that one can be sure of is that it will reproduce the terms of the sequence which were used to discover it.**

Example: 6.1-2.   Find a general term for the sequence 2, 7, 12, 17, ...

By trial and error $n + 1$ was tried. It satisfied the sequence for $n = 1$, but failed to satisfy it for $n = 2$. In turn, $3n - 1$ and $4n - 2$ were tried and both failed. Finally, $5n - 3$ satisfied all the given terms of the sequence, when $n = 1$, $n = 2$, $n = 3$, and $n = 4$ were substituted in it. Thus, for $5n - 3$ the sequence is

$$s_n = 2, 7, 12, 17, 22, 27, 32, \ldots, (5n - 3), \ldots .$$

Example: 6.1-3.   Find the first five terms in a sequence defined by

$$s(n) = \frac{(-1)^n(n - 4)}{2n}, \qquad n \in \{1, 2, 3, \ldots\}.$$

By substitution, $s(1) = \frac{3}{2}$; $s(2) = -\frac{1}{2}$; $s(3) = \frac{1}{6}$; $s(4) = 0$; $s(5) = -\frac{1}{10}$ the sequence is

$$s(n) = \frac{3}{2}, -\frac{1}{2}, \frac{1}{6}, 0, -\frac{1}{10}, \ldots, \frac{(-1)^n(n - 4)}{2n}, \ldots .$$

6.2 SERIES

Definition: 6.2-1.   **A series** *is the indicated sum of the terms in a sequence.*

The series that is associated with the sequence

$$2, 7, 12, 17, 22, 27, \ldots, (5n - 3), \ldots$$

is $2 + 7 + 12 + 17 + 22 + 27 + \cdots + (5n - 3) + \cdots$.

By letting the symbol for infinity ∞ represent an indefinitely large number of cases, by using the subscript instead of the function notation, and by using the so-called **sigma notation,** the indicated sum of a sequence may be expressed in the following very concise manner:

$$S_\infty = \sum_{i=1}^{\infty} s(i),$$

Σ is the Greek capital letter sigma, and i is the index of summation, which has a range from 1 to ∞.

Example: 6.2-1.   Generate the series represented by $S_n = \sum_{i=1}^{n} (5i - 3)$.

The sigma notation means to substitute into $(5i - 3)$ the values $i = 1$,

$i = 2$, and so on, until all the natural numbers up to and including n have been used. Thus, the series is

$$S_n = \sum_{i=1}^{n} (5i - 3) = 5(1) - 3 + 5(2) - 3 + 5(3) - 3 + \cdots + 5(n) - 3.$$

$$S_n = 2 + 7 + 12 + \cdots + (5n - 3).$$

Example: 6.2-2. Expand the series $\displaystyle\sum_{i=5}^{9} \left(\frac{2i}{1 - i}\right)$.

$$\sum_{i=5}^{9} \left(\frac{2i}{1 - i}\right) = \frac{2(5)}{1 - 5} + \frac{2(6)}{1 - 6} + \frac{2(7)}{1 - 7} + \frac{2(8)}{1 - 8} + \frac{2(9)}{1 - 9},$$

$$= -\frac{10}{4} - \frac{12}{5} - \frac{14}{6} - \frac{16}{7} - \frac{18}{8}.$$

This is a finite series where the directions demand that i begin with 5 and run successively, according to the natural numbers, to 9 inclusive.

EXERCISE 6.A

1. (a) Write a set that shows the sequence function for $s(n) = 2n + 3$; that is, determine $s(1)$, $s(2)$, and so on.
   (b) Actually write out the sequence in terms of numerals.

2. (a) Determine $s(1)$, $s(2)$, $s(3)$, and so on for the sequence function $s(n) = \dfrac{n - 2}{3}$.
   (b) Write the sequence in terms of numerals.

   For the following general terms write the first five terms of each sequence.

3. $s(n) = \dfrac{5}{1 - n^2}$.

5. $s(n) = \dfrac{(-1)^n(n - 1)}{n}$.

7. $s_r = r^3 - 17$.

4. $s(n) = \dfrac{1 + n}{n}$.

6. $s(n) = (-1)^{n-1}(2n + 5)$.

8. $s_t = \dfrac{8 - t^3}{t^2}$.

   First find a general term for each of the following sequences and then express each sequence in the sigma notation.

9. $1, 4, 9, 16, 25, \ldots$.
10. $3, 12, 27, 48, 75, \ldots$.
11. $-2, -1, 0, 1, 2, \ldots$.
12. $2, 5, 8, 11, 14, \ldots$.

13. $-3, 4, -5, 6, -7, \ldots$.
14. $0, 3, 8, 15, 24, \ldots$.
15. $4, 3\frac{1}{2}, 3\frac{1}{3}, 3\frac{1}{4}, 3\frac{1}{5}$.
16. $0, 5, 8, 17, 24$.

17. What is a sequence? Write out two sequences.
18. What is a series? Write out two series.

   Generate the series represented by each of the following sigma forms:

19. $\displaystyle\sum_{i=1}^{8} (i^2 - 1)$.

21. $\displaystyle\sum_{r=3}^{7} (2r^2 - 1)$.

23. $\displaystyle\sum_{t=1}^{5} \frac{(-1)^t}{t^3}$.

20. $\displaystyle\sum_{i=1}^{6} i^3$.

22. $\displaystyle\sum_{s=3}^{9} (s^2 + 5)$.

24. $\displaystyle\sum_{k=1}^{6} (-1)^k(1 - k^2)$.

25. $\displaystyle\sum_{i=1}^{4} \left(\frac{1}{1-i}\right)^{i}$.   **27.** $\displaystyle\sum_{i=1}^{\infty} i$.   **29.** $\displaystyle\sum_{j=3}^{\infty} j(j+2)$.

26. $\displaystyle\sum_{n=3}^{7} \frac{n}{(-1)^{n}(n-1)}$.   **28.** $\displaystyle\sum_{i=27}^{\infty} (i)$.   **30.** $\displaystyle\sum_{k=5}^{\infty} (k-1)^{k}(k-1)$.

Write each of the following infinite series in sigma notation:

31. $3(4) + 4(5) + 5(6) + 6(7) + \cdots$.
32. $\frac{3}{4} + \frac{4}{5} + \frac{5}{6} + \cdots$.

6.3 ARITHMETIC SEQUENCES AND SERIES

In Section 6.1-1 we generated the unique infinite sequence

$1, 4, 7, 10, 13, 16, \ldots$

by starting with the number 1 and adding the fixed number 3 to each preceding term to get the next term. At that point we mentioned that this was an arithmetic sequence. We will now define such a sequence.

Definition: 6.3-a.   An arithmetic sequence *is a sequence of numbers each of which differs from the next preceding one by a fixed number called the common difference.*

The expression "common difference" is used because any term in an arithmetic sequence, except the first one, less the preceding term always gives the common addend. As you can readily see for the sequence $1, 4, 7, 10, 13, 16, \ldots$, the common difference between 4 and 1, 7 and 4, 10 and 7, 13 and 10, and 16 and 13 is the fixed number 3. Thus, by Definition 6.3-a the sequence is an arithmetic sequence.

Definition: 6.3-b.   An arithmetic series *is the indicated algebraic sum of the corresponding terms of an arithmetic sequence.*

In developing an arithmetic sequence (or series) we will denote the **first term** of the sequence by **a**, the **common difference** between successive terms by **d**, the **number of terms** to be considered in a finite sequence by **n**, the **nth term** of the sequence by **L**, and the **sum or the indicated sum of the first n terms** by **S_n**.

The general expression for an arithmetic sequence, using the preceding notation, is

$a, a + d, a + 2d, a + 3d, a + 4d, \ldots, a + (n - 1)d$.

Since the nth term of the sequence is to be denoted by L, we can write what is known as the **nth term formula** *of an arithmetic sequence:*

$$L = a + (n - 1)d. \tag{A}$$

Because you have the privilege of considering any term in an arithmetic sequence as the nth term, you can use the formula $L = a + (n - 1)d$ to evaluate any term in the sequence.

The arithmetic series that corresponds to the general arithmetic sequence is

$$S_n = a + (a + d) + (a + 2d) + (a + 3d) + \cdots + a + (n - 1)d.$$

Substituting L for $a + (n - 1)d$ and writing the series first in ascending order and then in descending order, we obtain the following two series:

$$S_n = a + (a + d) + (a + 2d) + \cdots + (L - 2d) + (L - d) + L,$$

$$S_n = L + (L - d) + (L - 2d) + \cdots + (a + 2d) + (a + d) + a.$$

Adding these two series term-by-term, we get

$$2S_n = (a + L) + (a + L) + (a + L) + \cdots + (a + L) + (a + L) + (a + L)$$

or $2S_n = n(a + L)$.

Thus, the **sum formula** *for an arithmetic sequence* or its corresponding series is

$$S_n = \frac{n}{2}(a + L). \tag{B}$$

By substituting $a + (n - 1)d$ for L in the preceding sum formula we get

$$S_n = \frac{n}{2}[a + a + (n - 1)d],$$

which simplifies into the following second sum formula, a formula that can be used to find the sum without having to solve first for L.

$$S_n = \frac{n}{2}[2a + (n - 1)d]. \tag{C}$$

Formulas (A), (B), and (C) involve the five literal numbers L, a, n, d, and S. When any three of these five numbers are known, the formulas make it possible to determine the other two.

Example: 6.3a.   Find the 15th term and the sum of the first 15 terms for the finite arithmetic series $4 + 7 + 10 + 13 + \cdots$.

The value of the 15th term is   The sum of the first 15 terms is

$$L = a + (n - 1)d, \qquad\qquad S_n = \frac{n}{2}(a + L),$$

$$L = 4 + (15 - 1)3, \qquad\qquad S_{15} = \tfrac{15}{2}(4 + 46),$$

$$L = 46. \qquad\qquad\qquad\qquad S_{15} = 375.$$

6.3-1 Arithmetic Means

Definition: 6.3-1a.   *When two or more terms are to be inserted between the extremes, a and L, of an arithmetic sequence, the terms are called* **arithmetic means**.

Definition: 6.3-1b.   *The* **arithmetic mean** *is the sum of the numbers divided by the count of the numbers added.*

Example: 6.3-1a.   Generate an arithmetic sequence by inserting five arithmetic means between $a = 3$ and $L = 15$.
There will be a total of $2 + 5$ terms; so $n = 7$.

$$L = a + (n - 1)d,$$
$$15 = 3 + (7 - 1)d,$$
$$2 = d, \quad \text{the common difference.}$$

Thus, the sequence is 3, **5, 7, 9, 11, 13,** 15.

Example: 6.3-1b.   Find the **arithmetic mean** (the middle term) between $a = 7$ and $L = 35$, and write the sequence.
The easy way is to average a and L, that is,

$$\frac{a + L}{2} = \frac{7 + 35}{2} = \frac{42}{2} = 21$$

for the middle term. Then the sequence is 7, **21**, 35.
Also, in problems concerning the mean or the means we can always use

$$L = a + (n - 1)d,$$
$$35 = 7 + (3 - 1)d,$$
$$14 = d, \quad \text{the common difference.}$$

Again, the sequence is 7, **21**, 35.

6.3-2 Interest Rate Formula for Installment Buying

Our study of arithmetic sequences and series enables us to develop a formula for determining the simple interest rate charged when buying by the **installment plan.**

1. If F is the unpaid balance at the end of the first month, and
2. If F is reduced equally for each of n months so that the unpaid principal for the last month is $\dfrac{F}{n}$ dollars,

then the sequence showing the unpaid principal each month is

$$F, F - \frac{F}{n}, F - \frac{2F}{n}, F - \frac{3F}{n}, \ldots, \frac{F}{n}.$$

At simple interest it costs the same to owe different amounts of money over n consecutive months as it does to owe the sum of the n amounts for one month.
Thus, to owe

$$F, F - \frac{F}{n}, F - \frac{2F}{n}, F - \frac{3F}{n}, \ldots, \frac{F}{n}$$

over n different months is equivalent to owing

$$F + \left(F - \frac{F}{n}\right) + \left(F - \frac{2F}{n}\right) + \left(F - \frac{3F}{n}\right) + \cdots + \frac{F}{n}$$

for one month. Since this latter statement is an arithmetic series having $a = F$ and $L = \frac{F}{n}$ and the total principal $P = S_n$, it follows that we can find P by summing the series. That is,

$$P = S_n = \frac{n}{2}(a + L) = \frac{n}{2}\left(F + \frac{F}{n}\right) = \frac{F}{2}(n + 1).$$

If a certain principal P is invested annually at a simple interest rate r for a certain number of years t, the interest earned, I, is expressed by the formula

$$I = Prt.$$

By substituting $\frac{F}{2}(n + 1)$ for P and $\frac{1}{12}$ to change t to one month, we get

$$I = \frac{F}{2}(n + 1)r\left(\frac{1}{12}\right),$$

and $I = \frac{F}{24}(n + 1)r$.

Solving the equation for r, we find that the **installment formula for r,** the rate of interest charged, is

$$r = \frac{24I}{F(n + 1)}.$$

Example: 6.3-2a. A student bought a used typewriter at an installment price of \$51. He paid \$6 down and arranged to pay the rest in 6 equal monthly payments. The cash price was \$48. What was his monthly payment? What rate of interest did he pay?

$$\frac{51 - 6}{6} = \$7.50, \text{ the monthly payment}; 48 - 6 = \$42 = F.$$

$$I = \$3, n = 6,$$

$$r = \frac{24I}{F(n + 1)} = \frac{24(3)}{42(6 + 1)} = \frac{12}{49} \doteq 0.245 \doteq \textbf{24.5\%}.$$

Is 24.5\% a high rate of interest to pay for the use of money?

6.4 GEOMETRIC SEQUENCES AND SERIES

You may recall that in Section 6.1-3 we presented this sequence

$$2, 1, \tfrac{1}{2}, \tfrac{1}{4}, \tfrac{1}{8}, \tfrac{1}{16}, \cdots$$

and called it a geometric sequence. We are now ready to define geometric sequences and series.

Definition: 6.4-a. *A sequence of numbers each of which, except the first one, is obtained by multiplying the immediately preceding term by a fixed number is called a* **geometric sequence.**

Definition: 6.4-b. *A* **geometric series** *is the indicated algebraic sum of the corresponding terms of a geometric sequence.*

As with arithmetic sequences the **first term of a geometric sequence** will be labeled a, the **last term** L, the **number of terms** n, and the **sum of n terms** S_n. The **fixed multiplier** will be denoted by r and will be referred to as the **common ratio.** This is because the common ratio may be determined by taking any term, except the first one, and dividing it by the preceding term.

In terms of our notation, the general expression for a geometric sequence is

$$a, ar, ar^2, ar^3, \ldots, ar^{n-1}.$$

Because L and ar^{n-1} both represent the nth term, we have the following **nth term formula** for a geometric sequence:

$$L = ar^{n-1}. \tag{D}$$

The geometric series that corresponds to the preceding geometric sequence is

$$S_n = a + ar + ar^2 + ar^3 + \cdots + ar^{n-1}.$$

By multiplying each term of the preceding equation by r, this equivalent equation is obtained:

$$rS_n = ar + ar^2 + ar^3 + \cdots + ar^{n-1} + ar^n.$$

Subtracting the rS_n equation from the S_n equation, there results

$$S_n - rS_n = a - ar^n.$$

By factoring out and solving for S_n, one finds the **sum formula** *for either a geometric sequence or series* is:

$$S_n = \frac{a - ar^n}{1 - r}, \qquad (r \neq 1). \tag{E}$$

A more convenient formula to use in many situations, particularly in investment theory, may be obtained by changing $L = ar^{n-1}$ to $rL = ar^n$ and substituting rL for ar^n in formula (E) to get

$$S_n = \frac{a - rL}{1 - r} \quad \text{or} \quad S_n = \frac{rL - a}{r - 1}, \qquad (r \neq 1). \tag{F}$$

Example: 6.4-a.   Find the 8th term and the sum of the first 8 terms for the geometric sequence $1, -4, 16, -64, \ldots$

The 8th term is   The sum of the first 8 terms is

$$L = ar^{n-1}, \qquad S_n = \frac{rL - a}{r - 1},$$

$$L = 1(-4)^{8-1}, \qquad S_n = \frac{(-4)(-16,384) - 1}{-4 - 1},$$

$$L = -16,384. \qquad S_n = -13,107.$$

6.4-1 Geometric Means

Definition: 6.4-1a.   *If two or more terms are inserted between the extremes, a and L, of a geometric sequence, these terms are called* **geometric means.**

Definition: 6.4-1b.   *The* **geometric mean** *is the nth root of the product of n factors.*

Example: 6.4-1a.   Insert three geometric means between $a = 4$ and $L = 324$ and write the sequence.

The number of terms involved is $2 + 3 = 5 = n$.

$$L = ar^{n-1},$$
$$324 = 4r^{5-1},$$
$$81 = r^4,$$
$$\pm 3 = r, \quad \text{the common ratio.}$$

Therefore, the desired geometric sequence is

4, **12**, **36**, **108**, 324;   or 4, -12, 36, -108, 324

Example: 6.4-1b.   Find the geometric mean between 3 and 48 and write the sequence.

   1. By Definition 6.4-1b $\sqrt{3 \times 48} = \sqrt{144} = +12$ or -12.
The geometric sequence is either 3, **12**, 48 or 3, $-$**12**, 48.
   2. By the common ratio approach

$$L = ar^{n-1},$$
$$48 = 3r^2,$$
$$r = +4 \quad \text{or} \quad r = -4.$$

If $r = 4$, the sequence is 3, **12**, 48.
If $r = -4$, the sequence is 3, $-$**12**, 48.

EXERCISE 6.B

   1. Define an arithmetic sequence, an arithmetic mean, and an arithmetic series.
   2. Define a geometric sequence, a geometric series, and a geometric mean.

3. Which arithmetic formula would you use to insert two or more arithmetic means between two terms of the sequence?

4. What geometric formula is needed to insert two or more geometric means between two terms of the sequence?

5. Compute the 15th term of the sequence 1, 8, 15, 22, . . . and find the sum of its first 15 terms.

6. Find the 12th term and the sum of the first 12 terms of the sequence $2\sqrt{2}, 5\sqrt{2}, 8\sqrt{2}$, $11\sqrt{2}, \ldots$.

7. Given the series $4 + 8 + 16 + 32 + \cdots$. Find the 8th term and the sum of the first 8 terms of the series.

8. What is the 7th term and the sum of the first 7 terms of the series $\frac{1}{3} + \frac{1}{9} + \frac{1}{27} + \frac{1}{81} + \cdots$?

9. (a) Can you be certain that 3, 5, 7, . . . represents an arithmetic sequence of consecutive odd numbers? Explain.

(b) Is 3, 5, 7, 11, 13, 17, 19, 23, 29, 31, . . . a sequence of consecutive odd numbers? What kind of numbers are these?

10. (a) Is $1, \frac{1}{2}, \frac{1}{3}, \frac{1}{4}, \frac{1}{5}, \ldots$ an arithmetic sequence? Does it possess a common difference? What is its nth term?

(b) What kind of a sequence is $1, -5, 25, -125, \ldots$? What fact determined your decision? What is its general term?

11. Insert three arithmetic means between 2 and 37.

12. What is the arithmetic mean between r and s?

13. Find the geometric mean between 3 and 243.

14. Insert three geometric means between 5 and 500.

Find the sum of each of the following finite arithmetic series.

15. $\displaystyle\sum_{i=1}^{7} (2i + 3)$.   **17.** $\displaystyle\sum_{k=1}^{11} k$.   **19.** $\displaystyle\sum_{j=11}^{16} (20 - j)$.

16. $\displaystyle\sum_{i=3}^{8} (5i - 2)$.   **18.** $\displaystyle\sum_{t=4}^{13} \frac{t + 4}{2}$.   **20.** $\displaystyle\sum_{n=1}^{7} (1 - n)$.

Find the sum of the following finite geometric series.

21. $\displaystyle\sum_{i=1}^{5} 3^{(i-1)}$.   **23.** $\displaystyle\sum_{n=1}^{4} \left(\frac{1}{5}\right)^{n}$.   **25.** $\displaystyle\sum_{h=1}^{5} 4\left(-\frac{1}{3}\right)^{(h+1)}$.

22. $\displaystyle\sum_{i=4}^{8} 2^{i}$.   **24.** $\displaystyle\sum_{k=1}^{5} \left(\frac{1}{2}\right)^{(k-1)}$.   **26.** $\displaystyle\sum_{r=3}^{6} -\frac{1}{3}\left(\frac{1}{4}\right)^{(r-1)}$.

Write the terms of the series indicated by the given data.

27. $a = \frac{1}{3}, d = \frac{2}{3}, n = 9$.   **29.** $a = 128, r = \frac{1}{4}, L = \frac{1}{2}$.

28. $L = -24, d = -4, n = 7$.   **30.** $a = 5, L = 3{,}125, r = -5$.

31. If the 3rd term of an arithmetic sequence is -4 and the 8th term is $+8$, find the common difference and the 7th term.

32. If the 4th term of a geometric sequence is 5 and the 7th term is $\frac{5}{8}$ find the common ratio and the 2nd term.

33. Prove that the sum of the first k even integers beginning with zero is $k^2 - k$.

34. Prove that the sum of the first k odd integers beginning with one is k^2.

35. Each of 500 bacteria develops into two bacteria every 6 minutes. If this reproduction rate continues without change for one hour, how many bacteria will be in the colony?

36. Write a geometric sequence. Then write the reciprocal of each term of the sequence. Show that the reciprocal terms also form a geometric sequence. (*The reciprocal of a term is the number* 1 *divided by that term.*)

37. A bedroom suite is offered for $160 cash or $172 by the installment plan. Find the rate of interest involved in the installment plan if a down payment of $40 is required and payments of $11 a month for 12 months are to be paid.

38. A well-driller agrees to drill a 60-foot well for 40 cents the first foot and 10 cents more for each additional foot drilled. He is also willing to contract to drill the well for $180. Which is the better deal and how much better is it?

6.5 INFINITE GEOMETRIC SERIES

In the expansion of $\sum_{n=1}^{\infty} (\frac{1}{2})^{n-1}$, expressed by the table

N	1	2	3	4	5	6	7	$\cdots$	n	$\cdots$	(Natural numbers)
$s(n)$	1	$\frac{1}{2}$	$\frac{1}{4}$	$\frac{1}{8}$	$\frac{1}{16}$	$\frac{1}{32}$	$\frac{1}{64}$	$\cdots$	$\left(\frac{1}{2}\right)^{n-1}$	$\cdots$	(Sequence function)

there is no last term and the series is an **infinite geometric series.** Because the common ratio of this series is less than one and more than negative one, it is a special type of infinite series whose sum can be determined.

Definition 6.5-a. *A geometric series whose terms continue without end is called an* **infinite geometric series.**

The sum of an infinite geometric series is a different kind of sum than the sum of a finite number of terms. As n is permitted to get larger and larger, the sum of the n terms appears to approach some fixed number. We call this fixed number the sum of that particular infinite geometric series.

If an infinite series has a common ratio of $-1 < r < 1$, *then the sum of the infinite series will be the* **limit S_n.**
$n \to \infty$

The infinite geometric series $\sum_{n=1}^{\infty} (\frac{1}{2})^{n-1}$ has a common ratio of $\frac{1}{2}$ so that its r is greater than -1 and less than $+1$. The $s(n)$ values, as you can observe, become smaller and smaller as n is made larger and larger. If we take our sum formula for a finite geometric series, namely,

$$S_n = \frac{a - ar^n}{1 - r}, \qquad \text{written as } S_n = \frac{a}{1 - r}(1 - r^n) \qquad (r \neq 1),$$

and substitute $\frac{1}{2}$ for r in the formula, it becomes evident that as n is permitted to increase without limit, the value of $r^n = (\frac{1}{2})^n$ becomes so small that we are quite willing to call it zero. Thus, we state that the limit of S_n as n increases without bound is

$$\mathbf{\text{limit } S_n} = \frac{a}{1 - r}\left[1 - \left(\frac{1}{2}\right)^n\right] = \frac{a}{1 - r}.$$
$n \to \infty$

The **sum of an infinite geometric series** whose common ratio is $|r| < 1$ is the first term of the series divided by $1 - r$, that is,

$$S_\infty = \frac{a}{1 - r}. \tag{G}$$

Oddly enough, it is much easier to find the sums of infinite geometric series that have common ratios of $|r| < 1$ than to find the sum of the terms of finite geometric series.

6.5-1 Repeating Decimals

It was stated in Section 2.7 of Chapter 2 that many rational numbers can be expressed as **repeating decimal fractions.** For example,

$$\frac{1}{7} = 0.\overline{142857}.$$

As previously stated the horizontal bar means that the digits under it are to be repeated without end. Thus the rational number $\frac{1}{7}$ written as

$$0.142857 + 0.000000142857 + 0.000000000000142857 + \cdots$$

is, of course, an **infinite geometric series** with $a = 0.142857$ and $r = 0.000001$. The sum of the series is

$$S_\infty = \frac{a}{1 - r} = \frac{0.142857}{1 - 0.000001} = \frac{0.142857}{0.999999} = \frac{1}{7}.$$

The preceding example shows that any time a rational number expressed as a repeating decimal needs to be expressed in the rational number form $\frac{a}{b}$ this can be accomplished by using the sum formula for an infinite geometric series, namely,

$$S_\infty = \frac{a}{1 - r} \qquad (-1 < r < 1).$$

Example: 6.5-1a.   Find the common fraction equivalent to $3.\overline{117}$.
For the geometric series part of the number, $a = 0.117$ and $r = 0.001$. Then

$$\frac{a}{b} = 3 + \frac{a}{1 - r} = 3 + \frac{0.117}{1 - 0.001} = 3 + \frac{0.117}{0.999} = 3 + \frac{13}{111} = \frac{346}{111}.$$

As a check of the work you should divide 346 by 111 to see if you obtain the given decimal fraction as a quotient.

EXERCISE 6.C

1. Is the series $3 + 6 + 12 + 24 + \cdots + 3(2)^{n-1} + \cdots$ a geometric series? What is its common ratio? Can its sum be obtained? Explain.

2. What is the common ratio of the series

$$-\frac{1}{3} + \frac{1}{9} - \frac{1}{27} + \frac{1}{81} + \cdots + (-1)^n\left(\frac{1}{3}\right)^n + \cdots?$$

3. What condition must be imposed to guarantee that the sum of an infinite geometric series is obtainable?

4. Given the first term and the common ratio of an infinite geometric series to be $a = 1$ and $r = 1$, what is the sum of the series? Discuss.

Find the sum of each of the following geometric series.

5. $a = 4$ and $r = \frac{1}{4}$.   **7.** $a = 18$ and $r = -\frac{1}{3}$.   **9.** $\sqrt{20} + \sqrt{10} + \sqrt{5} + \cdots$.

6. $a = 7$ and $r = \frac{1}{2}$.   **8.** $a = -24$ and $r = \frac{1}{6}$.   **10.** $\sqrt[3]{50} + \sqrt[3]{10} + \sqrt[3]{2} + \cdots$.

11. $\displaystyle\sum_{i=1}^{\infty} \left(\frac{3}{5}\right)^i$.   **12.** $\displaystyle\sum_{n=1}^{\infty} \left(-\frac{2}{3}\right)^{n-1}$.

Find a common fraction equivalent for each of the following:

13. $0.\overline{27}$.   **15.** $2.1\overline{47}$.   **17.** $0.\overline{571428}$.

14. $0.\overline{54}$.   **16.** $5.0\overline{19}$.   **18.** $0.2\overline{85714}$.

19. A golf ball is dropped from a height of 80 feet. Each time the ball hits the pavement it rebounds $\frac{1}{2}$ the distance through which it has just fallen. Find the total distance traveled by the ball from the spot where it was first dropped to the point where it comes to rest.

20. Given a square with sides of 10 feet. Join the midpoints of the sides of the square to form another square. Repeat the same procedure continuously. Find the sum of the perimeters of all the squares.

6.6 BINOMIAL SERIES

Definition: 6.6-a.   *A* **binomial series** *is a series obtained by expanding the binomial $(a + b)^n$, where n is a natural number and $a, b \in R$.*

To begin with, we will form some binomial series by actually multiplying out the binomial for $n = 1, 2, 3, 4,$ and 5.

$$
\begin{array}{ll}
(a + b)^1 & a + b \\
(a + b)^2 & a^2 + 2ab + b^2 \\
(a + b)^3 & a^3 + 3a^2b + 3ab^2 + b^3 \\
(a + b)^4 & a^4 + 4a^3b + 6a^2b^2 + 4ab^3 + b^4 \\
(a + b)^5 & a^5 + 5a^4b + 10a^3b^2 + 10a^2b^3 + 5ab^4 + b^5
\end{array}
$$

If we drop the literal numbers, the numerical coefficients form what is known as **Pascal's triangle.**

$$
\begin{array}{ll}
(a + b)^1 & \quad\quad 1 \quad 1 \\
(a + b)^2 & \quad\quad 1 \quad 2 \quad 1 \\
(a + b)^3 & \quad 1 \quad 3 \quad 3 \quad 1 \\
(a + b)^4 & \quad 1 \quad 4 \quad 6 \quad 4 \quad 1 \\
(a + b)^5 & 1 \quad 5 \quad 10 \quad 10 \quad 5 \quad 1
\end{array}
$$

The interesting thing about Pascal's triangle is that each member is equal to the sum of the two nearest numbers directly above it, except for the 1's on the outside. For example, $5 = 1 + 4$, $10 = 4 + 6$, $3 = 1 + 2$, $4 = 3 + 1$, and so on. Knowing the principle involved in Pascal's triangle enables one to write the coefficients for $(a + b)$ to the next highest power. For example, if the coefficients for

$$(a + b)^5 \quad \text{are} \quad 1 \quad 5 \quad 10 \quad 10 \quad 5 \quad 1,$$

then the coefficients for

$$(a + b)^6 \quad \text{are} \quad 1 \quad (1 + 5) \quad (5 + 10) \quad (10 + 10) \quad (10 + 5) \quad (5 + 1) \quad 1,$$
$$\text{or} \quad 1 \quad 6 \quad 15 \quad 15 \quad 10 \quad 6 \quad 1.$$

Write out the coefficients for $(a + b)^7$, $(a + b)^8$, $(a + b)^9$.

Expanding binomials of the type $(a + b)^n$ by multiplying them out is a long, clumsy procedure. Such multiplications as have been done, along with the Pascal triangle arrangement, are sufficient to enable us to observe the factual nature of the binomial theorem without its being necessary for us to present a formal proof of it here.

6.6-1 Binomial Theorem

The binomial theorem states that, for any natural number n, and $a, b \in R$, the series obtained by expanding $(a + b)^n$ generates $(n + 1)$ terms with the following properties:

(A) The first term is a^n; the second term is $na^{n-1}b$; from term to term the exponents of a decrease by 1 while the exponents of b increase by 1; and the last term is b^n.

(B) The sum of the exponents of a and b in each term is n.

(C) The coefficient of any term is the product of the coefficient of the preceding term and the exponent of a of that term divided by the number of the preceding term in the series.

(D) The coefficients of the expanded terms of the series form an ordered set of integers which is reversible; that is, reading from the coefficient of the last term to the coefficient of the first term is exactly the same series of numbers as reading from the coefficient of the first term to the coefficient of the last term.

6.6-2 Factorial Numbers

Before applying the properties of the binomial theorem to $(a + b)^n$, we need to give attention to a concise method of writing the product of consecutive natural numbers, such as will appear in the expansions.

Definition: 6.2-2a.   *The symbol n! read **n factorial** represents the product of all natural numbers from 1 to n (or vice versa). That is*

$$n! = n(n - 1)(n - 2)(n - 3)(n - 4)(n - 5) \cdots 5 \cdot 4 \cdot 3 \cdot 2 \cdot 1.$$

Thus,

$$6! = 1 \cdot 2 \cdot 3 \cdot 4 \cdot 5 \cdot 6 = 6 \cdot 5 \cdot 4 \cdot 3 \cdot 2 \cdot 1$$

$$10! = 10 \cdot 9 \cdot 8 \cdot 7 \cdot 6 \cdot 5 \cdot 4 \cdot 3 \cdot 2 \cdot 1.$$

$$(n - r)! = (n - r)(n - r - 1)(n - r - 2)(n - r - 3) \cdots 5 \cdot 4 \cdot 3 \cdot 2 \cdot 1.$$

Let us take the relation

$$n! = (n)(n - 1)!$$

and substitute 1 for n to obtain

$$(1)! = (1)(1 - 1)!.$$

Then $(1)! = (1)(0)!$,

and $\quad 1 = 1 \cdot 0!.$

To guarantee completeness of the factorial idea it now becomes evident that the following definition is necessary.

Definition: 6.6-2b. **The number 0!** *is defined as* 1 *in order to make the statement* $1 = 1 \cdot 0!$ *consistent.*

Example: 6.6-2a. Expand and simplify $\dfrac{4!8!}{6!}$.

$$\frac{4!8!}{6!} = \frac{(4 \cdot 3 \cdot 2 \cdot 1)(8 \cdot 7 \cdot 6 \cdot 5 \cdot 4 \cdot 3 \cdot 2 \cdot 1)}{(6 \cdot 5 \cdot 4 \cdot 3 \cdot 2 \cdot 1)} = (24)(56) = \mathbf{1{,}344}.$$

Example: 6.6-2b. Write the product of $8 \cdot 9 \cdot 10 \cdot 11 \cdot 12$ in factorial form.

$$\frac{1 \cdot 2 \cdot 3 \cdot 4 \cdot 5 \cdot 6 \cdot 7 \cdot 8 \cdot 9 \cdot 10 \cdot 11 \cdot 12}{1 \cdot 2 \cdot 3 \cdot 4 \cdot 5 \cdot 6 \cdot 7} = \frac{12!}{7!}.$$

This is an example of using the factorial notation to write an indicated product of natural numbers that does not begin with 1.

6.6-3 Binomial Formula

In the following expansion of $(a + b)^n$ either r or $r + 1$ may be considered to be the general term of the series.

$$(a + b)^n = a^n + \frac{na^{n-1}}{1!}b + \frac{n(n - 1)}{2!}a^{n-2}b^2 + \frac{n(n - 1)(n - 2)}{3!}a^{n-3}b^3 +$$

the general term r $\qquad \cdots + \dfrac{n(n - 1)(n - 2) \cdots n - r + 2}{(r - 1)!}a^{n-r+1}b^{r-1} +$

the general term $(r + 1) \cdots + \dfrac{n(n - 1)(n - 2) \cdots n - r + 1}{r!} a^{n-r}b^r +$

the last term $\cdots + b^n.$ (H)

This formula has been generated by applying the properties stated in Section 6.6-1 for the binomial theorem. You should carefully check to see if the properties in the theorem have been correctly applied.

Since the coefficient of the $(r + 1)$ term may be expressed as

$$\left[\frac{n(n - 1)(n - 2) \cdots (n - r + 1)}{r!}\right]\frac{(n - r)!}{(n - r)!} = \frac{n!}{r!(n - r)!},$$

it follows that the $(r + 1)$ **general term** may be more concisely written as

$$\frac{n!}{r!(n - r)!}a^{n-r}b^r$$

Example: 6.6-3a.   Find the 6th term in the expansion of $(x - 2y)^6$.
Using the $(r + 1)$ general term where $r + 1 = 6$ or $r = 5$, $n = 6$, $a = x$, and $b = (-2y)$,

$$\frac{n!}{r!(n - r)!}a^{n-r}b^r = \frac{6!}{5!(6 - 5)!}x^{6-5}(-2y)^5 = -192xy^5.$$

EXERCISE 6.D

Expand the factorial numbers and simplify.

1. $7!$

2. $9!$.

3. $\dfrac{11!}{8!}$.

4. $\dfrac{8!}{7!}$.

5. $5!7!$.

6. $\dfrac{12!3!}{6!}$.

7. $\dfrac{(7 - 2)!}{(3 + 2)!}$.

8. $\dfrac{(4 + 9)!}{(8 - 3)!}$.

9. $\dfrac{n!}{(n - 1)!}$.

10. $\dfrac{(n + 1)!}{n!}$.

11. $\dfrac{(n + 3)!}{(n + 1)(n + 2)!}$.

12. $\dfrac{n!}{(n - r)!r!}$.

13. Write $19 \cdot 20 \cdot 21 \cdot 22 \cdot 23$ in factorial form.
14. Express $75 \cdot 76 \cdot 77 \cdot 78$ in factorial form.

In applying the properties of the binomial theorem to a binomial expansion one must never change a term until the entire expansion has been completed. Expand each of the following into a binomial series.

15. $(x + y)^7$.
16. $(a + 2b)^5$.
17. $(2w - 3)^7$.
18. $\left(\dfrac{y}{2} - 5\right)^6$.

19. $(s^2 - t)^5$.
20. $(1 + i)^9$.
21. $(2a - 3b)^9$.
22. $(3x - 4y)^5$.

23. $(1 + 0.06)^5$.
24. $(1 + 0.08)^4$.
25. $(1 - 0.05)^6$.
26. $(1 - 0.03)^7$.

27. Use one of the general terms of the binomial formula to find the 10th term of $(x - 2y)^{20}$.

28. Determine the 13th term of $(3x - y)^{30}$.

Accepting the fact that it can be proved that the binomial theorem holds when n is a negative integer or a rational number, expand the following:

29. $(x - 2)^{-2}$

31. $\sqrt{9.6}$ Hint: $(9 + 0.6)^{1/2}$.

30. $(2a + b)^{-1}$.

32. $(24.7)^{1/2}$.

33. The amount of \$1000 invested at 6 per cent compounded annually for 6 years is expressed by the formula $A = 1000(1 + 0.06)^6$. Find the amount at the end of 6 years.

34. If you invest \$500 in a business venture at 4 per cent compounded annually and no interest is paid until the end of five years, how much money do you expect to collect?

Trigonometry in Terms of Circular Functions

During the twentieth century, trigonometry has become more than just an applied portion of mathematics used to solve problems in surveying, navigation, astronomy, and other phases of science and engineering. *The circular and trigonometric functions of trigonometry and their many relations are now widely used in the development of many sections of mathematical theory.* Consequently, the theoretical aspects of circular functions are being given greater emphasis.

Circular and trigonometric functions are of extreme importance in phenomena which repeat themselves in a periodic fashion, such as sound waves of all kinds, tides of large bodies of water, back and forth motion of pendulums, movement of planets around their orbits, voltage of an alternating electric current, and so on.

The basic notions of circular and trigonometric functions are so much alike that they can be treated, and some authors do treat them, as being identical. However, because (1) **the circular functions will have subsets of real numbers as domains** and (2) **the trigonometric functions will have sets of angles as domains,** this book will discuss these functions in separate chapters. The circular functions will be developed in this chapter, and in Chapter 9 the trigonometric functions will be presented.

7.1 THE NATURE OF CIRCULAR FUNCTIONS

The unit circle will be used as the geometric basis for defining circular functions.

Definition: 7.1-1. *A circle whose distance from its center to each point on its circumference is one unit is called* **a unit circle.**

We shall begin our study of circular functions by assuming that each arc of a unit circle centered at the origin of a rectangular coordinate system and measured counterclockwise from $(1, 0)$ to point $P(x, y)$ has a length t.

140

It should become clear as we proceed with the study of circular functions that—

1. A real number can be represented by a distance along the arc of a unit circle the same as a real number can be represented by a distance along a number line.

2. Both the domain and the range of circular functions are expressed in terms of real numbers.

Definition: 7.1-2. *A* **circular function** *is a function defined in terms of an arc length and the rectangular coordinates of a point as it moves around the circumference of a unit circle which has its center at the origin of the rectangular coordinate system.*

Since the center of the unit circle and the origin of the rectangular coordinate system are made to coincide (see Figure 7.1-1), then it follows that for any

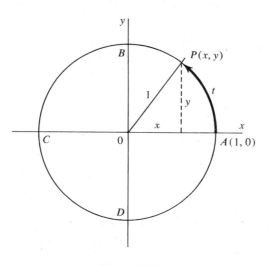

Figure 7.1-1

point $P(x, y)$ on the circumference of the circle the relation of x, y, and 1, by authority of the Pythagorean theorem, is $\{(x, y) \mid x^2 + y^2 = 1\}$.

The distance around the circumference of any circle of radius r is $2\pi r$. So the distance around the circumference of a unit circle would be 2π units. Then dividing the unit circle into four equal parts as is shown in Figure 7.1-1, the **arc distance** from A to B is $\frac{\pi}{2}$ units, from A to C moving counterclockwise is π units, counterclockwise from A to D is $3\frac{\pi}{2}$ units, and counterclockwise from A to A is 2π units.

Definition: 7.1-3.   *Distances measured around the circumference of a circle are called* **arc distances.** *Arc distances measured counterclockwise are positive, clockwise negative.*

The distance measured clockwise from A to D in Figure 7.1-1 is $-\dfrac{\pi}{2}$ units, from A to C is $-\pi$ units, from A to B is $-3\dfrac{\pi}{2}$ units, and from A to A is -2π units.

You will see as we proceed that we make much use of the numbers $\dfrac{\pi}{2}$, π, $3\dfrac{\pi}{2}$, 2π, and their neg 'ive counterparts.

7.2 WINDING AROUND A UNIT CIRCLE

A flexible vertical line which is assumed to represent all the real numbers is used to show the functional relation between the real numbers and the points on the circumference of a unit circle (see Figure 7.2-1). This is how it is done:

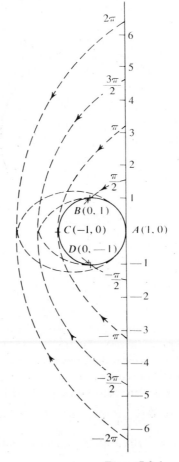

Figure 7.2-1

1. Let the positive numbers on the vertical line be represented by the upper part of the line, the negative numbers by the lower part.

2. Place the zero point of the number line on the point A $(1, 0)$ where the circumference of the unit circle cuts the x axis.

3. Take the unit of measure on the vertical number line to be the same as the radius of the unit circle, locate the points which represent the real numbers $\frac{\pi}{2}$, π, $3\frac{\pi}{2}$, 2π, and their negatives, on the number line. Actually, all real numbers are involved, but these will be our guide numbers.

4. With the zero of the vertical line fixed at $A(1, 0)$, wind the flexible vertical line **counterclockwise** around the circumference of the unit circle. Since a line has no thickness, this winding can continue around the circle as many times as you please.

5. Likewise with the zero of the vertical line fixed at $A(1, 0)$, wind the negative part of the vertical line **clockwise** around the unit circle as many times as you please.

The winding should help you to understand that *each positive or negative real number corresponds to one and only one point on the circumference of a unit circle.* The converse is not true. This means that *a one-to-many correspondence exists between the real numbers t and the points P(x, y) on the circumference of a unit circle.*

7.3 QUADRANTAL NUMBERS

Notice particularly the numbers $\frac{\pi}{2}$, π, $3\frac{\pi}{2}$, and 2π. These numbers are associated respectively with the points $(0, 1)$, $(-1, 0)$, $(0, -1)$, and $(1, 0)$, which divide the unit circle into four equal quadrants (see Figure 7.3-1). Likewise, the numbers $-\frac{\pi}{2}$, $-\pi$, $-3\frac{\pi}{2}$, and -2π, obtained by going around the circle clockwise, have their terminal points on one of the coordinate axes. Thus,

Definition: 7.3-1. *A number which is represented by a terminal point of an arc that falls on one of the coordinate axes is called a* **quadrantal number.**

Since neither time nor space permit us to discuss the circular functions of every real number, these quadrantal numbers provide us the numbers necessary to determine the **maximum and minimum points** as well as other **critical points** of these functions.

Definition: 7.3-2. *A* **maximum point** *is a point on a graph that is higher than any other point in the immediate neighborhood of that point.*

Definition: 7.3-3. *A* **minimum point** *is a point on a graph that is lower than any other point in the immediate neighborhood of that point.*

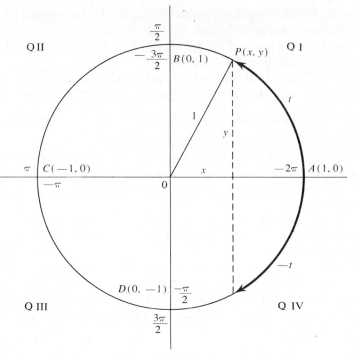

Figure 7.3-1

7.4 THE CIRCULAR FUNCTIONS DEFINED

Definition: 7.4-1.   *If t in Figure 7.4-1 is any real number measured from the point where the circumference of the unit circle crosses the positive x axis and P, with rectangular coordinates x and y, marks the end point of t, then the* **circular**

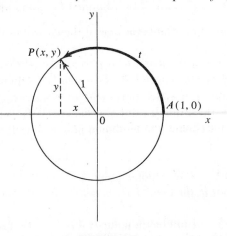

Figure 7.4-1

functions of the real number t *are*

$$\text{sine } t = \text{the ordinate of } P = y,$$

$$\text{cosine } t = \text{the abscissa of } P = x,$$

$$\text{tangent } t = \frac{\text{the ordinate of } P}{\text{the abscissa of } P} = \frac{\text{sine } t}{\text{cosine } t} = \frac{y}{x} \qquad (x \neq 0),$$

$$\text{cotangent } t = \frac{\text{cosine } t}{\text{sine } t} = \frac{x}{y} \qquad (y \neq 0),$$

$$\text{secant } t = \frac{1}{\text{cosine } t} = \frac{1}{x} \qquad (x \neq 0),$$

$$\text{cosecant } t = \frac{1}{\text{sine } t} = \frac{1}{y} \qquad (y \neq 0).$$

The abbreviations that will be used in writing these six circular functions will be sin, cos, tan, cot, sec, and csc. Except when we are working with inverse function, it will be usual practice in this book to write the names of the circular functions in lowercase form, that is, sin t, never Sin t.

From the definitions of the six circular functions you can easily see that the **sine and cosine functions are the two basic functions** and that the other four functions are obtained from them.

By using the relation $y^2 + x^2 = 1$ as indicated by Figure 7.4-2 and the

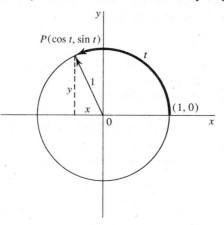

Figure 7.4-2

definitions $y = \sin t$ and $x = \cos t$, we get this very interesting relation involving the sine and cosine functions:

$$y^2 + x^2 = 1,$$

$$(\sin t)^2 + (\cos t)^2 = 1,$$

$$\mathbf{\sin^2 t + \cos^2 t = 1}.$$

It is much neater and less expensive from a printing standpoint to write $(\sin t)^2$ as $\sin^2 t$ and $(\cos t)^2$ as $\cos^2 t$. In all such cases, however, you must have a correct understanding of what these more abbreviated forms actually mean.

7.5 BEHAVIOR OF THE SINE AND COSINE FUNCTIONS

The data necessary to build a table of values for the sine and cosine functions for $0 \leq t \leq 2\pi$ is suggested by Figure 7.3-1 in Section 7.3.

Although Table 7.5-1 involves only a few special numbers, you should

Table 7.5-1

t	$P(x, y)$	$\sin t$	$\cos t$
0	$(1, 0)$	0	1
$\dfrac{\pi}{2}$	$(0, 1)$	1	0
π	$(-1, 0)$	0	-1
$3\dfrac{\pi}{2}$	$(0, -1)$	-1	0
2π	$(1, 0)$	0	1

understand, of course, that the **domain of t includes all the real numbers.** One of the important things shown by Table 7.5-1 is that the **ranges of the sine and cosine functions are identical,** that is,

$$\{n \mid -1 \leq n \leq 1 ; n \in R\}.$$

No matter what real number you take, the sine or cosine of that number will never be less than -1 or more than $+1$.

Instead of taking special numbers for t as we have done in Table 7.5-1, let us think of t as being continuously extended counterclockwise from $A(1, 0)$ where $t = 0$ around the circumference of the circle to the point where $t = 2\pi$. Table 7.5-2 indicates how $\sin t$ and $\cos t$ vary as t varies continuously.

Notice that if t were extended in Table 7.5-2 so that it would continue to move from 2π to $5\dfrac{\pi}{2}$, the sine values would vary from 0 to 1 exactly as these values varied when t was moved from 0 to $\dfrac{\pi}{2}$. Thus, when t has moved from 0 counterclockwise to 2π, any further increase of t begins an identical second cycle. An endless number of such cycles can be made forming what is called the **sine wave** or a **sinusoidal curve.** The cosine function behaves in precisely the same manner. The graph of the cosine function also forms a **sinusoidal curve.**

Definition: 7.5-1.   *The* **period** *of a function for any real number t is the smallest positive number m for which the relation $P(t + m) = P(t)$ is true.*

Table 7.5-2

Quadrant	As t Varies from:	sin t Values Vary from:	cos t Values Vary from:	Signs of Values for: sin t	cos t
I	0 to $\dfrac{\pi}{2}$	0 to 1	1 to 0	$+$	$+$
II	$\dfrac{\pi}{2}$ to π	1 to 0	0 to -1	$+$	$-$
III	π to $3\dfrac{\pi}{2}$	0 to -1	-1 to 0	$-$	$-$
IV	$3\dfrac{\pi}{2}$ to 2π	-1 to 0	0 to 1	$-$	$+$

Letting $m = 2\pi n$, where n is an integer, and letting t be increased or decreased by $2\pi n$, then $P(t + 2\pi n)$ and $P(t)$ terminate at exactly the same point and have the same coordinates. Thus,

$$P(t + 2\pi n) = P(t).$$

Applying Definition 7.5-1 to the sine function and the cosine function, we have

$$\sin(t + 2\pi n) = \sin t, \qquad (A)$$

and $\cos(t + 2\pi n) = \cos t.$ $\qquad (B)$

The smallest positive value for m where $m = 2\pi n$ (n an integer) is obtained when $n = 1$. Thus, substituting in (A) and (B),

1. If $n = 1$, $m = 2\pi$ **is the period for sin t.**
2. If $n = 1$, $m = 2\pi$ **is the period for cos t.**

The sine and cosine functions are known as **periodic functions** with periods of 2π. Having already obtained in Table 7.5-2 the critical values for these two functions for $0 \le t \le 2\pi$, the preceding formulas (A) and (B) enable us to conclude that the values for all t are the same as the values for $0 \le t \le 2\pi$.

In addition to the periodic nature of the sine and cosine functions, we need to be able to tell something about the maximum departure of each of these curves from its average value. Thus we will need to know the **amplitude** of these functions.

Definition: 7.5-2. *The **amplitude** of a periodic function is half the sum of the absolute values of its maximum and minimum values (see Definitions 7.3-2 and 7.3-3).*

7.6 FUNCTIONS OF NEGATIVE NUMBERS

If t is a measure of the distance counterclockwise from $(1, 0)$ on a unit circle to $P_1(a, b)$ and $-t$ is a measure of the distance clockwise from $(1, 0)$ to $P_2(a, -b)$, the two points are said to be **symmetrical** to a line—the horizontal axis. By the sine definition it follows that $\sin t = b$ and $\sin(-t) = -b$. Changing $\sin t = b$ to $-\sin t = -b$, and applying the transitive law we get

$$\sin(-t) = -\sin t. \tag{C}$$

Theorem: 7.6-1.   The **sine of a negative number** is equal to the negative of the sine of the same positive number.

The **sine function** is an **odd function** because the sine values of the negative numbers differ in sign from the sine values of the same positive numbers.

Applying the preceding data to the cosine function, we have $\cos t = a$ and $\cos(-t) = a$, and again by the transitive law we obtain

$$\cos(-t) = \cos t. \tag{D}$$

Theorem: 7.6-2.   The **cosine of a negative number** is equal to the cosine of the same positive number.

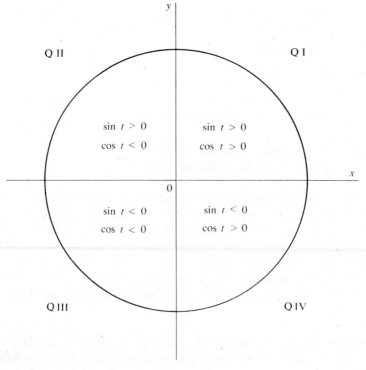

Figure 7.6-1

Because the cosine function, by definition, involves the x coordinates, we get the same cosine values regardless of whether we take a positive number or its comparable negative number. For this reason the **cosine function** is an **even function**. (Algebraic proofs of Theorems 7.6-1 and 7.6-2 will be given in Section 7.17.)

Whether one is using positive or negative numbers, the proper signs for sin t and cos t, within the four quadrants of a unit circle, are indicated in Figure 7.6-1.

EXERCISE 7.A

1. What is the domain of sin t? What is its range?

2. State the domain of cos t. What is its range?

3. State the length of the radius of the circle used in defining the circular functions.

4. Would the circular function definitions be changed in any way if the radius of the circle of reference were permitted to vary?

5. In terms of what are the sine and cosine function defined?

6. Is this a correct definition of the sine function? $\{(t, y) \mid y = \sin t\}$?

7. What is the numerical value of the number one third of the way from $\frac{\pi}{2}$ to π?

8. Find the numerical value of a number two thirds of the way from 0 to $-\frac{\pi}{2}$. Why is this number negative?

9. If P is the point at the end of each arc distance t, does it follow that each t is represented by a point P on the unit circle? Does each P on the unit circle represent exactly one t? Is there one-to-one correspondence between t and P? Explain.

10. If you wound a string around a unit circle (either way) to π, would the t at the end of the semicircle have a unique end point P? Should you continue the winding one full circle and come back to that same point P, would the new t have a unique end point P? Does this end point P represent one and only one t?

11. (a) Can cos t be expressed in terms of sin t? If so, do it.

(b) Express the cotangent function in terms of sines only.

12. (a) Write sin t in terms of cosines only.

(b) Express tan t in terms of cos t.

13. What is the maximum value of the sine function? its minimum value? Under what condition could the sine value be -2? $+3$?

14. (a) State the maximum and minimum values for cos t.

(b) Is $\{t \mid 1 < \cos t < -1\}$ a correct expression for (a)? If not, correct it.

15. How do the sine values vary as t moves from $\frac{\pi}{2}$ to π? Is the sine function **a decreasing function (a function whose $f(x)$ value decreases as x, the independent value, increases)** between $\frac{\pi}{2}$ and π? between 0 and $\frac{\pi}{2}$?

16. As t moves from $3\frac{\pi}{2}$ to 2π, how do the sine values vary? Between these limits is the sine function **an increasing function (a function whose $f(x)$ value increases as x, the independent variable, increases)**? Is it an increasing function between π and $3\frac{\pi}{2}$?

17. What special name is given to the length of one cycle of the sine function? Why is the sine function called a periodic function?

18. Does the expression "sinusoidal curve" refer to just the sine curve? just the cosine curve? or both? What is the period of the sine curve?

19. What is the smallest value that n can have in the statement $\sin(t + 2\pi n) = \sin t$? Could $n = \frac{1}{4}$? Explain.

20. In $\cos(t + 2\pi n) = \cos t$ assume t to be $\dfrac{\pi}{2}$ and show that the statement is true for $n = 10$ and $n = 2$. Is the statement true for $n = \frac{1}{2}$? What is the smallest number for n for which the equation is true?

21. What is the amplitude for $\sin t$ if its maximum sine value is $+1$ and its minimum value is -1?

22. What is the maximum and minimum value for $\cos(-t)$? What is its amplitude?

23. Show that $\sin(-t) = -\sin t$. The sine function is called an odd function. Why?

24. Explain why the statement $\cos(-t) = \cos t$ is true. Is the cosine an odd or an even function?

25. Name the quadrants in which the sine and the cosine functions are both negative, both positive.

26. In which quadrant is $\cos t$ positive and $\sin t$ negative? In which quadrant is $\cos t$ negative and $\sin t$ positive?

27. For $t < 2\pi$, what value of t makes $\cos t = -1$? $\sin t = -1$?

28. For $t < 2\pi$, what value of t makes $\sin t = 1$? $\cos t = 1$?

7.7 GRAPH OF THE SINE FUNCTION $y = \sin t$

In the following pages detailed instructions will be given concerning the construction and interpretation of several types of sine curves. Your responsibility is to come to understand these procedures so completely that you can proceed to develop similar details for the basic cosine curve and its variations.

The graph in Figure 7.7-1 for the basic sine function $y = \sin t$ has been

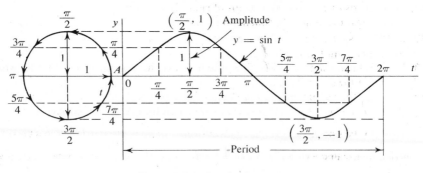

Figure 7.7-1. Graph of $y = \sin t$.

constructed in the following manner:

1. With t as the horizontal axis and y the vertical axis of a rectangular coordinate system, a unit circle was drawn with its center on the t axis.

2. Since the distance around one cycle of the unit circle is 2π, it was considered sufficient for demonstration purposes to divide it into eight parts so that the distances counterclockwise from A would be $\dfrac{\pi}{4}, \dfrac{\pi}{2}, \dfrac{3\pi}{4}, \pi, \dfrac{5\pi}{4}, \dfrac{3\pi}{2}, \dfrac{7\pi}{4}$, 2π. If there were any purpose in doing it, one could divide 2π into a multitude of equal parts.

3. Because the radius of the unit circle is 1, the unit of measurement along the y axis of the coordinate system is taken as 1. The t axis is divided into equal lengths of $\pi/4$, that is 0.7854 approximately. Actually, one can use any unit of measurement he chooses along the t axis without changing the basic characteristics of the graph.

4. To help in showing how the graph of the sine curve represents data indicated by the unit circle, these horizontal lines were drawn:

(a) A horizontal line was drawn from $\pi/4$ and $3\pi/4$ on the unit circle until it intersected vertical lines through $\pi/4$ and $3\pi/4$ on the t axis.

(b) A horizontal line was drawn from $\pi/2$ on the unit circle until it intersected the vertical line through $\pi/2$ on the t axis.

(c) A horizontal line was drawn from $5\pi/4$ and $7\pi/4$ on the unit circle until it intersected vertical lines through $5\pi/4$ and $7\pi/4$ on the t axis.

(d) A horizontal line was drawn from $3\pi/2$ on the unit circle until it intersected a vertical line through $3\pi/2$ on the t axis.

5. To complete the sine curve for the function $y = \sin t$, a smooth curve was drawn through the intersection of the horizontal and vertical lines. This sine curve represents the sine values for all real numbers t between 0 and 2π.

The graph of the sine curve clearly shows the following facts concerning the sine function.

1. The graph shows the measures of sin t (the ordinates) for one complete counterclockwise winding.

2. The graph shows that the cycle is completed at 2π so that the period is 2π. If winding is continued beyond 2π, the curve repeats itself.

3. The average of the maximum and minimum ordinates of the graph is $\dfrac{1 + |-1|}{2} = 1$. The graph shows that the amplitude of the curve is 1.

4. The curve shows that $\sin 0 = 0$, $\sin \dfrac{\pi}{2} = 1$, $\sin \pi = 0$, $\sin \dfrac{3\pi}{2} = -1$, and $\sin 2\pi = 0$.

5. The graph shows that the values of the sine in quadrants I and II are all positive; in quadrants III and IV they are all negative.

6. The graph shows that sin t is an increasing function from 0 to $\pi/2$, a decreasing function from $\pi/2$ to $3\pi/2$, and an increasing function from $3\pi/2$ to 2π.

7. The graph shows that the range of the sine value involves all real numbers from -1 to $+1$ inclusive.

7.8 THE GENERAL SINE FUNCTION AND ITS GRAPH, $y = a \sin bt$

The **sine function $y = \sin t$ is basic.** The shape of its graph should be so clearly impressed upon your mind that you can make a reasonably accurate sketch of it as quickly as you can push a pencil across a sheet of paper.

A more general form of $y = \sin t$ is the function

$y = a \sin bt,$

where a and b are positive constants. The general shape of its graph is similar to the graph of $y = \sin t$.

While a and b in $y = a \sin bt$ do not necessarily have to be limited, for the sake of simplicity they will be limited to positive constants throughout our discussion of the various types of sine functions.

In order to discover the effects of including a and b in the basic function $y = \sin t$, let us consider the two forms

$y = a \sin t$ and $y = \sin bt,$

and make a detailed study of each form.

For $y = a \sin t$, $(a > 0)$,

assume $a = 1$, then $y = \sin t$ (the basic sine definition);

assume $a = 2$, then $y = 2 \sin t$;

assume $a = \frac{1}{2}$, then $y = \frac{1}{2} \sin t$.

Enough assumptions for a have been made to show that its effect is to alter the amplitude of the basic sine function $y = \sin t$. Since the amplitude for $y = \sin t$ has a maximum ordinate of 1, we conclude that the measure of **the amplitude for $y = a \sin t$ is a.**

For $y = \sin bt$ $(b > 0)$,

assume $b = 1$, then $y = \sin t$ (the basic sine definition);

assume $b = 2$, then $y = \sin 2t$;

assume $b = \frac{1}{2}$, then $y = \sin \frac{1}{2}t$.

As t moves from 0 to 2π, the graph of $y = \sin t$ completes one cycle of values. Similarly, as $2t$ moves from 0 to 2π, that is **as t moves from 0 to π, the graph of $y = \sin 2t$ completes one cycle.** Likewise, as $t/2$ moves from 0 to 2π, that is **as t moves from 0 to 4π, $y = \sin\frac{t}{2}$ completes one cycle.** By the same approach, **as bt moves from 0 to 2π, t moves from 0 to $2\pi/b$.** Therefore, the **period for the function $y = \sin bt$ is $2\pi/b$.**

For a and b positive constants and t a real number, the **graph of $y = a \sin bt$** *is a sinusoidal curve having an* **amplitude of a** *and a* **period of $2\pi/b$.**

To be able to make a quick sketch of the graph of the function $y = a \sin bt$, you must know that the general shape of all sine graphs is going to be the same as the shape of the graph of $y = \sin t$. Then you can quickly and easily sketch the curve for $y = a \sin bt$ by isolating the following data:

1. Determine the amplitude and the period.
2. Find the coordinates of the maximum and minimum points of the curve.

   (a) The maximum point will be at $\left(\dfrac{\text{period}}{4}, \text{amplitude}\right)$.

   (b) The minimum point will be at $\left(\dfrac{3 \text{ period}}{4}, -\text{amplitude}\right)$.

3. Find the coordinates for the points where the curve crosses the t axis.
These points will be located at $(0, 0)$, $\left(\dfrac{\text{period}}{2}, 0\right)$, and (period, 0).

4. Finally, draw a smooth curve through the critical points obtained by items 2 and 3. The graph can be extended either to the right or to the left, or both ways, as many cycles as needed.

Example: 7.8-1.   Make a graph of the function $y = 3 \sin 2t$.

1. The amplitude is $a = 3$. The period is $2\pi/2$ or π.
2. (a) The maximum point is $(\pi/4, 3)$;
   (b) The minimum point is $(3\pi/4, -3)$.
3. The curve crosses the t axis at $(0, 0)$, $(\pi/2, 0)$ and $(\pi, 0)$.
4. Notice in Figure 7.8-1 that t has been extended beyond π to give a second

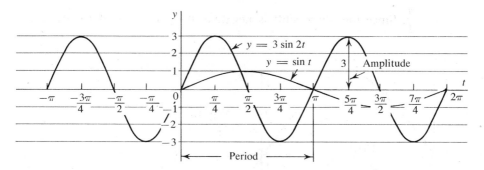

Figure 7.8-1. Graph $y = 3 \sin 2t$.

cycle on the right. Also, negative values have been taken from 0 to $-\pi$ to give one cycle to the left of the origin.

7.9 PHASE SHIFT

The details used in graphing the general sine function $y = a \sin bt$ can be used to good advantage in plotting the function

$y = a \sin(bt + c)$,

where a and b are positive constants and c and t are real numbers.

As the real number $bt + c$ moves from 0 to 2π, bt would have to move from $-c$ to $(2\pi - c)$ and t would move so that the period of the sine function would be from $-\dfrac{c}{b}$ to $\left|\dfrac{2\pi}{b} - \dfrac{c}{b}\right|$.

Definition: 7.9-1.   *In the function* $y = a \sin(bt + c)$, *where* a *and* b *are positive constants and* c *and* t *are real numbers, the* c *is known as the* **phase number** *and* $-\dfrac{c}{b}$ *is called the* **phase shift.**

1. **If $c > 0$,** making the value of $-\dfrac{c}{b}$ **negative,** the entire curve is shifted $\dfrac{c}{b}$ distance to the left of the origin.

2. **If $c < 0$,** making the value of $-\dfrac{c}{b}$ **positive,** the entire curve is shifted $\dfrac{c}{b}$ to the right of the origin.

Example: 7.9-1.   Determine the *amplitude*, the *period*, the *phase shift*, and draw the graph for the function $y = 2 \sin(2t + \pi)$.

$a = 2$ **is the amplitude. The period is** $\dfrac{2\pi}{b} = \dfrac{2\pi}{2} = \pi$. **The phase shift is**

$-\dfrac{c}{b} = -\dfrac{\pi}{2}$. Since the phase shift is negative, the top curve in Figure 7.9-1

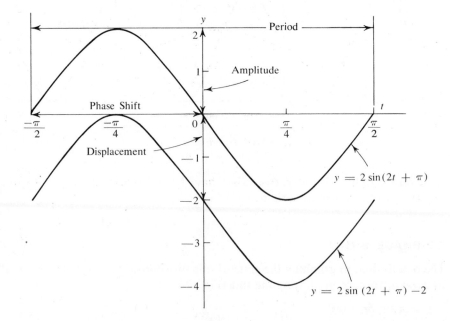

Figure 7.9-1

has been shifted $\dfrac{\pi}{2}$ to the left of the origin and then graphed in the usual sine

curve pattern. (The lower curve applies to the discussion in the next section.)

If the t in the function $y = a \sin(bt + c)$ is thought of as a time variable instead of a distance variable, the equation can be used to study the velocity of a point as it moves along the circumference of a circle. This application applied to periodic functions is called **simple harmonic motion.**

7.10 DISPLACEMENT OF A SINE FUNCTION

While a phase shift moves the entire curve either to the right or to the left of the point $(0, 0)$, a **displacement** moves the entire curve either up or down.

Consider the function

$$y = a \sin(bt + c) + d,$$

where a and b are positive constants and c, d, and t are real numbers. Looking at $y = a \sin(bt + c) + d$, it becomes immediately evident that no matter what the length of the ordinate that represents the value of $a \sin(bt + c)$ is, *a positive real number d added to it will make each ordinate reach d higher* and *a negative real number d subtracted from it will make each ordinate reach d lower*. Thus,

Definition: 7.10-1. *In the function* $y = a \sin(bt + c) + d$, *the d is called the* **displacement** *of the function*:

1. **If $d > 0$**, the entire curve is **displaced upward**.
2. **If $d < 0$**, the entire curve is **displaced downward**.

How would the graph of $y = 2 \sin(2t + \pi) - 2$ differ from the graph of $y = 2 \sin(2t + \pi)$? If you will look back to Figure 7.9-1, you will see that the displacement $d = -2$ in the function $y = 2 \sin(2t + \pi) - 2$ displaces the entire curve down 2 units below the graph of $y = 2 \sin(2t + \pi)$.

Quite obviously, the function $y = 2 \sin(bt + \pi) - 2$ is the sum of the two simpler functions $y = 2 \sin(2t + \pi)$ and $y = -2$. Because these two functions have a common domain, we could have graphed them separately, then added their ordinates to get the desired graph. This process is called **graphing by composition of ordinates.**

7.11 GRAPH OF THE COSINE FUNCTION $x = \cos t$

As stated at the beginning of Section 7.5, it will be up to you to develop most of the details for the cosine function. You are to accomplish this by working all the problems in Exercise 7.B and using Sections 7.7 through 7.10 as your guides.

However, to make sure that you have the correct approach, we will present the graph for the **basic cosine function** $x = \cos t$.

Using the same unit circle as for the sine curve; the same division of 2π into eight parts so that the distances counterclockwise from A are $\pi/4$, $\pi/2$, $3\pi/4$, π, $5\pi/4$, $3\pi/2$, $7\pi/4$, 2π; the unit of measurement along the x axis as 1; and the unit along the t axis as $\pi/4 \doteq 0.7854$; we have sketched vertical and

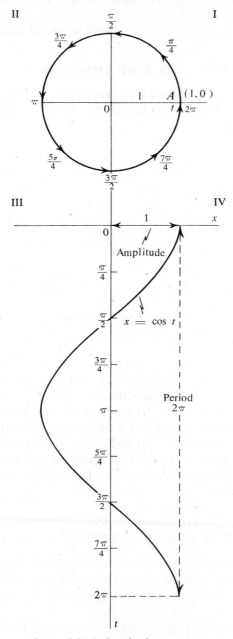

Figure 7.11-1. Graph of $x = \cos t$.

horizontal lines according to item 4 in Section 7.7 and have drawn a smooth curve through their intersections to form the cosine curve as you see it in Figure 7.11-1.

Each distance involved in establishing this cos *t* curve represents an *x* value. Note that all *x* values in quadrants I and IV are positive values, and all *x* values in quadrants II and III are negative values.

For convenience in our future use of the cosine graph, we have altered the position of the cosine curve as it is shown in Figure 7.11-1 so that the *t* axis is made horizontal (see Figure 7.11-2) and so that the abscissas represented by *x* are plotted along or parallel to the vertical axis.

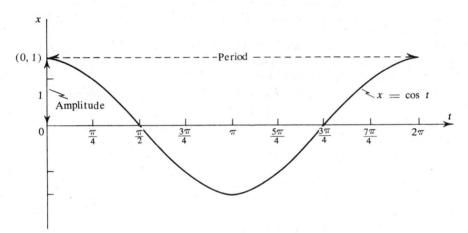

Figure 7.11-2. Graph of x = cos t.

EXERCISE 7.B

1. Use Figure 7.11-2 to decide in which quadrants the cos *t* values are positive. In which quadrants are the cos *t* values negative?

2. Write the coordinates of the maximum point of the cosine curve and state its maximum value. State the minimum value and the coordinates of the minimum point.

3. State the coordinates of the points from 0 to 2π inclusive, where cos *t* = 0.

4. What is the amplitude and the period of $y = \sin t$? of $x = \cos t$?

5. For $t = 0$ show that $\sin\left(t + \dfrac{\pi}{2}\right) = \cos t$. Is the preceding equation also true for $t = \pi/2$? for $t = \pi$? for $t = 3\pi/2$? for all *t*?

6. What is the phase number for $\sin\left(t + \dfrac{\pi}{2}\right)$? What is its phase shift? Does this mean that if you shifted left to $-\pi/2$ and made a graph of sin *t* the graph from the origin to the right would be a replica of the graph of cos *t*? Try it.

7. In which two quadrants is the cosine curve an increasing function? a decreasing function? (See Problems 15 and 16, Exercise 7.A.)

8. What is the domain of cos *t*? the range of cos *t*?

9. For the cosine function $x = 4 \cos 2t$:

(a) State the amplitude and the period.

(b) Find the coordinates for the maximum and the minimum points, $t \leq \pi$.

(c) Find the coordinates for the points where $4 \cos 2t = 0$, $t \leq \pi$.

(d) Sketch the curve from $t = 0$ to $t = 5\pi/4$. (See Section 7.8.)

10. For the cosine function $x = \frac{1}{2} \cos \frac{1}{2}t$:

(a) Determine the amplitude and the period.

(b) Find the coordinates for the maximum and the minimum points, $t \leq 4\pi$.

(c) Find the coordinates of the points where $\frac{1}{2} \cos \frac{1}{2}t = 0$, $t \leq 4\pi$.

(d) Sketch the curve from $t = 0$ to $t = 9\pi/2$.

11. Assume $t = \pi/2$ in $\cos(t + 2\pi n) = \cos t$. Show that the equation is true for $n = 2$, for $n = 10$. Is the statement true for $n = \frac{1}{4}$? What is the smallest value for n for which the equation is true?

12. For any real number t, what is the largest integral value that n can have in the equation $\cos t = \cos(t + 2\pi n)$ and preserve the equality? How many cycles does this value of n represent? How many periods?

13. If the coordinates of t are $P_1(1/\sqrt{2}, 1/\sqrt{2})$, what are the coordinates for $(-t)$ where its end point P_2 is symmetrical to P_1? (See Section 7.6.)

14. If the coordinates of $(-t)$ are $P_1(-1, -3)$, what are the coordinates of t where its end point P_2 is symmetrical to P_1?

15. State the amplitude, period, and phase shift for the cosine function $x = 5 \cos(3t - \pi)$. Should the graph of this curve be shifted to the right or to the left of the origin? Why?

16. Find the phase number, the phase shift, the amplitude, and the period for $x = \frac{1}{4} \cos(\frac{1}{4}t + \frac{1}{4}\pi)$. Should the graph of this curve be shifted to the right or the left of the origin? Why?

17. Make a graph of the curve in Problem 15 from $-\pi/2$ to π.

18. Sketch a graph of the curve in Problem 16 from $-\pi$ to 10π.

19. Draw a graph of $2 \cos(-t)$ where $-6\pi \leq t \leq 0$. Should this graph fall to the right or the left of the origin? How many cycles are involved? Is it a sinusoidal curve?

20. Make a graph of the curve $x = 2 \cos(-4t)$ where $-\pi \leq t \leq \pi$. Write an expression in terms of cosines that is equivalent to $2 \cos(-4t)$.

21. How does the graph of $x = 2 \cos(-4t) + 4$ differ from the graph $x = 2 \cos(-4t)$? Has the latter curve been displaced up or down?

22. Make a graph of $x = 2 \cos(-t) - \pi$ by graphing $x = 2 \cos(-t)$ and $x = -\pi$ on the same axes. What is the displacement number?

23. (a) Distinguish between phase shift and displacement.

(b) State the amplitude, period, phase shift, and displacement for

$$x = 3 \cos\left(2t - \frac{\pi}{2}\right) + 0.5.$$

24. What is the amplitude, period, phase number, phase shift, and displacement of $x = \frac{2}{3} \cos(-\frac{2}{3}t + \pi) - \frac{3}{4}$?

25. When you substitute values for t in $\cos t$ and plot the results, are the values actually abscissas or ordinates? If the t values are plotted along the horizontal axis, where are the $\cos t$ values plotted?

26. What is the definition for the cosine function? Does it follow then that the vertical distances used to draw the curve in Figure 7.11-2 are all abscissas? Does Figure 7.11-1 show these distances to be abscissas or ordinates?

7.12 EXTENSION OF SINE AND COSINE FUNCTIONS

You should notice that in the preceding pages we have given very special emphasis to the sine and cosine functions. This has been done because **the sine and cosine functions are basic to the remaining four circular functions, namely, the tangent, cotangent, secant, and cosecant functions.** The dependence of these other circular functions on the sine and cosine functions can best be shown by repeating the definitions given in Section 7.3.

$$\tan t = \frac{\sin t}{\cos t} \qquad (\cos t \neq 0),$$

$$\cot t = \frac{\cos t}{\sin t} \qquad (\sin t \neq 0),$$

$$\sec t = \frac{1}{\cos t} \qquad (\cos t \neq 0),$$

$$\csc t = \frac{1}{\sin t} \qquad (\sin t \neq 0).$$

The algebraic signs for each sine value and each cosine value have already been listed in Table 7.5-2. This information, along with preceding definitions for tan t, cot t, sec t, and csc t, should enable you to verify the sign for each circular function given in the following table.

Table 7.12-1 *Signs for the Circular Functions*

Functions	sin t	cos t	tan t	cot t	sec t	csc t
Quadrant I	+	+	+	+	+	+
Quadrant II	+	−	−	−	−	+
Quadrant III	−	−	+	+	−	−
Quadrant IV	−	+	−	−	+	−

7.13 EXACT VALUES OF THE CIRCULAR FUNCTIONS OF π/6, π/4, π/3, AND THEIR MULTIPLES

In studying circular functions we have been using the numbers 0, $\pi/4$, $\pi/2$, $3\pi/4$, π, $5\pi/4$, $3\pi/2$, $7\pi/8$, and 2π. We are now going to give special attention to $\pi/6$, $\pi/4$, $\pi/3$, **located in Quadrant I,** and their multiples

$$\frac{2\pi}{3}, \frac{3\pi}{4}, \text{ and } \frac{5\pi}{6} \text{ in Quadrant II,}$$

$$\frac{7\pi}{6}, \frac{5\pi}{4}, \text{ and } \frac{4\pi}{3} \text{ in Quadrant III,}$$

and $\dfrac{5\pi}{3}, \dfrac{7\pi}{4},$ and $\dfrac{11\pi}{6}$ in **Quadrant IV**.

The exact numerical values of the circular functions $\pi/6$, $\pi/3$, and $\pi/4$ and their multiples can readily be obtained by using some elementary plane geometry and the six definitions for circular functions. The word "exact" as used here means that the values are 100 per cent accurate. The following examples demonstrate how these exact values are obtained.

Example: 7.13-a.   Find the numerical values for the six circular functions if $t = \pi/6$.

$P(c, d)$ is a point on the unit circle in Figure 7.13-a such that the length of its arc from A is AP, that is $\overset{\frown}{AP} = \pi/6$. Also, $P(c, -d)$ is another point on the unit circle symmetrical to P with respect to the x axis (see Section 7.6) such that its length of arc is $\overset{\frown}{AP'} = -\pi/6$. It follows then that

$$\overset{\frown}{P'P} = \frac{\pi}{6} + \left| -\frac{\pi}{6} \right| = \frac{\pi}{3}, \qquad \overset{\frown}{PB} = \frac{\pi}{2} - \frac{\pi}{6} = \frac{\pi}{3},$$

and $\overset{\frown}{P'P} = \overset{\frown}{PB}$.

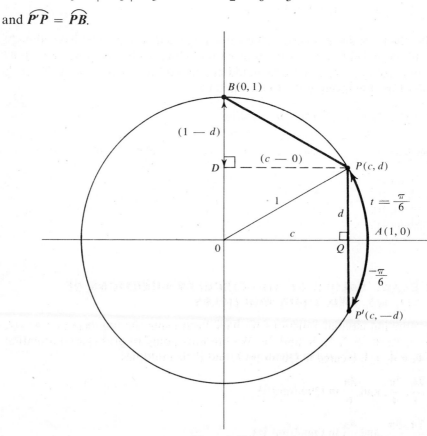

Figure 7.13-a

Arcs of equal lengths are subtended by chords of equal lengths. Therefore, chords

$P'P = PB$.

By using the fact that in the unit circle of Figure 7.13-a $c^2 + d^2 = 1$ and applying the Pythagorean theorem to triangle DPB, the length of PB is found to be

$$PB = \sqrt{(c - 0)^2 + (1 - d)^2} = \sqrt{c^2 + 1 - 2d + d^2} = \sqrt{2 - 2d}.$$

The length of $P'P = QP + QP' = d + |-d| = 2d$.

So $$2d = \sqrt{2 - 2d},$$

$$4d^2 = 2 - 2d,$$

$$2d^2 + d - 1 = 0,$$

$$(d + 1)(2d - 1) = 0 \quad \text{and} \quad d = \tfrac{1}{2} \quad \text{or} \quad d = -1.$$

For $\pi/6$ it is evident that d falls in Quadrant I and must be positive. Thus, the only acceptable value for d is $\tfrac{1}{2}$. If $d = \tfrac{1}{2}$, then from $c^2 + d^2 = 1$, $c^2 = 1 - \tfrac{1}{4}$ and $c = \sqrt{3}/2$. Therefore, the coordinates for point P are

$$(c, d) = \left(\frac{\sqrt{3}}{2}, \frac{1}{2}\right).$$

With the coordinates of the end point of the arc which represents the length of $\pi/6$ available to us we can now write the following numerical values for:

Circular Functions of $\dfrac{\pi}{6}$

$$\sin \frac{\pi}{6} = \frac{1}{2} \qquad \tan \frac{\pi}{6} = \frac{1}{\sqrt{3}} \qquad \sec \frac{\pi}{6} = \frac{2}{\sqrt{3}}$$

$$\cos \frac{\pi}{6} = \frac{\sqrt{3}}{2} \qquad \cot \frac{\pi}{6} = \sqrt{3} \qquad \csc \frac{\pi}{6} = 2$$

Example: 7.13-b.   Find the numerical values for the six circular functions if $t = \pi/4$.

Figure 7.13-b shows $P(c, d)$ to be a point on the unit circle such that the length of $\widehat{AP}$ is $\pi/4$. Also, the length of $\widehat{PB}$ is $\dfrac{\pi}{2} - \dfrac{\pi}{4} = \dfrac{\pi}{4}$. Therefore, $\widehat{AP} = \widehat{PB}$ and chords $AP = PB$.

Applying the Pythagorean theorem to triangles EAP and DPB and using the fact that $c^2 + d^2 = 1$ for the unit circle,

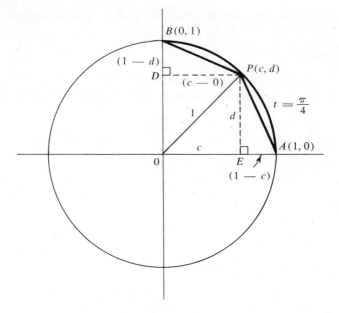

Figure 7.13-b

$(AP)^2 = (1 - c)^2 + (d - 0)^2 = 1 - 2c + c^2 + d^2 = 2 - 2c;$

$(PB)^2 = (c - 0)^2 + (1 - d)^2 = c^2 + 1 - 2d + d^2 = 2 - 2d.$

Since $AP = PB$, it follows that $(AP)^2 = (PB)^2$ and $2 - 2c = 2 - 2d$.

$\therefore$ $c = d$.

Substituting c for d in $c^2 + d^2 = 1$ gives $c = 1/\sqrt{2}$ and $d = 1/\sqrt{2}$.

$\therefore$ $(c, d) = \left(\dfrac{1}{\sqrt{2}}, \dfrac{1}{\sqrt{2}} \right)$.

Knowing the coordinates for P, at the end point of the arc $\pi/4$, enables us to write the numerical values for:

Circular Functions of $\dfrac{\pi}{4}$

$$\sin \frac{\pi}{4} = \frac{1}{\sqrt{2}} \qquad \tan \frac{\pi}{4} = 1 \qquad \sec \frac{\pi}{4} = \sqrt{2}$$

$$\cos \frac{\pi}{4} = \frac{1}{\sqrt{2}} \qquad \cot \frac{\pi}{4} = 1 \qquad \csc \frac{\pi}{4} = \sqrt{2}$$

Example: 7.13-c.   Find the numerical values for the six circular functions if $t = \pi/3$.

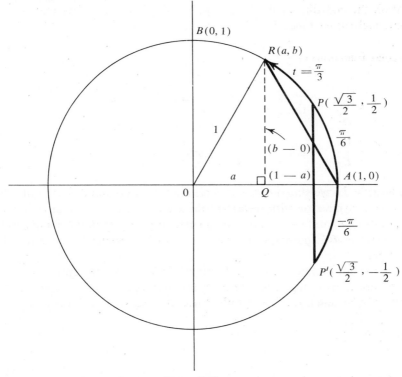

Figure 7.13-c

Let $R(a, b)$ be a point on the unit circle in Figure 7.13-c such that the length of $\widehat{AR} = \pi/3$. From Example 7.13-a we already know that the coordinates of P and P' are respectively $\left(\dfrac{\sqrt{3}}{2}, \dfrac{1}{2}\right)$ and $\left(\dfrac{\sqrt{3}}{2}, -\dfrac{1}{2}\right)$ and that $\widehat{P'P} = \pi/3$. It follows, then, that

$\widehat{AR} = \widehat{P'P}$ and chords $AR = P'P$.

Applying the Pythagorean theorem to the triangle QAR, and using the fact that in the unit circle $a^2 + b^2 = 1$, we get

$$(AR)^2 = (1 - a)^2 + (b - 0)^2 = 1 - 2a + a^2 + b^2 = 2 - 2a;$$
$$(P'P)^2 = (d + |-d|)^2 = (\tfrac{1}{2} + |-\tfrac{1}{2}|)^2 = 1.$$

Since $AR = P'P$, then $(AR)^2 = (P'P)^2$ and $2 - 2a = 1$ or $a = \tfrac{1}{2}$.

If $a = \tfrac{1}{2}$, then by $a^2 + b^2 = 1$, $b^2 = 1 - \tfrac{1}{4}$ and $b = \dfrac{\sqrt{3}}{2}$. Thus, the co-ordinates for point R are

$$(a, b) = \left(\frac{1}{2}, \frac{\sqrt{3}}{2}\right).$$

With the coordinates of the end point of $\pi/3$ available, we can write these numerical values for:

Circular Functions of $\dfrac{\pi}{3}$

$$\sin\frac{\pi}{3} = \frac{\sqrt{3}}{2} \qquad \tan\frac{\pi}{3} = \sqrt{3} \qquad \sec\frac{\pi}{3} = 2$$

$$\cos\frac{\pi}{3} = \frac{1}{2} \qquad \cot\frac{\pi}{3} = \frac{1}{\sqrt{3}} \qquad \csc\frac{\pi}{3} = \frac{2}{\sqrt{3}}$$

In Section 7.6 we stated that if a circle contains two points (c, d) and $(c, -d)$ the curve is **symmetric with respect to the x axis.** Likewise, if a circle contains two points (c, d) and $(-c, d)$, it is **symmetric with respect to the y axis,** and if a circle contains two points (c, d) and $(-c, -d)$, it is **symmetric with respect to the origin.**

Once the coordinates of the end points of the arc which represent $\pi/6$, $\pi/4$, and $\pi/3$ are known, the coordinates of the multiples of these numbers can be obtained by **symmetry.** For example, since the coordinates of the end point of $\dfrac{\pi}{3}$ are $\left(\dfrac{1}{2}, \dfrac{\sqrt{3}}{2}\right)$,

(a) by symmetry about the y axis the coordinates of $\dfrac{2\pi}{3}$ are $\left(-\dfrac{1}{2}, \dfrac{\sqrt{3}}{2}\right)$;

(b) by symmetry about the origin the coordinates of $\dfrac{4\pi}{3}$ are $\left(-\dfrac{1}{2}, -\dfrac{\sqrt{3}}{2}\right)$;

(c) by symmetry about the x axis the coordinates of $\dfrac{5\pi}{3}$ are $\left(\dfrac{1}{2}, -\dfrac{\sqrt{3}}{2}\right)$.

It will be left for the reader to use the concepts of symmetry and the coordinates of the end points of the arcs which represent $\pi/6$, $\pi/4$, and $\pi/3$, to find the numerical coordinates for $3\pi/4$, $5\pi/4$, $7\pi/4$, $5\pi/6$, $7\pi/6$, and $11\pi/6$.

Summarizing the results of Examples 7.13-a, b, and c, we obtain Table 7.13a.

Example: 7.13-d.   Find the values of the six circular functions for integral multiples of $\pi/6$, $\pi/4$, and $\pi/3$ in Quadrant II.

Exact values of integral multiples of $\pi/6$, $\pi/4$, and $\pi/3$ in Quadrants II, III, and IV may be obtained by using the equilateral triangle and the isosceles right triangle as they were used in Examples 7.13-a, b, and c for Quadrant I. In all cases the corresponding **absolute values of the circular functions** for the multiples of $\pi/6$, $\pi/4$, and $\pi/3$ will not change, but the true values will differ in signs according to the quadrant considered.

Figure 7.13-d shows the multiples of $\pi/6$, $\pi/4$, and $\pi/3$ for Quadrant II.

Table 7.13-a *Circular Function Values for* $\dfrac{\pi}{6}, \dfrac{\pi}{4},$ *and* $\dfrac{\pi}{3}$

t	$\sin t$	$\cos t$	$\tan t$	$\cot t$	$\sec t$	$\csc t$
$\dfrac{\pi}{6}$	$\dfrac{1}{2}$	$\dfrac{\sqrt{3}}{2}$	$\dfrac{1}{\sqrt{3}}$	$\sqrt{3}$	$\dfrac{2}{\sqrt{3}}$	2
$\dfrac{\pi}{4}$	$\dfrac{1}{\sqrt{2}}$	$\dfrac{1}{\sqrt{2}}$	1	1	$\sqrt{2}$	$\sqrt{2}$
$\dfrac{\pi}{3}$	$\dfrac{\sqrt{3}}{2}$	$\dfrac{1}{2}$	$\sqrt{3}$	$\dfrac{1}{\sqrt{3}}$	2	$\dfrac{2}{\sqrt{3}}$

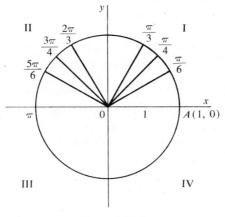

Figure 7.13-d

This is how these multiples were determined:

A multiple of $\dfrac{\pi}{6}$ in Quadrant II is $\left(\pi - \dfrac{\pi}{6}\right) = \dfrac{5\pi}{6}$.

A multiple of $\dfrac{\pi}{4}$ in Quadrant II is $\left(\pi - \dfrac{\pi}{4}\right) = \dfrac{3\pi}{4}$.

A multiple of $\dfrac{\pi}{3}$ in Quadrant II is $\left(\pi - \dfrac{\pi}{3}\right) = \dfrac{2\pi}{3}$.

Table 7.13-b shows the exact values obtained by applying the definitions of the circular functions to $2\pi/3$, $3\pi/4$, and $5\pi/6$.

Again it should be emphasized that the values in Table 7.13-b are, except for the algebraic signs, identical to those obtained for $\pi/6$, $\pi/4$, and $\pi/3$ as

Table 7.13-b *Circular Function Values for Multiples of $\frac{\pi}{6}, \frac{\pi}{4}$, and $\frac{\pi}{3}$ in Quadrant II*

t	$\sin t$	$\cos t$	$\tan t$	$\cot t$	$\sec t$	$\csc t$
$2\left(\dfrac{\pi}{3}\right)$	$+\dfrac{\sqrt{3}}{2}$	$-\dfrac{1}{2}$	$-\sqrt{3}$	$-\dfrac{1}{\sqrt{3}}$	-2	$+\dfrac{2}{\sqrt{3}}$
$3\left(\dfrac{\pi}{4}\right)$	$+\dfrac{1}{\sqrt{2}}$	$-\dfrac{1}{\sqrt{2}}$	-1	-1	$-\sqrt{2}$	$+\sqrt{2}$
$5\left(\dfrac{\pi}{6}\right)$	$+\dfrac{1}{2}$	$-\dfrac{\sqrt{3}}{2}$	$-\dfrac{1}{\sqrt{3}}$	$-\sqrt{3}$	$-\dfrac{2}{\sqrt{3}}$	$+2$

shown in Table 7.13-a. As indicated by Table 7.12-1, *the algebraic sign for a circular function depends upon the quadrant in which the end point of the arc that represents the number lies.*

The student is to work out tables similar to Table 7.13-b for multiples of $\pi/6$, $\pi/4$, and $\pi/3$ for Quadrant III and Quadrant IV.

7.13-1 Graphs of the Circular Functions from 0 to 2π

The graphs of the six circular functions can be of considerable help to you in visualizing and recalling the facts possessed by these functions. As you continue to study and work problems involving the circular and trigonometric functions you should refer often to these six graphs.

Turning to Section 7.4, you can see that there exists a reciprocal relationship between certain pairs of circular functions. That is,

$$\csc t = \frac{1}{\sin t}; \qquad \sec t = \frac{1}{\cos t}; \qquad \cot t = \frac{1}{\tan t}.$$

In each relationship the functions are, of course, interchangeable. To show to

Table 7.13-1a *Numbers Used in Plotting the Circular Functions*

t	0	$\dfrac{\pi}{6}$	$\dfrac{\pi}{3}$	$\dfrac{\pi}{2}$	$\dfrac{2\pi}{3}$	$\dfrac{5\pi}{6}$	π	$\dfrac{7\pi}{6}$	$\dfrac{4\pi}{3}$	$\dfrac{3\pi}{2}$	$\dfrac{5\pi}{3}$	$\dfrac{11\pi}{6}$	2π
$\sin t$	0	0.5	0.9	1.0	0.9	0.5	0	-0.5	-0.9	-1.0	-0.9	-0.5	0
$\csc t$	—	2.0	1.2	1.0	1.2	2.0	—	-2.0	-1.2	-1.0	-1.2	-2.0	—
$\cos t$	1.0	0.9	0.5	0	-0.5	-0.9	-1.0	-0.9	-0.5	0	0.5	0.9	1.0
$\sec t$	1.0	1.2	2.0	—	-2.0	-1.2	-1.0	-1.2	-2.0	—	2.0	1.2	1.0
$\tan t$	0	0.6	1.7	—	-1.7	-0.6	0	0.6	1.7	—	-1.7	-0.6	0
$\cot t$	—	1.7	0.6	0	-0.6	-1.7	—	1.7	0.6	0	-0.6	-1.7	—

best advantage the graphs of these functions that are reciprocally related, both graphs will be plotted on the same coordinate axes.

Except as indicated by the dash marks "—" in Table 7.13-1a and by the points of discontinuity indicated by the graphs in Figures 7.13-1a, 1b, and 1c, the graphs

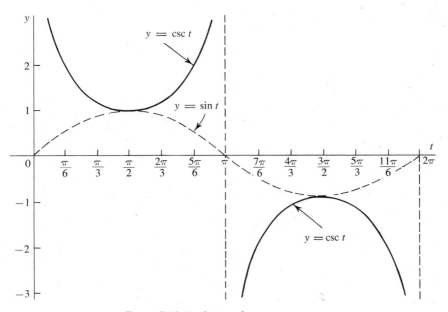

Figure 7.13-1a. Sine and cosecant curves.

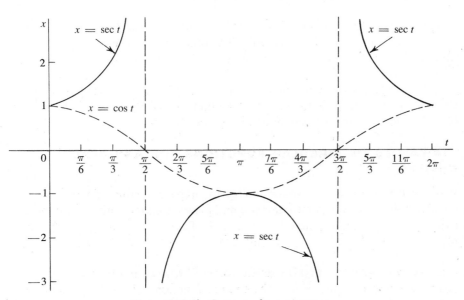

Figure 7.13-1b. Cosine and secant curves.

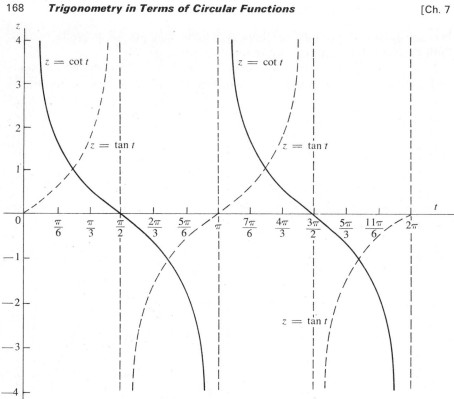

Figure 7.13-1c. Tangent and cotangent curves.

of the functions are continuous for all admissible real numbers. However, we will plot the graphs from 0 to 2π only. The numbers and their function values used in the plotting have been previously developed and are summarized in Table 7.13-1a.

It is suggested that each student practice making quick sketches of these circular function graphs. The sketches should be carefully drawn at the critical points, otherwise just a freehand drawing is sufficient.

7.14 VALUES OF CIRCULAR FUNCTIONS FOR ANY REAL NUMBER

It is the usual practice in trigonometry to prepare a table of values of the circular functions, accurate to four decimal places, for all positive real numbers from 0 to $\pi/2$ inclusive. Table I on page 390 of this book is a **circular function table.** To make this table serve for all real numbers you must know:

(a) How to select a "first quadrant number" whose circular function value can be made to be equivalent to the circular function value of a second quadrant, a third quadrant, or a fourth quadrant number.

(b) How to change any number greater than 2π to a number whose arc ends at the same point but is less than 2π.

Definition: 7.14-a.   *The positive arc from 0 to $\pi/2$ inclusive that represents any real number on the unit circle will be called the* **corresponding arc** *and will be symbolized by* C_A.

Definition: 7.14-b.   *Arcs that have their initial points at $A(1, 0)$ on the unit circle and have the same point $P(x, y)$ for their terminal points will be called* **coterminal arcs.**

Definition: 7.14-c.   *Numbers that have coterminal arcs are called* **coterminal numbers.**

A review of Section 7.13 should help to make the following statements evident:

1. The circular function value of a real number whose arc falls in Quadrant II is the circular function of its corresponding arc, namely, π less the given number, with proper signs prefixed.

2. The circular function of a real number whose arc falls in Quadrant III is the circular function of its corresponding arc, namely, the given number less π, with the proper signs prefixed.

3. The circular function of a real number whose arc falls in Quadrant IV is the circular function of its corresponding arc, namely, 2π less the given number, with the proper signs prefixed.

4. The circular function of any real number t whose arc is greater than 2π (such as $t + 2\pi n$, where $n = 1, 2, 3, \ldots$,) is identical to the circular function of its coterminal arc, which is less than 2π. Then, to find the circular function of the corresponding arc for the coterminal arc less than 2π, use either statement 1, 2, or 3 above, depending on which one applies.

The four preceding statements apply both to positive and negative numbers. For help in dealing with negative numbers, we should recall these two facts presented in Section 7.6:

$$\sin (-t) = -\sin t, \tag{C}$$
$$\text{and } \cos (-t) = \cos t. \tag{D}$$

From (C) and (D) and the fact that $\tan t$, $\cot t$, $\sec t$, and $\csc t$ were defined in Section 7.12 in terms of the sine and cosine functions, it follows that

$$\tan(-t) = \frac{\sin(-t)}{\cos(-t)} = \frac{-\sin t}{\cos t} = -\tan t;$$
$$\cot(-t) = -\cot t$$
$$\sec(-t) = \frac{1}{\cos(-t)} = \frac{1}{\cos t} = \sec t;$$
$$\csc(-t) = -\csc t.$$

7.14-1 How to Find the Corresponding Arc C_A for Any Real Number

1. Sketch the arc that represents the given number.
2. Note in which quadrant the end point of the arc falls.
3. Determine the corresponding arc and write the six circular functions for the number which this arc represents.
4. Prefix the proper sign for each circular function for the quadrant in which the end point of the arc of the given number falls.

Example: 7.14-1a.   Find the function value for $\cos \dfrac{3\pi}{4}$.

The arc ends in Quadrant II. The corresponding arc is $\pi - \dfrac{3\pi}{4} = \dfrac{\pi}{4}$.

$$\cos \frac{\pi}{4} = \frac{1}{\sqrt{2}}.$$

All cosine values in Quadrant II (Figure 7.14-1a) are negative.

$$\therefore \ \cos \frac{3\pi}{4} = -\frac{1}{\sqrt{2}}.$$

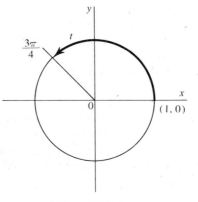

Figure 7.14-1a

Example: 7.14-1b.   Find the function value for $\tan \dfrac{4\pi}{3}$.

The arc ends in Quadrant III. The *corresponding arc* is $\dfrac{4\pi}{3} - \pi = \dfrac{\pi}{3}$.

$$\tan \frac{\pi}{3} = \sqrt{3}.$$

All tangent values in Quadrant III (Figure 7.14-1b) are positive.

$$\therefore \ \tan \frac{4\pi}{3} = \sqrt{3}.$$

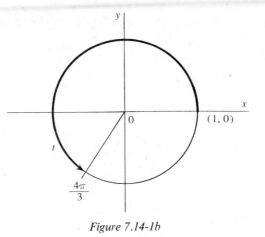

Figure 7.14-1b

Example: 7.14-1c.   Find the function value for $\cot \dfrac{11\pi}{6}$.

The arc ends in Quadrant IV. The *corresponding arc* is $2\pi - \dfrac{11\pi}{6} = \dfrac{\pi}{6}$.

$\cot \dfrac{\pi}{6} = \sqrt{3}.$

All cotangent values in Quadrant IV (Figure 7.14-1c) are negative.

$\therefore \ \mathbf{\cot \dfrac{11\pi}{6}} = -\sqrt{3}.$

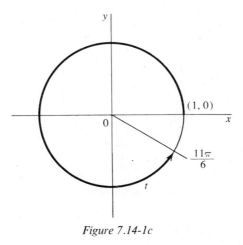

Figure 7.14-1c

Example: 7.14-1d.   Find the function value for $\tan \dfrac{16\pi}{3}$.

The arc goes around the circle twice and finally ends in Quadrant III (Figure 7.14-1d). Using $\dfrac{16\pi}{3} = \dfrac{4\pi}{3} + \dfrac{12\pi}{3} = t + 2\pi n$, where $n = 2$, we find that

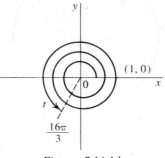

Figure   7.14-1d

$t = 4\pi/3$ is coterminal with $16\pi/3$ and is less than 2π. Now our problem is to find $\tan \dfrac{4\pi}{3}$. This was determined in Example 7.14-1b to be $\sqrt{3}$.

$\therefore$ $\tan \dfrac{16\pi}{3} = \sqrt{3}.$

Example: 7.14-1e.   Find the function value for $\sin \dfrac{(-7\pi)}{4}$.

Moving clockwise from (1, 0) the arc ends in Quadrant I (Figure 7.14-1e).

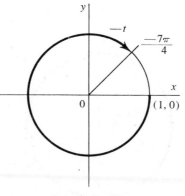

Figure   7.14-1e

The *corresponding arc* is $2\pi - \dfrac{7\pi}{4} = \dfrac{\pi}{4}.$

$\sin \dfrac{\pi}{4} = \dfrac{1}{\sqrt{2}},$

All sin values in Quadrant I are positive.

$$\therefore \ \sin\left(-\frac{7\pi}{4}\right) = \frac{1}{\sqrt{2}}.$$

Efficient computation of the values of circular functions for real numbers requires more complicated mathematics than this book will present. However, for your information, we will list the two basic infinite series used in conjunction with an electronic computing machine to build a circular function table. They are

$$\sin t = t - \frac{t^3}{3!} + \frac{t^5}{5!} - \frac{t^7}{7!} + \cdots,$$

and

$$\cos t = 1 - \frac{t^2}{2!} + \frac{t^4}{4!} - \frac{t^6}{6!} + \cdots.$$

where t is any real number and the symbol $n!$ (see Section 6.6-2) means the product of all the positive integers from 1 to n inclusive.

The preceding series for $\sin t$ converges in the sense that the more terms used, the more nearly the approximated value for $\sin t$ will approach the true value of $\sin t$. The same is true for $\cos t$.

Example: 7.14-1f.   Find the value of sin 1 by the infinite sine series.

$$\sin 1 = 1 - \frac{(1)^3}{1\cdot 2\cdot 3} + \frac{(1)^5}{1\cdot 2\cdot 3\cdot 4\cdot 5} - \frac{(1)^7}{1\cdot 2\cdot 3\cdot 4\cdot 5\cdot 6\cdot 7} + \cdots.$$

$$= 1 - 0.16666 + \ + 0.00833 + \ -\ 0.00198 + \cdots$$

$$\doteq 0.83334$$

$$\doteq 0.84167$$

$$\doteq 0.84148$$

$\therefore$ **sin 1** $\doteq$ **0.8415**   (accurate to four digits).

Check the value for sin 1 in Table I, the circular function table on page 390.

If either coordinate of the end point P of the arc t in a unit circle is given, then by the Pythagorean theorem the other coordinate and the numerical values of the six circular functions can be computed.

Example: 7.14-1g.   Find the numerical values of the six circular functions if the real number t ends in the second quadrant of the unit circle in Figure 7.14-1g and the ordinate from P to the x axis is $y = \frac{4}{5}$.

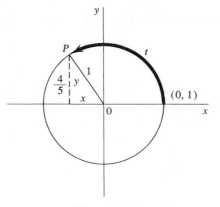

Figure 7.14-1g

$y = \frac{4}{5}$ is given.

$$x = -\sqrt{1 - y^2} = -\sqrt{\frac{25}{25} - \frac{16}{25}} = -\frac{3}{5}.$$

The six numerical values are:

$$\begin{aligned}
\sin t &= \tfrac{4}{5}, &\quad \cot t &= -\tfrac{3}{4}, \\
\cos t &= -\tfrac{3}{5}, &\quad \sec t &= -\tfrac{5}{3}, \\
\tan t &= -\tfrac{4}{3}, &\quad \csc t &= \tfrac{5}{4}.
\end{aligned}$$

EXERCISE 7.C

In answering the following questions keep in mind that the circumference of a unit circle is the real number 2π. The exact number 2π is equal approximately to $6.28 \cdots$, $\pi = 3.14 \cdots$, $\pi/2 = 1.57 \cdots$, etc.

1. Make a table similar to Table 7.13-a showing the circular function values for multiples of $\pi/6$, $\pi/4$, and $\pi/3$ in Quadrant III.

2. Make a table similar to Table 7.13-a showing the circular function values for multiples of $\pi/6$, $\pi/4$, and $\pi/3$ in Quadrant IV.

3. On a unit circle draw an arc that represents each of the following numbers. Then find the number its *corresponding arc* represents.

(a) $\dfrac{5\pi}{6}$. (c) $\dfrac{5\pi}{4}$. (e) 15.

(b) $\dfrac{5\pi}{3}$. (d) $-\dfrac{3\pi}{4}$. (f) -17.

4. (a) Draw an arc on a unit circle to represent

(i) $\dfrac{2\pi}{3}$ (iii) $\dfrac{7\pi}{4}$ (v) 7.

(ii) $-\dfrac{2\pi}{3}$ (iv) $-\dfrac{7\pi}{4}$.   (vi) -5.

(b) Find the *corresponding arc* for each number in (a).

5. Which of the following circular functions have nonnegative values?

(a) $\sin \dfrac{2\pi}{3}$.

(d) $\sec 1$.

(g) $\sin \dfrac{11\pi}{4}$.

(b) $\cos 3$.

(e) $\csc \left(-\dfrac{\pi}{4}\right)$.

(h) $\cos \left(-\dfrac{7\pi}{6}\right)$.

(c) $\tan \dfrac{5\pi}{4}$.

(f) $\cot 5$.

(i) $\tan 32$.

6. Which of the following circular functions have negative values?

(a) $\sec 3$.

(d) $\cot \left(-\dfrac{2\pi}{3}\right)$.

(g) $\sin 24$.

(b) $\tan \dfrac{\pi}{5}$.

(e) $\tan(2\pi + 3)$.

(h) $\cos 15$.

(c) $\cos(\pi + 1)$.

(f) $\csc \left(-\dfrac{3\pi}{4}\right)$.

(i) $\tan \dfrac{3\pi}{4}$.

7. State the quadrant or quadrants in which the real number t will terminate if

(a) $\sin t < 0$.

(d) $\tan t > 0$ and $\sec t < -1$.

(b) $\sin t > 0$ and $\cot t < 0$.

(e) $\cos t > 0$ and $\sin t > 0$.

(c) $0 < \cot t < 1.55$.

(f) $\cot t < 0$ and $\tan t > 0$.

8. In which quadrant or quadrants will the end point of the real number t fall if

(a) $\cos t > 0$.

(d) $\csc t < -1$ and $\cot t > 0$.

(b) $\cos t < 0$ and $\tan t > 0$.

(e) $\cos t > 0$ and $\sin t > 0$.

(c) $-1 < \tan t < 0$.

(f) $\tan t < 0$ and $\cot t > 0$.

9. How many arcs have their end points at $P_1(x_1, y_1)$ on a unit circle? Where are their initial points located?

10. Write out the numerical values of any five arcs that have their end points at $3\pi/4$.

11. If one of the coordinates of the end point of the arc that represents t has the value $y = 12/13$ in Quadrant II, (a) find the corresponding x coordinate of the end point of this arc; (b) state the numerical values of the six circular functions for t.

12. If $x = 24/25$ is one of the coordinates of the end points of the arc that represents t in Quadrant III, (a) compute the corresponding y; (b) determine the numerical values of the six circular functions for t.

13. If $\sin t = \frac{1}{2}$ in Quadrant IV, what are the numerical values of the other five circular functions?

14. If $\cos t = -\frac{3}{5}$ in Quadrant II, determine the numerical values of the other five circular functions.

15. Use the infinite sine series to find the value of $\sin 0.4$ accurate to four decimal places. Then compare your answer with the value of $\sin 0.4$ in **Table I.**

16. Find the value of $\cos 0.6$ accurate to four decimal places by using the infinite cosine series. Compare your answer with the value for $\cos 0.6$ in Table I.

17. Show that the statement $\sin^2 \left(\dfrac{\pi}{4}\right) + \cos^2 \left(\dfrac{\pi}{4}\right) = 1$ is true.

18. Is the statement $\tan \dfrac{2\pi}{3} = -\dfrac{\sin \dfrac{\pi}{3}}{\cos \dfrac{\pi}{3}}$ true or false? Show why.

19. Which of these statements are false?

(a) $\sin t = 4$.

(c) $\tan \dfrac{\pi}{2} = 1$.

(e) $\sec t = 0.5$.

(b) $\cos t = 1.1$.

(d) $\cot 0 = 0$.

(f) $\csc t = 0.8$.

20. Which of these statements are true?

(a) $\sin t = 0.98$.

(c) $\tan 0 = 0$.

(e) $\sec t = -2$.

(b) $\cos t = -0.99$.

(d) $\cot \dfrac{\pi}{4} = 1$.

(f) $\csc t = 1.5$.

21. Find the product of $\sin \dfrac{\pi}{3} \cdot \cos \dfrac{11\pi}{6} \cdot \tan^3 \dfrac{\pi}{4}$.

22. Find the product of $\sec \dfrac{2\pi}{3} \cdot \csc\left(-\dfrac{\pi}{6}\right) \cdot \cot^2\left(-\dfrac{\pi}{4}\right)$.

23. Prepare a table of *exact* values obtained when the six circular functions are applied to these numbers:

$$0, \frac{\pi}{6}, \frac{\pi}{4}, \frac{\pi}{3}, \frac{\pi}{2}, \frac{2\pi}{3}, \frac{3\pi}{4}, \frac{5\pi}{6}, \pi, \frac{7\pi}{6}, \frac{5\pi}{4}, \frac{4\pi}{3}, \frac{3\pi}{2}, \frac{5\pi}{3}, \frac{7\pi}{4}, \frac{11\pi}{6}, 2\pi.$$

Keep this table for future reference.

24. In the list of numbers in Problem 23

(a) which numbers are quadrantal numbers?

(b) which numbers are multiples of $\dfrac{\pi}{3}$?

(c) which number is the corresponding arc of the arc that represents the number $\dfrac{65\pi}{4}$?

(d) the sine of which numbers has the value $-\dfrac{1}{\sqrt{2}}$?

(e) the cosine of which numbers has the value $-\dfrac{\sqrt{3}}{2}$?

25. Use Figure 7.13-1a to determine

(a) the range of the sine curve;
(b) the range of the cosecant curve;
(c) the ordered pairs that represent the intersection of the two curves.

26. Use Figure 7.13-1b to determine

(a) the range of the cosine curve;
(b) the range of the secant curve;
(c) the ordered pairs that represent the intersection of the two curves.

27. Use Figure 7.15-1c to determine

(a) the range of the tangent curve;
(b) the range of the cotangent curve;
(c) the common intersecting points of the two curves between 0 and π.

28. Use Figure 7.13-1c to determine

(a) the period of the tangent curve;
(b) the period of the cotangent curve;
(c) the inadmissible value of the domain of the tangent function between 0 and π.

7.15 THE EIGHT FUNDAMENTAL IDENTITIES AND THEIR APPLICATIONS

Definition 4.2-2 states that *an identical equation is an equation that is true for all admissible values of the variable.* Likewise,

   Definition: 7.15-1.   *A **trigonometric identity** is a statement that is true for every value of the real number t for which both sides of the equation are defined.*

   For example, the identity $\cot t = \dfrac{\cos t}{\sin t}$, which happens to be one of the circular function definitions, is not defined for $t = 0$, π, 2π, 3π, and so on. All numbers presented by $n\pi$, $n \in I$, are inadmissible values. With these exceptions, the equation is a trigonometric identity.

   There are literally thousands of trigonometric identities. One of our main interests in these identities is learning how to manipulate them so that we can transform complicated trigonometric expressions into simpler ones. For example, in the statement $\cot t = \dfrac{\cos t}{\sin t}$ it is much simpler to write $\cot t$ than $\dfrac{\cos t}{\sin t}$, or $\cos t$ than $\sin t \cot t$.

   From the unit circle in Figure 7.15-1 and the six circular functions, the

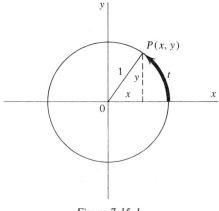

Figure 7.15-1

following *eight fundamental identities* can be easily justified. These eight basic identities should be memorized just as you have memorized the six circular functions.

The Eight Fundamental Identities

Ratio identities:

1. $\tan t = \dfrac{y}{x} = \dfrac{\sin t}{\cos t}$ $(\cos t \neq 0)$.

2. $\cot t = \dfrac{x}{y} = \dfrac{\cos t}{\sin t}$ $(\sin t \neq 0)$.

Reciprocal identities:

3. $\cot t = \dfrac{\cos t}{\sin t} = \dfrac{1}{\dfrac{\sin t}{\cos t}} = \dfrac{1}{\tan t}$ $(\tan t \neq 0)$.

4. $\sec t = \dfrac{1}{x} = \dfrac{1}{\cos t}$ $(\cos t \neq 0)$.

5. $\csc t = \dfrac{1}{y} = \dfrac{1}{\sin t}$ $(\sin t \neq 0)$.

Pythagorean relationships:

6. Since $y^2 + x^2 = 1$, then $\sin^2 t + \cos^2 t = 1$.

7. Since $1 + \dfrac{x^2}{y^2} = \dfrac{1}{y^2}$, then $1 + \cot^2 t = \csc^2 t$.

8. Since $1 + \dfrac{y^2}{x^2} = \dfrac{1}{x^2}$, then $1 + \tan^2 t = \sec^2 t$.

You should note that *each of the eight fundamental identities can be written in three different ways*, and you should practice writing them in these different forms. For example, by algebraic procedure

$$\tan t = \frac{\sin t}{\cos t} \qquad \text{or} \quad \sin t = \cos t \cdot \tan t \qquad \text{or} \quad \cos t = \frac{\sin t}{\tan t}.$$

$$\sin t = \frac{1}{\csc t} \qquad \text{or} \quad \sin t \cdot \csc t = 1 \qquad \text{or} \quad \csc t = \frac{1}{\sin t}.$$

$$\sin^2 t + \cos^2 t = 1 \quad \text{or} \quad \sin t = \pm\sqrt{1 - \cos^2 t} \quad \text{or} \quad \cos t = \pm\sqrt{1 - \sin^2 t}.$$

$$1 + \cot^2 t = \csc^2 t \quad \text{or} \quad \csc t = \pm\sqrt{1 + \cot^2 t} \quad \text{or} \quad \cot t = \pm\sqrt{\csc^2 t - 1}.$$

The verification of trigonometric identities may at first be frustrating to you, but in time it becomes fun. More important than the fun, of course, is the mathematical strength the verification of identities brings to you.

1. It helps you to master the other basic data of circular functions.
2. It helps you to simplify complicated equations.
3. It makes it possible for you to express all circular functions in terms of one of the functions. (See Example 7.15-1 that follows.)

4. It helps strengthen your trigonometric preparation for advanced mathematics courses.

Several examples are given to show you how trigonometric identities are verified by (a) using the eight fundamental identities, and (b) by performing the algebraic techniques necessary to simplify the expressions. The rest is up to you. You are to assume, of course, that the eight fundamental identities are true and therefore hold for all values of t for which the functions are defined.

Example: 7.15-1.   Express the other five circular functions in terms of sin t.

1. $\sin t = \sin t$.   (Given)

2. $\cos t = \pm\sqrt{1 - \sin^2 t}$.   [Fundamental identity (6)]

3. $\tan t = \dfrac{\sin t}{\cos t} = \dfrac{\sin t}{\pm\sqrt{1 - \sin^2 t}}$.   [*F. i.* (1) and (6)]

4. $\cot t = \dfrac{\cos t}{\sin t} = \dfrac{\pm\sqrt{1 - \sin^2 t}}{\sin t}$.   [*F. i.* (2) and (6)]

5. $\sec t = \dfrac{1}{\cos t} = \dfrac{1}{\pm\sqrt{1 - \sin^2 t}}$.   [*F. i.* (4) and (6)]

6. $\csc t = \dfrac{1}{\sin t}$.   [*F. i.* (5)]

In a similar manner the six circular functions can be expressed in terms of any other one of the circular functions.

Example: 7.15-2.   Prove that $\cos t - \sec t = -\sin t \tan t$.

In this identity we will make our changes on the right side only. By substituting $\dfrac{\sin t}{\cos t}$ for tan t we get

$$\cos t - \sec t = -(\sin t)\frac{\sin t}{\cos t}$$ [Fundamental identity (1)]

$$= -\frac{\sin^2 t}{\cos t}$$

$$= -\left(\frac{1 - \cos^2 t}{\cos t}\right)$$ [*F. i.* (6)]

$$= -\frac{1}{\cos t} + \frac{\cos^2 t}{\cos t}$$

$$= -\sec t + \cos t.$$ [*F. i.* (4)]

$\therefore$ **cos** $t -$ **sec** $t =$ **cos** $t -$ **sec** t.

Generally, no comment will be made concerning the algebraic procedures used in the examples in this section. It is assumed that they are familiar to you.

There are no definite rules for working identities. This is a learning situation in which one has to learn by doing. So, you should keep making substitutions such that each step will lead you to a less complicated expression. Ultimately you should be able to recognize that the left and right members of the identity are equivalent.

Identities can be proved in one of three ways:

1. By working only on the expression on the right side of the equality sign until it becomes identical to the expression on the left side (see Example 7.15-2).

2. By working only on the expression on the left side of the equality sign until it becomes identical to the expression on the right side (see Example 7.15-3).

3. By working on the expressions on both sides of the equality sign until the two members become identical (see Example 7.15-4).

Usually, it is best to work on the more complicated member of the identity. If all other approaches fail, try to change all the given functions to sines and/or cosines, then proceed. The latter procedure is longest but it may be easier for you to follow.

Example: 7.15-3.   Verify that

$$\cos^4 t - \sin^4 t = \cos^2 t - \sin^2 t.$$

It seems best to work with the left side of this identity.

$$(\cos^2 t)^2 - (\sin^2 t)^2 = \cos^2 t - \sin^2 t$$
$$(\cos^2 t + \sin^2 t)(\cos^2 t - \sin^2 t) = \cos^2 t - \sin^2 t \text{ (Factoring)}$$
$$(1)(\cos^2 t - \sin^2 t) = \cos^2 t - \sin^2 t \text{ [Fundamental identity (6)]}$$
$$\therefore \ \mathbf{\cos^2 t - \sin^2 t = \cos^2 t - \sin^2 t.}$$

Example: 7.15-4.   Prove that

$$\sin^2 t \sec^2 t = \sec^2 t - 1.$$

In this example we will attempt to reduce both sides to a common number.

$$\sin^2 t \frac{1}{\cos^2 t} = \frac{1}{\cos^2 t} - 1 \qquad\qquad \text{[Fundamental identity (4)]}$$

$$\tan^2 t = \frac{1 - \cos^2 t}{\cos^2 t} \qquad\qquad [F.\,i.\,(1)]$$

$$\tan^2 t = \frac{\sin^2 t}{\cos^2 t} \qquad\qquad [F.\,i.\,(6)]$$

$$\therefore \quad \mathbf{\tan^2 t = \tan^2 t.} \qquad\qquad [F.\,i.\,(1)]$$

Example: 7.15-5. Verify that

$$\frac{\sec t}{\sin t} - \frac{2 \sin t}{\cos t} = \cot t - \tan t.$$

Here again both sides of the identity will be simplified and the necessary algebraic steps will be taken to bring both members of the identity to some common number.

$$\frac{\sec t \cos t - 2 \sin t \sin t}{\sin t \cos t} = \frac{\cos t}{\sin t} - \frac{\sin t}{\cos t} \qquad \text{[Fundamental identities (1) and (2)]}$$

$$\frac{1 - 2 \sin^2 t}{\sin t \cos t} = \frac{\cos^2 t - \sin^2 t}{\sin t \cos t} \qquad [F.\,i.\,(4)]$$

$$\frac{1 - 2 \sin^2 t}{\sin t \cos t} = \frac{(1 - \sin^2 t) - \sin^2 t}{\sin t \cos t} \qquad [F.\,i.\,(6)]$$

$$\therefore \qquad \mathbf{1 - 2 \sin^2 t = 1 - 2 \sin^2 t.} \qquad [E_5]$$

Example: 7.15-6. Prove that

$$\sin t + \cos t = \frac{\sin t}{1 - \cot t} + \frac{\cos t}{1 - \tan t}.$$

The more complicated expression is on the right side of this identity; so we will substitute the needed fundamental identity and apply the algebraic procedure necessary to transform it into $\sin t + \cos t$.

$$\sin t + \cos t = \frac{\sin t}{1 - \dfrac{\cos t}{\sin t}} + \frac{\cos t}{1 - \dfrac{\sin t}{\cos t}} \qquad \text{[Fundamental identities (1) and (2)]}$$

$$= \frac{\sin^2 t}{\sin t - \cos t} + \frac{\cos^2 t}{\cos t - \sin t}$$

$$= \frac{\sin^2 t - \cos^2 t}{\sin t - \cos t}$$

$$= \frac{(\sin t + \cos t)(\sin t - \cos t)}{\sin t - \cos t}.$$

$$\therefore \mathbf{\sin t + \cos t = \sin t + \cos t.}$$

EXERCISE 7.D

Verify the following identities for all admissible values of t:

1. $\cot t = \cos t \csc t$ **2.** $\sin t = \cos t \tan t$

3. $\dfrac{\cos t}{1 - \sin t} = \dfrac{1 + \sin t}{\cos t}.$

7. $(1 - \sin^2 t)(1 + \tan^2 t) = 1.$

4. $1 - \sin t = \dfrac{\cos^2 t}{1 + \sin t}.$

8. $\csc^2 t - \sec^2 t = \cot^2 t - \tan^2 t.$

5. $\dfrac{\cos t}{\sec t} = 1 - \dfrac{\sin t}{\csc t}.$

9. $\tan^2 t - \sin^2 t = \tan^2 t \sin^2 t.$

6. $\dfrac{1}{\csc^2 t} = 1 - \dfrac{1}{\sec^2 t}.$

10. $\cot^2 t - \cos^2 t = \cot^2 t \cos^2 t.$

Transform the first expression into the second one.

11. $(1 - \cos t)(1 + \cos t)$ into $\sin^2 t.$

12. $(\sec t - 1)(\sec t + 1)$ into $\tan^2 t.$

13. $\dfrac{1 + \cot^2 t}{\sec t}$ into $\csc t \cot t.$

14. $\cot t + \csc t$ into $\dfrac{1 + \cos t}{\sin t}.$

15. $\dfrac{\cos t}{\sin t} - \dfrac{\csc t}{\cos t}$ into $\tan(-t).$

16. $\dfrac{\sin t}{\cos t} - \csc t \sec t$ into $\cot(-t).$

Prove the following identities:

17. $\dfrac{\cot t + 1}{\cot t - 1} = \dfrac{1 + \tan t}{1 - \tan t}.$

18. $\dfrac{\cos t - 1}{\cos t + 1} = \dfrac{1 - \sec t}{1 + \sec t}.$

19. $(\tan t + \cot t)(\sin t + \cos t) = \csc t + \sec t.$

20. $(\sec t - \csc t)(\cos t + \sin t) = \tan t - \cot t.$

21. $\sin t \cos t \cot t + \sin t \cos t \tan t = 1.$

22. $(\sin t - \cos t)^2 + (\sin t + \cos t)^2 = 2.$

23. $\dfrac{\csc t + \cot t}{\tan t + \sin t} = \cot t \csc t.$

24. $\dfrac{1 + \sec t}{1 - \sec t} = \dfrac{\tan t + \sin t}{\sin t - \tan t}.$

25. $\sin t \tan t = \sec t - \cos t.$

26. $2 \tan^2 t + 1 = \sec^4 t - \tan^4 t.$

27. $\sin t + \cos t = \dfrac{\sin t}{1 - \cot t} + \dfrac{\cos t}{1 - \tan t}.$

28. $\dfrac{\cos t}{1 - \cos^2 t} = \dfrac{\cot t + \csc t}{\tan t + \sin t}.$

29. $(1 - \cos t)(2 - 2 \sin t) = (1 - \sin t - \cos t)^2.$

30. $\tan t \sin^2 t = \dfrac{\sin t}{\cos t} - \sin t \cos t.$

7.16 TRIGONOMETRIC EQUATIONS

In this section we will attempt to find the numbers that satisfy equations that contain circular functions.

Definition: 7.16-1. *An equation that contains circular functions "of unknown real numbers" is called a* **trigonometric equation.**

A trigonometric equation differs from a trigonometric identity in that it is not true for all admissible values of the variable. It is a conditional equation (see Definition 4.2-1) and therefore selects from its universal set only those values that make the equation true. For this reason it becomes necessary to check each value for t to see whether or not it satisfies the equation.

When we say "solve a trigonometric equation," we mean for you to find all the real numbers that satisfy the equation, within the limits specified. In general, a trigonometric equation has an unlimited number of solutions. The principal solutions (or roots) desired may be found

(a) by algebraic processes—such as factoring, correctly treating both sides of the equality the same, correctly taking powers and roots, clearing of fractions, etc;

(b) by circular function transformations—such as using $\sec^2 t$ for $1 + \tan^2 t$, using 1 for $\sin t \csc t$, etc.;

(c) by a combination of both (a) and (b) above.

Three distinct steps are involved in solving a trigonometric equation:

STEP 1.   Reduce the given equation to one or more simple trigonometric equations.

STEP 2.   Determine the value of the real number (or numbers) that satisfies each simple equation.

STEP 3.   Check each number obtained to see if it satisfies the given trigonometric equation.

Unless otherwise stated, we shall restrict our solutions of trigonometric equations to numbers where $0 \le t \le 2\pi$. Our reason for doing this is that *coterminal numbers have the same circular function values* (see Definition 7.14-c). This means that $t + 2\pi n$, where $n = 1, 2, \ldots$, is a solution whenever t is a solution.

Example: 7.16-1.   Solve the trigonometric equation

$\sin t = \cos t \quad (0 \le t \le 2\pi).$

Obviously, $\sin t = \cos t$ is not a trigonometric identity because $\sin 0 \neq \cos 0$. Also, $\sin \dfrac{\pi}{3} \neq \cos \dfrac{\pi}{3}$. Actually, it only requires one counterexample to prove that $\sin t = \cos t$ is not a trigonometric identity.

STEP 1. $\sin t = \cos t.$ (Given)

$\dfrac{\sin t}{\cos t} = 1,$ (Dividing by $\cos t \neq 0$)

$\tan t = 1.$ [Fundamental identity (1)]

STEP 2.   If $\tan t = 1$, then it follows that

$t = \dfrac{\pi}{4} \quad \text{or} \quad t = \dfrac{5\pi}{4}.$

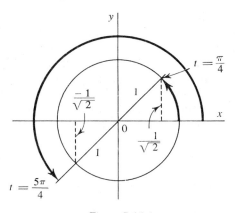

Figure 7.16-1

STEP 3.   Check, using Figure 7.16-1.

$\sin \dfrac{\pi}{4} = \dfrac{1}{\sqrt{2}} \quad \text{and } \cos \dfrac{\pi}{4} = \dfrac{1}{\sqrt{2}},$

$\therefore \sin \dfrac{\pi}{4} = \cos \dfrac{\pi}{4}.$

$\sin \dfrac{5\pi}{4} = -\dfrac{1}{\sqrt{2}} \quad \text{and } \cos \dfrac{5\pi}{4} = -\dfrac{1}{\sqrt{2}},$

$\therefore \sin \dfrac{5\pi}{4} = \cos \dfrac{5\pi}{4}.$

Before proceeding to the next example, let us consider *how to read the Circular Function table*. Table I on page 390 was constructed by using the infinite sine and cosine series. It is easy enough to find in Table I the values of the circular functions for numbers such as

$$\sin 0.30 \doteq 0.2955, \qquad \cot 1.00 \doteq 0.6421, \qquad \csc 1.57 \doteq 0.0008.$$

But it is not so easy if the function involves a real number not listed in the table. For example, what is the value of sin 1.054? In addition to Table I the answer to this question requires the use of *linear interpolation*.

Definition: 7.16-2.   Linear interpolation *is a process based upon proportion which uses the value of consecutive entries in a table to compute the approximate value of the function of a number that falls between the two consecutive entries.* (The process, of course, is reversible.)

Thus, from Table I

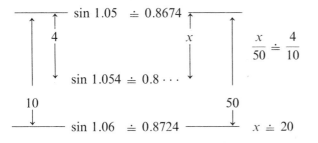

$$\therefore \; \textbf{sin 1.054} \doteq \textbf{0.8694}, \qquad \text{by linear interpolation.}$$

Next, let us consider the equation $\sin t \doteq 0.800\overline{0}$ which will make its appearance in Example 7.16-2. No number for t where $\sin t \doteq 0.800\overline{0}$ is given in the body of Table I; so here again we must use linear interpolation.

From Table I we read

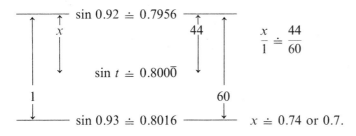

The result of the proportion means that x is seven-tenths of the change between 0.92 and 0.93 and $t \doteq 0.927$.

$$\therefore \; \textbf{sin 0.927} \doteq \textbf{0.800}\overline{\textbf{0}}.$$

Note that in a unit circle $\sin t = 0.800\bar{0}$ can also represent an arc that ends in Quadrant II. In this case $\sin(\pi - 0.927) \doteq \sin(3.142 - 0.927)$.

$\therefore$ **$\sin 2.215 \doteq 0.800\bar{0}$.**

Example: 7.16-2.   Find all roots of the trigonometric equation

$\cos t = 1 - 2 \sin t$ $(0 \le t \le 2\pi)$.

STEP 1. $\cos^2 t = 1 - 4 \sin t + 4 \sin^2 t$,   (Squaring both members)

$1 - \sin^2 t = 1 - 4 \sin t + 4 \sin^2 t$,   [$F. i. (6)$]

$5 \sin^2 t - 4 \sin t = 0$,

$\sin t (5 \sin t - 4) = 0$,

$\sin t = 0$ or $\sin t = \frac{4}{5} \doteq 0.800\bar{0}$.

STEP 2.   If $\sin t = 0$, then **$t = 0$** or **$t = \pi$** (see Figure 7.16-2a). If $\sin t =$

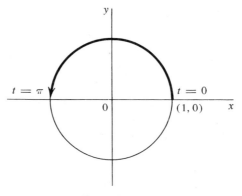

Figure 7.16-2a

$0.800\bar{0}$, then from Table I

$t \doteq 0.927$ or   **$t \doteq (\pi - 0.927) \doteq 2.215$** (see Figure 7.16-2b).

STEP 3.   Check the following:
Substituting $t = 0$ in

$\cos t = 1 - 2 \sin t$
gives $\cos 0 = 1 - 2 \sin 0$
or $1 = 1$.
$\therefore$ **$t = 0$ is a root.**

Substituting $t = \pi$ into $\cos t = 1 - 2 \sin t$ gives

$\cos \pi = 1 - 2 \sin \pi$
$-1 \ne 1 - 0$.

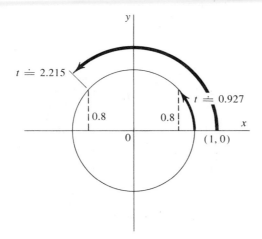

Figure 7.16-2b

∴ *t* = π **is not a root**.

Substituting *t* ≐ 0.927 into cos *t* = 1 − 2 sin *t* gives

$$\cos 0.927 \doteq 1 - 2 \sin 0.297.$$
Using Table I $0.6002 \doteq 1 - 2(0.7998),$
and $0.6002 \neq 1 - 1.5996,$
but $0.6 \neq -0.6.$

∴ *t* ≐ **0.927 is not a root**.

Substituting *t* ≐ 2.215 into cos *t* = 1 − 2 sin *t* gives

$$\cos 2.215 \doteq 1 - 2(\sin 2.215),$$
$$-0.6002 \doteq 1 - 1.5996,$$
and $-0.6 \doteq -0.6.$
∴ *t* ≐ **2.215 is a root**.

Example: 7.16-3.   Solve the quadratic trigonometric equation

$$2 \sec^2 t - 3 \sec t - 2 = 0 \qquad (0 \le t \le 2\pi).$$

STEP 1. $(2 \sec t + 1)(\sec t - 2) = 0,$ (Factoring)
$$2 \sec t + 1 = 0,$$
$$\sec t - 2 = 0,$$
so $\sec t = 2$ and $\sec t = -\frac{1}{2}.$

STEP 2.   If sec *t* = 2, then

$$t = \frac{\pi}{3} \text{ in Quadrant I}$$

and $t = \dfrac{5\pi}{3}$ in Quadrant IV (see Figure 7.16-3).

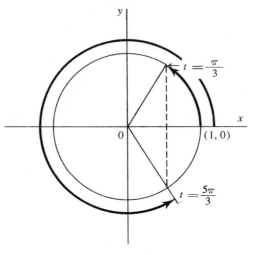

Figure 7.16-3

If sec $t = -\frac{1}{2}$, t is not defined. The value of the secant of a real number can never fall between -1 and $+1$.

STEP 3.   Check. Substituting $\pi/3$ into $2 \sec^2 t - 3 \sec t - 2 = 0$ gives

$$2 \sec^2 \frac{\pi}{3} - 3 \sec \frac{\pi}{3} - 2 = 0,$$

$$2(4) - 3(2) - 2 = 0,$$

and $8 - 8 = 0$

$\therefore t = \dfrac{\pi}{3}$ is a solution.

$t = \dfrac{5\pi}{3}$ is also a solution. Check it out to be sure.

Keep in mind that in each of the preceding examples whenever t is a solution $(t + 2\pi n)$, where $n = 1, 2, \ldots$, can also be a solution for all $t > 2\pi$.

EXERCISE 7.E

Solve each of the following trigonometric equations for all possible solutions of t, where $0 \le t \le 2\pi$. Check each answer.

1. $2 \sin t - \sqrt{3} = 0$.
2. $\sec t + \sqrt{2} = 0$.
3. $\sqrt{3} \tan t + 1 = 0$.
4. $\frac{1}{2} \csc t + 1 = 0$.
5. $5 \cos t - \sin t = 0$.

6. $3 \sin^2 t - \sin t - 2 = 0$.
7. $3 \tan t = 4 \sin t$.
8. $1 + \cot t = \csc^2 t$.
9. $7 - \cos t = 8 \sin t$.
10. $\sin t + \cos t = 1$.

11. $\tan^2 t = 3 \tan t - 2$.

12. $1 - \cos^2 t = 0.5$.

13. $\cot^2 t + \cot t = 0$.

14. $\csc^2 t - 1 = \sqrt{3}$.

15. $\sin^2 t = 1 - 2 \sin t \cos t$.

16. $1 - 2 \sin^2 t + \sin t = 0$.

17. $3 \tan^2 t + 3 \cot^2 t = 10$.

18. $2 \cos^2 t + \cos t - 1 = 0$.

19. $5 \tan t = 2(\tan t - 1)$.

20. $4 \sin^4 t - 3 \sin^2 t = 0$.

21. $\sin^2 t - 1 = 3 \cot t \cos t - 2 \cos^2 t$.

22. $\sec^2 t - \cos^2 t \sec^2 t = 3 \tan t - 2$.

23. $2 \cos^2 t - \cos t = 2 \sin t \cos t - \sin t$.

24. $\tan^2 t - 3 = 3 \cos t - \cos t \tan^2 t$.

25. $4 \sec^2 t + \cos^2 t - \sin^2 t = \dfrac{4}{1 + \tan^2 t}$.

26. $6 \cot t \cos t - 24 \tan t \sin t = 0$.

7.17 CIRCULAR FUNCTION IDENTITIES INVOLVING COMBINATIONS OF NUMBERS

The six circular function definitions and the eight fundamental identities all deal with circular functions of **single numbers.** We are now about to develop formulas that will deal with the **sum of two numbers** such as $\sin(s + t)$; the **difference of two numbers,** such as $\cos(s - t)$; **double the number,** such as $\tan 2t$; and **half the number,** such as $\cos \dfrac{t}{2}$. These more general circular function formulas are of considerable importance and will be used extensively in this course, in analytic geometry, in calculus, and in other higher mathematics.

One of our main objectives in the next several pages is to prove that circular functions containing more than one number are equivalent to expressions containing circular functions of single numbers. As examples:

$$\tan(s + t) = \frac{\tan s + \tan t}{1 - \tan s \tan t},$$

and $\cos(s - t) = \cos s \cos t + \sin s \sin t$.

In mathematics you never multiply a word, such as "cosine," through parentheses. For example, you would never write $\cos(s - t) = \cos s - \cos t$. The word "cosine" is prefixed to $(s - t)$ to make it possible for you to identify and define a specific circular function. The function $\cos(s - t)$ means cosine *of* $(s - t)$ but never cosine *times* $(s - t)$.

7.17-1 Distance Formula Between Two Points

At this point the **distance formula** for finding the distance between two points will be derived in order that we might make use of it in the proof of

$$\cos(s - t) = \cos s \sin t + \sin s \cos t.$$

Take any two points A and B in the plane as shown in Figure 7.17-1a. Project A and B perpendicularly on the x axis into M_1 and M_2 and on the y axis into

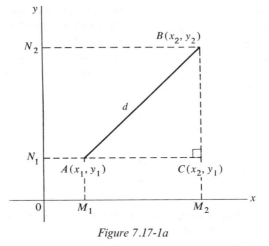

Figure 7.17-1a

N_1 and N_2. Then the intersection of BM_2 and the extension of N_1A at C will form a right angle and by the Pythagorean theorem

$$(AB)^2 = (AC)^2 + (CB)^2$$
$$= (M_1M_2)^2 + (N_1N_2)^2,$$
$$\therefore \ AB = \sqrt{(M_1M_2)^2 + (N_1N_2)^2}.$$

Definition: 7.17-1a.   *The distance between* **two points** *on a coordinate axis, such as M_1M_2 in Figure 7.17-1a is the absolute value of the difference between their coordinates.*

By Definition 7.17-1a $M_1M_2 = |x_2 - x_1|$ and $N_1N_2 = |y_2 - y_1|$ and therefore,

$$AB = d = \sqrt{(x_2 - x_1)^2 + (y_2 - y_1)^2}. \qquad \text{(Distance formula)}$$

7.17-2 Cosine of the Difference of Two Numbers

As indicated by Figure 7.17-2a, the coordinates at the end point of arc t are P_t (cos t, sin t) and the coordinates at the end point of arc s are P_s (cos s, sin s).

The difference of the two arc lengths in the unit circle is $s - t$ and the chord which corresponds to this difference is P_sP_t. Using the formula for finding the distance between two points, and letting $x_1 = \cos t$, $y_1 = \sin t$, $x_2 = \cos s$, and $y_2 = \sin s$, we get

$$P_sP_t = \sqrt{(\cos s - \cos t)^2 + (\sin s - \sin t)^2},$$
$$= \sqrt{\cos^2 s - 2 \cos s \cos t + \cos^2 t + \sin^2 s - 2 \sin s \sin t + \sin^2 t}.$$

Since $\cos^2 s + \sin^2 s = 1$ and $\cos^2 t + \sin^2 t = 1$ by Fundamental identity (6),

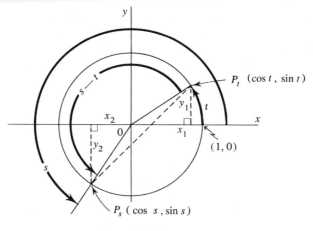

Figure 7.17-2a

then

$$P_s P_t = \sqrt{2 - 2(\cos s \cos t + \sin s \sin t)}.$$

Next consider Figure 7.17-2b which is an exact duplicate of Figure 7.17-2a

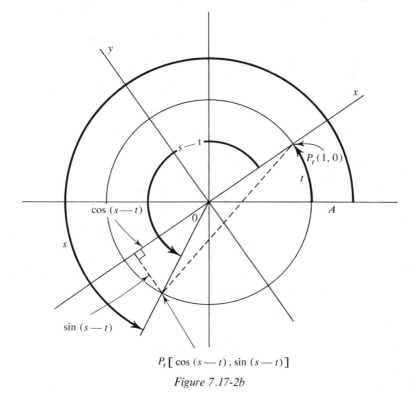

Figure 7.17-2b

except that the coordinate system has been rotated so that the positive side of the x axis passes through the terminal point of the arc t at P_t. Under this rotation the coordinates of P_t are $(1, 0)$ and the coordinates of P_s are $[\cos(s - t), \sin(s - t)]$. Again, computing the length of the chord P_sP_t, which corresponds to the difference of the two arc lengths, we get

$$P_sP_t = \sqrt{[\cos(s - t) - 1]^2 + [\sin(s - t) - 0]^2},$$

$$= \sqrt{\cos^2(s - t) - 2\cos(s - t) + 1 + \sin^2(s - t)}.$$

By fundamental identity (6), $\cos^2(s - t) + \sin^2(s - t) = 1$. Therefore, $P_sP_t = \sqrt{2 - 2\cos(s - t)}$.

We have proved P_sP_t to be equivalent to two different expressions. Then it follows by the transitive law that

$$\sqrt{2 - 2\cos(s - t)} = \sqrt{2 - 2(\cos s \cos t + \sin s \sin t)}.$$

Squaring both members of this identity and simplifying these results

$$2 - 2\cos(s - t) = 2 - 2(\cos s \cos t + \sin s \sin t).$$

Therefore,

$$\cos(s - t) = \cos s \cos t + \sin s \sin t.$$

Thus, we have reached one of our objectives, which was to prove that the circular function of two or more numbers can be expressed as circular functions of the given numbers taken singly. Specifically, we have proved this theorem:

Theorem: 7.17-2a. The cosine of the difference of two numbers is equal to the sum of the product of the cosines of the two numbers and the product of the sines of the two numbers.

The cosine of the difference of two numbers, namely,

$$\cos(s - t) = \cos s \cos t + \sin s \sin t,$$

is one of the most basic and valuable formulas in all trigonometry. Now that its proof has been validated we can use it to prove the validity of the circular functions of negative numbers in terms of their corresponding positive numbers (see Section 7.14) and to prove a large number of other relationships. All the identities that are directly or indirectly derived from $\cos(s - t)$ in the following pages should be thoroughly memorized.

7.17-3 Prove that $\cos(-t) = \cos t$

PROOF: Assume $s = 0$ and substitute 0 for s in

$$\cos(s - t) = \cos s \cos t + \sin s \sin t.$$

Then $\cos(0 - t) = \cos 0 \cos t + \sin 0 \sin t,$

$$\cos(-t) = 1 \cdot \cos t + 0 \cdot \sin t,$$

and $\quad$ **$\cos(-t) = \cos t$** $\qquad\qquad$ (even function, see Definition 7.6-2).

7.17-4 Prove that $\cos\left(\dfrac{\pi}{2} - t\right) = \sin t$

PROOF:$\quad$ Assume $s = \pi/2$ and substitute $\pi/2$ for s in

$$\cos(s - t) = \cos s \cos t + \sin s \sin t,$$

Then $\cos\left(\dfrac{\pi}{2} - t\right) = \cos \dfrac{\pi}{2} \cos t + \sin \dfrac{\pi}{2} \sin t,$

$$\cos\left(\dfrac{\pi}{2} - t\right) = (0)(\cos t) + (1) \sin t,$$

and $\quad$ $\cos\left(\dfrac{\pi}{2} - t\right) = \sin t.$

7.17-5 Prove that $\sin(-t) = -\sin t$

PROOF:$\quad$ Assume $t = -t$ and substitute $-t$ for t in

$$\cos\left(\dfrac{\pi}{2} - t\right) = \sin t.$$

Then $\qquad\qquad \cos\left[\dfrac{\pi}{2} - (-t)\right] = \sin(-t),$

$$\cos\left(\dfrac{\pi}{2} + t\right) = \sin(-t),$$

$$\cos\left[t - \left(-\dfrac{\pi}{2}\right)\right] = \sin(-t),$$

$$\cos t \cos\left(-\dfrac{\pi}{2}\right) + \sin t \sin\left(-\dfrac{\pi}{2}\right) = \sin(-t),$$

$$\cos t \cdot (0) + \sin t \cdot (-1) = \sin(-t),$$

$$-\sin t = \sin(-t),$$

and $\qquad\qquad$ **$\sin(-t) = -\sin t.$** $\qquad\qquad$ (an odd function, see Definition 7.6-1).

7.17-6 Prove that $\tan(-t) = -\tan t$

PROOF:$\quad$ $\tan(-t) = \dfrac{\sin(-t)}{\cos(-t)} = \dfrac{-\sin t}{\cos t} = -\tan t,$

and $\tan(-t) = -\tan t$ (an odd function).

7.17-7 Prove that cot $(-t) = -\cot t$

The proof is left for the reader.

7.17-8 Prove that sin$\left(\dfrac{\pi}{2} - t\right) = \cos t$

PROOF: Assume $t = \dfrac{\pi}{2} - t$ and substitute $\left(\dfrac{\pi}{2} - t\right)$ for t in

$$\cos\left(\frac{\pi}{2} - t\right) = \sin t.$$

Then $\cos\left[\dfrac{\pi}{2} - \left(\dfrac{\pi}{2} - t\right)\right] = \sin\left(\dfrac{\pi}{2} - t\right),$

$$\cos t = \sin\left(\frac{\pi}{2} - t\right),$$

and $\sin\left(\dfrac{\pi}{2} - t\right) = \cos t.$

7.17-9 Prove that tan $\left(\dfrac{\pi}{2} - t\right) = \cot t$

PROOF: $\tan\left(\dfrac{\pi}{2} - t\right) = \dfrac{\sin\left(\dfrac{\pi}{2} - t\right)}{\cos\left(\dfrac{\pi}{2} - t\right)} = \dfrac{\cos t}{\sin t} = \cot t,$

and $\tan\left(\dfrac{\pi}{2} - t\right) = \cot t.$

7.17-10 Prove that cot $\left(\dfrac{\pi}{2} - t\right) = \tan t$

The proof is left for the reader.

7.17-11 Prove that cos $(s + t) = \cos s \cos t - \sin s \sin t$

PROOF: Assume $t = -t$ and substitute $-t$ for t in

$$\cos(s - t) = \cos s \cos t + \sin s \sin t.$$

$$\cos[s - (-t)] = \cos t \cos(-t) + \sin t \sin(-t)$$

Then $\cos(s + t) = \cos s \cos t - \sin s \sin t.$

7.17-12 Prove that sin(s + t) = sin s cos t + cos s sin t

PROOF: Assume $t = s + t$ and substitute $(s + t)$ for t in

$$\sin t = \cos\left(\frac{\pi}{2} - t\right).$$

Then $\sin(s + t) = \cos\left[\dfrac{\pi}{2} - (s + t)\right]$

$$= \cos\left[\left(\frac{\pi}{2} - s\right) - t\right],$$

$$= \cos\left(\frac{\pi}{2} - s\right)\cos t + \sin\left(\frac{\pi}{2} - s\right)\sin t,$$

and $\sin(s + t) = \sin s \cos t + \cos s \sin t.$

7.17-13 Prove that sin(s − t) = sin s cos t − cos s sin t

PROOF: Assume $t = -t$ and substitute $-t$ for t in

$\sin(s + t) = \sin s \cos t + \cos s \sin t.$
Then $\sin(s - t) = \sin s \cos(-t) + \sin s \sin(-t),$
and $\sin(s - t) = \sin s \cos t - \cos s \sin t.$

7.17-14 Prove that $\tan(s + t) = \dfrac{\tan s + \tan t}{1 - \tan s \tan t}$

PROOF: $\tan(s + t) = \dfrac{\sin(s + t)}{\cos(s + t)},$

$$= \frac{\sin s \cos t + \cos s \sin t}{\cos s \cos t - \sin s \sin t}.$$

The proof is complete except that a mathematician wants his formulas expressed in the most convenient form. So in this case he would continue by dividing each term in the numerator and the denominator by $\cos s \cos t$, where $\cos s \cos t \neq 0$.

Then $\tan(s + t) = \dfrac{\dfrac{\sin s \cos t}{\cos s \cos t} + \dfrac{\cos s \sin t}{\cos s \cos t}}{\dfrac{\cos s \cos t}{\cos s \cos t} - \dfrac{\sin s \sin t}{\cos s \cos t}},$

and $\tan(s + t) = \dfrac{\tan s + \tan t}{1 - \tan s \tan t}.$

7.17-15 Prove that $\cot(s + t) = \dfrac{\cot s \cot t - 1}{\cot s + \cot t}$

The proof is left for the reader.

7.17-16 Prove that $\tan(s - t) = \dfrac{\tan s - \tan t}{1 + \tan s \tan t}$

The proof is left for the reader. (Assume $t = -t$ and substitute $(-t)$ for t in Section 7.17-14.)

7.17-17 Prove that $\cot(s - t) = \dfrac{\cot s \cot t + 1}{\cot t - \cot s}$

The proof is left for the reader. (Assume $t = -t$ and substitute $-t$ for t in Section 7.17-15.)

In general, *the identity formulas for cotangents, secants, and cosecants will not be proved, because by reciprocal relations they can readily be obtained from the sines, cosines, and tangents.*

If in the identities $\sin(s + t)$, $\cos(s + t)$, and $\tan(s + t)$ we substitute t for s we get the **circular functions of double a number.**

7.17-18 Prove that $\sin 2t = 2 \sin t \cos t$

PROOF: Assume $s = t$ and substitute t for s in

$$\sin(s + t) = \sin s \cos t + \cos s \sin t.$$
Then $\sin(t + t) = \sin t \cos t + \cos t \sin t$,
and $\sin 2t = 2 \sin t \cos t.$

7.17-19 Prove that $\cos 2t = \cos^2 t - \sin^2 t = 1 - 2 \sin^2 t$
$= 2 \cos^2 t - 1$

PROOF: Assume $s = t$ and substitute t for s in

$$\cos(s + t) = \cos s \cos t - \sin s \sin t.$$
Then $\cos(t + t) = \cos t \cos t - \sin t \sin t$,
and $\cos 2t = \cos^2 t - \sin^2 t.$

In $\cos 2t = \cos^2 t - \sin^2 t$ substitute $(1 - \sin^2 t)$ for $\cos^2 t$.

Then $\cos 2t = 1 - \sin^2 t - \sin^2 t$,
and $\cos 2t = 1 - 2 \sin^2 t.$

In $\cos 2t = \cos^2 t - \sin^2 t$ substitute $(1 - \cos^2 t)$ for $\sin^2 t$.

Then $\cos 2t = \cos^2 t - (1 - \cos^2 t)$,
and $\cos 2t = 2 \cos^2 t - 1.$

7.17-20 Prove that $\tan 2t = \dfrac{2 \tan t}{1 - \tan^2 t}$

The proof is left for the reader.

In the formulas in 7.17-18, 19, and 20 notice that the right-hand part of the formula has a single t, but the left-hand member always has twice that t. This is why we call these formulas "double number" formulas.

In the next three formulas the right-hand part of the formulas will have a single t but the left member will have $\dfrac{t}{2}$ for its argument. So these formulas have been named **half a number formulas.**

7.17-21 Prove that $\sin\dfrac{t}{2} = \pm\sqrt{\dfrac{1-\cos t}{2}}$

PROOF: Assume $t = t/2$ and substitute $t/2$ for t in

$$\cos 2t = 1 - 2\sin^2 t.$$

Then $\cos 2\left(\dfrac{t}{2}\right) = 1 - 2\sin^2\left(\dfrac{t}{2}\right)$

$$\sin^2\frac{t}{2} = \frac{1-\cos t}{2},$$

and $\sin\dfrac{t}{2} = \pm\sqrt{\dfrac{1-\cos t}{2}}$ or $\left|\sin\dfrac{t}{2}\right| = \sqrt{\dfrac{1-\cos t}{2}}.$

7.17-22 Prove that $\cos\dfrac{t}{2} = \pm\sqrt{\dfrac{1+\cos t}{2}}$

PROOF: Assume $t = t/2$ and substitute $t/2$ for t in

$$\cos 2t = 2\cos^2 t - 1.$$

Then $\cos 2\left(\dfrac{t}{2}\right) = 2\cos^2\dfrac{t}{2} - 1,$

$$\cos t - 2\cos^2\frac{t}{2} = -1,$$

$$\cos^2\frac{t}{2} = \frac{1+\cos t}{2},$$

and $\cos\dfrac{t}{2} = \pm\sqrt{\dfrac{1+\cos t}{2}}$ or $\left|\cos\dfrac{t}{2}\right| = \sqrt{\dfrac{1+\cos t}{2}}.$

7.17-23 Prove that $\tan\dfrac{t}{2} = \pm\sqrt{\dfrac{1-\cos t}{1+\cos t}} = \dfrac{\sin t}{1+\cos t}$

$$= \frac{1-\cos t}{\sin t} \quad \text{or} \quad \left|\tan\frac{t}{2}\right| = \sqrt{\frac{1-\cos t}{1+\cos t}}$$

The proofs are left for the reader. Use Sections 7.17-21 and 7.17-22.

In some of the advanced courses in mathematics and in certain computations involving circular functions, it is often desirable and helpful to be able to express the *product of two circular functions in terms of their sum or their difference,* and the *sum or difference of functions in terms of their product*. So we will use appropriate identities, from those we have already proved, to develop some **basic identities that relate products, sums, and differences.**

7.17-24 Prove that sin s cos t = $\frac{1}{2}$[sin(s + t) + sin(s − t)]

PROOF: Take $\sin(s + t) = \sin s \cos t + \cos s \sin t$,

and $\sin(s - t) = \sin s \cos t - \cos s \sin t$.

Add $\sin(s + t) + \sin(s - t) = 2 \sin s \cos t$ and solve for $\sin s \cos t$ to get

sin s cos t = $\frac{1}{2}$[sin(s + t) + sin(s − t)].

7.17-25 Prove that cos s sin t = $\frac{1}{2}$[sin(s + t) − sin(s − t)]

PROOF: Take $\sin(s + t) = \sin s \cos t + \cos s \sin t$,

and $\sin(s - t) = \sin s \cos t - \cos s \sin t$.

Subtract $\sin(s + t) - \sin(s - t) = 2 \cos s \sin t$. Then

cos s sin t = $\frac{1}{2}$[sin(s + t) − sin(s − t)].

7.17-26 Prove that cos s cos t = $\frac{1}{2}$[cos(s + t) + cos(s − t)]

The proof is left for the reader. (Hint: Add $\cos(s + t)$ and $\cos(s - t)$, similar to Section 7.17-24.)

7.17-27 Prove that sin t sin t = $-\frac{1}{2}$[cos(s + t) − cos(s − t)]

The proof is left for the reader. (Hint: Subtract $\cos(s - t)$ from $\cos(s + t)$, similar to Section 7.17-25.)

Because products can be calculated by logarithms much easier than can sums, the product identities developed in Sections 7.17-24 to 7.17-27 can readily be transformed into sum identities by assuming that $u = s + t$ and $v = s - t$. Then, solve

$$\left.\begin{array}{l} s + t = u \\ s - t = v \end{array}\right\} \text{simultaneously to get } s = \frac{u + v}{2} \text{ and } t = \frac{u - v}{2}.$$

These relations for s, t, u, and v will be used to prove Sections 7.17-28 to 7.17-31.

7.17-28 Prove that sin u + sin v = $2 \sin \dfrac{u + v}{2} \cos \dfrac{u - v}{2}$

PROOF: Rewrite $\sin s \cos t = \frac{1}{2}[\sin(s + t) + \sin(s - t)]$ as

$\sin(s + t) + \sin(s - t) = 2 \sin s \cos t$

and substitute the s, t, u, and v relations. Then

sin u + sin v = $2 \sin \dfrac{u + v}{2} \cos \dfrac{u - v}{2}$.

7.17-29 Prove that sin u − sin v = 2 cos $\dfrac{u + v}{2}$ sin $\dfrac{u - v}{2}$

The proof is left for the reader.

7.17-30 Prove that cos u + cos v = 2 cos $\dfrac{u + v}{2}$ cos $\dfrac{u - v}{2}$

PROOF: Rewrite cos s cos t = $\frac{1}{2}$[cos(s + t) + cos(s − t)] as

cos(s + t) $+$ cos(s − t) = 2 cos s cos t,

and substitute the s, t, u, and v relations. Then

$$\cos u + \cos v = 2 \cos \frac{u + v}{2} \cos \frac{u - v}{2}.$$

7.17-31 Prove that cos u − cos v = −2 sin $\dfrac{u + v}{2}$ sin $\dfrac{u - v}{2}$

The proof is left for the reader.

   It is hoped that the development of these basic identities in one continuous block will mean that by the time you have studied them you will either have them memorized or that you will be sufficiently familiar with them to know readily how to develop the ones you do not remember. The preceding identity formulas are summarized here for your convenience.

Summary of Formulas as Developed in Section 7.17

Distance Formula

$$d = \sqrt{(x_2 - x_1)^2 + (y_2 - y_1)^2} \qquad\qquad 7.17\text{-}1$$

Sum and Difference of Two Numbers

$$\cos(s - t) = \cos s \cos t + \sin s \sin t. \qquad\qquad 7.17\text{-}2$$

$$\cos(s + t) = \cos s \cos t - \sin s \sin t. \qquad\qquad 7.17\text{-}11$$

$$\sin(s + t) = \sin s \cos t + \cos s \sin t. \qquad\qquad 7.17\text{-}12$$

$$\sin(s - t) = \sin s \cos t - \cos s \sin t. \qquad\qquad 7.17\text{-}13$$

$$\tan(s + t) = \frac{\tan s + \tan t}{1 - \tan s \tan t}. \qquad\qquad 7.17\text{-}14$$

$$\tan(s - t) = \frac{\tan s - \tan t}{1 + \tan s \tan t}. \qquad\qquad 7.17\text{-}16$$

$$\cot(s + t) = \frac{\cot s \cot t - 1}{\cot s + \cot t}. \qquad\qquad 7.17\text{-}15$$

$$\cot(s - t) = \frac{\cot s \cot t + 1}{\cot t - \cot s}. \qquad\qquad 7.17\text{-}17$$

Special Reduction Formulas

$$\sin(-t) = -\sin t$$
7.17-5

$$\cos(-t) = \cos t.$$
7.17-3

$$\tan(-t) = -\tan t.$$
7.17-6

$$\cot(-t) = -\cot t.$$
7.17-7

$$\sin\left(\frac{\pi}{2} - t\right) = \cos t.$$
7.17-8

$$\cos\left(\frac{\pi}{2} - t\right) = \sin t.$$
7.17-4

$$\tan\left(\frac{\pi}{2} - t\right) = \cot t.$$
7.17-9

$$\cot\left(\frac{\pi}{2} - t\right) = \tan t.$$
7.17-10

Double Numbers

$$\sin 2t = 2 \sin t \cos t.$$
7.17-18

$$\cos 2t = \cos^2 t - \sin^2 t = 1 - 2 \sin^2 t = 2 \cos^2 t - 1.$$
7.17-19

$$\tan 2t = \frac{2 \tan t}{1 - \tan^2 t}.$$
7.17-20

Half a Number

$$\sin \frac{t}{2} = \pm \sqrt{\frac{1 - \cos t}{2}}.$$
7.17-21

$$\cos \frac{t}{2} = \pm \sqrt{\frac{1 + \cos t}{2}}.$$
7.17-22

$$\tan \frac{t}{2} = \frac{\sin t}{1 + \cos t} = \frac{1 - \cos t}{\sin t} = \pm \sqrt{\frac{1 - \cos t}{1 + \cos t}}$$
7.17-23

Product of Two Functions

$$\sin s \cos t = \tfrac{1}{2}[\sin(s + t) + \sin(s - t)].$$
7.17-24

$$\cos s \sin t = \tfrac{1}{2}[\sin(s + t) - \sin(s - t)].$$
7.17-25

$$\cos s \cos t = \tfrac{1}{2}[\cos(s + t) + \cos(s - t)].$$
7.17-26

$$\sin s \sin t = -\tfrac{1}{2}[\cos(s + t) - \cos(s - t)].$$
7.17-27

Sum of Two Functions

$$\sin u + \sin v = 2 \sin \frac{u + v}{2} \cos \frac{u - v}{2}.$$
7.17-28

$$\sin u - \sin v = 2 \cos \frac{u + v}{2} \sin \frac{u - v}{2}. \qquad 7.17\text{-}29$$

$$\cos u + \cos v = 2 \cos \frac{u + v}{2} \cos \frac{u - v}{2}. \qquad 7.17\text{-}30$$

$$\cos u - \cos v = -2 \sin \frac{u + v}{2} \sin \frac{u - v}{2}. \qquad 7.17\text{-}31$$

If you have mastered the definitions of the six Circular Functions and the eight Fundamental Identities and can select from the identities in the preceding summary the appropriate changes to be substituted, and if you can handle the necessary algebraic manipulations properly, then solving trigonometric identities will prove very satisfying and profitable to you. Usually, there are several ways of verifying an identity, some of them easy and some very difficult.

Example: 7. 17-1. Show that

$$\frac{\sin 2t}{\sin t} - \frac{\cos 2t}{\cos t} = \sec t \qquad (\sin t, \cos t \neq 0).$$

There are several very easy ways of proving this identity. We will work entirely with the left member and proceed by changing each term of the left member so that it has a common denominator. Thus,

$$\frac{\sin 2t \cos t - \cos 2t \sin t}{\sin t \cos t} = \sec t. \qquad (A)$$

It is now hoped that you will observe, before you read further, that the numerator of the left member of the identity in (A) is equal to $\sin(2t - t)$. See formula 7.17-13. Substituting $\sin(2t - t)$ in (A) gives

$$\frac{\sin(2t - t)}{\sin t \cos t} = \sec t,$$

$$\frac{\sin t}{\sin t \cos t} = \sec t,$$

$$\frac{1}{\cos t} = \sec t,$$

and $\qquad$ **sec t = sec t.**

Another way to prove Example 7.17-1, working only from the left side, would be to write $\sin 2t$ as $2 \sin t \cos t$ and $\cos 2t$ as $2 \cos^2 t - 1$; that is,

$$\frac{2 \sin t \cos t}{\sin t} - \frac{2 \cos^2 t}{\cos t} + \frac{1}{\cos t} = \sec t.$$

Then $2 \cos t - 2 \cos t + \sec t = \sec t$

and $\qquad\qquad\qquad$ **sec t = sec t.**

Example: 7.17-2.   Verify that

$$\frac{\sin 7t - \sin 5t}{\cos 7t + \cos 5t} = \tan t \quad (\cos 7t + \cos 5t \neq 0).$$

FIRST TRIAL

If one attempted to reduce the left-hand functions to functions in terms of single numbers the verification would prove very difficult. For example, one could write

$$\cos 5t = \cos(3t + 2t) = \cos 3t \cos 2t - \sin 3t \sin 2t$$

$$= \cos(2t + t) \cos 2t - \sin(2t + t) \sin 2t$$

$$= (\cos 2t \cos t - \sin 2t \sin t) \cos 2t - (\sin 2t \cos t$$

$$+ \cos 2t \sin t) \sin 2t.$$

Then the *double number functions* could be changed to *single number functions* and an effort made to simplify the expression. This will not be done. Note also that there are three other functions like cos 5*t* that would have to be evaluated. Certainly, we have gone far enough to show the difficulty and the time-consuming nature of this approach and to cause us to hope that there might be a better way to verify this identity. So let us try again to verify that

$$\frac{\sin 7t - \sin 5t}{\cos 7t + \cos 5t} = \tan t. \tag{A}$$

SECOND TRIAL

$$\sin 7t - \sin 5t = 2 \cos\left(\frac{7t + 5t}{2}\right) \sin\left(\frac{7t - 5t}{2}\right) \qquad \text{(by 7.17-29)} \quad (B)$$

$$\cos 7t + \cos 5t = 2 \cos\left(\frac{7t + 5t}{2}\right) \cos\left(\frac{7t - 5t}{2}\right). \qquad \text{(by 7.17-30)} \quad (C)$$

Substituting (*B*) and (*C*) in (*A*), we get

$$\frac{2 \cos 6t \sin t}{2 \cos 6t \cos t} = \tan t.$$

Simplifying, **tan *t* = tan *t*.**

From Trials I and II you can see that the important thing is to learn how to make the best choice of the basic identity formulas that are applicable to the identity to be verified.

Example: 7.17-3.   Prove that

$$\frac{2 \cos t \left(\sin^2 \frac{t}{2}\right)}{\cos t + 1} = 1 - \cos t - \tan^2 \frac{t}{2}.$$

From Section 7.17-21 we know that $\sin^2 \dfrac{t}{2} = \dfrac{1 - \cos t}{2}$,

and from Section 7.17-23 we know that $\tan^2 \dfrac{t}{2} = \dfrac{1 - \cos t}{1 + \cos t}$.

Substituting, $\dfrac{2 \cos t \,(1 - \cos t)}{2 \,(\cos t + 1)} = (1 - \cos t) - \dfrac{(1 - \cos t)}{(1 + \cos t)}$,

and $\dfrac{\cos t - \cos^2 t}{1 + \cos t} = \dfrac{1 - \cos^2 t - 1 + \cos t}{1 + \cos t}$ (L.C.D.)

$\therefore$ $\dfrac{\cos t - \cos^2 t}{1 + \cos t} = \dfrac{\cos t - \cos^2 t}{1 + \cos t}$.

Example: 7.17-4.   Prove that

$4 \sin t \sin 4t \cos 2t = \cos t - \cos 3t + \cos 5t - \cos 7t$.

Using Section 7.17-31 and substituting in it the equivalent of $\cos t - \cos 3t$ and $\cos 5t - \cos 7t$, the given statement is changed to

$$4 \sin t \sin 4t \cos 2t = -2\left[\left(\sin \frac{4t}{2}\right)\left(-\sin \frac{2t}{2}\right)\right] + (-2)\left[\left(\sin \frac{12t}{2}\right)\left(-\sin \frac{2t}{2}\right)\right]$$

$$= 2 \sin 2t \sin t + 2 \sin 6t \sin t$$

$$= 2 \sin t \,(\sin 2t + \sin 6t)$$

$$= 2 \sin t \,(2)\left(\sin \frac{8t}{2} \cos \frac{4t}{2}\right). \qquad \text{(by 7.17-28)}$$

$\therefore$ **$4 \sin t \sin 4t \cos 2t = 4 \sin t \sin 4t \cos 2t$.**

Example: 7.17-5.   Use the sine of two numbers to find the value of $\sin \dfrac{11\pi}{12}$.

$$\sin \frac{11\pi}{12} = \sin\left(\frac{2\pi}{3} + \frac{\pi}{4}\right) = \sin \frac{2\pi}{3} \cos \frac{\pi}{4} + \cos \frac{2\pi}{3} \sin \frac{\pi}{4} \qquad \text{(by 7.17-12)}$$

$$= \frac{\sqrt{3}}{2} \cdot \frac{\sqrt{2}}{2} + \left(-\frac{1}{2}\right)\left(\frac{\sqrt{2}}{2}\right)$$

$$= \frac{\sqrt{2}}{4}(\sqrt{3} - 1).$$

$\therefore$ $\sin \dfrac{11\pi}{12} \doteq 0.2588$.

Example: 7.17-6.   Evaluate $3 \tan t = \tan 2t$ for $0 \le t \le \pi$.

$$3 \tan t = \frac{2 \tan t}{1 - \tan^2 t},$$

$$(1 - \tan^2 t)(3 \tan t) = \left(\frac{2 \tan t}{1 - \tan^2 t}\right)(1 - \tan^2 t),$$

$$3 \tan t - 3 \tan^3 t = 2 \tan t,$$

$$\tan t - 3 \tan^3 t = 0,$$

$$\tan t (1 - 3 \tan^2 t) = 0.$$

Then $\qquad\qquad \tan t = 0 \quad$ so $\quad t = 0 \quad$ and $\quad t = \pi,$

or $\qquad\qquad \tan t = \dfrac{1}{\sqrt{3}} \quad$ so $\quad t = \dfrac{\pi}{6}$

or $\qquad\qquad \tan t = -\dfrac{1}{\sqrt{3}} \quad$ so $\quad t = \dfrac{5\pi}{6}.$

The reader should check the values $t = 0, \pi, \dfrac{\pi}{6},$ and $\dfrac{5\pi}{6}$ to determine if some of them are extraneous numbers.

EXERCISE 7.F

Verify the following identities **for all admissible values** of s and t.

1. $\dfrac{\sin(s + t)}{\cos s \cos t} = \tan s + \tan t.$

2. $\dfrac{\cos(s - t)}{\cos s \cos t} = 1 + \tan s \tan t.$

3. $\sin\left(t + \dfrac{\pi}{3}\right) - \cos\left(t + \dfrac{\pi}{6}\right) = \sin t.$

4. $\cos(s + t) \cos(s - t) = \cos^2 s - \sin^2 t.$

5. $\sin\left(t - \dfrac{2\pi}{3}\right) = -\dfrac{(\sqrt{3} \cos t + \sin t)}{2}.$

6. $\cos\left(t + \dfrac{4\pi}{3}\right) = \dfrac{\sqrt{3} \sin t - \cos t}{2}.$

7. $\cos 2t + 1 = 2 \sin t(\csc t - \sin t)$

8. $\tan 2t = \dfrac{2 \sin t \cos t}{1 - 2 \sin^2 t}.$

9. $\sin 2t = \dfrac{2 \cot t}{1 + \cot^2 t}.$

10. $\tan 2t = \dfrac{2 \tan t}{1 - \tan^2 t}.$

11. $\tan(-s) - \tan(\pi - s) = \tan 2\pi.$

12. $\sin \dfrac{4\pi}{3} + \cos \dfrac{3\pi}{2} \cos\left(\dfrac{-\pi}{3}\right) = \sin \dfrac{4\pi}{3}$.

13. $\cos 2s = \cos^4 s - \sin^4 s$.

14. $\dfrac{\cos^4 t - \sin^4 t}{\cos 2t} = 1$.

15. $\sin 3t = \sin 2t \cos t + \cos 2t \sin t$.

16. $\cos 3t = \cos 2t \cos t - \sin 2t \sin t$.

17. $4 \sin^3 s + \sin 3s = 3 \sin s$.

18. $4 \cos^3 t - 3 \cos t = \cos 3t$.

19. $\sin 4s = 4 \sin s \cos s \cos 2s$.

20. $\cos 4t = 8 \cos^4 t - 8 \cos^2 t + 1$.

21. $\cos\left(\dfrac{\pi}{4} + s\right) = \dfrac{\sqrt{2}(\cos s - \sin s)}{2}$.

22. $\cos\left(\dfrac{\pi}{6} + t\right) + \sin t = \cos\left(\dfrac{\pi}{6} - t\right)$.

23. $\tan\left(\dfrac{\pi}{3} - t\right) = \dfrac{\sqrt{3} - \tan t}{\sqrt{3} \tan t + 1}$.

24. $\cot\left(\dfrac{\pi}{6} - s\right) = \dfrac{\sqrt{3} \cot s + 1}{\sqrt{3} - \cot t}$.

If s and t both fall in Quadrant I (see Figure 7.F-1) and $\tan s = \frac{5}{12}$ and $\sec t = \frac{5}{4}$, then:

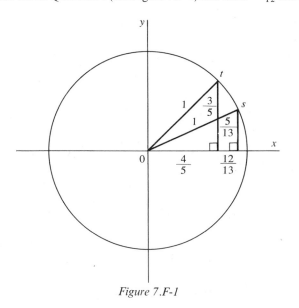

Figure 7.F-1

25. Find the value of $\sin(s + t)$.

26. Find the value of $\tan(s + t)$.

27. Find the value of $\tan(s - t)$.

28. Find the value of $\cos(s - t)$.

29. Find the value of $\tan 2t$.

30. Find the values of $\cos 2s$.

31. Find the value of $\tan \dfrac{s}{2}$.

32. Find the value of $\sin \dfrac{t}{2}$.

Express each of the following as the sum and difference of two functions:

33. $\sin 4t \cos 2t$.

34. $\cos 12t \sin 6t$.

35. $2 \cos 7t \cos 3t$.

36. $2 \sin(s + t) \sin(s - t)$.

Express each of the following as the product of two functions:

37. $\sin \dfrac{\pi}{4} + \sin \dfrac{\pi}{12}$.

38. $\cos \dfrac{\pi}{3} - \cos \dfrac{\pi}{6}$.

39. $\sin \dfrac{\pi}{2} - \sin \dfrac{\pi}{3}$.

40. $\cos \dfrac{\pi}{3} + \cos \dfrac{\pi}{4}$.

Verify the following identities **for all admissible values** of s and t.

41. $\dfrac{\tan(s - t)}{\tan(s + t)} = \dfrac{\sin 2s - \sin 2t}{\sin 2s + \sin 2t}$.

42. $\dfrac{\sin s + \sin t}{\sin s - \sin t} = \dfrac{\tan \dfrac{s + t}{2}}{\tan \dfrac{s - t}{2}}$.

43. $\dfrac{\sin 6t - \sin 2t}{\cos 2t - \cos 6t} = \cot 4t$.

44. $\dfrac{\sin 2t + \sin 5t}{\cos 2t + \cos 5t} = \tan 3.5t$.

45. $2 \sin s \sin 3s = \cos 2s - \cos 4s$.

46. $\cos 2s \sin 3t = \tfrac{1}{2}[\sin(2s + 3t) - \sin(2s - 3t)]$.

47. $\dfrac{\sin^2 3t}{\sin t} = \sin t + \sin 3t + \sin 5t$.

48. $\cos \dfrac{3t}{2} \cos \dfrac{5t}{2} 2 \sin t = \sin 2t - \sin 3t + \sin 5t$.

49. Find all t for $0 \le t \le 2\pi$ for $\cos^2 2t = \dfrac{1 - \cos 2t}{2}$.

50. Find all s for $0 \le s \le 2\pi$ for $\sec^2 s = 4 + 2 \tan s$.

7.18 INVERSE CIRCULAR FUNCTIONS

Inverse functions, symbolized by f^{-1}, have been discussed in Section 3.9 of Chapter 3. Compare the following definition for an inverse function with the one given in Definition 3.9-a.

Definition: 7.18-a.   *If no two of the ordered pairs* (x, y) *of the function* f *have the same* y, *then the set of ordered pairs obtained by interchanging the* x *and* y *in each ordered pair of the function* f *is called the* **inverse function** *of* f.

The preceding definition demands that:

1. *The domain of* f *become the range of* f^{-1}.
2. *The range of* f *become the domain of* f^{-1}.

This has been demonstrated in Section 3.9, in statements (A) through (F) and will be shown again later in connection with the sine function.

Before proceeding further you should review carefully all of Section 3.9 to be certain you have the fundamental concepts clearly in mind.

7.18-1 Basic Facts Concerning Inverse Functions

(a) To have a function there must be a set of ordered pairs (x, y) such that no two distinct pairs have the same first element x.

(b) If a function f exists and it possesses the property that no two distinct pairs have the same second element y, one-to-one correspondence has been satisfied.

(c) Only when function f satisfies one-to-one correspondence is an inverse function possible.

(d) Only when a horizontal line intersects the graph of function f in exactly one point does an inverse function exist.

(e) An inverse function exists if and only if the composite of f and f^{-1} are commutative.

(f) It is usually possible to restrict a function that does not normally have an inverse function so that under the restriction it does have an inverse.

For the circular function whose equation is $y = \sin t$ two questions may be asked:

QUESTION 1.   What is the value of y if $y = \sin t$?

QUESTION 2.   What is the value of t whose sine is y?

The second question implies the inverse of the first one and immediately points up the need for some new notation to express it. Two different symbols are in common use, namely,

If $y = \sin t$, then $t = \arcsin y$,
or If $y = \sin t$, then $t = \sin^{-1} y$.

Each of the two forms, $t = \arcsin y$ or $t = \sin^{-1} y$, may be read

"the set of numbers t whose sine is y,"

which means that arcsin y is the set of real numbers for which the value of the sine is y.

Now, returning to the equation $y = \sin t$ in Question 1. We know that for each t in $y = \sin t$ we will get a unique y. But what can we expect in Question 2 if y is some given number, such as $\frac{1}{2}$, and the value (or values) of t is desired?

If you will apply the horizontal-line test [7.18-1(d)] to the graph of the sine function, $y = \sin t$, remembering that this function is periodic, you will readily see that through any selected point of the range of the curve the horizontal line will intersect the sine curve many times. Thus, *the sine function (and this is equally true for the other five circular functions) does not have an* **inverse function.** *It has an* **inverse relation,** which for $y = \frac{1}{2}$ may be written as

$$t = \arcsin \tfrac{1}{2}.$$

Another approach to an answer for Question 2 is to attempt to find those numbers whose sine is $\frac{1}{2}$. For example,

If $\sin t = \dfrac{1}{2}$, then $t = \dfrac{\pi}{6} + 2\pi n$ (*n* any nonnegative integer)

or $t = \dfrac{5\pi}{6} + 2\pi n$ (*n* any nonnegative integer)

Here you can see that arcsin $\frac{1}{2}$ is an infinite set, its solution set being

$$\left\{ t \mid t = \frac{\pi}{6} + 2\pi n \text{ or } t = \frac{5\pi}{6} + 2\pi n; n = 0, 1, 2, \ldots \right\}.$$

Thus again we find that in its original form the sine function does not have an inverse function.

It so happens that not only the sine but *all the circular functions can be restricted in such a way as to guarantee inverse functions for the restricted functions,* and there are many ways of making these restrictions.

Restricting the domain of a circular function will, of course, limit the range of its corresponding inverse relation. For example, restricting the sine function to $-\pi/2 \le t \le \pi/2$ means that we no longer have the set of real numbers as the range of its inverse relation, which is represented by arcsin y. Assuming $y = \frac{1}{2}$, the inverse relation expressed by arcsin $\frac{1}{2}$, under the restrictions set for the sine, becomes the inverse function expressed by arcSin $\frac{1}{2}$. The values represented by arcSin $\frac{1}{2}$ are called the principal values of arcsin $\frac{1}{2}$. Generalizing:

Definition: 7.18-1a. *The values of the inverse function represented by arcSin y are called* **the principal values** *of the inverse relation represented by arcsin y.*

To avoid the possibility of confusing the inverse symbol $\text{Sin}^{-1} y$ with exponents, we will work primarily with the arcSine symbol in this text. *When we are dealing with the principal values of arcsin y (and similarly for the other functions), we will always capitalize the first letter of the sine function, writing the inverse function as arcSin y.*

We will state the restrictions commonly used on the sine, cosine, and tangent functions in Table 7.18-1a and leave their reciprocal functions for you to

Table 7.18-1a *Restrictions on Circular Functions*

Function	Equation	Domain	Range
Sine	$y = f(t) = \text{Sin } t$	$-\dfrac{\pi}{2} \le t \le \dfrac{\pi}{2}$	$-1 \le y \le 1$
Cosine	$x = f(t) = \text{Cos } t$	$0 \le t \le \pi$	$-1 \le x \le 1$
Tangent	$z = f(t) = \text{Tan } t$	$-\dfrac{\pi}{2} < t < \dfrac{\pi}{2}$	All real numbers

investigate. As mentioned before, there are several possible ways of selecting these restrictions.

There are several things about Table 7.18-1b that we want to reemphasize

Table 7.18-1b *Domain and Range of Inverse Circular Functions*

Function	Equation	Domain	Range
arcSine	$y = \text{arcSin } t$	$-1 \le t \le 1$	$-\dfrac{\pi}{2} \le y \le \dfrac{\pi}{2}$
arcCosine	$x = \text{arcCos } t$	$-1 \le t \le 1$	$0 \le x \le \pi$
arcTangent	$z = \text{arcTan } t$	all real numbers	$-\dfrac{\pi}{2} < z < \dfrac{\pi}{2}$

and summarize for you.

1. When the **inverse circular relations,** namely, arcsin t, arccos t and arctan t, have the first letter of the function capitalized; that is, arcSin t, arcCos t or arcTan t, they refer specifically to **inverse circular functions.**

2. The inverse circular functions, arcSin t, arcCos t, and arcTan t, are generally referred to as the **principal values** of arcsin t, arccos t or arctan t.

3. When the inverse circular functions are written in their **equivalent form** the first letter of the circular function will also be capitalized to aid in identifying the inverse circular functions. That is,

$y = \text{arcSin } t$ is equivalent to Sin $y = t$.
$x = \text{arcCos } t$ is equivalent to Cos $x = t$.
$z = \text{arcTan } t$ is equivalent to Tan $z = t$.

4. Note that the **domain** for any function in Table 7.18-1a is identical to the **range** of its corresponding inverse function in Table 7.18-1b, and vice versa.

5. Also note that when the **sine function** is $\{(t, y)|y = \text{Sin } t\}$, the corresponding **inverse sine function** is $\{(t, y) \mid t = \text{Sin } y \text{ or } y = \text{arcSin } t\}$, and

similarly for the other functions and their inverses. The inverse circular function $y = \text{arcSin } t$ has been obtained by repeating the argument from (A) through (D) in Section 3.9, Chapter 3, in the following manner:

Given function: $f = \{(t, y) | y = \text{Sin } t, t \text{ and } y \in R\}$ (A)

Inverse function: $f^{-1} = \{(y, t) | y = \text{Sin } t, t \text{ and } y \in R\}$.   (B)

If the inverse function is left in form (B) we will not be able to graph (A) and (B) on the same axes. Thus, we would not be able to make any graphical comparisons of the function f and its inverse f^{-1}. For this reason (B) is re-written so that its ordered pairs follow the same order as does the original function f. Thus, the

Inverse function: $f^{-1} = \{(t, y) | t = \text{Sin } y, t \text{ and } y \in R\}$.   (C)

Written in terms of arc notation:

Inverse function: $f^{-1} = \{(t, y) | y = \text{arcSin } t, t \text{ and } y \in R\}$.   (D)

The inverse functions $x = \text{arcCos } t$ and $z = \text{arcTan } t$ are obtained by the same line of argument.

7.18-2 The Identity Function and Inverse Circular Functions

Preliminary to the graphing of the inverse circular functions we need to review Section 3.8 and Figure 3.8-1 which have to do with the **identity function.**

$I_f = \{(x, y) | y = x, x \text{ and } y \in R\}$

expresses the identity function symbolically. Its graph exactly divides the first and third quadrants of the rectangular coordinate system.

7.18-3 Graph of the Inverse Sine Function

A graph of the sine function $y = \text{Sin } t$, with its domain limited to $\dfrac{\pi}{2} \leq t \leq \dfrac{\pi}{2}$ is shown in Figure 7.18-3a.

Figure 7.18-3b is a graph of the inverse sine function $y = \text{arcSin } t$ with domain $-1 \leq t \leq 1$.

If the graphs of the sine function and its inverse are plotted on the same axes, as shown in Figure 7.18-3c, it becomes apparent that the graph of the inverse sine function is an exact reflection of the graph of the sine function across the graph of the identity function $y = t$. Actually, $y = t$ **is an axis of symmetry.**

Definition: 7.18-3a. *If a line and two curves form two congruent figures such that when one is folded over on the other along the line they coincide, then this line is called an* **axis of symmetry.**

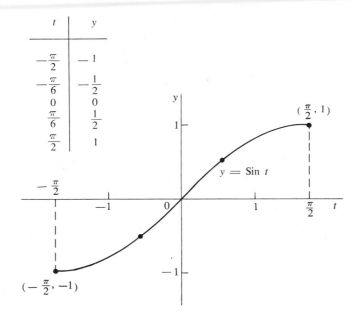

t	y
$-\dfrac{\pi}{2}$	-1
$-\dfrac{\pi}{6}$	$-\dfrac{1}{2}$
0	0
$\dfrac{\pi}{6}$	$\dfrac{1}{2}$
$\dfrac{\pi}{2}$	1

Figure 7.18-3a

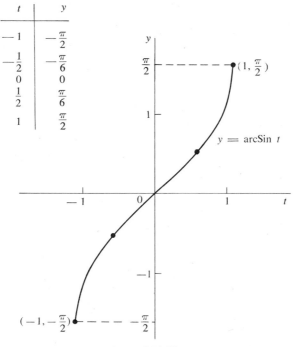

t	y
-1	$-\dfrac{\pi}{2}$
$-\dfrac{1}{2}$	$-\dfrac{\pi}{6}$
0	0
$\dfrac{1}{2}$	$\dfrac{\pi}{6}$
1	$\dfrac{\pi}{2}$

Figure 7.18-3b

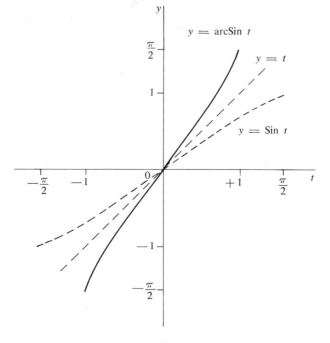

Figure 7.18-3c

Thus, the easy and rapid way to plot a graph of the inverse sine function is to plot the sine function and reflect it across the graph of the identity function $y = t$.

The **graph of any inverse function,** *circular or otherwise, is the graph of its corresponding function reflected across the graph of the identity function.*

The graphs of the sine function and its inverse in Figure 7.18-3c show very clearly that:

1. The domain of $y = \text{Sin } t$ is the range of $y = \text{arcSin } t$, and
2. The range of $y = \text{Sin } t$ is the domain of $y = \text{arcSin } t$.

7.18-4 Graph of the Inverse Cosine Function

The circular cosine function was originally defined as $\cos t = x$. For clarity we will hold to this original form. Values of t will be plotted on the horizontal axis and x values on or parallel to the vertical axis.

The graph of $x = \text{Cos } t$ with its domain restricted to $0 \le t \le \pi$ is shown in Figure 7.18-4a. In Figure 7.18-4b the restricted cosine function is shown along with its inverse cosine function. The function $x = \text{arcCos } t$ was plotted by reflecting the graph of $x = \text{Cos } t$ across the graph of the identity function $x = t$.

Check the graph for $x = \text{arcCos } t$ by using the given set of ordered pairs.

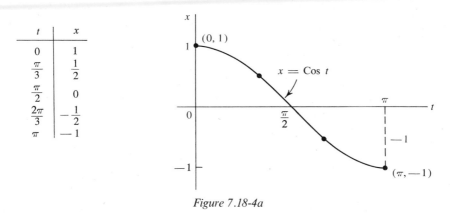

t	x
0	1
$\dfrac{\pi}{3}$	$\dfrac{1}{2}$
$\dfrac{\pi}{2}$	0
$\dfrac{2\pi}{3}$	$-\dfrac{1}{2}$
π	-1

Figure 7.18-4a

Some features of Figure 7.18-4b which you should note are:

1. For $x = \text{Cos } t$ each t has a unique x and each x has a unique t. This is equally true of $x = \text{arcCos } t$. This guarantees one-to-one correspondence and tells that each function has an inverse function.

2. The graph of $x = \text{Cos } t$ is symmetrical to the graph of $x = \text{arcCos } t$ with respect to the axis of symmetry (or identity function) represented by $x = t$.

3. The domain of $x = \text{Cos } t$ is the range of arcCos t, and the range of $x = \text{Cos } t$ is the domain of $x = \text{arcCos } t$.

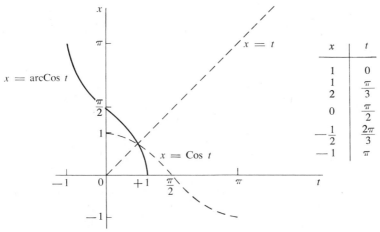

x	t
1	0
$\dfrac{1}{2}$	$\dfrac{\pi}{3}$
0	$\dfrac{\pi}{2}$
$-\dfrac{1}{2}$	$\dfrac{2\pi}{3}$
-1	π

Figure 7.18-4b

7.18-5 Graph of the Inverse Tangent Function

Since the original definition for the tangent function

$$\tan t = \frac{y}{x} = \frac{\sin t}{\cos t} \qquad (x \neq 0).$$

involves both x and y, it seems wise to use some other letter such as z to represent the tangent function. This means that in graphing the restricted tangent function and its inverse,

$z = \text{Tan } t$

and $z = \text{arcTan } t$,

the t values will be plotted along the horizontal axis and the z values will be plotted along or parallel to the vertical axis.

The graph of $z = \text{Tan } t$ with its domain restricted to $-\pi/2 < t < \pi/2$ is shown in Figure 7.18-5(1). Figure 7.18-5(2) shows the graph of the tangent

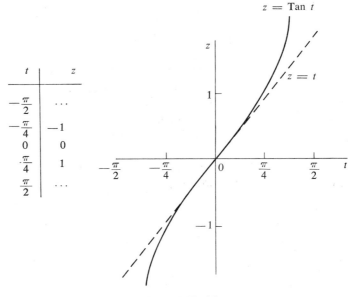

t	z
$-\dfrac{\pi}{2}$	$\ldots$
$-\dfrac{\pi}{4}$	-1
0	0
$\dfrac{\pi}{4}$	1
$\dfrac{\pi}{2}$	$\ldots$

Figure 7.18-5(1)

function $z = \text{Tan } t$ along with the graph of its inverse function $z = \text{arcTan } t$ obtained by reflecting the original function across the graph of the identity function $z = t$.

In the examples, and in Exercise 7.G which follows, you must be very careful to interpret each expression correctly. For example, arcSin $\frac{1}{2}$ is definitely calling for the evaluation of an inverse sine "function," not an inverse sine "relation." This is why the first letter of the sine function has been capitalized. On the other hand, arcsin $\frac{1}{2}$, where the sine function begins with a small case s, means that you are dealing with an inverse sine relation and not an inverse sine function.

To avoid possible confusion we will use the symbols w, w_1, w_2 and so on, rather than the letters x, y, and z in the following examples.

If you encounter Sin $w = \frac{1}{2}$, which of course is equivalent to $w = \text{arcSin } \frac{1}{2}$, you should know immediately that the capital "S" in Sin $w = \frac{1}{2}$ is there to

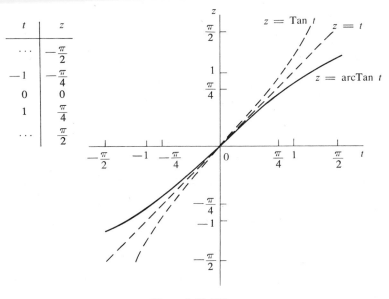

Figure 7.18-5(2)

tell you that you are dealing with an inverse function. Likewise, Cos $w = 1$ and Tan $w = 1$ are inverse functions.

Example: 7.18-5a.　Find the value of arcSin $\frac{1}{2}$.

Given:　$w = $ arcSin $\frac{1}{2}$.

Then　Sin $w = \frac{1}{2}$　(equivalent form).

But if　sin $w = \frac{1}{2}$　(See Example 7.13-a, Section 7.13),

then　　　$w = \dfrac{\pi}{6} \pm 2\pi n$, where $n = 0, 1, 2, \ldots$.

To guarantee an inverse sine function we know that the sine function has to be restricted to $-\dfrac{\pi}{2} \le w \le \dfrac{\pi}{2}$.

Therefore, **$w = \dfrac{\pi}{6}$**.

Example: 7.18-5b.　Find the exact value for arcTan(-1).

Given:　$w = $ arcTan(-1).

Its equivalent form is Tan $w = -1$ (see Figure 7.18-5b). The restriction on the tangent function that guarantees an inverse tangent is $-\pi/2 < w < \pi/2$.

Therefore, **$w = -\dfrac{\pi}{4}$**.

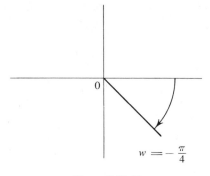

Figure 7.18-5b

Example: 7.18-5c.   Find the cot(arcTan 2).

Let $w = \text{arcTan } 2$.
Then Tan $w = 2$.

The problem is to find cot w. From Figure 7.18-5c, which correctly shows the

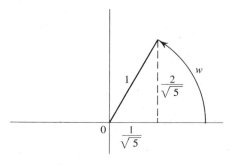

Figure 7.18-5c

location of Tan $w = 2$ on a unit circle, we read

$$\cot w = \dfrac{\dfrac{1}{\sqrt{5}}}{\dfrac{2}{\sqrt{5}}} = \dfrac{1}{2}.$$

Example: 7.18-5d.   Show that arcSin $\frac{1}{2}$ + arcCos $\frac{1}{2}$ = arcSin 1.

Let $w = \text{arcSin } \frac{1}{2}$ so that Sin $w = \frac{1}{2}$. Then $w = \pi/6$.
Let $w_1 = \text{arcCos } \frac{1}{2}$ so that Cos $w_1 = \frac{1}{2}$. Then $w_1 = \pi/3$.
Let $w_2 = \text{arcSin } 1$ so that Sin $w_2 = 1$. Then $w_2 = \pi/2$.

Because of the restrictions placed upon the circular sine and cosine functions

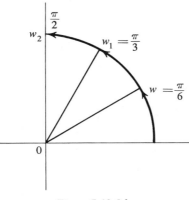

Figure 7.18-5d

the values shown in Figure 7.18-5d are the only possible ones for w, w_1, and w_2.

So $w + w_1 = w_2$,

$$\frac{\pi}{6} + \frac{\pi}{3} = \frac{\pi}{2},$$

and $\frac{\pi}{2} = \frac{\pi}{2}.$

Example: 7.18-5e.   Find the solution set for $\arccos(-\frac{1}{2})$.

Let $w = \arccos(-\frac{1}{2})$.
Then $\cos w = -\frac{1}{2}$.

$$\therefore \quad \textbf{arccos}(-\tfrac{1}{2}) = \left\{ w \mid w = \frac{2\pi}{3} + 2\pi n;\, n = 0, 1, 2, \ldots \right\}$$

or $\textbf{arccos}(-\tfrac{1}{2}) = \left\{ w \mid w = \dfrac{4\pi}{3} + 2\pi n;\, n = 0, 1, 2, \ldots \right\}.$

This example, you should notice, is a *relation* and has no restrictions on the cosine function.

Example: 7.18-5f.   Evaluate $\arcSin \frac{3}{5} + \arcTan \frac{3}{5}$.

Let $w = \arcSin \frac{3}{5} + \arcTan \frac{3}{5}$.
Then $w = w_1 + w_2$.

If $w_1 = \arcSin \frac{3}{5}$, then $\text{Sin } w_1 = \frac{3}{5}$; $\text{Cos } w_1 = \frac{4}{5}$. If $w_2 = \arcTan \frac{3}{5}$, then $\text{Tan } w_2 = \frac{3}{5}$, and

$$\text{Cos } w_2 = \frac{5}{\sqrt{34}}; \quad \text{Sin } w = \frac{3}{\sqrt{34}} \text{ (see Figure 7.18-5f)}.$$

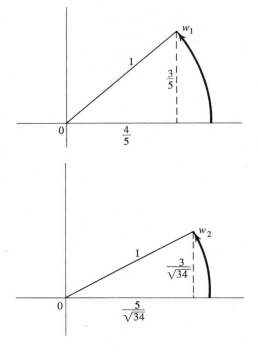

Figure 7.18-5f

Since $w = w_1 + w_2$,

$\quad$ Sin $w =$ Sin$(w_1 + w_2)$,

$\qquad\qquad =$ Sin w_1 Cos $w_2 +$ Cos w_1 Sin w_2,

$\quad$ Sin $w = \dfrac{3}{5} \cdot \dfrac{5}{\sqrt{34}} + \dfrac{4}{5} \cdot \dfrac{3}{\sqrt{34}}$,

$\quad$ Sin $w = \dfrac{27}{5\sqrt{34}}$ or $\dfrac{27\sqrt{34}}{170}$.

Therefore, $w =$ **arcSin** $\dfrac{27\sqrt{34}}{170}$.

EXERCISE 7.G

Do not use the tables in the back of the text to work the problems in this exercise. Figures 7.13-1(a), (b), and (c), should be of help to you in obtaining information about the cotangent, secant, and cosecant functions.

State the value, or values, for each expression from 1 through 12.

1. arcSin 1.   3. Sin $w = \frac{1}{2}$.   5. arcCos 0.
2. arcCos 1.   4. Tan $w = 1$.   6. arcSin$(-\frac{3}{2})$.

7. arcTan$(-1/\sqrt{3})$.   **9.** arcCot 0.   **11.** arctan(-1).
8. arcCos $\frac{1}{2}$.   **10.** arcTan 0.   **12.** arcsec 2.

Find the value of each expression:

13. tan[arcSin$(-\frac{1}{2})$].   **17.** sin(arcTan $\sqrt{3}$).   **21.** cos[arcTan$(-\frac{5}{12})$].
14. tan[arcTan(-2)].   **18.** cos(arcCot $\sqrt{3}$).   **22.** sin[arcCot$(-\frac{5}{12})$].
15. sin(arcCos $1/\sqrt{2}$).   **19.** cos[arcSin$(-\frac{3}{5})$].   **23.** arcSin(cos $\pi/3$).
16. cos(arcSin $1/\sqrt{2}$).   **20.** sin[arcCos$(-\frac{3}{5})$].   **24.** arcCos(sin $\pi/6$).

Evaluate the following expressions:

25. arcSin $\frac{3}{5}$ + arcSin $\frac{4}{5}$.   **29.** arcTan 3 $-$ arcTan(-2).
26. arcSin $\frac{1}{4}$ + arcCos $\frac{1}{4}$.   **30.** arcCos $\frac{3}{5}$ $-$ arcSin $\frac{5}{13}$.
27. sin(arcCos $\frac{1}{2}$ + arcSin $\frac{3}{5}$).   **31.** cos(arcSin w + arcCos w).
28. tan(arcTan $\frac{1}{5}$ + arcTan $\frac{3}{5}$).   **32.** sin(arcSin w + arcCos w).

Prove the following statements:

33. arcSin w + arcCos w = $\pi/2$.
34. arcTan w + arcCot w = $\pi/2$, $w \geq 0$.

35. arcSin $\dfrac{v}{\sqrt{1 + v^2}}$ = arcTan v.

36. arcCos $\sqrt{1 - v^2}$ = 2 arcSin v.
37. 4 arcTan $\frac{1}{7}$ + 8 arcTan $\frac{1}{3}$ = π.
38. arcTan $\frac{1}{3}$ $-$ arcTan $\frac{1}{4}$ = arcTan $\frac{1}{13}$.

Sketch the graphs of (a) and (b) on the same coordinate system.

39. (a) z = Cot t.   (b) z = arcCot t.
40. (a) x = Sec t.   (b) x = arcSec t.
41. (a) y = Csc t.   (b) y = arcCsc t.

8

Exponential and Logarithmic Functions

Most of the functions which we have been studying up to this point have been polynomial functions or power functions, such as $f(x) = x^3 - 5x^2 + 1$ or $y = x^5$, which can be generated by algebraic operations. These are known as **algebraic functions.** A characteristic of all such functions is that the independent variable is the base and the exponent attached to the independent variable is always a constant.

There are many functions, called **transcendental functions,** which cannot be expressed algebraically in terms of a base which is a variable and an exponent which is a constant. Such functions include the circular and trigonometric functions (see Chapters 7 and 9) and the exponential and logarithmic functions which will be discussed in this chapter.

8.1 EXPONENTIAL FUNCTIONS

What difference can you detect between

(1) $y = x^5$, which defines an algebraic function, and
(2) $y = 5^x$, which defines an exponential function?

Did you observe that in the polynomial, $y = x^5$, the independent variable x is the base and the exponent 5 attached to the base is a constant? Did you notice that just the reverse took place in the exponential function, that is, the base is the constant 5 and its exponent is the independent variable, x? This is a basic distinction between algebraic and exponential functions.

It should be recognized, of course, that $y = x^x$ is also an exponential function. It is essential that the following definition be sufficiently general to include exponential functions of the type $y = x^x$.

Definition: 8.1-1. *An equation which contains the variable quantity as an exponent is called an* **exponential equation.**

The equation $y = b^x$, where b is a positive real number and x a rational num- ber, is an exponential equation. Mathematically, it is completely logical to state that x can be any real number, and we will use x in that sense even though we do not have the mathematical equipment to justify it at this point. Thus, if we choose to do so we can work with exponential equations such as $y = 3^{\cos 4}$, $y = 5^\pi$, $y = 4^{\sqrt{2}}$, and so on. We can now strengthen our exponential defini- tion in this manner:

Definition: 8.1-2. *For $x \in R$ the function f, defined by $y = b^x$ where $b > 0$ and $b \neq 1$, is called an* **exponential function.** *Expressed symbolically,*

$$f = \{(x, y) \mid y = b^x, b > 0, b \neq 1\}.$$

This is an ideal spot to note that if $b = 1$ the function f degenerates into a linear function denoted by

$$f = \{(x, y) \mid y = 1^x, b > 0\}$$

and its graph would be a horizontal line cutting the y axis at $(0, 1)$. Each x will give a unique y, but when $b = 1$ each y will not give a unique x.

In order to see how an exponential curve behaves, a graph of the function $y = e^x$, where $e = 2.718 \ldots$ is presented.

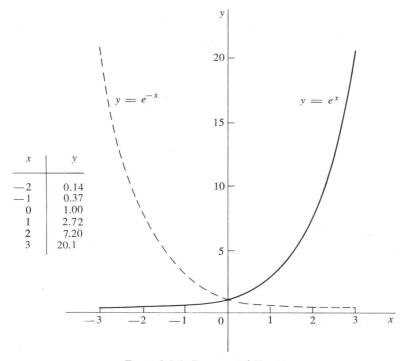

x	y
-2	0.14
-1	0.37
0	1.00
1	2.72
2	7.20
3	20.1

Figure 8.1-1. Exponential Function.

Definition: 8.1-3.   *If $f(x_a) < f(x_b)$ for all $x_a < x_b$, then the function is a* **monotone increasing function.**

Definition: 8.1-4.   *If $f(x_a) > f(x_b)$ for all $x_a < x_b$, then the function is a* **monotone decreasing function.**

Some of the basic properties of the general exponential function $y = b^x$ ($b > 1$) as defined by $y = e^x$ are:

1. The function is continuous for all $x \in R$.
2. The function consistently rises as x increases; so it is a **monotone increasing function** (see Definition 8.1-3).
3. As x gets smaller and smaller the function approaches zero but never reaches it.
4. There is no zero value of the function.
5. The graph is entirely above the x axis so that the function is positive for all x. This means $0 < y < \infty$.
6. Should the exponential function be defined by $y = e^{-x}$, its graph would be symmetrical to the graph of $y = e^x$ about the y axis, and would intersect the y axis at $y = 1$. This graph is indicated by the dotted curve in Figure 8.1-1. $y = e^{-x}$ is the mirror image of $y = e^x$ about the y axis and is a **monotone decreasing function** (see Definition 8.1-4).

8.2 EXPONENTS AND THE LAWS OF EXPONENTS

The development of exponents has followed the usual pathways of all mathematical efforts. The theoretical aspects of the subject had to be developed first. Then, on the basis of this theory the practical aspects made their appearance. Both in theory and practice the concepts and principles of exponents have greatly clarified and simplified mathematical procedures and applications.

An exponent is a positive integer usually written a little smaller and a little above and to the right of the base number b to indicate how many times the base number is to be used as a factor. For example,

$$4^6 = 4 \cdot 4 \cdot 4 \cdot 4 \cdot 4 \cdot 4,$$

and $b^9 = b \cdot b \cdot b \cdot b \cdot b \cdot b \cdot b \cdot b \cdot b$.

Or more generally,

Definition: 8.2-1.   *For any real number b and the positive integer n, called the power of b, the symbol b^n is the product of n factors of b. Thus*

$b^n = b \cdot b \cdot b \cdot b \cdot b \cdot b \cdot b \cdots$ **(to n factors of b).**

From Definition 8.2-1 the following five very significant theorems of exponents are derived.

Theorem: 8.2-1.   If b is in R and n and m are positive integers, then

$$b^n b^m = b^{(n+m)}.$$ (I)

PROOF: $b^n = b \cdot b \cdot b \cdot b \cdot b \cdots$ (to n factors of b),   (Definition 8.2-1)

$$b^m = b \cdot b \cdot b \cdot b \cdot b \cdot b \cdot b \cdots \text{ (to } m \text{ factors of } b),$$
(Definition 8.2-1)

$$b^n b^m = b \cdot b \cdot b \cdot b \cdot b \cdot b \cdot b \cdot b \cdot b \cdot b \cdot b \cdot b \cdots \text{ (to } n + m \text{ factors of } b).$$

∴ $b^n b^m = b^{(n+m)}.$

There are available more rigorous mathematical proofs for the laws of exponents than the counting method used in the preceding proof, but the counting method is sufficient for our purpose. It is suggested that you use this method to prove the following four theorems.

Theorem: 8.2-2.   If $b \neq 0 \in R$, and n and m are positive integers, then

$$\frac{b^m}{b^n} = b^{(m-n)}, \qquad \text{if } m > n.$$ (IIA)

$$\frac{b^m}{b^n} = \frac{1}{b^{(n-m)}}, \qquad \text{if } m < n.$$ (IIB)

$$\frac{b^m}{b^n} = 1, \qquad \text{if } m = n.$$ (IIC)

Theorem: 8.2-3.   If $b \in R$ and m and n are positive integers, then

$$(b^m)^n = b^{mn}.$$ (III)

Theorem: 8.2-4.   If a and $b \in R$ and n is a positive integer, then

$$(ab)^n = a^n b^n.$$ (IV)

Theorem: 8.2-5.   If a and $b \in R$, $(b \neq 0)$, and n is a positive integer, then

$$\left(\frac{a}{b}\right)^n = \frac{a^n}{b^n}.$$ (V)

While these theorems of exponents as presented are true only when the exponents are positive integers, yet one can set up definitions that will assure that these five laws of exponent will hold for zero exponents, for negative exponents and, in fact, for any exponent that is a rational number. The definitions are:

Definition: 8.2-2.   *If* $b \neq 0 \in R$, *then* $b^0 = 1$.

To show that this definition satisfies Theorem 8.2-2 (IIC), take

$\dfrac{b^m}{b^n} = 1$, if $m = n$. But if $m = n$, by Theorem 8.2-2 (IIA),

$$\frac{b^m}{b^n} = b^{m-n} = b^{n-n} = b^0.$$

$\therefore\ \boldsymbol{b^0 = 1}.$

Thus, $b^0 = 1$ satisfies Theorem 8.2-2 and it can easily be shown that it also satisfies the other theorems on exponents.

Definition: 8.2-3.   *If $b \neq 0 \in R$ and n a positive integer, then*

$$\boldsymbol{b^{-n} = \frac{1}{b^n}.}$$

Definition 8.2-3 could have been written as $(b)^{-n} = (1/b)^n$, that is, b to a negative exponent is equal to the reciprocal of b to the same positive exponent.

The important thing to keep in mind is that Definition 8.2-2 and Definition 8.2-3 have been defined in such a way that Theorems 8.2-1, 8.2-2, 8.2-3, 8.2-4, and 8.2-5, which were limited to positive integral exponents only, will now hold true for all **integral exponents.**

Our next problem is to define $b^{m/n}$ so that the five basic theorems of exponents will hold for all **fractional exponents.** In the rationalizations which follow only Theorems 8.2-1 and 8.2-3 will be involved, but you are to understand that all the theorems of exponents must be satisfied.

No meaning has been assigned to the symbol $b^{1/2}$ up to this point in this book. However, if b is restricted to the nonnegative real numbers, then by Theorem 8.2-1 is

$$b^{1/2} \cdot b^{1/2} = b^{(1/2 + 1/2)} = b^1 = b,$$

and $\sqrt{b} \cdot \sqrt{b} = \sqrt{b^2}\ \ = |b| = b.$

To preserve Theorem 8.2-1, the definition would have to be

$$b^{1/2} = \sqrt{b}, \qquad b \geq 0. \tag{A}$$

By taking n to be any positive integer so that the fraction $1/n$ is also positive, a rationalization similar to the preceding one leads to

Definition: 8.2-4.

$$b^{1/n} = \sqrt[n]{b}, \qquad b \geq 0. \tag{B}$$

The number b has n nth roots. In order to obtain a root of b which is unique (see Definition 4.8-4) one of the following facts must apply.

The *principal nth root of b, that is* $b^{1/n}$ *or* $\sqrt[n]{b}$, *is*

(a) *positive* if b is a positive real number and n is a positive integer,
(b) *negative* if b is a negative real number and n is an odd integer, and
(c) *not defined* if b is a negative real number and n is an even integer.

We are now ready to consider $b^{m/n}$ where the m and n are positive integers and $b \neq 0$. According to Theorem 8.2-3 and (B)

$$b^{m/n} = (b^{1/n})^m = (\sqrt[n]{b})^m,$$

or $b^{m/n} = (b^m)^{1/n} = \sqrt[n]{b^m}$.

Therefore, to guarantee that Theorem 8.2-3 will be satisfied $b^{m/n}$ must be defined as follows:

Definition: 8.2-5.

$$b^{m/n} = \sqrt[n]{b^m} = (\sqrt[n]{b})^m. \qquad\qquad (C)$$

Note that $b^{m/n}$ is the principal nth root of b^m (see Definition 4.8-3). Observe also in (C) that the denominator n of the rational exponent is the same n that represents the root index of the radical, and the numerator m of the rational exponent is also the power of b under the radical sign.

In recent years there has been a sharp trend in mathematical manipulations toward the use of expressing numbers with fractional exponents rather than by the radical form of expression.

Since it is assumed that you already have had experience in working with exponents and radicals, only a brief exercise will be given to enable you to check your understanding of the five laws of exponents and the three definitions which extend the laws to apply to rational numbers.

Example: 8.2-1.   Find the value of $\dfrac{2^8 \cdot 2^3}{2^4}$.

This example requires the use of both Theorem 8.2-1 and Theorem 8.2-2 of exponents. Thus

$$\frac{2^8 \cdot 2^3}{2^4} = 2^{(8+3-4)} = 2^7 = \mathbf{128}.$$

Example: 8.2-2.   Simplify $\dfrac{b^{5/2} \cdot a^{-2}}{b^{1/2}(a^2)^0}$ by eliminating all zero, negative and fractional exponents.

$(a^2)^0 = 1$ because any number except 0 to the zero power is 1.

(Definition 8.2-2)

$$a^{-2} = \frac{1}{a^2} \text{ and } \frac{1}{b^{\frac{1}{2}}} = b^{-\frac{1}{2}}. \qquad\qquad \text{(Definition 8.2-3)}$$

Therefore, $\dfrac{b^{\frac{1}{2}} \cdot a^{-2}}{b^{\frac{1}{2}}(a^2)^0} = \dfrac{b^{\frac{1}{2}} \cdot b^{-\frac{1}{2}}}{a^2} = \dfrac{b^2}{a^2}.$

Check the expression against the simplified form of the given expression by assuming $b = 4$ and $a = 2$.

$$\frac{(4)^{\frac{1}{2}} \cdot 2^{-2}}{4^{\frac{1}{2}} \cdot (2^2)^0} = \frac{\frac{32}{4}}{2 \cdot 1} = 4,$$

and $\qquad \dfrac{(4)^2}{(2)^2} = \dfrac{16}{4} = 4.$ ⟵ check

Example: 8.2-3.　　Find the product of $(x^{\frac{1}{2}} - y^{\frac{1}{2}})(x^{\frac{1}{2}} + y^{\frac{1}{2}})$.

$$(x^{\frac{1}{2}} - y^{\frac{1}{2}})(x^{\frac{1}{2}} + y^{\frac{1}{2}}) = (x - x^{\frac{1}{2}}y^{\frac{1}{2}} + x^{\frac{1}{2}}y^{\frac{1}{2}} - y) = x - y.$$

Example: 8.2-4.　　What value of x satisfies the equation $x^{-1} = 5$?

If　　　　$x^{-1} = 5,$

then　　　　$\dfrac{1}{x} = 5,$ 　　　　　　　　　　　　　(Definition 8.2-3)

and　　　　$1 = 5x.$

Therefore, $x = \dfrac{1}{5}.$

EXERCISE 8.A

Evaluate the following expressions:

1. $(81)^{1/4}$

2. $(169)^{1/2}$

3. $(-3)^{-5}$.

4. $\left(\dfrac{1}{2}\right)^{-7}$.

5. $\left[\dfrac{3}{8^0} + \left(\dfrac{3}{8}\right)^0\right]^{-3}$.

6. $[4^{3/2} + 9^0]^2$.

7. $(16)^{3/4} + \dfrac{1}{16^0}$.

8. $32^{4/5} - \dfrac{1}{32^{-0}}$.

9. $\left[\dfrac{4^{-2} - 3^{-3}}{4^{-2} + 3^{-3}}\right]^{-1/2}$.

10. $2^{3/2}[2^{-3/2} - 2(2^{-1}) + 5(2^{-1/2})]$.

Simplify each of the following expressions and check each answer by substituting numerical values of your choice for each letter.

11. $(16)^{-3/2}(a^{-5})$.

12. $\dfrac{2b^4 c}{(2b)^4 c^{-1}}$.

13. $\dfrac{s^{-1} + s^0}{s^{-1} + r^0}$.

14. $\dfrac{b^2 a^{-4}}{b^{-2} a^{-6}}$.

15. $\dfrac{(xy)^5 (xy)^0}{(xy)^{-4}(x-y)^0}$.

16. $\dfrac{(x-y)^3 (w+z)^0}{(x-y)^2 [(w+z)^3]^0}$.

Write the following in radical form and simplify.

17. $b^{2/3}$.

18. $(4a4b^2c^6)^{1/2}$.

19. $32w^{3/5}$.

20. $(32w)^{3/4}$.

21. $(7x^2y^2)^{2/3}$.

22. $(x^2 - y^2)^{1/2}$.

Write the following in fractional exponent form and simplify.

23. $\sqrt[5]{c}$.

24. $\sqrt[7]{9}$.

25. $\sqrt[6]{(3x - 4y)^3}$.

26. $\sqrt{(x^2 + y^2)^2}$.

27. $\sqrt[4]{\left[\dfrac{e^{2x} + e^{-2x}}{2}\right]^2}$.

28. $\sqrt[6]{(x^2 - y^2)^{12}}$.

Perform the indicated operation and simplify.

29. $(x^{1/3} + y^{1/3})(x^{2/3} - x^{1/3}y^{1/3} + y^{2/3})$.

30. $(3x^{-1/2} + 2)(2x^{-1/2} + x^{-1} - 4)$.

31. $(x^{-2} - x^{-1} - 2) \div (x^{-1} + 1)$.

32. $(x^{-2} + 5x^{-1} + 6) \div (x^{-1} + 2)$.

Solve these equations:

33. $x^{3/4} = 27$.

34. $y^{2/3} = 64$.

35. $y^{-1/2} = \dfrac{1}{4}$.

36. $x^{-1/5} = \dfrac{1}{32}$.

37. $x^{-1/2} + (3y)^0 = 9$.

38. $\dfrac{x^{-1/2}}{[(x - y)^{1/2}]^0} = 121$.

8.3 INVERSE OF EXPONENTIAL FUNCTIONS

For the exponential function $\{(x, y) \mid y = b^x, b > 0, b \neq 1\}$ *the domain of definition is the set of real numbers and the range is the set of positive real numbers.* With the exception of $b = 1$, which produces a linear function whose graph is a horizontal line through $y = 1$, it is evident that each value of y increases as x increases. So by ruling out $b = 1$, each y in the range of the exponential function corresponds to a unique x in the domain of the function. This assures us that the **exponential function**

$$f = \{(x, y) \mid y = b^x, b > 0, b \neq 1\}$$

has an **inverse function;** that is, a function obtained from function f by interchanging the elements in its defining equation. (Study again all of Section 3.9 in Chapter 3 on Inverse Fractions.)

The inverse function f^{-1} maps each number in the range of f onto that number in the domain of f which generated it. This means that

1. *the domain of f becomes the range of the inverse function* f^{-1}.
2. *the range of f becomes the domain of* f^{-1}.

Since y in the exponential function f maps into x uniquely when $b \neq 1$, all that has to be done to write the inverse function of f, is to interchange the x and y in the defining relation $y = b^x$ and express the result explicitly in terms of y. Thus,

$$f = \{(x, y)\,|\,y = b^x, b > 0, b \neq 1\} \qquad \textbf{(Exponential function).}$$

$$f^{-1} = \{(x, y)\,|\,x = b^y, b > 0, b \neq 1\} \qquad \textbf{(Inverse exponential function).}$$

Then writing $x = b^y$ in its equivalent logarithmic notation, we obtain the inverse of the exponential function and call it *the logarithmic function*. That is,

$$f^{-1} = \{(x, y)\,|\,y = \log_b x, b > 0, b \neq 1\} \qquad \textbf{(Logarithmic function).}$$

8.4 LOGARITHMIC FUNCTIONS

For the logarithmic function

$$f^{-1} = \{(x, y)\,|\,y = \log_b x, b > 0, b \neq 1\},$$

the domain x is the set of all positive numbers and the range y is the set of real numbers.

In working with logarithms, it is well to keep in mind this equivalent relationship:

$y = \log_b x$ if and only if $x = b^y$.

As we did with the exponential function, let us take $y = \log_e x$ as a special case of the logarithmic function $y = \log_b x$ and make a graph of it.

Some basic properties of the logarithmic function $y = \log_e x$ as indicated by Figure 8.4-1 are

1. The function is continuous for all positive values of x.
2. The zero value of the function is at $x = 1$.
3. The function is an **increasing function** for all $b > 1$ (see Definition 8.1-3).
4. The function is negative for values $0 < x < 1$.
5. The function is positive for values $1 < x < \infty$.
6. The function is not defined for negative values of x.

If the b in $y = \log_b x$ has values $0 < b < 1$, the function is a **decreasing function** (see Definition 8.1-4). Check this out by making a graph of $y = \log_{0.5} x$.

Once again you need to study Sections 3.8 and 3.9 in Chapter 3 where the identity function $I_f = \{(x, y)\,|\,y = x\}$ was first developed and used. It was explained in Figure 3.9-a that the graph of any function f which has an inverse can be reflected across the graph of the identity function $y = x$ to give the graph of its inverse function f^{-1}. Using this same procedure, we can now obtain the graph of the logarithmic function $y = \log_e x$ by reflecting the graph of the exponential function $y = b^x$ across the graph of the identity function $y = x$.

Figure 8.4-2 indicates the action. See Figures 8.1-1 and 8.4-1 for the data used in plotting the two curves.

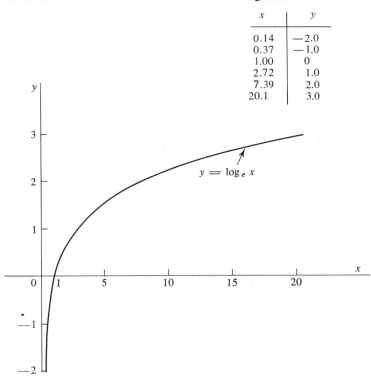

x	y
0.14	−2.0
0.37	−1.0
1.00	0
2.72	1.0
7.39	2.0
20.1	3.0

Figure 8.4-1. Logarithmic Function.

The arrows in Figure 8.4-2 are to indicate that function $y = e^x$ has been reflected across $y = x$ to give its inverse function $y = \log_e x$. Since *any function is the inverse of its inverse function*, it would be equally possible to graph the logarithmic function and reflect it across $y = x$ to get the exponential function.

In Section 3.7, Chapter 3, composite functions were studied. There we learned that *two functions are inverses of each other if and only if they are commutative*. This demands that

$$f[f^{-1}(x)] = f^{-1}[f(x)].$$

Let us justify that $y = \log_e x$ is the inverse of $y = e^x$ by writing them in functional notation as

$$f(x) = e^x \quad \text{and} \quad f^{-1}(x) = \log_e x,$$

and substitute their values in the commutative relationship $f[f^{-1}(x)] = f^{-1}[f(x)]$.

$$f[f^{-1}(x)] = f[\log_e x] = e^{\log_e x} = x, \tag{A}$$

and $f^{-1}[f(x)] = f^{-1}[e^x] \quad = \log_e e^x = x.$ $\hfill (B)$

Therefore, $y = \log_e x$ **is the inverse of** $y = e^x$ and vice versa.

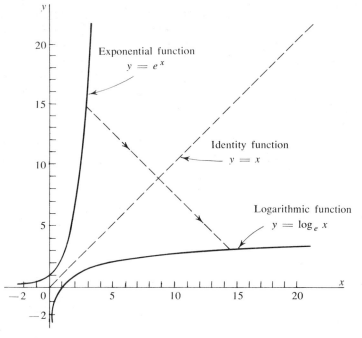

Figure 8.4-2

The relations:

(A)   (B)

$$x = e^{\log_e x} \quad \text{and} \quad x = \log_e e^x,$$

when generalized to

$$x = b^{\log_b x} \quad \text{and} \quad x = \log_e b^x$$

are very important to us. For example, $x = b^{\log_b x}$ means that $\log_b x$ is the exponent to which the power b must be raised to give the number x. This is precisely
the way we will define "logarithm" in a later section. It can be noticed also
in Section 8.8 that $x = b^{\log_b x}$ is used in developing some of the proofs of the
laws of logarithms.

8.5 THE NUMBER *e*

Certain numbers that never occur in the solution of algebraic equations are
called **transcendental numbers. The number *e* is a transcendental number** and
may be defined as the limit of a binomial expansion in this manner.

Definition: 8.5-1.   *The* **transcendental number *e*** *is equal to*

$$\lim_{n \to \infty} \left(1 + \frac{1}{n}\right)^n = 2.7182818 \ldots \qquad (n > 0)$$

By the following trials you can see that as n increases without limit the value of $\left(1 + \dfrac{1}{n}\right)^n$ approaches 2.71828 . . .

If $n = 1$,   then $\left(1 + \dfrac{1}{1}\right)^1 = 2$.

If $n = 100$,   then $\left(1 + \dfrac{1}{100}\right)^{100} = 2.705+$.

If $n = 10{,}000$,   then $\left(1 + \dfrac{1}{10{,}000}\right)^{10{,}000} = 2.717+$.

If n goes the limit, then $\left(1 + \dfrac{1}{n}\right)^n = 2.71828 \ldots = e$.

By the binomial expansion of $\left(1 + \dfrac{1}{n}\right)^n$ (see Section 6.6),

$$\left(1 + \frac{1}{n}\right)^n = (1)^n + \frac{n(1)^{n-1}}{1!}\left(\frac{1}{n}\right) + \frac{(n)\,(n-1)}{2!}(1)^{n-2}\left(\frac{1}{n}\right)^2$$

$$+ \frac{n(n-1)(n-2)}{3!}(1)^{n-3}\left(\frac{1}{n}\right)^3 + \cdots,$$

$$= 1 + 1 + \frac{n(n-1)}{2!(n)(n)} + \frac{n(n^2 - 3n + 2)}{3!(n)(n^2)} + \cdots.$$

$$\therefore \left(1 + \frac{1}{n}\right)^n = 1 + 1 + \frac{1 - \dfrac{1}{n}}{2!} + \frac{1 - \dfrac{3}{n} + \dfrac{2}{n^2}}{3!} + \cdots.$$

This expansion is sufficient to show that as n becomes infinitely large, all terms having n in the denominator become zero, and the expanded infinite series becomes

$$\operatorname*{limit}_{n \to \infty} \left(1 + \frac{1}{n}\right)^n = 1 + \frac{1}{1!} + \frac{1}{2!} + \frac{1}{3!} + \frac{1}{4!} + \frac{1}{5!} + \frac{1}{6!} + \cdots + \frac{1}{(n-1)!} + \cdots.$$

(See Chapter 6, Section 6.6-2 for discussion of **factorial numbers**.)

The number e plays an important role in mathematics. It is used as the base for natural logarithms, it is used throughout calculus, it has many applications in statistics, it appears in the mathematics of investments, it is the base used in defining hyperbolic functions, and on and on. We will only indicate in the briefest way how it functions in hyperbolic functions and in finding the compound amount of money by continuous interest.

8.6 HYPERBOLIC FUNCTIONS

Hyperbolic functions *are functions associated with an equilateral hyperbola much the same as circular functions are associated with the unit circle.* We define the hyperbolic sine and cosine as follows:

Definition: 8.6-1. $\sinh t = \dfrac{e^t - e^{-t}}{2}.$ **(Hyperbolic sine)**

Definition: 8.6-2. $\cosh t = \dfrac{e^t + e^{-t}}{2}.$ **(Hyperbolic cosine)**

The *h* is inserted to emphasize the hyperbolic function.

With these definitions you could proceed to work out the other four hyperbolic functions much the same as you worked with circular functions. For example,

Definition: 8.6-3. $\tanh t = \dfrac{\sinh t}{\cosh t} = \dfrac{e^t - e^{-t}}{e^t + e^{-t}}.$ **(Hyperbolic tangent)**

Values for *e* can be obtained from Table V on page 409.

8.7 COMPOUND AMOUNT BY CONTINUOUS INTEREST

If money is compounded continuously (or if one considers the laws of organic growth which behave much the same) one finds that *e* plays a prominent role. For example, if P dollars were invested at r per cent a year, at the end of the first year there would be $P + Pr$ or $P(1 + r)^1$ dollars. Likewise, at the end of the second year there would be $P(1 + r)(1 + r)$ or $P(1 + r)^2$ dollars, third year $P(1 + r)^2(1 + r)$ or $P(1 + r)^3$ dollars, and so on, and after n years the amount A would be

$$A = P(1 + r)^n.$$ **(Compound amount formula)**

Should there be k interest conversion periods each year, then the number of conversion periods would be nk and the rate of interest per conversion period would be r/k. Thus,

$$A = P\left(1 + \frac{r}{k}\right)^{nk}.$$ $\left(\begin{array}{l}\textbf{Compound amount formula for}\\ \textbf{\textit{k} conversions each year}\end{array}\right)$

Then, by letting $r/k = 1/x$ so that $k = rx$, and substituting in A, we get

$$A = P\left[\left(1 + \frac{1}{x}\right)^x\right]^{nr}.$$

Since r is a fixed number, as k increases indefinitely so must x increase indefinitely. Therefore, the value of the compound amount A for interest converted continuously is expressed by

$$A = P\left[\text{limit}_{x \to \infty} \left(1 + \frac{1}{x}\right)^x\right]^{nr}.$$

Then by substituting e for $\text{limit}_{x \to \infty} \left(1 + \frac{1}{x}\right)^x$ we get

$$A = Pe^{nr}.$$

$$\left(\begin{array}{l}\textbf{Compound amount formula for}\\ \textbf{interest converted continuously}\end{array}\right)$$

EXERCISE 8.B

1. What happens to the exponential function $y = b^x$ if $b = 1$? Is the function an increasing or decreasing function?

2. If $0 < b < 1$ in $y = b^x$, is the function increasing or decreasing?

3. Write an equation whose graph is a mirror image of $y = b^x$ about the x axis. Why is it a monotone decreasing function?

4. Write an equation whose graph is a mirror image of $y = b^x$ about the y axis. Why is it a monotone decreasing function?

5. Write a formula for the inverse of the exponential function and state the domain of the inverse function.

6. What is the range of the inverse function of $y = b^x$?

7. What common properties do the graphs of $y = b^x$ have for $b = 2, b = e, b = 10$?

8. What common properties do the graphs of $y = \log_b x$ have for $b = 2, b = e, b = 10$?

9. If the exponential function has zero values, state them. Where does its graph intersect the x axis?

10. Write the formula for the inverse of the logarithmic function and state the domain of definition for this inverse.

11. Does the base b for logarithms include all positive numbers? If there are exceptions state them and explain why they are excluded.

12. Which of these statements is equivalent to $y = \log_b x$?

    (a) $y = b^x$.   (b) $x = b^y$.

Write the inverse of each of the following functions:

13. (a) $f(x) = x^2$.   (b) $f^{-1}(x) = x$.   (c) $y = b^x$.   (d) $x = y^2 + 5$.

14. (a) $f(x) = 1/x$.   (b) $f^{-1}(x) = x - 4$.   (c) $y = \log_b x$.   (d) $x = 4y + 1$.

15. Sketch a graph of the identity function. What purpose does the identity function serve in regard to a function and its inverse?

16. If the graphs of $y = \log_b x$ and $y = -\log_b x$ are symmetrical about the x axis, is $y = 0$ the identity function? Explain.

17. Prove that $f(x) = x - 2$ and $f^{-1}(x) = x + 2$ are truly inverse functions.

18. Show that the functions $y = x^3$ and $y = \sqrt[3]{x}$ are commutative. Does it follow then that each function is the inverse of the other?

19. One form of the equation of a **catenary,** the curve formed if a very flexible rope is allowed to hang between two posts, is

$$y = \cosh x = \frac{e^x + e^{-x}}{2}.$$

Make a graph of this hyperbolic function from $0 \leq x \leq 4$.

20. If the population of a city increases exponentially so that $y = ce^{kt}$, where $y =$ population, $t =$ years, $c = y$ when $t = 0$, and $k = 0, 1, \ldots$, how many years would it take for the population to change from 50,000 to 150,000 people?

How long would it take $3,256 to double if it were invested as follows:

21. (a) 6% compounded annually.   (b) 6% converted 1,000 times a year.
22. (a) 6% compounded quarterly.   (b) 6% compounded continuously.

8.8 LOGARITHMS AND THE LAWS OF LOGARITHMS

Up until the impact of the computing machine on our society logarithms were one of the greatest time and labor saving devices ever invented by man. But in spite of the influence of the computing machine, and in spite of the fact that the major emphasis today is placed upon the theoretical aspects of logarithmic functions, as a means of computing the results of complicated multiplications and divisions logarithms still hold a significant place in mathematics. Consequently, the basic facts and principles of logarithms must continue to be a part of our mathematical study.

As was stated in Section 8.2 and as is indicated by the next definition:

LOGARITHMS ARE EXPONENTS.

Definition: 8.8-1.   *For x a positive real number, $y \in R$, and $b > 0$, $b \neq 1$, the **logarithm of x** is the exponent y which indicates the power to which a number b, called the base, must be raised to produce x.*

The preceding definition may be expressed in these equivalent forms:

(A) **The logarithmic form:** $\log_b x = y$ $(b > 0, b \neq 1)$;
(B) **The exponential form:** $x = b^y$ $(b > 0, b \neq 1)$;
(C) **The antilogarithmic form:** $x = \text{antilog}_b y$ $(b > 0, b \neq 1)$.

Definition: 8.8-2.   *The number x required when the logarithm y is known is called the **antilogarithm**.*

Note these two things:

1. The exponent y in the exponential form $x = b^y$ is identical to the y in the logarithmic form $\log_b x = y$.

$\therefore x = b^{\log_b x}$. (A)

2. If y is known in $\log_b x = y$ and you want to find the number x, you do so by taking the antilogarithm of y.

That is,

$\therefore \text{antilog}_b y = x$. (B)

The base of a system of logarithms can be any positive integer except 1. The base 1 is ruled out because it would cause $\log_b x = y$ to degenerate into a line function. You might find it interesting to investigate this situation.

Actually, in working with logarithms only two bases are in common use, the base 10 and the base e, where e is the symbol for the irrational number 2.7182818284 . . . (see Section 8.5). As the use of the digital computer increases the number 2 as a base for logarithms is used and may become more common.

Logarithms using base 10, designated by the symbol $\log_{10} x$ **are called common logarithms. Logarithms using the base e,** designated by $\log_e x$, or more neatly $\ln x$, **are called natural logarithms.** Natural logarithms find their greatest use in the calculus and higher mathematics. As a matter of fact, logarithmic tables are first computed for base e, by higher mathematics, and then changed to the base 10 by this relationship:

$$\log_{10} x = (\log_e x)(\log_{10} e). \tag{C}$$

Because $\log_{10} e = 0.43429448$ . . . , the above statement becomes

$$\log_{10} x = (0.43429448 \ldots) \log_e x. \tag{C_1}$$

Since *logarithms are exponents,* the five theorems or laws of exponents are used to prove the following theorems concerning logarithms.

Theorem: 8.8-1. The logarithm of the product of two (or more) numbers is the sum of their logarithms. Or, symbolically,

$$\log_b (xy) = \log_b x + \log_b y, \qquad \text{for } x, y \in R \text{ and positive and } b > 1.$$

PROVE: $\log_b (xy) = \log_b x + \log_b y$.

By Definition 8.8-1 $\log_b x$ is the power to which b must be raised to give the number x.

Then $x = b^{\log_b x}$ and $y = b^{\log_b y}$.

The product of xy is: $xy = b^{\log_b x} b^{\log_b y}$.

By Theorem 8.2-1: $xy = b^{(\log_b x + \log_b y)}$.

Writing the above exponential statement in logarithmic form, we obtain

$$\log_b (xy) = \log_b x + \log_b y.$$

Theorem: 8.8-2. The logarithm of the quotient of two numbers is the logarithm of the numerator minus the logarithm of the denominator. That is, $\log_b (xy) = \log_b x - \log_b y$, for all positive x and y.

PROVE: $\log_b \left(\dfrac{x}{y}\right) = \log_b x - \log_b y$.

Again, because $\log_b x$ is the power to which b must be raised to give x, it follows that $x = b^{\log_b x}$ and $y = b^{\log_b y}$.   (Definition 8.8-1)

Dividing x by y: $\dfrac{x}{y} = \dfrac{b^{\log_b x}}{b^{\log_b y}} = b^{(\log_b x - \log_b y)}$.   (Theorem 8.2-2)

Writing the above exponential in logarithmic form we get

$$\log_b \frac{x}{y} = \log_b x - \log_b y.$$

Theorem: 8.8-3.   The logarithm of the y power of a number x is y times the logarithm of x to the base b. Or, in symbols,

$\log_b (x^y) = y \log_b x$, for x positive and y a real number.

The proof of this theorem is similar to the preceding ones. It and the next theorem that follow will be left for the reader to prove.

Theorem: 8.8-4.   The logarithm of the real yth root of a number x is the logarithm of x divided by y. That is, $\log_b (x)^{1/y} = \dfrac{\log_b x}{y}$, for x a positive number and y a real number different from zero.

Theorem: 8.8-5.   If b is different from 1 and positive and the base is e, then

$$\log_e b = \frac{1}{\log_b e}.$$

PROVE: $\log_e b = \dfrac{1}{\log_b e}$.

Since $\log_e b$ is the power to which e must be raised to give b, it is true that

$b = e^{\log_e b}$.   (Definition 8.8-1)

Applying the preceding principle to $\log_b e$, we obtain

$e = b^{\log_b e}$.   (Definition 8.8-1)

Taking the $1/\log_b e$ power of both sides of $b^{\log_b e} = e$, we get

$b^{(\log_b e)(1/\log_b e)} = e^{1/\log_b e}$,

and $b = e^{1/\log_b e}$.

By the transitive postulate, since

$b = e^{\log_e b}$ and $b = e^{1/\log_b e}$,

it follows that

$$\log_e b = \frac{1}{\log_b e}.$$

From (C) under Section 8.8, we have

$$\log_{10} x = (\log_e x)(\log_{10} e),$$

or $\log_e x = \dfrac{\log_{10} x}{\log_{10} e}$.

Then, by Theorem 8.8-5, $\log_e x = (\log_{10} x)(\log_e 10)$, (D)

or $$\log_e x = (2.302585 \ldots) \log_{10} x. \qquad (D')$$

In the back of this book on page 394 you will find **Table II,** a table of four-place **Common Logarithms; Table V,** a table of **Exponential Functions** on page 409; and **Table VI,** a table of **Natural Logarithms of Numbers** on page 410.

Tables of logarithms up to 33-digit accuracy have been obtained, but 4-digit accuracy is sufficient for our purpose. As you notice, Table II provides the logarithms of 3-digit numbers without interpolation and 3-digit numbers if linear interpolation is used.

8.9 HOW TO FIND THE COMMON LOGARITHM OF A NUMBER

The advantage of 10 as the base of the common logarithmic system may be seen from the following table:

Table 8.9-1

Numbers in Exponent Form	Numbers in Logarithmic Form
. .	. .
. .	. .
. .	. .
$0.001 = 10^{-3}$	$\log_{10} 0.001 = -3$
$0.01\ \ = 10^{-2}$	$\log_{10} 0.01\ \ = -2$
$0.1\ \ \ = 10^{-1}$	$\log_{10} 0.1\ \ \ = -1$
$1\ \ \ \ = 10^0$	$\log_{10} 1\ \ \ \ = 0$
$10\ \ \ = 10^1$	$\log_{10} 10\ \ \ = 1$
$100\ \ = 10^2$	$\log_{10} 100\ \ = 2$
$1,000\ \ = 10^3$	$\log_{10} 1,000 = 3$
. .	. .
. .	. .
. .	. .

These selected numbers with integral powers working on the base 10 can be extended without end in either direction, and the logarithm of each number has an integral logarithmic value. Not only do numbers that have integral exponents have logarithms, but numbers that have fractional exponents, such as $10^{2.6857} \doteq 485$ also have logarithms. As an example we will show that $\log_{10} 485 \doteq 2.6857$.

Looking at Table 8.9-1, it is evident that the number 485 is more than 100 and less than 1,000; so its logarithm has to be between 2 and 3. Thus, the integral part of the logarithm is 2. The fractional part, the part that is to be added to 2, will be obtained by changing the number 485 to **standard form** (*scientific notation*) and using Table II.

To write any number in standard form, place a decimal point after the first left-hand nonzero digit of the number. This forms the first of two factors. Then make a count of the number of digits that must be passed over to move from the new to the original decimal point of the number. The number that represents this count is the power that must be applied to 10 to reproduce the original number. *The base* 10 *to some power is always the second factor of the standard form.* If as you move you count over digits to the right, then 10 to the power of the count is positive. If you count to the left, 10 to the power of the count is negative. For example,

Number	Standard Form (Scientific Notation)	
4.85	$= 4.85 \times 10^0$	(A)
485	$= 4.85 \times 10^2$	(B)
0.00485	$= 4.85 \times 10^{-3}$	(C)
4,850,000	$= 4.85 \times 10^6$	(D)
0.485	$= 4.85 \times 10^{-1}$	(E)

Notice these things:

1. (B) and (D) have positive exponents because you have to move to the right to count to the original decimal point.
2. (C) and (E) have negative exponents because you have to move to the left to count to the original decimal point.
3. The standard form of a number always consists of two factors:
   (a) the left factor has a value between 1 and 10;
   (b) the right factor is always 10 to some integral power.
4. The exponent on 10 always gives the integral part of the logarithm and is called the **characteristic of the logarithm.**
5. The value between 1 and 10 gives the fractional part of the logarithm and is called the **mantissa of the logarithm.**
6. A mantissa value is determined by using Table II. **Table II contains logarithmic values for numbers between 1 and 10 only.**

From here on, *when the base is omitted in the writing of the logarithm form, it is to be understood that the base is* 10. Let us now return to the problem of finding the logarithm of 485.

$$\log 485 = \log(4.85 \times 10^2) = \log 4.85 + \log 10^2,$$
$$= \log 4.85 + 2 \log 10.$$

Finding the 4 and 8 in the left column of Table II and moving horizontally to the column headed 5, we read

   log 4.85 ≐ 0.6857.

Since log 10 = 1,   2 log 10 = 2.

Therefore, **log 485 ≐ 2.6857.**

This means that $10^{2.6857}$ is the exponential form approximately equal to 485.

   We have found that the exponent on the factor 10, where the number is expressed in standard notation, gives the characteristic (the integral part of the logarithm). From this fact we can speed up the action by writing these directives:

   1. **To find the characteristic of a number,** begin to the right of the first left-hand nonzero digit and count the digits passed over to return to the original decimal point.
   (a) If the count is to the right the characteristic is positive.
   (b) If the count is to the left the characteristic is negative.
   The logarithm of the other factor of the number whose value is between 1 and 10 is the mantissa. **In this text, mantissas are positive without exception and fractional in nature.**
   2. **To find the mantissa of a number,** use Table II, which is actually a table of mantissas, commonly but wrongly called a table of logarithms. To have a complete table of logarithms the characteristics as well as the mantissas would have to be given. This is done in tables of logarithms of trigonometric functions and for logarithms of numbers to bases other than 10.

   Example: 8.9-1.   Find the value of log 564,300.
   According to the preceding directives, the characteristic of log 5̪64,30̪0 is +5. The plus sign does not need to be written. To get the mantissa, find 56 in the left column of Table II, move horizontally into the column headed 4 and read 0.7513. Then continue horizontally to the right into the proportional parts section of the table under the column headed 3 and read 2. Add this 0.0002 to 0.7513 to get 0.7515 as the desired mantissa.

Therefore, **log 564,300 ≐ 5.7515.**

   The proportional parts section in Table II has been placed there to save the time involved in making **linear interpolations** such as the following:

Then $\dfrac{x}{0.007} \doteq \dfrac{300}{1000}$, $x \doteq 0.0002$.

Therefore, **log 564,300 $\doteq$ 5.7515.**

Linear interpolation takes considerably more time and labor, as you can see.

Example: 8.9-2. Find the value of log 0.00295.

As the arrow in log 0.00295 indicates, the characteristic is -3. Characteristics can be negative, but mantissas cannot. The mantissa of 0.00295 is found by placing 29 in the left-hand column of Table II and moving horizontally to column 5 and reading 0.4698.

The question now arises: What is the proper way of recording a logarithm where the integral part (the characteristic) is negative and the fractional part (the mantissa) is positive? There are three equivalent and acceptable ways:

1. log 0.00295 $\doteq \overline{3}.4698$.   *The bar over the* 3 *means that the characteristic is negative, that is,* -3.

2. log 0.00295 $\doteq 0.4698 - 3$.   The negative characteristic -3 is written to the right of the positive mantissa.

3. (a) log 0.00295 $\doteq 7.4698 - 10$.   No matter which one of these forms
   (b) log 0.00295 $\doteq 17.4698 - 20$.   you use, by adding the positive and
   (c) log 0.00295 $\doteq 27.4698 - 30$.   the negative integrals you get the characteristic -3.

Form 1 is certainly the most compact, but for computational purposes Form 3 is usually preferred.

Example: 8.9-3. What is the antilogarithm (that is, the number) if log $x \doteq \overline{4}.2846$?

In Table II the mantissa of $\overline{4}.2846$, which is 0.2846, falls between column 2 and column 3 in row 1.9; so the first three digits of the number are 1.92. The fourth digit must be found by linear interpolation.

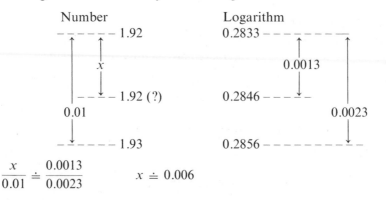

$\dfrac{x}{0.01} \doteq \dfrac{0.0013}{0.0023}$ $x \doteq 0.006$

Therefore, for log $w \doteq 0.2848$, $w \doteq 1.92 + 0.006 \doteq 1.926$,

and for log $N \doteq \overline{4}.2848$, $N \doteq 0.0001926$.

That is, **antilog $\overline{4}.2848 \doteq 0.0001926 = N$.**

Here again the proportional parts section of Table II could have greatly speeded up the interpolation. For example, take the number horizontally to the right of 1.9 in column 2, which is 0.2833, and subtract it from the given mantissa 0.2846 to get 13. Move horizontally in the 1.9 row into the proportional parts section of Table II until you find 13. The number at the top of that column is 6. Annex it to 1.92 and you have 1.926, which is the number when the logarithm is 0.2846. Finally,

If log $N = 4.2846$, then $N = 0.0001926$.

Example: 8.9-4.   Use logarithms to find the value of $\dfrac{(\sqrt[3]{52.76})(35.27)^2}{769.0}$.

$\log \dfrac{(52.76)^{1/3}(35.27)^2}{769.0} = \tfrac{1}{3} \log 52.76 + 2 \log 35.27 - \log 769.0$,

$$\log x \doteq \tfrac{1}{3}(1.7223) + 2(1.5474) - 2.8859,$$

$$\log x \doteq 0.5741 + 3.0948 - 2.8859,$$

$$\log x \doteq 0.7830.$$

Therefore, $x \doteq 6.067$ and $\dfrac{\sqrt[3]{\mathbf{52.76}}(\mathbf{35.27})^2}{\mathbf{769.0}} \doteq \mathbf{6.067}.$

Example: 8.9-5.   Find the value of $\dfrac{\sqrt[7]{0.6273}}{\sqrt[3]{(0.0005241)^2}}$.

$\log \dfrac{(0.6273)^{1/7}}{(0.0005241)^{2/3}} \doteq \tfrac{1}{7} \log 0.6273 - \tfrac{2}{3} \log 0.0005241$,

$$\log x \doteq \tfrac{1}{7}(9.7975 - 10) - \tfrac{2}{3}(6.7194 - 10),$$

$$\log x \doteq \tfrac{1}{7}(69.7975 - 70) - \tfrac{2}{3}(26.7194 - 30).$$

In the preceding line the actual values of the characteristics have not been changed but, for the convenience of dividing by 7 and 3 and meeting the demand that characteristics must be kept integral, the form of the characteristics have been changed. Then, multiplying by $\tfrac{1}{7}$ and $\tfrac{2}{3}$ respectively, we obtain

      $\log x \doteq (9.9711 - 10) - (17.8130 - 20)$

or $\log x \doteq (9.9711 - 10) - (7.8130 - 10)$,

and $\log x \doteq 2.1581$.

Therefore, $x \doteq 143.9$ and $\dfrac{\sqrt[7]{0.6273}}{\sqrt[3]{(0.0005241)^2}} \doteq 143.9$.

It would also be correct to write

antilog $2.1581 \doteq 143.9$.

Example: 8.9-6.   Find the value of $(0.472)^x = 27.5$.

If $(0.472)^x = 27.5$,

then $x \log 0.472 = \log 27.5$,

and $x = \dfrac{\log 27.5}{\log 0.472} \doteq \dfrac{1.4393}{9.6739 - 10}$.

Note that $\dfrac{\log 27.5}{\log 0.472}$ **has an entirely different meaning than** $\log \dfrac{27.5}{0.472}$. Actually, 1.4393 has to be divided by -0.3261, the difference between 9.6739 and -10.

Therefore, $x \doteq \dfrac{1.4393}{-0.3261} \doteq -4.41$.

If negative numbers are involved in expressions to be worked by logarithms, one has to study the data and determine what effect the negative numbers will have on the final answers. Then apply the logarithmic principles as if no negative signs were involved, but at the very last, adjust the answers so that they will have the proper signs for the given data.

EXERCISE 8.C

1. Write the equivalent of $x = b^y$ in logarithmic form.
2. If $y = \log_a x$ express its equivalent in exponent form.
3. In the symbol antilog$_b$ y, what purpose does b serve? What special kind of number does the y represent?
4. What does the symbol antilog$_{10}$ 2 mean? Find its numerical value.
5. Which number in the positive integers cannot be used as the base for a system of logarithms? Show why.
6. Logarithmic tables are available to you for what bases? Does this mean you cannot evaluate statements to other bases?
7. Evaluate $y = \log_2 32$. (Hint: change to an equivalent form.)
8. Find y if $y = \log_5 125$.
9. Determine y, if $y = \log (81)^{-1/2}$.
10. Evaluate $y = \log_{12} 144$.
11. Prove that $\log_b (x)^y = y \log_b x$ ($y \in R$ and $x \in R+$).
12. Prove that $\log_b \sqrt[y]{x} = (1/y)(\log_b x)(y \in R$ and $x \in R+$).
13. Without the help of tables evaluate $\log_{100} 10$.

14. Use Table VI page 410 and $\log_e 67$ to find $\log_{10} 67$.

Change these numbers to standard, or scientific, notation. *Always keep the nonzero digits in the left-hand factor.*

15. (a) 673.   (b) 87,640.   (c) 0.0047.   (d) 0.0000972.
16. (a) 0.714.   (b) 5,231   (c) 0.0236.   (d) 96,000.

17. A number in standard notation contains how many factors? In terms of logarithms, what does the exponent on the base 10 tell you?

18. Write the number 5 in standard notation. What is its characteristic? Are there any characteristics recorded in Table II? Then is Table II a table of mantissas? a table of logarithms? or both under the specified condition that it represents logarithms of numbers from 1 to 10 only?

Use Table II to find the logarithms of the numbers in Problems 19 and 20.

19. (a) 47.8.   (b) 0.0479.   (c) 83,230.   (d) 0.2473.
20. (a) 27,000.   (b) 0.0004.   (c) 97.36.   (d) 289.4.

Given the number 86.34 to four significant digits, write the number so that the characteristic of the logarithm of the number is:

21. (a) 1.   (b) 0.   (c) -2.   (d) $\bar{3}$.   (e) $9 - 10$.
22. (a) 4.   (b) -3.   (c) -2.   (d) $7 - 10$.   (e) $\bar{1}$.

Use the laws of logarithms and Table II to evaluate the following. Keep the same number of significant digits in the answers as are in the least accurate number used. (Study Sections 9.4-6 to 9.4-11.)

23. $34.6 \times 672 \times 0.0542$.   **24.** $0.672 \times 738 \times 901$.
25. 64.85×0.007238.   **26.** 11.82×27.51.
27. $84,630 \div 72.94$.   **28.** $576.4 \div 21.68$.

29. $\dfrac{54.5 \times 1.07}{0.412 \times 8.23}$.   **30.** $\dfrac{276 \times 43.1}{0.00571 \times 96,700}$.

31. $\dfrac{(\sqrt{0.67214})(44.71)^2}{\sqrt[3]{(247.9)^2}}$.   **32.** $\dfrac{(6.472)^{1/2}\sqrt[3]{987.2}}{(0.01435)^{3/2}}$.

Solve for x:

33. $x^{3.572} = 842.9$.   **34.** $(1.728)^x = 4.321$.
35. $x^{0.57} = 6.4$.   **36.** $(3.872)^{x-1} = 428.9$.

37. The area of a sphere is $A = 4\pi r^2 = 75.42$ square inches. Find its radius.

38. Find the perimeter of an equilateral triangle whose area is 67.7 square feet.

39. Find the volume of a sphere if $V = \frac{4}{3}\pi r^3$ and $r = 12.25$ feet.

40. In a vacuum a body falls according to the formula $s = \frac{1}{2}gt^2$, where g is approximately 32.2 feet per second per second, s is distance in feet, and t is time in seconds. Find the distance s a body has fallen after 1 hour and 45 minutes.

Trigonometry in Terms of Angles

In Chapter 7 the circular functions and their applications were presented. The circular function approach is commonly called **analytic trigonometry** and is based upon the concept of a real number. The domains and the ranges of the circular functions are subsets of the real number system.

The analytic trigonometric approach is especially pleasing to the mathematician because it enables him to subject the circular functions to the same basic operations as are applied to other elementary functions.

Angle trigonometry, which will be discussed in this chapter, has traditionally been a mathematical discipline highly adaptable to practical applications, especially those problems having to do with the sides and angles of triangles.

9.1 ANGLES

To make a logical connection between the **analytic trigonometry of real numbers** and **angle trigonometry** we must have a clear understanding of these two questions:

1. What is an angle?
2. How is the central angle θ in a circle related to the real number t which measures its intercepted arc?

Definition: 9.1-1. *To form an* **angle** *rotate a ray, a line with a fixed point at one end of it, about its fixed point from an initial to a terminal position.*

The end point of the ray or half-line is called the **vertex,** the initial position of the half-line is called its **initial side,** and its terminal position is called its **terminal side.** The amount of rotation gives the **measure of an angle.** It is not unusual for authors to use just the word "angle" in place of "the measure of an angle." This practice will be followed. In this book angles will be measured

Table 9.2-1

t as a Real Number Expressing Arc Length	θ as an Angle Measured in Radians		θ as an Angle Measured in Degrees	
Circle	=	2π	=	360
Semicircle	=	π	=	180
Quarter-circle	=	$\pi/2$	=	90
One-sixth circle	=	$\pi/3$	=	60
One-eighth circle	=	$\pi/4$	=	45
One-twelfth circle	=	$\pi/6$	=	30

You should be able to change quickly from radian measure to degrees and from degrees to radians. Two relations that are helpful in making these changes are

$$1 \text{ radian} = \left(\frac{180}{\pi}\right)^{\circ} \quad \text{and} \quad 1 \text{ degree} = \frac{\pi}{180} \text{ radian.}$$

Since $\pi(\text{radians}) = 180°$,

$$\text{then} \quad 1 \text{ radian} = \left(\frac{180}{\pi}\right)^{\circ} = 57.2958\ldots^{\circ}$$

$$\text{and} \quad 1 \text{ degree} = \frac{\pi}{180} = 0.017453\ldots \text{ radian.}$$

One of the advantages of expressing the measure of angles in terms of radians is that it provides an efficient method of determining the length of the arc regardless of the length of the radius of the circle.

In plane geometry we learned that **the intercepted arcs of circles are to each other as their corresponding radii.** Applying this to Figure 9.2-2 we read

$$\frac{s}{r} = \frac{t}{1},$$

and $s = rt$.

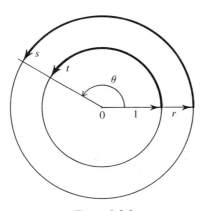

Figure 9.2-2

It has already been established that $t = \theta$, provided θ is expressed in radians. So $s = rt$ becomes, by substitution,

$s = r\theta$ (θ measured in radians).

In general, *the* **length of an arc of a circle** *is equal to the radius of the circle times the radians in its central angle.*

Example: 9.2-1. Express the numbers, $\pi/2$, $(-\pi/4)$, and 2π, that represent length of arcs on a unit circle, in term of degrees.

(a) $t = \pi/2$ corresponds to $\theta = \pi/2$ in radians, hence $\theta = 90°$.
(b) $t = -\pi/4$ corresponds to $\theta = -\pi/4$ in radians, hence $\theta = -45°$.
(c) $t = 2$ corresponds to $\theta = 2$ in radians, hence $\theta \doteq 114.6°$.

Example: 9.2-2. Express these angles, $60°$, $405°$, and $20°$ in terms of numbers on a unit circle.

(a) $\theta = 60°$ corresponds to $\theta = \pi/3$ in radians, hence $t = \pi/3$ as a measure of length.
(b) $\theta = 405°$ corresponds to $\theta = 9\pi/4$ in radians, hence $t = 9\pi/4$ as a length of arc.
(c) $\theta = 20°$ corresponds to $\theta = \dfrac{20\pi}{180}$ in radians, hence $t = \pi/9$ as a length of arc.

Example: 9.2-3. How far does a man on a bicycle travel in 12 revolutions if the wheels on his bicycle have a diameter of 26 inches?

In this problem (and all other problems in this text that involve either measurements or other approximate numbers) the basic concepts of computing with approximate data are expected to be applied. The answers in the back of the book will reflect this practice after you have studied "computing with approximate data" in Section 9.4.

Using $s = r\theta$ where $r = 13''$ and $\theta = 12(2\pi)$ radians, we get $s = (13)(24)\pi$. Because the given data is two-digit accuracy we will take $\pi \doteq 3.14$.

$s \doteq (312)(3.14) \doteq 989.68$ inches.

We are to keep no more significant digits in our answer than is in the least accurate number in our given data. Therefore, there is no sense in keeping more than two significant digits in our answer. So the man traveled

990 inches.

9.3 USE OF TABLE I AND TABLE III

In Table I located on page 390 you can find the value of any circular function or its corresponding trigonometric function in three ways:

Use the left-hand column of Table I either for t a real number or for its equivalent angular measure θ in radians. If θ is given in degrees, use the right-hand column of the table to obtain the value of the function.

1. If $t = 1.00$, then $\cos t = \cos 1.00 \doteq 0.5403$.
2. If $t = 1.00$, then $\theta = 1.00$ and $\cos \theta = \cos 1.00 \doteq 0.5403$.
3. If $\theta = 1.00$ (radian), then $\theta \doteq 57.3°$ and $\cos 57.3° \doteq 0.5403$.

As you can see, it makes no difference whether or not you look up the function of the real number $t = 1.00$, the angle expressed as a radian $\theta = 1.00$, or the angle expressed as 57.3 degrees.

Table I is, of course, reversible. If you are given the value of a circular or trigonometric function you look for that value under the proper functional value heading. Then look horizontally to the right or left for the angle in degrees, the angle in radians, or the real number which measures the length of arc. For example, if $\tan t \doteq 1.009$, then $t \doteq 45° \; 16'$ or 0.79 of a radian, or 0.79 of a unit of length.

In Table I note that the real number values are evenly and conveniently spaced, but the corresponding angles in degrees do not follow an even pattern. Table III on page 396 differs from Table I mainly in that the angles in degrees are conveniently and evenly spaced, but the radians do not follow an even pattern.

In Tables I and III, as in most all tables, linear interpolation often has to be used to evaluate a given number or angle. For example, to evaluate $\cos 57° \; 18'$ in Table III, linear interpolation is necessary. From Table III,

$$\begin{array}{ll} \cos 57° \; 10' \doteq 0.5422 \\ \cos 57° \; 18' \doteq 0.54\ldots \\ \cos 57° \; 20' \doteq 0.5398 \end{array}$$

By proportion $\dfrac{x}{24} \doteq \dfrac{8}{10}$ and $x \doteq 19$.

As the angles increase the cosine values decrease. Therefore, subtract 0.0019 from 0.5422 to get

$\cos 57° \; 18' \doteq 0.5403$.

This is the same value given for $\cos 57° \; 18'$ in Table I.

9.4 COMPUTING WITH APPROXIMATE DATA

All numbers t, or angles θ, which we have been using to represent measurements, are **approximate numbers.** Other sources of approximate numbers are logarithmic tables, trigonometric tables and most other tables that contain numbers rounded to a certain place value accuracy.

Definition: 9.4-a.   *An* **approximate number** *is a record of a measurement, or a rounding of a number, to a certain degree of accuracy.*

An approximate number never expresses absolute precision or accuracy as does an **exact number.**

Definition: 9.4-b.   *An* **exact number** *is a number obtained by counting indivisible units.*

Much valuable time and effort can be saved in working out the problems in applied mathematics if one realizes that *computations with approximate data can never make results more accurate than were the data used to obtain them.*

9.4-1 Unit of Measurement

The **unit of measurement** is the basic idea in all measurements.

Definition: 9.4-1a.   *The* **unit of measurement** *is the smallest unit used in making a specific measurement.*

Suppose, for example, the cylinder bore of an automobile is 3.270 inches. The unit of measurement is 0.001 inch and there are 3,270 such units. Never, for any reason, omit the 0 in a case like 3.270 inches. The 0 must be retained to show that the measurement was taken to 0.001 inch and that the true measurement is somewhere between 3.2695 and 3.2705 inches.

Likewise, if a bunch of bananas weighs $7\frac{0}{16}$ lb, the unit of weight is $\frac{1}{16}$ lb, and there are 112 such units. If the 0 were not retained you would never know the size of the unit of measurement.

9.4-2 Absolute Error of a Measurement

An approximate number implies a closeness to the true number.

Definition: 9.5-2a.   *The* **absolute** (*or greatest possible*) **error** *of a measurement is one-half the unit of measurement.*

Assume a measurement of 27.3 feet. The unit of measurement is 0.1 foot and the absolute error is $+0.05$ foot or -0.05 foot. This means that the unit of measurement can be in error not more than 0.05 foot either side of the given measurement and that the true measurement is somewhere between 27.25 feet and 27.35 feet.

9.4-3 Precision of a Measurement

Exact numbers are 100 *per cent precise.* Computations with them produce exact results. All numbers that are not exact are approximate, and we need to know how to judge the precision of these approximate numbers.

Definition: 9.4-3a.   *The maximum amount a measurement can vary from the true measurement is called the* **precision of the measurement.**

The first three entries in Table 9.4-3a show that *the smaller the unit of measurement used the greater is the precision.*

Table 9.4-3a

Measurements	Precision of Measurement in Terms of:	
	Unit of Measurement	Absolute Error
674 ft	1 ft	0.5 ft
67.4 ft	0.1 ft	0.05 ft
6.74 ft	0.01 ft	0.005 ft
7.050 ft	0.001 oz	0.0005 oz
$11\frac{0}{8}$ in	$\frac{1}{8}$ in.	$\frac{1}{16}$ in
25° 11′	1 min	0.5 min

Precision may be measured either by the unit of measurement or by absolute error, which is one-half the unit of measurement.

9.4-4 Rounding Numbers

Definition: 9.4-4a. *The process of dropping one or several digits from the right end of a number is called* **rounding the number.**

The basic rules for rounding numbers as used in this text are as follows:
1. If the right-hand digit to be dropped from a number is less than five, do not change the digit to its immediate left.
2. If the right-hand digit to be dropped from a number is five or more, increase the digit to its immediate left by one.
3. (a) If the left-hand digit of several digits to be dropped is less than five, do not change the digit to its immediate left.
(b) If the left-hand digit of several digits to be dropped is five or more, increase the digit to its immediate left by one.
4. When dropping digits from the right end of a whole number replace them with zeros.

9.4-5 Addition and Subtraction of Approximate Data

Precision is the controlling concept in addition or subtraction of approximate data.

The sum (or difference) of a set of approximate numbers should have the same precision as the least precise approximate number used in the set.

Standard practice in the addition or subtraction of approximate numbers is to round the numbers to one more digit than the least precise number before adding or subtracting.

(A)————►(B)		(C)————————►(D)	
3.825 ft	3.8	27.492 inches	27.49
523.1 ft	523.1	6.7 inches	6.7
89 ft	89	20.792 inches	20.79
615.925 ft	615.9	20.8 inches	**20.8 inches**
616 ft	**616 ft**		

In Example (B) 89 feet is the least precise measure given so the sum of the measurement should be expressed to the nearest foot, that is, 616 feet is the "best" answer. In Example (D), 6.7 inches is the least precise measurement so the difference should be expressed to the nearest tenth of an inch, that is, 20.8 inches is the "best" answer.

By "best" answer, we mean the most reasonable or the most dependable answer.

9.4-6 Significant Digits

Definition: 9.4-6. *If each digit of a number except the right-hand one is exactly correct, and the error in the right-hand digit is not more than one-half the unit of measurement, then each digit of that number is said to be a* **significant digit.**

The nonzero digits in an approximate number are always significant. As Table 9.4-6a will show, the zero digits may or may not be significant.

Table 9.4-6a

Measurement	Unit of Measurement	Count of Units of Measurement	Number of Significant Digits in Measurement
(a) 0.009 ft	0.001 ft	9	1
(b) 50 ft	10 ft	5	1
(c) 0.70 ft	0.01 ft	70	2
(d) $18\frac{0}{4}$ ft	$\frac{1}{4}$ ft	72	2
(e) 13° 42′	1 min	822	3
(f) 18 lb. 11 oz	1 oz	299	3

Table 9.4-6a demonstrates these facts:

1. **In a measurement a zero digit is significant if and only if it is needed to record the correct count of the number of units of measure in the measurement.**

(a) In 0.009 ft in the table the two zeros to the right of the decimal point are not needed to express the count of the units of measure, so they are not significant. *In a decimal fraction the zeros between the decimal point and the first nonzero digit to the right are never significant.*

(b) The zero on the right end of the whole number 50 in the table is not needed and is not significant. Of course, *zeros on the right end of a whole number may or may not be significant depending entirely on the unit of measure stated.*

(c) The zero on the right end of 0.70 in the table is significant because it is needed to give the correct count of units of measure. In fact, *zeros on the right end of any decimal or mixed decimal fraction are significant.*

2. **The significance of digits depends entirely on the count of the units of measure in a measurement and is completely independent of the position of the decimal point in the number.** Note from the table that 0.009 ft and 50 ft each have one significant digit and that 0.70 ft and $18\frac{9}{4}$ ft each have two significant digits.

9.4-7 Relative Error

Definition: 9.4-7a. Relative error *is the ratio of the absolute error of an approximate number to the approximate number.*

Suppose two measurements 6 ft and 9 ft are measured to the nearest foot. Then the *absolute error* of each is 0.5 ft and their *relative errors* are:

$$\frac{0.5}{6} \doteq 0.083\overline{3}, \qquad \frac{0.5}{9} \doteq 0.05\overline{5}.$$

Since the absolute error of 0.5 foot is the same in the 6-foot measure as in the 9-foot measurement, the 9-foot measurement is more accurate. Also, the fact that the 9-foot measurement has the smaller relative error indicates that it is more accurate.

9.4-8 Accuracy of a Measurement

We have introduced the concepts of **significant digits** and **relative error** for the purpose of using them to express the **accuracy of an approximate number.**

From the significant digit viewpoint,

Definition: 9.4-8a. *The* **accuracy of an approximate number** *is the count of the significant digits in that number.*

The measurement 36 pounds has two significant digits so we say that it has two-digit accuracy. The circular function cos 1 $\doteq$ 0.5403 has four significant digits and four-digit accuracy.

Measurements that have the same number of significant digits, such as 879 ft and 902 ft, have the same digit accuracy. But note that for any two approximate numbers, such as 879 and 902, the number having the larger left-hand digit is actually the more accurate. This is because 902 is closer to a four-digit accurate number than is 879.

From the relative error viewpoint,

Definition: 9.4-8b. *The* **accuracy of an approximate number** *may be expressed in terms of the relative error. That is, for any two approximate numbers the one having the smaller relative error is the more accurate number.*

As you can see by referring to Table 9.4-8a, *the relative error is a more reliable and a more mathematical type of approach to the determination of accuracy than is the significant digit method.*

Table 9.4-8a

Measurement	Unit of Measurement	Precision or Absolute Error	Accuracy By: Significant Digits	Relative Error	Per Cent Error	Degree of Accuracy (in Per Cent)
1 lb	1 lb	0.5 lb	1	0.5	50	50
9 lb	1 lb	0.5 lb	1	0.0555	5.6	94.4+
10 gal	1 gal	0.5 gal	2	0.05	5.0	95.5
99 gal	1 gal	0.5 gal	2	0.0051−	0.51	99.49+
100 ft	1 ft	0.5 ft	3	0.005	0.50	99.50
999 ft	1 ft	0.5 ft	3	0.0005	0.05+	99.95+

Notice especially in Table 9.4-8a the columns headed "Per Cent Error" and "Degree of Accuracy."

Definition: 9.4-8c.   Per Cent Error *is relative error expressed in per cent form.*

Definition: 9.4-8d.   Degree of Accuracy *is per cent error subtracted from* 100 *per cent.*

Definitions 9.4-8c and 8d should help considerably in the comparison of the accuracy of one number with another.

9.4-9 Multiplication of Approximate Numbers

When adding or subtracting approximate numbers we based our procedure on **precision** (Section 9.4-5), to get the "best" answer. Now, notice that in multiplication or division we depend upon the idea of **accuracy** as indicated by significant digits or by relative error to obtain the most reasonable or "best" answer.

The standard procedure in multiplying or dividing approximate numbers is to round the more accurate numbers until they contain one more digit than the least accurate number, then complete computation and round the answer until it contains the same number of digits as the least accurate number used.

When either approximate numbers or exact and approximate numbers are multiplied together, keep in the final product the same number of significant digits as is in the least accurate factor.

If an exact number does enter into a computation you need to keep in mind that it is 100 per cent precise and accurate. It is precise and accurate to an unlimited number of digits. **An exact number represents a true count.** For example, 4 cows mean 4.0000000000 . . . cows.

In multiplying 47.46 ft by 6.02 ft, you must understand that all the digits are correct for each measurement except the right-hand digit which is only
significant.

$$
\begin{array}{r}
47.46 \\
6.02 \\
\hline
94\ 92 \\
28476\ 0 \\
\hline
28570\ 92
\end{array}
$$

286 square feet
(best answer)

This means that the measurements 47.46 ft and 6.02 ft were closer to the
right-hand digits 6 and 2 than to any other digits. The slant lines through the
digits in the partial products and the product are there to show you the digits
that are not correct because of the influence of the 6 and the 2. You can see
also that only the 2 and the 8 in the final product are correct. The 6 is not
correct but it is significant. Thus, the "best" answer is **286 sq ft.** It contains
the same number of significant digits as does 6.02, the least accurate factor.

9.4-10 Division of Approximate Numbers

*When approximate numbers, or an exact and an approximate number, are
divided, keep in the quotient the same number of significant digits as is in the
least accurate of the two numbers.*

In cutting a 46-inch rod into 6 equal parts, note that

(a) the 6 is an exact number,
(b) the quotient has been computed to one extra significant digit and then
rounded to two significant digits.

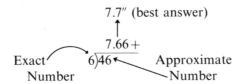

7.7″ (best answer)
↑
7.66+
Exact   6)46   Approximate
Number   Number

9.4-11 Square Roots of Approximate Numbers

To find the square root of an approximate number, one should determine the
value of one of its two equal factors to one more significant digit than is in the
given number. Round this quotient by one digit to get the "best" answer. The
example shows the square root of 59, to two significant digits, to be **7.7.**

$$
\begin{array}{r}
7.76 \text{ or } 7.8 \\
7.6)\overline{59} \\
532 \\
\hline
58 \\
532 \\
\hline
48 \\
456
\end{array}
$$

Average $\dfrac{7.6 + 7.8}{2} = $ **7.7**

9.4-12 Computing with Approximate Data in Trigonometry

If we could confine our work in trigonometry to circular functions which involve real numbers there would be no further problems concerning computations with approximate data. But in discussing angle trigonometry in the following sections we will be associating approximate angles with approximate lengths. These approximations make it necessary that the measurements expressed by angles and the measurements expressed by length be made consistent. Table 9.4-12a should help to indicate what must be done.

Table 9.4-12a

Angle	Units of Measure	Count of Units	If Given Angle Has a Count of Units of Measure from:	The Significant Digits Used in Circular or Trigonometric Ratios Should Be Not More than:
$9°$	$1°$	9	1 to 9 units	$1 + 1 = 2$ digits
$1° \, 39'$	$1'$	99	10 to 99	$2 + 1 = 3$
$16° \, 39'$	$1'$	999	100 to 999	$3 + 1 = 4$
$2° \, 46' \, 39''$	$1''$	9999	1000 to 9999	$4 + 1 = 5$

The whole point of Table 9.4-12a is to emphasize the fact that you must know how to find the number of significant digits implied by the measure of the given angle. Then in computing you must use a trigonometric ratio that does not exceed this count of significant digits by at most more than one. For example, the first four columns on the left of Table 9.4-12a show that the angle $1° \, 39'$ involves two significant digits. Then for computational purposes the right-hand column of the table tells you to keep not more than three significant digits in the trigonometric ratio that is to be associated with the angle. It is a total waste of time to keep any more.

EXERCISE 9.A

The rules for computing with approximate data are to be properly applied to all problems that involve approximate numbers. In the Answers to Odd-Numbered Problems you will occasionally find the computed answer in parentheses immediately followed by the answer properly adjusted to the number of significant digits justified. For example, the answer for Problem 9 is listed as (0.1267) 0.1.

$$\text{One radian} = \left(\frac{180}{\pi}\right)° = 57.2938\ldots°$$

$$\text{One degree} = \frac{\pi}{180} = 0.017453\ldots \text{radian}.$$

1. For each of the following, state the unit of measurement and the number of times the unit of measurement is contained in the measurement.

(a) 22 tons.
(b) 6.00 ft.
(c) 13 ft 7 inches.
(d) 3,500 miles.
(e) 5°.
(f) $5\frac{4}{8}''$.
(g) 6 lb 4 oz.
(h) 27° 14'.
(i) 39.26 sec.

2. Find the absolute error and state the precision for each of the following measurements:

(a) 49 inches.
(b) 6.9 ft.
(c) 26,000 gal.
(d) 732 miles.
(e) 0.004 gm.
(f) 5° 4' 13".
(g) 4.281 mm.
(h) $8\frac{0}{8}$ inches.
(i) $\frac{27}{32}$ inches.

3. Round these numbers to (a) three significant digits; (b) to one significant digit:

(a) 28.67.
(b) 10.842.
(c) 36,327.
(d) 47,380.
(e) 78,055.01
(f) 2.5451.

4. State the number of significant digits and the digit accuracy for each of these approximate numbers:

(a) 1,002 qt.
(b) 1.470 inches.
(c) 61° 5'.
(d) 4.110 mm.
(e) $11\frac{0}{4}$ inches.
(f) 3 yd 2 ft.
(g) 0.0060 cm.
(h) 19 ft 6 inches.
(i) 1.0001 gm.

5. What is the "best" answer for the sum of these approximate numbers?

    37,   24.79,   54.7,   221.583.

6. If a measure of 6 feet is subtracted from a measurement of 18.48 feet, what is the "best" answer?

7. Find the relative error for each of the following:

(a) 340 ft.
(b) 0.004 cm.
(c) 0.035 inches.
(d) $9\frac{0}{16}''$.
(e) 42.36 mm.
(f) 18° 32'.

8. Work out (a) the per cent error and (b) the degree of accuracy for each number in Problem 7.

9. Find the product of 7.543 inches × 0.006 inch × 2.8 inches.

10. (a) Divide 74.6 square inches by 37.281 inches.

  (b) Determine the proper square root of 64.00 square feet.

11. Sketch each of these angles in standard position. Indicate by arrow the direction of rotation and label its initial and terminal side.

(a) 40°.   (b) −120°.   (c) 10π/9.   (d) −π.   (e) −300°.

12. Draw an angle coterminal with each of the following. Label the initial and terminal sides of both angles.

(a) π/4.   (b) 180°.   (c) 7π/4.   (d) −330°.   (e) 150°.

13. How many radians are there in the central angle of a circle whose radius is 12 inches long and the length of the intercepted arc is 1 foot?

14. If the radius of a circle is 6 inches, how long must an arc on the circumference of the circle be to subtend an angle of one radian?

15. Change the following angle measures from radians to degrees:

(a) 3π/2.
(b) −0.02.
(c) 10.00.
(d) 1.00.
(e) 3.00.
(f) 1.004.
(g) −3π/4.
(h) π/9.
(i) 3/π.
(j) 3.6.
(k) −π/3.
(l) −0.3π.

16. Change the following angle measures from degrees to radians:

(a) 120°.
(b) 10° 30'.
(c) 119° 13'.
(d) −60°.
(e) −36° 10'.
(f) −70° 9'.
(g) −215°.
(h) −0°.
(i) 27.2°.
(j) 20°.
(k) 600°.
(l) −10°.

17. Write the answers for Problem 16 in terms of revolutions.

18. Write the answers for Problem 15 in terms of revolutions.

19. One angle of a triangle is 42.0°, the other one $\pi/8$ radians, what is the measure of the third angle in degrees?

20. Through how many radians does the hour hand of a clock move in thirty minutes?

21. Express each of the following as a single angle and change it to radians.

(a) $30° + 60°$.

(b) $27° \, 10' + 32° \, 50'$.

(c) $82° \, 10' - 47° \, 40'$.

(d) $21° \, 42' + 78° \, 51'$.

22. Express each of the following as a single angle and change it to degrees.

(a) $\dfrac{\pi}{3} + \dfrac{\pi}{6}$.

(b) $\dfrac{\pi}{4} - \dfrac{\pi}{3}$.

(c) $1.45 + 2.81$.

(d) $\pi - \dfrac{\pi}{2} - \dfrac{\pi}{3}$.

23. Find the length of the arc of a circle if $r = 12$ feet and $\theta = 0.21$ radians.

24. Find the length of the arc of a circle if $r = 0.06$ feet and $\theta = 60°$.

25. If a point on the rim of a 20.00-inch flywheel travels 2,764 feet a minute, through how many radians does the wheel turn in a second?

26. A belt 48 feet long passes around a 16-inch pulley. As the belt makes one complete revolution how many revolutions does the pulley make?

27. Use Table I to find the value of csc $\pi/10$. Check by using Table III.

28. Use Table III to find the value of cot 37° 13'. Check by using Table I.

29. Use Table III to find θ in sec $\theta = 1.547$. Check by using Table I.

30. Use Table I to find t in sin $t = 0.4219$. Check by using Table III.

9.5 THE TRIGONOMETRIC FUNCTIONS DEFINED

In Section 9.2 it was shown that the arc in a unit circle represented by the real number t had the same value as the angle θ measured in radians. In other words,

$$t = \theta.$$

It follows then that the circular functions defined in terms of arc lengths and the trigonometric functions of their subtended angles are represented by the same numbers. Thus,

$$\sin t = \sin \theta, \qquad \tan t = \tan \theta, \qquad \sec t = \sec \theta,$$
$$\cos t = \cos \theta, \qquad \cot t = \cot \theta, \qquad \csc t = \csc \theta.$$

On the basis of the unit circle shown in Figure 9.5-1, with θ in standard

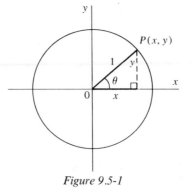

Figure 9.5-1

position and (x, y) as the coordinates at the end point of the arc t, the defini-tions of the *angle functions equivalent* to the *circular functions* are

$$\sin \theta = \frac{\text{ordinate of } P}{\text{distance to } P} = \frac{y}{1} = y.$$

$$\cos \theta = \frac{\text{abscissa of } P}{\text{distance to } P} = \frac{x}{1} = x.$$

$$\tan \theta = \frac{\text{ordinate of } P}{\text{abscissa of } P} = \frac{y}{x} \qquad (x \neq 0).$$

$$\cot \theta = \frac{\text{abscissa of } P}{\text{ordinate of } P} = \frac{x}{y} \qquad (y \neq 0).$$

$$\sec \theta = \frac{\text{distance to } P}{\text{abscissa of } P} = \frac{1}{x} \qquad (x \neq 0).$$

$$\csc \theta = \frac{\text{distance to } P}{\text{ordinate of } P} = \frac{1}{y} \qquad (y \neq 0).$$

Compare these definitions with those given for the circular functions in Section 7.4.

It already has been established in Section 9.2 that the length of the arc of any circle can be obtained by the formula

$$s = r\theta \qquad \text{(iff } \theta \text{ is in radians).}$$

This formula has a value of

$$s = \theta \qquad \text{for } r = 1;$$

$$s = 2\theta \qquad \text{for } r = 2;$$

$$s = 3\theta \qquad \text{for } r = 3;$$

and so on, showing that *a direct proportion exists between the radians of a circle and its length of arc.*

From the geometric relations shown in Figure 9.5-2, it is true also that a direct proportion exists between θ in standard position, the radii, the abscissas, and the ordinates for circles of any size. Thus, the **general definitions** for the **trigonometric functions** based on angle θ and the radius r are

$$\sin \theta = \frac{\text{ordinate of } P}{\text{radius to } P} = \frac{y}{r}.$$

$$\cos \theta = \frac{\text{abscissa of } P}{\text{radius to } P} = \frac{x}{r}.$$

$$\tan \theta = \frac{\text{ordinate of } P}{\text{abscissa of } P} = \frac{y}{x} \qquad (x \neq 0).$$

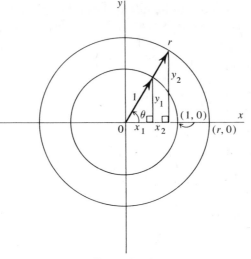

Figure 9.5-2

$$\cot\theta = \frac{\textbf{abscissa of } \textit{P}}{\textbf{ordinate of } \textit{P}} = \frac{x}{y} \qquad (y \neq 0).$$

$$\sec\theta = \frac{\textbf{radius to } \textit{P}}{\textbf{abscissa of } \textit{P}} = \frac{r}{x} \qquad (x \neq 0).$$

$$\csc\theta = \frac{\textbf{radius to } \textit{P}}{\textbf{ordinate of } \textit{P}} = \frac{r}{y} \qquad (y \neq 0).$$

Now that both the circular functions and the trigonometric functions have been defined we will list in Table 9.5-1 their domains and ranges.

9.6 TRIGONOMETRIC VALUES FOR ANGLES OF 0°, 30°, 45°, 60°, and 90°

In Section 7.13 we developed the circular functions for $\pi/6$, $\pi/4$, and $\pi/3$, and from Section 9.2 you should understand that

$\pi/6$ as a real number is the same number as $\pi/6$ as a radian;
$\pi/4$ as a real number is the same number as $\pi/4$ as a radian;
$\pi/3$ as a real number is the same number as $\pi/3$ as a radian; and
$\pi/2$ as a real number is the same number as $\pi/2$ as a radian.

But these radians expressed in terms of degrees are $\pi/6 = 30°$, $\pi/4 = 45°$, $\pi/3 = 60°$, and $\pi/2 = 90°$. Table 9.6-1 gives the values of the trigonometric functions of these particular angles in degrees. The dash sign means that there is no value possible. Compare Table 9.6-1 with Table 7.13-a.

If θ is any positive acute angle you can obtain the multiple of θ in Quadrants

Table 9.5-1 *Domain and Range of Circular and Trigonometric Functions*
(*t* stands for real numbers, θ stands for angles)

Function	Domain	Range
$y = \sin t$	all t	$-1 \le y \le 1$
$y = \sin \theta$	all θ	$-1 \le y \le 1$
$x = \cos t$	all t	$-1 \le x \le 1$
$x = \cos \theta$	all θ	$-1 \le x \le 1$
$z = \tan t$	all t except odd multiples of $\pi/2$	all real numbers
$z = \tan \theta$	all θ except odd multiples of 90°	all real numbers
$z = \cot t$	all t except even multiples of $\pi/2$	all real numbers
$z = \cot \theta$	all θ except even multiples of 90°	all real numbers
$x = \sec t$	all t except odd multiples of $\pi/2$	all real numbers R $\ge +1$ and ≤ -1
$x = \sec \theta$	all θ except odd multiples of 90°	all $R \ge +1$ and ≤ -1
$y = \csc t$	all t except even multiples of $\pi/2$	all real numbers R $\ge +1$ and ≤ -1
$y = \csc \theta$	all θ except even multiples of 90°	all $R \ge +1$ and ≤ -1

Table 9.6-1 *Trigonometric Values*

Angle	sin	cos	tan	cot	sec	csc
0°	0	1	0	—	1	—
30°	$\dfrac{1}{2}$	$\dfrac{\sqrt{3}}{2}$	$\dfrac{1}{\sqrt{3}}$	$\sqrt{3}$	$\dfrac{2}{\sqrt{3}}$	2
45°	$\dfrac{1}{\sqrt{2}}$	$\dfrac{1}{\sqrt{2}}$	1	1	$\sqrt{2}$	$\sqrt{2}$
60°	$\dfrac{\sqrt{3}}{2}$	$\dfrac{1}{2}$	$\sqrt{3}$	$\dfrac{1}{\sqrt{3}}$	2	$\dfrac{2}{\sqrt{3}}$
90°	1	0	—	0	—	1

II, III, and IV in this way:

180° − θ gives multiple in Quadrant II;
180° + θ gives multiple in Quadrant III;
and 360° − θ gives multiple in Quadrant IV.

By the preceding expressions we find that

the multiples of 30° are 150°, 210°, and 330°;
the multiples of 45° are 135°, 225°, and 315°;
the multiples of 60° are 120°, 240°, and 300°.

The six trigonometric functions of a positive acute angle and its multiples have **identical absolute values.** The proper values for the different angles differ only in the prefixing of signs to indicate the quadrants in which the angles fall.

For example, tan 45° = 1,   tan 225° = 1,
tan 135° = −1,   tan 315° = −1.

9.7 TRIGONOMETRIC FUNCTIONS FOR ANGLES OF ANY SIZE

While it is important to know how to find the multiples of an acute angle in the different quadrants of a coordinate system, it is equally important to know how to interpret any angle greater than 90° in terms of its *corresponding positive acute angle*. There will be trouble unless an efficient way of finding corresponding positive acute angles is provided, because Table III at the end of this book lists only the trigonometric values for angles to 90° inclusive.

To meet this situation we will introduce what is sometimes called the **related angle** or the **reference angle** but what we will call, in order to be a little more specific, the **corresponding acute angle.**

Definition: 9.7-1.   *The* **corresponding acute angle** *is that positive acute angle* ϕ *between the terminal side of any nonquadrantal angle* θ *and the nearest side of the x axis* (see Figure 9.7-1).

Definition: 9.7-2.   **Quadrantal angles** *are the angles* 0°, 90°, 180°, 270°, *and all angles coterminal with them.*

A quadrantal angle has no corresponding acute angle ϕ.

The **corresponding acute angle** ϕ **(phi) is** considered to be **a positive angle,** no matter in which quadrant it happens to fall. A trigonometric function of this corresponding acute angle produces the "absolute value" of that particular function. Then to make this absolute value represent the function of the given angle you must place before it the proper sign of the quadrant in which it falls.

As an example let us write out the values for the six trigonometric functions of 300°. The *corresponding acute angle* by Figure 9.7-2 is **60°.** Therefore,

$$\sin 300° = -\sin 60° = -\frac{\sqrt{3}}{2}; \quad \cos 300° = \quad \cos 60° = +\frac{1}{2};$$

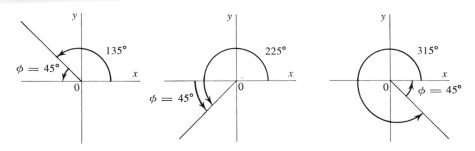

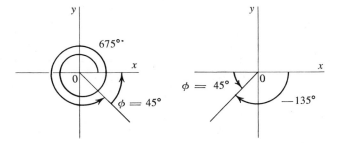

Figure 9.7-1. Corresponding acute angles.

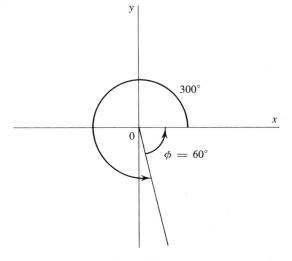

Figure 9.7-2

$$\tan 300° = -\tan 60° = -\sqrt{3}; \quad \cot 300° = -\cot 60° = -\frac{1}{\sqrt{3}};$$

$$\sec 300° = \quad \sec 60° = +2; \quad \csc 300° = -\csc 60° = -\frac{2}{\sqrt{3}}.$$

When we say large angles we do not necessarily mean angles less than 360°. The problem could be to find the six trigonometric functions of 863°.

Angles whose measures differ from each other by either 360° or 720° or 1080°, or by any other number of complete revolutions, have exactly the same values for the six trigonometric functions. That is,

$$\sin 863° = \sin(863° - 720°) = \sin 143° = \sin(180° - 143°) = \sin 37°.$$

To find sin 37° turn to Table III on page 396, in which all trigonometric function values for angles from 0 to 90° inclusive are given, and read sin 37° ≐ 0.6018.

Thus, as indicated in Figure 9.7-3

$$\sin 863° = \sin 143° = +\sin 37° \doteq +0.6018;$$
$$\cos 863° = \cos 143° = -\cos 37° = -0.7986;$$
$$\tan 863° = \tan 143° = -\tan 37° = -0.7536;$$
$$\cot 863° = \cot 143° = -\cot 37° \doteq -1.327;$$
$$\sec 863° = \sec 143° = -\sec 37° \doteq -1.252;$$
$$\csc 863° = \csc 143° = +\csc 37° \doteq +1.662.$$

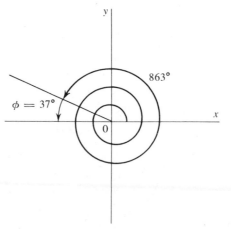

Figure 9.7-3

You can see, therefore, no matter whether a given angle is less than 360° or more, it has a *corresponding acute angle* which can be used along with Table III to find the trigonometric values of the angle.

Further, the corresponding acute angle procedure works just as well for negative as positive angles (see Figure 9.7-4). Making use of the following relations, as proved in Section 7.17,

$$\sin(-\theta) = -\sin\theta, \qquad \cos(-\theta) = \cos\theta,$$
$$\csc(-\theta) = -\csc\theta, \qquad \sec(-\theta) = \sec\theta,$$
$$\tan(-\theta) = -\tan\theta,$$
$$\cot(-\theta) = -\cot\theta.$$

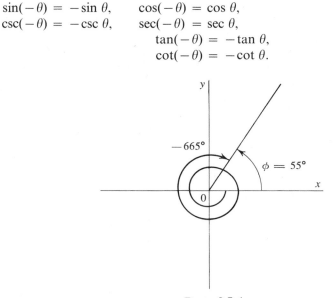

Figure 9.7-4

the values of the six trigonometric functions for $(-665°)$ are

$$\sin(-665°) = -\sin 665° = -\sin 305° = -(-\sin 55°) \doteq +0.8192;$$
$$\cos(-665°) = +\cos 665° = +\cos 305° = +\cos 55° \doteq +0.5736;$$
$$\tan(-665°) = -\tan 665° = -\tan 305° = -(-\tan 55°) \doteq +1.428;$$
$$\cot(-665°) = -\cot(665°) = -\cot 305° = -(-\cot 55°) \doteq +0.7002;$$
$$\sec(-665°) = +\sec(665°) = +\sec 305° = +\sec 55° \doteq +1.743;$$
$$\csc(-665°) = -\csc(665°) = -\csc 305° = -(-\csc 55°) \doteq +1.221.$$

Thus, the procedure of finding the value of any nonquadrantal angle (positive or negative) can be summarized in this theorem:

Theorem: 9.7-1. The value of a trigonometric function of a nonquadrantal angle θ is equal to either plus or minus the value obtained when the same trigonometric function is applied to its corresponding positive acute angle.

The trigonometric function of the corresponding acute angle θ looked up in Table III, with proper quadrant sign prefixed, is the trigonometric value of the given angle.

9.8 TRIGONOMETRIC FUNCTIONS OF AN ACUTE ANGLE

By referring back to the use made of the corresponding acute angle in Section 9.7 you can see that ϕ was always a part of a right triangle, with ϕ at the origin, one side on the *x* axis, and the other side in one of the quadrants. The projection of the end point of the terminal side on the *x* axis always formed a right angle.

Definition: 9.8-1.   *The **projection of a point** is the foot of the perpendicular from the point to a line or a plane.*

It is necessary to refer every angle greater than 90° to its **corresponding acute angle** ϕ in order to evaluate trigonometric functions of the angle. One form of such a right angled *reference triangle* with ϕ in standard position is shown in Figure 9.8-1(a).

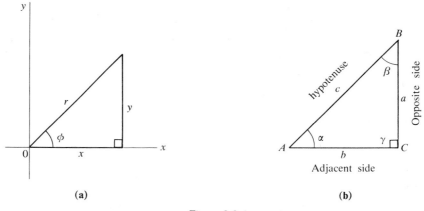

(a)   (b)

Figure 9.8-1

In Figure 9.8-1(b) we have duplicated the right triangle in Figure 9.8-1(a), but we have not referred it to a coordinate system. In fact, we are now about to point out that the right triangle *ABC* in Figure 9.8-1(b) can exist in any position whatsoever. However, to keep our *positive acute angle trigonometry* consistent with our *general angle and real number trigonometry* we will replace *y* with *a*, where *a* represents the side opposite α; we will replace *x* with *b*, where *b* is the side opposite β; and we will replace *r* with *c*, where *c* is the side opposite the right angle γ and is called the hypotenuse. Thus, from Figure 9.8-1b our six trigonometric definitions for the positive acute angle α are

$$\sin \alpha = \frac{\text{opposite side}}{\text{hypotenuse}} = \frac{a}{c};$$

$$\cos \alpha = \frac{\text{adjacent side}}{\text{hypotenuse}} = \frac{b}{c};$$

$$\tan \alpha = \frac{\text{opposite side}}{\text{adjacent side}} = \frac{a}{b};$$

$$\cot \alpha = \frac{\text{adjacent side}}{\text{opposite side}} = \frac{b}{a};$$

$$\sec \alpha = \frac{\text{hypotenuse}}{\text{adjacent side}} = \frac{c}{b}.$$

$$\csc \alpha = \frac{\text{hypotenuse}}{\text{opposite side}} = \frac{c}{a}.$$

To see how this positive acute angle trigonometry works, let us assume that $\cos \alpha = \frac{5}{13}$, $0 < \alpha < 90°$, and find the other five trigonometry functions.

Constructing α and the resulting right triangle in any position we choose (see Figure 9.8-2), and placing 5 on the side adjacent to α and 13 on the hypot-

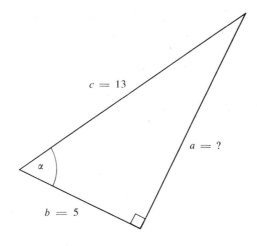

Figure 9.8-2

enuse, we can work out, by the Pythagorean relationship, the side a opposite the angle α to be

$$a = \sqrt{(13)^2 - (5)^2} = \sqrt{169 - 25} = 12.$$

Then $\sin \alpha = \dfrac{12}{13}$, $\cot \alpha = \dfrac{5}{12}$,

$\cos \alpha = \dfrac{5}{13}$, $\sec \alpha = \dfrac{13}{5}$,

$\tan \alpha = \dfrac{12}{5}$, $\csc \alpha = \dfrac{13}{12}$.

9.9 COFUNCTIONS AND RECIPROCAL FUNCTIONS

It is common practice to list the six trigonometric functions as
sine, and cosine which stands for the complement of the sine;
tangent, and cotangent which stands for the complement of the tangent;
secant, and cosecant which stands for the complement of the secant.

Definition: 9.9-1. *If the name of one trigonometric function is obtained
from another either by prefixing or dropping the syllable co, the functions are
called* **cofunctions.**

Definition: 9.9-2. *If the sum of two acute angles is equal to 90°, the angles
are said to be* **complementary angles,** *and either angle is the complement of the
other.*

Thus, in Figure 9.9-1 α and β are complementary, $\alpha + \beta = 90°$, and
$\beta = 90° - \alpha$.

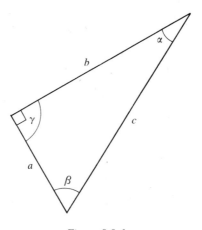

Figure 9.9-1

Theorem: 9.9-1. A trigonometric function of a positive acute angle is
equal to the corresponding cofunction of its complementary angle.
Theorem 9.9-1 means that

$$\sin \alpha = \frac{a}{c} = \cos \beta, \qquad \cot \alpha = \frac{b}{a} = \tan \beta,$$

$$\cos \alpha = \frac{b}{c} = \sin \beta, \qquad \sec \alpha = \frac{c}{b} = \csc \beta,$$

$$\tan \alpha = \frac{a}{b} = \cot \beta, \qquad \csc \alpha = \frac{c}{a} = \sec \beta.$$

Substituting $90° - \alpha$ for β, we obtain these

COFUNCTIONS OR COMPLEMENTARY FORMULAS

$\sin \alpha = \cos(90° - \alpha), \quad \tan \alpha = \cot(90° - \alpha),$
$\cos \alpha = \sin(90° - \alpha), \quad \cot \alpha = \tan(90° - \alpha),$
$$\sec \alpha = \csc(90° - \alpha),$$
$$\csc \alpha = \sec(90° - \alpha).$$

One of the most important applications of the preceding cofunction relations is in the building of Table III located on page 396.

Using $\sin \alpha \quad = \cos(90° - \alpha)$, it works like this:
For $\alpha = 1°$, $\sin 1° \quad = \cos(90° - 1°) = \cos 89°$.
For $\alpha = 20°$, $\sin 20° = \cos(90° - 20°) = \cos 70°$.
For $\alpha = 30°$, $\sin 30° = \cos(90° - 30°) = \cos 60°$.
For $\alpha = 45°$, $\sin 45° = \cos(90° - 45°) = \cos 45°$.

These samples are enough to suggest that if angles from 0° to 45° are listed in the left column of Table III and the values of the sine function are listed in the column headed sin, then these same values will serve for the cosine values of angles from 45° to 90°, provided the angles are read in the right-hand column of the table and the values of the cosine functions are read in the column labelled **cos** at the bottom of the table.

The other functions and their cofunctions are read in the same manner. For example,

$\sin 5°$ (left) $\doteq 0.0872 \doteq \cos 85°$ (right),
$\sin 85°$ (right) $\doteq 0.9962 \doteq \cos 5°$ (left),
$\tan 40°$ (left) $\doteq 0.8391 \doteq \cot 50°$ (right),
$\tan 50°$ (right) $\doteq 1.192 \doteq \cot 40°$ (left),
$\sec 30°$ (left) $\doteq 1.155 \doteq \csc 60°$ (right),
$\sec 60°$ (right) $\doteq 2.000 \doteq \csc 30°$ (left).

It becomes evident, therefore, that the cofunction relationships save at least half of the time and expense involved in preparing tables of trigonometric values for angles from 0° to 90°.

This is a good place to observe that the definitions of the trigonometric functions of any angle, or any real number, may be classified either as *cofunctions* or *reciprocal relations, the reciprocal of a number being* 1 *divided by that number*.

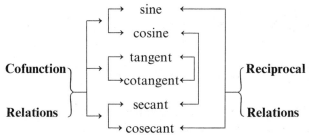

9.10 DEPENDENT NATURE OF TRIGONOMETRIC FUNCTIONS

We will demonstrate that the trigonometric functions are dependent by taking the value of one function and determining the values of the other functions from it.

Example: 9.10-1.   Find the six trigonometric values for an angle of 30°.

We have already learned that the value of a circular function of a real number is the same number as the value of the trigonometric function of its corresponding angle. However, the method of finding these values does differ.

To evaluate the six circular functions for $\pi/6$ we use the data properly adjusted to a unit circle as shown in Figure 9.10-1(a). But in angle trigonometry

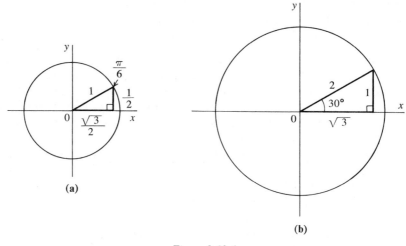

(a)

(b)

Figure 9.10-1

the data can be applied to a circle of any radius. For example, in Figure 9.10-1(b), which shows a 30°–60°–90° triangle in standard position, it is more convenient to use a circle of radius 2. Then the hypotenuse of the right triangle is 2, the side opposite the 30° is 1, and by the Pythagorean theorem the third side is computed to be $\sqrt{3}$. The resulting values of the six trigonometric functions for 30° are:

$$\sin 30° = \frac{1}{2}, \qquad \tan 30° = \frac{1}{\sqrt{3}}, \qquad \sec 30° = \frac{2}{\sqrt{3}},$$

$$\cos 30° = \frac{\sqrt{3}}{2}, \qquad \cot 30° = \sqrt{3}, \qquad \csc 30° = 2.$$

Note that by applying the circular functions to $\pi/6$ in Figure 9.10-1(a) we would obtain exactly the same results for the six functions.

Example: 9.10-2. Given that $\sec \theta = -\frac{13}{12}$, find the other five functions.

(a) Approaching this problem from the unit circle viewpoint and substituting t for θ, we know that

$$\sec t = \frac{1}{\cos t} = -\frac{13}{12}.$$

Therefore,

$$\cos t = -\frac{12}{13} = x.$$

Then by the Pythagorean theorem

$$y = \sin t = \pm\sqrt{1 - \frac{144}{169}} = \pm\frac{5}{13}.$$

The cosine value can be negative and the sine value positive in Quadrant II or the cosine value can be negative and the sine value negative in Quadrant III; therefore, as indicated in Figure 9.10–2(a), both Quadrant II values and Quadrant III values will have to be considered.

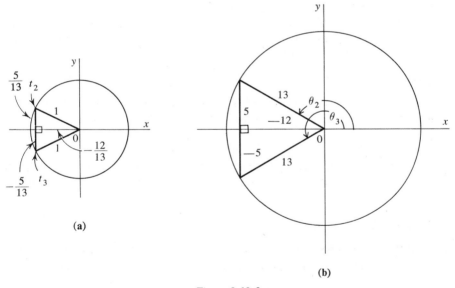

(a)

(b)

Figure 9.10-2

(b) Now, notice in Figure 9.10-2(b) how much easier it is to get the desired results by *angle trigonometry*. If $\sec \theta = -\frac{13}{12}$, then by the definition of the secant of the corresponding acute angle, the hypotenuse is 13 and the adjacent side is 12, both in Quadrants II and III. By the Pythagorean theorem the opposite side is ± 5. That is, 5 is in Quadrant II and -5 is in Quadrant III.

Then by our trigonometric definitions we have for Quadrant II:

$$\sin \theta_2 = \tfrac{5}{13}, \qquad \tan \theta_2 = -\tfrac{5}{12}, \qquad \sec \theta_2 = -\tfrac{13}{12},$$

$$\cos \theta_2 = -\tfrac{12}{13} \qquad \cot \theta_2 = -\tfrac{12}{5}, \qquad \csc \theta_2 = \tfrac{13}{5}.$$

Should you apply the circular function to Quadrant II in Figure 9.10-2(a), you would get the same values. Later you will be asked to finish this problem by writing out the functional values for θ_3 in Quadrant III.

9.11 VALUES OF TRIGONOMETRIC FUNCTIONS—TABLE III

We have already been using Table III (page 396). In case you need further help in using the table, these examples should help you.

Example: 9.11-1.   Find the tangent of 20° 30'.
In Table III at the top of the table headed *Degrees*, read down the column to 20° 30'. Then move horizontally to the column headed **tan** and read:

tan 20° 30′ ≐ 0.3739.

Example: 9.11-2.   Find the cosine of 67° 10'.
From the bottom of the Table III headed *Degrees* read up the column to 67° 10'. Then move horizontally to the left to the column headed **cos** at the bottom of the page and read:

cos 67° 10′ ≐ 0.3881.

As will be shown in Example 9.11-3, it becomes more difficult if the value of a function is given and we have to find the measure of its angle.

Example: 9.11-3.   If cot θ ≐ 7.269, find θ.
This time we do the reverse of Example 9.11-1. We find 7.269 in the column headed **cot** at the top of the page. Then we move to the left and read the angle. Thus,

If cot θ ≐ 7.269, then θ ≐ 7° 50′.

For cot θ ≐ 0.1376 we would find 0.1376 in the column headed **cot** from the bottom of the page. In this case we would move to the right and read

If cot θ ≐ 0.1376, then θ ≐ 82° 10′.

Interpolation, of course, has to be used if the value or the angle does not match an entry in the table.

Example: 9.11-4.   If tan θ ≐ 0.7841, find θ.
In the **tan** column of the table we find a value of 0.7813, which is slightly less than 0.7841, and 0.7860, which is slightly more. So we set up these data:

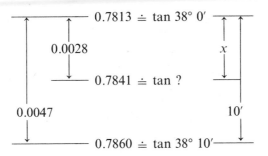

$$0.7813 \doteq \tan 38° 0'$$

$$0.0028$$

$$0.7841 \doteq \tan \ ?$$

$$0.0047$$

$$0.7860 \doteq \tan 38° 10'$$

The ratio of the values is 0.0028/0.0047 or 28/47. It is usual practice to omit the decimal points and zeros and just use 28/47. Thus, the proportion is

$$\frac{x}{10} \doteq \frac{28}{47}.$$

and $x \doteq 5.9$ or $6'$.

So $6'$ should be added to $38° 0'$. Thus, by linear interpolation we have

tan 38° 6′ ≐ 0.7841.

EXERCISE 9.B

Keep in mind that the comparisons between real numbers and angles are
$0 = 0°$, $\pi/6 = 30°$, $\pi/4 = 45°$, $\pi/3 = 60°$, $\pi/2 = 90°$, $2\pi/3 = 120°$, etc.

1. Make a sketch for each angle and write out the numerical values for the six trigonometric functions at

(a) 0°.   (b) 45°.   (c) 60°.

2. Same as Problem 1:

(a) 30°.   (b) 90°.   (c) 120°.

3. For the sine, tangent and secant functions write out

(a) their domains;   (b) their ranges.

4. For the cosine, cotangent, and cosecant functions, write out

(a) their domains;   (b) their ranges.

5. How do the values of the trigonometric functions of 30° differ from those of 210°?

6. How do the values of the trigonometric functions at 45° differ from those of 315°?

7. What purpose is served by the *corresponding acute angle* idea?

8. Is the *corresponding acute angle* ever considered to be a negative angle? Does the *corresponding acute angle* always have to be in standard position?

9. What are the *corresponding acute angles* for each of these angles?

(a) 68°.   (c) 230°.   (e) 520°.   (g) −210°.
(b) 140°.   (d) 342°.   (f) 826°.   (h) −740°.

10. Make a sketch showing the location of the *corresponding acute angle* for each angle given in Problem 9.

11. By use of the *corresponding acute angle* and Table III find the numerical values for the six trigonometric functions of the angle 428°.

12. Use the corresponding acute angle and Table III to find the numerical values for the six trigonometric functions of the angle $(-534°)$.

13. Write the proper function of the complementary angle of each of the following:

(a) sin 39°.   (c) sec(α + 14°).   (e) cos(α + β + 24°).
(b) cot 82°.   (d) csc(50° − α).   (f) tan(90° − β).

14. Write the cofunction of

(a) tan 76°.   (c) cot(90° − α).   (e) csc(40° − β).
(b) sec 2°.   (d) sin(α + 2).   (f) cos(89° + α).

15. Use Figure 9.B-1 to write out the six trigonometric functions of β.

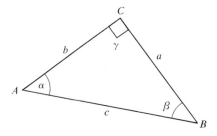

Figure 9.B-1

16. Write out the six trigonometric functions of α in Figure 9.B-1.

17. Write a reciprocal trigonometric function which is equal to

(a) sin θ.   (b) tan θ.   (c) sec θ.

18. What is the value of (a) cos θ multiplied by its reciprocal? (b) cot θ multiplied by its reciprocal? (c) csc θ multiplied by its reciprocal?

19. If sin $\alpha = -\dfrac{7}{25}$ in Quadrant IV, determine the value of each of the other functions.

20. Given that tan $\beta = \dfrac{\sqrt{3}}{3}$ in Quadrant III, find the value of each of the other functions.

21. Refer to Figure 9.10-2a and write out the value for each circular function for Quadrant III.

22. Write out the value for each angle function for Quadrant III in Figure 9.10-2b.

23. Find the value for each of the other possible trigonometric functions if cos $\theta = 8/17$.

24. If cot $\theta = 7/24$, find the values for each of the other possible trigonometric functions.

25. If cot $\theta = -4/3$ and sin $\theta > 0$, find the value of 2 sin θ cos θ.

26. Find the value of cos² θ − sin² θ if tan $\theta = \frac{3}{4}$ and sin $\theta < 0$.

27. Use Table III to find the value of

(a) tan 43° 17′.   (b) θ if sin $\theta = -0.4625$.

28. Find the value of

(a) csc 78° 13′.   (b) θ if cot $\theta = 0.6850$.

29. Evaluate $\dfrac{\tan 150° + \tan 210°}{1 - \tan 150° \tan 210°}$.

30. Evaluate $\sin 30° \cos 120° - \cos 30° \sin 120°$.

9.12 VECTORS

There are certain physical phenomena such as velocity, acceleration, force, and displacement, that involve direction as well as magnitude. These phenomena are called **vector quantities.**

Definition: 9.12-a.   *Any quantity determined by both magnitude and direction is called a* **vector quantity.**

The technical way of talking about the wind is to say that it is blowing a certain number of miles per hour (magnitude) from a certain point (direction). For example, a wind of 15 miles per hour blowing from the north is a vector quantity.

Definition: 9.12-b.   *A directed line segment, totally determined by its length and its direction, is called a* **vector.**

It is customary to represent a vector by an arrow whose length (stem) corresponds to the magnitude and which points in the proper direction.

If for the 15 mile-per-hour wind *blowing from the north* 1 unit of measure on the line segment represents 5 miles, then 3 units would represent the magnitude of the vector quantity, and an arrow from the north toward the south would represent the direction the vector would act.

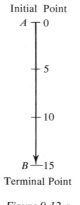

Initial Point

Terminal Point

Figure 9.12-a

As indicated by Figure 9.12-a, the point at which a vector originates is called the **initial point,** and the point at which the line segment ends is called the **terminal point.** One way of denoting vector AB is $\overrightarrow{AB}$.

Definition: 9.12-c. *A* **zero (or null) vector** *has no length and, consequently, an indeterminate direction.*

A **zero vector** may be symbolized by $\overrightarrow{AA}$, which indicates that only a point is being considered. Or it may be symbolized by $[0, 0]$ which indicates that there is zero magnitude and no direction.

Definition: 9.12-d. *Two vectors $\overrightarrow{AB}$ and $\overrightarrow{CD}$ are* **equivalent** *if they are parallel, if the direction of vector $\overrightarrow{AB}$ is the same as the direction of $\overrightarrow{CD}$, and if the magnitude of $\overrightarrow{AB}$ equals the magnitude of $\overrightarrow{CD}$.*

The relationship of the three vectors shown in Figure 9.12-b is $\overrightarrow{AB} = \overrightarrow{CD} \neq \overrightarrow{EF}$.

While it is true that the length of $\overrightarrow{EF}$ is exactly the same as the lengths of $\overrightarrow{AB}$ and $\overrightarrow{CD}$, the action of $\overrightarrow{EF}$ is in the opposite direction. In a case like this, we say that the **sense** of $\overrightarrow{EF}$ is opposite to $\overrightarrow{CD}$ or $\overrightarrow{AB}$. An acceptable relationship that shows that $\overrightarrow{CD}$ and $\overrightarrow{EF}$ have equal lengths but act in opposite directions is

$$\overrightarrow{CD} = -\overrightarrow{EF}.$$

The idea of oppositeness in sense can, of course, be applied to a single vector. To show that moving from F to E along line segment FE is opposite to moving from E to F along EF, we write

$$\overrightarrow{EF} = -\overrightarrow{FE},$$

As one becomes better acquainted with the notion of vectors he will find it much simpler in many cases to denote the vectors by lowercase letters expressed

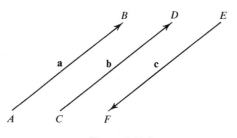

Figure 9.12-b

in boldfaced type. Thus, in Figure 9.12-b these substitutions can be made:

$$\overrightarrow{AB} = \mathbf{a}, \qquad \overrightarrow{CD} = \mathbf{b}, \qquad \overrightarrow{EF} = \mathbf{c}.$$

By using boldfaced lowercase letters to represent the vectors we have the usual lowercase letters, such as a, b, c, etc., available to represent the **scalar quantities.**

Definition: 9.12-e. *A* **scalar quantity** *represents magnitude but not direction.*

9.12-1 Vector Addition

If two winches are pulling on a boat at an acute angle with each other, the path of the boat will be somewhere between the pull of the winches. The force applied to the boat is greater than the force produced by either winch but not as great as if the two winches were pulling from the same position. To find the single force, called the **resultant force** for problems of this type, **vector addition** is used.

When two vectors act on a body simultaneously, it may be preferable to use the *parallelogram law of addition of vectors* to obtain the resultant vector. Both it and the *triangular law for addition of vectors* will be demonstrated in the following examples.

Example: 9.12-1a. If forces of 5 pounds and 4 pounds are acting on a body at an angle of 60°, find the magnitude and the direction of the resultant of the forces.

First select a unit of measurement such that one unit represents one pound of force. Lay off 5 units on a line segment. From the initial point on the line segment, construct an angle of 60° and on the terminal side of this angle lay off a line segment 4 units long. Then place the initial point of the 4-unit vector on the terminal point of the 5-unit vector and draw a line segment parallel to and equal to the 4-unit vector. Next, the initial point of the 5-unit vector is placed on the terminal point of the 4-unit vector and a line segment parallel and equal to the 5-unit vector is drawn. This completes the parallelogram.

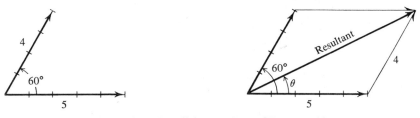

Figure 9.12-1a. Parallelogram Law of Vector Addition.

The resultant force is represented by the diagonal of the parallelogram drawn from the initial point of action. The magnitude of about 8 pounds is a measure of the line segment which represents the resultant. Angle θ of about 26° is the direction of action of the single force with respect to the 5-unit vector.

Definition: 9.12-1a. *The **vector sum (or resultant)** of two vectors **a** and **b** is the single vector **c**. In symbols* $\mathbf{a} + \mathbf{b} = \mathbf{c}$.

Example: 9.12-1b. Find the magnitude and the direction of the resultant for the data in Example 9.12-1a by the *triangle law for the addition of vectors*. Select a unit of measurement such that *one unit represents one pound* and construct a line segment 5 units long (see Figure 9.12-1b). Then place the initial end of the 4-unit vector at the terminal end of the 5-unit vector and draw it so that it makes an angle of 120° with the 5-unit vector. The resultant is the line segment from the initial end of the 5-unit vector to the terminal end of the 4-unit vector and gives the magnitude of the resultant force to be about 8 pounds. The direction of action of the single force with respect to the 5-unit vector is $\theta \doteq 26°$.

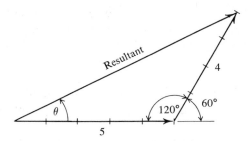

Figure 9.12-1b. Triangle Law of Vector Addition.

The sum of several vectors can be obtained by repeating the procedures indicated as many times as each situation demands. As indicated in Figure 9.12-1c, $\overrightarrow{OD}$ is the resultant obtained by adding the vectors $\overrightarrow{OA}$, $\overrightarrow{AB}$, $\overrightarrow{BC}$, and $\overrightarrow{CD}$.

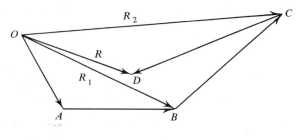

Figure 9.12-1c

Definition: 9.12-1b. *Any two vectors that produce a resultant vector are called* **components of the resultant vector.**

As Figure 9.12-1d indicates, a resultant vector can have an unlimited number of pairs of components. For the resultant $\overrightarrow{OB}$ the pairs of components may be $\overrightarrow{OA}$ and $\overrightarrow{AB}$ or $\overrightarrow{OC}$ and $\overrightarrow{CB}$ or $\overrightarrow{OD}$ and $\overrightarrow{DB}$. The pair of components $\overrightarrow{OD}$ and $\overrightarrow{DB}$ are at right angles to each other and are called **orthogonal projections.** *In our use of components in this course we will confine ourselves principally to orthogonal projections.*

9.12-2 Vector Subtraction

Similar to subtraction with numbers, **the subtraction of vectors is the inverse of the addition of vectors.**

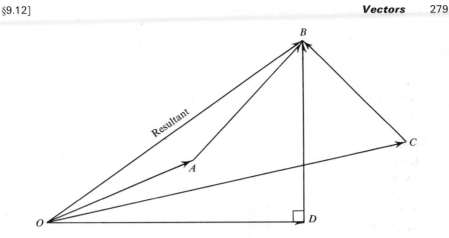

Figure 9.12-1d

Definition: 9.12-2a.   *The* **subtraction of vector b from vector a** *is vector* **c**, *such that* **a = b + c.** *Symbolically,*

a − b = c if and only if a = b + c.

Suppose we attempt to subtract vector $\overrightarrow{CB}$ as shown in Figure 9.12-2a

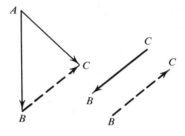

Figure 9.12-2a

from vector $\overrightarrow{AB}$. Keeping in mind that subtracting a vector is equivalent to adding its negative, then

$$\overrightarrow{AB} - \overrightarrow{CB} = \overrightarrow{AB} + (-\overrightarrow{CB}) = \overrightarrow{AB} + \overrightarrow{BC}.$$

The preceding statement shows that $\overrightarrow{BC}$ is equal in length and is parallel to $\overrightarrow{CB}$ but has its arrow pointing in the opposite direction. Therefore,

$$\overrightarrow{AB} - \overrightarrow{CB} = \overrightarrow{AB} + \overrightarrow{BC} = \overrightarrow{AC}.$$

9.12-3 Multiplication of a Vector by a Scalar

For any two points A and B the magnitude (the measure) of $\overrightarrow{AB}$ will be denoted by $|\overrightarrow{AB}|$ or its equivalent, $|\mathbf{a}|$.

Theorem: 9.12-3a.   If $\overrightarrow{AB}$ is a vector represented by **a** and n is a scalar, then the product na of a scalar and a vector is the vector such that its magnitude is $|n\mathbf{a}| = |n| \cdot |\mathbf{a}|$. *Its direction is*

(a) unchanged if **a** is a nonzero vector and $n > 0$;
(b) the opposite of **a** if **a** is a nonzero vector and $n < 0$;
(c) undetermined if $n = 0$.

9.12-4 Some Properties of Vectors

It is most interesting to observe how a system based upon the operations of addition and multiplication, *with vectors as the elements,* parallels the postulates used in connection with the real number system.

Vector quantities as expressed by the vectors **0, a, b,** and **c** and the scalars $0, 1, m,$ and n, obey the following algebraic laws:

Under Addition

9.12-4a. Commutative law: $\mathbf{a} + \mathbf{b} = \mathbf{b} + \mathbf{a}$
9.12-4b. Associative law: $(\mathbf{a} + \mathbf{b}) + \mathbf{c} = \mathbf{a} + (\mathbf{b} + \mathbf{c})$
9.12-4c. Identity law: $\mathbf{a} + \mathbf{0} = \mathbf{a}$
9.12-4d. Inverse law: $\mathbf{a} + (-\mathbf{a}) = \mathbf{0}$

Under Multiplication

9.12-4e. Identity Law: $\mathbf{a} \cdot 1 = \mathbf{a}$
9.12-4f. Zero element: $\mathbf{a} \cdot 0 = \mathbf{0}$
9.12-4g. Associative law: $(m \cdot n)a = m \cdot (n \cdot a)$

Distributive laws

9.12-4h. Distributive law: $(m + n)a = ma + na$
9.12-4i. Distributive law: $m(\mathbf{a} + \mathbf{b}) = m\mathbf{a} + m\mathbf{b}$

These properties can, of course, be proved. We will present a proof of the commutative law and leave the others to be justified by the reader.

Theorem: 9.12-4a.   Given the vectors **a** and **b** to prove that $\mathbf{a} + \mathbf{b} = \mathbf{b} + \mathbf{a}$. Let the two vectors be as shown in Figure 9.12-4a. Then to find $\mathbf{a} + \mathbf{b}$,

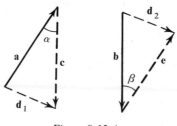

Figure 9.12-4a

draw **c**, equal to and parallel to **b**, from the terminal end of **a**. It follows that

$$\mathbf{a} + \mathbf{c} = \mathbf{a} + \mathbf{b} = \mathbf{d}_1.$$

To find $\mathbf{b} + \mathbf{a}$, draw **e** from the terminal point of **b**, parallel and equal to **a**.

Then

$$\mathbf{b} + \mathbf{e} = \mathbf{b} + \mathbf{a} = \mathbf{d}_2.$$

Since vector $\mathbf{a} = \mathbf{e}$ and vector $\mathbf{c} = \mathbf{b}$, and angle $\alpha =$ angle β, the two triangles are congruent ($s, a, s = s, a, s$) and

$$\mathbf{d}_1 = \mathbf{d}_2.$$

Therefore, by the transitive law

$$\mathbf{a} + \mathbf{b} = \mathbf{b} + \mathbf{a}.$$

The following laws applying to the magnitude of vector quantities should be understood. For any vectors $\mathbf{a}$ and $\mathbf{b}$ and scalar n,

9.12-4j. $|\mathbf{a} + \mathbf{b}| \leq |\mathbf{a}| + |\mathbf{b}|$
9.12-4k. $|\mathbf{a} - \mathbf{b}| \geq |\mathbf{a}| - |\mathbf{b}|$
9.12-4m. $|n \cdot \mathbf{a}| = |n| \cdot |\mathbf{a}|$
9.12-4n. $|\mathbf{a}| \geq 0,$ and $|\mathbf{a}| = 0$ iff $\mathbf{a} = \mathbf{0}.$

Vector quantities are more than single numbers, as you can see. Yet we find that vectors and numbers have several of the field postulates in common.

9.12-5 Fixed Vectors

The vectors we have been dealing with so far are sometimes called **free vectors.** For free vectors it made no difference as to where the vectors were positioned in a plane or in space. Now we propose to deal with **fixed vectors.** We plan to associate them with the rectangular coordinate system. By doing this we can use the positive x axis of the coordinate system (or a line parallel to it) as the **reference line for a vector.** We can use an angle properly related to the x axis or a reference line parallel to it to determine the direction of the vector, and we can use the length of the line segment along the terminal side of the angle to find the magnitude of the vector.

Definition: 9.12-5a. *An orthogonal (a right angled) projection of a vector on the x axis or on a line parallel to the x axis is called the* **x component of the vector.**

Definition: 9.12-5b. *The orthogonal projection of a vector on the y axis or on a line parallel to the y axis is called the* **y component of the vector.**

Definition: 9.12-5c. *In terms of rectangular coordinates a* **two-dimensional vector v** *is an ordered pair expressed as* $\mathbf{v} = [v_x, v_y]$. (Note that special brackets are used to enclose an ordered pair that represents a vector.)

To further simplify our notation we will let the vector $\overrightarrow{OB}$ in Figure 9.12-5a be represented by $\mathbf{v}$, the component of $\overrightarrow{OB}$ along the x axis by $\mathbf{v}_x$ and the component along the y axis by $\mathbf{v}_y$. The scalar distances of these vectors are represented by the same symbols but not boldfaced type, that is, v_x and v_y.

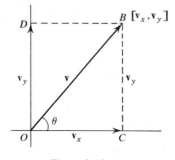

Figure 9.12-5a

Applying trigonometry,

$v_x = |\mathbf{v}| \cos \theta,$

$v_y = |\mathbf{v}| \sin \theta,$

$|\mathbf{v}| = \sqrt{(v_x)^2 + (v_y)^2}$ **(the modulus).**

Other important relations are

$$\tan \theta = \frac{v_y}{v_x}, \qquad \theta = \arctan \frac{v_y}{v_x}.$$

9.12-6 Algebraic Nature of Vectors from Component Viewpoint

As indicated by Figure 9.12-5a, $\overrightarrow{OB}$ may be denoted by $[v_x, v_y]$.

Definition: 9.12-6a.   *Vectors* $[v_{xa}, v_{ya}]$ *and* $[v_{xb}, v_{yb}]$ *are* **equivalent** *if and only if* $v_{xa} = v_{xb}$ *and* $v_{ya} = v_{yb}$.

Definition: 9.12-6b.   *The sum of the vectors*

$[v_{xa}, v_{ya}] + [v_{xb}, v_{yb}]$ *is* $[v_{xa} + v_{xb}, v_{ya} + v_{yb}]$.

This definition assures us that the sum of the horizontal components of two or more vectors is the horizontal component of the resultant vector. The sum of the vertical components of two or more vectors is the vertical component of the resultant vector.

If $\mathbf{w} = [v_x, v_y]$, it follows that $-\mathbf{w} = [-v_x, -v_y]$ and we have this definition for the subtraction of vectors.

Definition: 9.12-6c.   *The* **difference** *of the vectors*

$[v_{xa}, v_{ya}] - [v_{xb}, v_{yb}]$ *is* $[v_{xa} - v_{xb}, v_{ya} - v_{yb}]$.

The difference of the horizontal components of two vectors is the horizontal component of the resultant. The difference of the two vertical components of the vectors is the vertical component of the resultant.

The following two relationships have been discussed before, but we will state them again in terms of horizontal and vertical components:

$$n[v_x, v_y] = [nv_x, nv_y].$$

$$[v_x, v_y] - [v_x, v_y] = [0, 0]. \qquad\qquad\text{(The Zero Vector)}$$

9.13 AZIMUTH AND BEARING ANGLES

The north line, the positive y axis in a rectangular coordinate system, is the reference line from which all angles are measured in ship and airplane navigation and in many other activities where angles are involved.

Definition: 9.13-1. *The nonnegative angle through which the north line must be rotated clockwise to coincide with the line that represents the course is called the* **azimuth angle.**

Azimuth angles *are nonnegative angles from* $0 \leq \beta \leq 360°$. The azimuth of $\overrightarrow{OB}$ in Figure 9.13-a is the angle 150°.

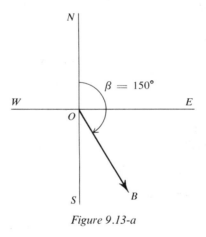

Figure 9.13-a

In land surveying we do not usually call for the *azimuth of a line.* Either the angle which gives the bearing of a line or the angle between two lines is commonly used.

Definition: 9.13-2. *The angle made by a line segment with a north or south direction is called the* **bearing angle (or bearing)** *of that line segment.*

Figure 9.13-b shows how a surveyor would write bearings of lines. Either the letter "N" or "S" must always come first, then the angle, and then the appropriate letter "E" or "W."

In this text all problems will have to do with plane sailing or plane surveying; that is, the line segments are considered to be in a plane surface.

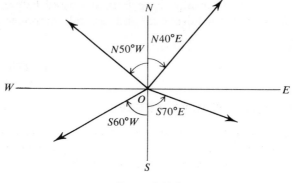

Figure 9.13-b

Example: 9.13-1. Two forces are acting on an object, one exerting a 50.0-pound pull to the north, the other a 20.0-pound pull to the east. Find the azimuth and the magnitude of the resultant.

$$\tan \beta \doteq \frac{20}{50} \doteq 0.400,$$

$$\doteq 21° \ 48' \qquad\qquad\qquad\qquad \text{(By Table III)}$$

or $\beta \doteq 21° \ 50'$ (to three-digit accuracy).

$$\cos \beta \doteq \frac{50}{|\overrightarrow{OB}|},$$

$$|\overrightarrow{OB}| \doteq \frac{50}{\cos 21° \ 48'}.$$

$$\log |\overrightarrow{OB}| \doteq \log 50 - \log \cos 21° \ 48' \qquad\qquad \text{(By Tables III and IV)}$$

$$\doteq 1.6990 - (9.9678 - 10),$$

$$\log |\overrightarrow{OB}| \doteq 1.7312.$$

$$\therefore \quad |\overrightarrow{OB}| \doteq 53.85$$

or $|\overrightarrow{OB}| \doteq$ **53.9 pounds**   (to three-digit accuracy).

Check OB by using the Pythagorean theorem. Figure 9.13-1 also provided an approximate check of the results.

Example: 9.13-2. A ship captain passing buoy B knows the azimuth to lighthouse L to be 155° and the distance from the buoy to it to be 5.4 nautical miles. He also knows that he must set a course of 142° to guarantee safe sailing (see Figure 9.13-2). What is his closest distance to the lighthouse as he passes it? How far has he traveled? (There are 6,080.27 feet in a nautical mile.)

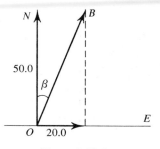

Figure 9.13-1

$\overrightarrow{BL} + \overrightarrow{LC} = \overrightarrow{BC}.$

$\quad |\overrightarrow{LC}| \doteq 5.4 \sin 13° \doteq 5.4 \times 0.2250$

$\qquad\qquad \doteq$ **1.2** nautical miles.

$\quad |\overrightarrow{BC}| = 5.4 \cos 13° \doteq 5.4 \times 0.974,$

$\qquad |\overrightarrow{BC}| = BC \doteq$ **5.3** nautical miles.

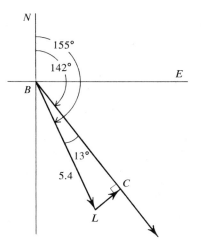

Figure 9.13-2

Example: 9.13-3. A surveyor runs a line bearing N 15° 13′ W, as shown in Figure 9.13-3, for a distance of 364.8 feet. Then he continues the line on a course bearing S 32° 55′ E for 204.0 feet. How far north is he from his starting point? What is the angle between the two lines?

$\quad |\overrightarrow{BE}| \doteq 364.8 \cos 15° \; 13′$

$\qquad \doteq 364.8 \,(0.9650),$

$BE \doteq 352.0$ feet.

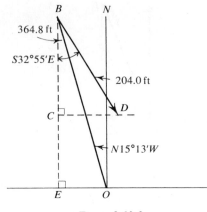

Figure 9.13-3

$|\overrightarrow{BC}| \doteq 204.0 \cos 32° \ 55'$

$\doteq 204.0 \ (0.8395),$

$BC \doteq 171.3.$

$EC \doteq BE - BC.$

$\doteq 352.0 - 171.3.$

$\therefore \ EC \doteq \textbf{180.7 feet}$ (to four-digit accuracy).

Angle $OBD \doteq 32° \ 55' - 15° \ 13' \doteq 17° \ 42'.$

Example: 9.13-4. An airplane is headed due west at an air speed of 465 miles per hour. A wind from the north is blowing at 38.5 miles per hour (refer to Figure 9.13-4). Find the course of the plane and its ground speed.

$\overrightarrow{OA} = \overrightarrow{CB}$ is the **wind vector.**

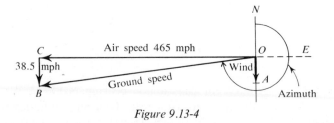

Figure 9.13-4

We always speak of the wind as "blowing from."

$\overrightarrow{OC}$ is the **air speed vector** and is the line segment along which the plane is **heading.**

$\overrightarrow{OB}$ is the **ground speed vector,** or the resultant of the air speed and wind vectors. The azimuth of $\overrightarrow{OB}$ is the **course of the plane.**

The angle between the **heading** $\overrightarrow{OC}$ and the course of the plane $\overrightarrow{OB}$ is called the **drift angle.**

$$\tan(COB) \doteq \frac{|\overrightarrow{CB}|}{|\overrightarrow{OC}|} \doteq \frac{38.5}{465} \doteq 0.0828,$$

∴ **Angle $COB \doteq 4° \ 44'$**   (drift angle).

The azimuth of the *heading* is 270°.

The course of the plane is $270° - 4° \ 44' \doteq 265° \ 16'$ or   **265°.**

The ground speed is $|\overrightarrow{OB}| \doteq \dfrac{|\overrightarrow{CB}|}{\sin 4° \ 44'} \doteq \dfrac{38.5}{0.0826} \doteq 466.1$ or **466 miles per hour.**

All answers have been written to three-digit accuracy.

EXERCISE 9.C

1. How does a vector quantity differ from a scalar quantity?

2. What is the magnitude of the vector $\overrightarrow{AA}$? What is its direction?

3. State the conditions that will guarantee the equality $\overrightarrow{AB} = \overrightarrow{CD}$.

4. What is the relation between the vectors $\overrightarrow{EF}$ and $-\overrightarrow{FE}$?

5. If two vectors are equal and parallel but have a different sense, are they equal?

6. To construct an angle between two vectors, what special arrangement of the vectors is necessary?

7. Discuss the details involved in finding the resultant of two vectors by the parallelogram law of vector addition.

8. Discuss the details involved in finding the resultant of two vectors by the triangular law of vector addition.

9. For any given resultant vector how many pairs of components are possible?

10. If the components of a resultant vector meet at right angles, what technical name do we give to the projections?

11. Explain how to find the length of the horizontal component of the resultant of the sum of any three vectors.

12. Explain how to find the length of the vertical component of the resultant of the difference of two vectors.

13. If a vector is multiplied by a scalar, does one get a vector or a scalar?

14. (a) If a is any real number, what is the identity element?

   (b) If a is a vector, what is the identity element?

15. Prove that vectors satisfy the associative law under addition.

16. Prove that vectors satisfy the associative law under multiplication.

17. Distinguish between (v_x, v_y) and $[v_x, v_y]$.

18. What is the modulus of the vector $|\mathbf{v}|$?

19. Write the vector $[4, 60°]$ in rectangular form. (See Section 10.5.)

20. Write the vector $[4, 60°]$ in rectangular form with the initial point at $(3, -2)$.

In the following problems the principles for computing with approximate data must be applied to each problem.

21. Find the horizontal and vertical components of a 173.9-pound force acting at an angle of inclination with the horizontal of 37° 29′.

22. Find the horizontal and vertical components of a 512.0-pound force acting at an angle of depression from the horizontal of 49° 37′.

23. If the wind is blowing 28.0 miles per hour from the south and the plane is flying east at an air speed of 340.0 miles per hour, find its drift angle, the azimuth of the course, and the ground speed.

24. If the wind is blowing 34.0 miles per hour from the west and the plane is flying south at an air speed of 170.0 miles per hour, find its drift angle, the direction of the course, and the ground speed.

9.14 SOLUTIONS OF RIGHT TRIANGLES

A right triangle possesses a right angle, two acute angles, and three sides. If we know an acute angle and a side or any two sides, we can then, by use of the six trigonometric definitions for an acute angle and Table III, find all the other parts.

9.14-1 How to Solve a Right Triangle

1. Represent the data on a reasonably accurate drawing.

2. Select the trigonometric formula that includes the two parts that are known and the part required. There may be more than one trigonometric relation that will satisfy the preceding requirements. Take the one that is easiest to solve.

Solve for the unknown part, but keep in mind as you do so that proper application of the principles of computing with measurements and other approximate data must be followed.

9.14-2 Angles of Elevation and Depression

Because of their common occurrence in right-triangle problems, *angle of elevation* and *angle of depression* need to be defined.

Definition: 9.14-2(1).   *As line segment AB, anchored at point A, swings up from the horizontal line AH in a vertical plane, the angle formed is called the* **angle of elevation.**

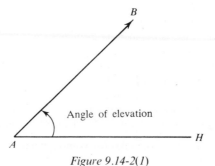

Figure 9.14-2(1)

Definition: 9.14-2(2).   *As line segment AB, anchored at point B, swings down from the horizontal line HB, the angle formed is called the* **angle of depression.**

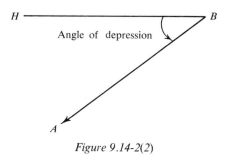

Figure 9.14-2(2)

Example: 9.14-2a.   If *AC* in Figure 9.14-2a is 205 feet long and the angle of elevation to the top of the church steeple, to the nearest 10 minutes, is 30° 10′, find the height to the top of the steeple.

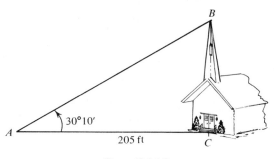

Figure 9.14-2a

Either the tangent or the cotangent function can be used, but the tangent is best. So,

$$\frac{BC}{205} \doteq \tan 30° \ 10' \doteq 0.5812, \qquad\qquad \text{(From Table III)}$$

$$BC \doteq 205(0.5812) \doteq 119.146,$$

and **BC** $\doteq$ **119 feet**   (best answer).

Review Example 9.14-2a and note particularly that 205 has three significant digits and, therefore, three-digit accuracy. There are (30)(6) + 1 or 181 ten-minute units in 30° 10′; so it, too, has three-digit accuracy. Following standard practice in all computations, we used the tangent value to four-digit accuracy, that is, (3 + 1)-digit accuracy, and then the final answer was rounded to three significant digits to match the least accurate measurement used.

Example: 9.14-2b.   How far is it from the balloon indicated in Figure 9.14-2b to the smoke stack of a ship if the angle of depression to the ship is 37° and the balloon is 5,200 feet above the top of the smoke stack?

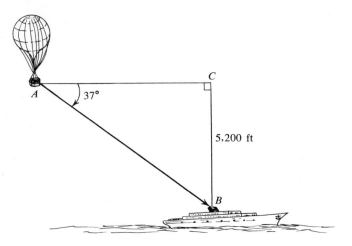

Figure 9.14-2b

For this problem the cosecant function is preferred over the sine function because the former is easier.

$$\frac{AB}{5,200} \doteq \csc 37° \doteq 1.66.$$

To the nearest degree 37° is a two-digit number, and, as far as one can tell from the data given, 5,200 feet is a measurement to the nearest 100 feet, with two-digit accuracy. Therefore, in our computations we should use only three digits for our cosecant value and round the final result to two digits (see Section 9.4-9).

$$AB \doteq 5,200(1.66),$$
$$AB \doteq 8,630.$$
$$\therefore AB \doteq \mathbf{8,600} \text{ feet} \qquad \text{(best answer)}.$$

Remember that **a result can be no more accurate than the data used in obtaining it** (read Section 9.4 again).

Example: 9.14-2c.   Find the length AB of one of the sides of the roof in Figure 9.14-2c built in the form of an isosceles triangle. The nonequal angle of the triangle is 86° 28′ and its perimeter is 22.54 feet. (*Hint*: What is the angle of elevation of each side?)

$$\text{Angle } \alpha \text{ at } A \doteq \frac{180° - 86° 28'}{2} \doteq \mathbf{46° \ 46'.}$$

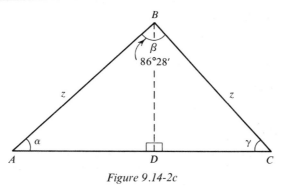

Figure 9.14-2c

Let z equal one of the two equal sides. Then

$$22.54 - 2z \doteq AC \quad \text{and} \quad AD \doteq \frac{22.54 - 2z}{2} \doteq 11.27 - z.$$

$$\cos 46° \, 46' \doteq \frac{11.27 - z}{z},$$

$$0.6849z \doteq 11.27 - z,$$

$$1.6849z \doteq 11.27,$$

$$z \doteq \frac{11.27}{1.6849} \doteq 6.6888.$$

$$\therefore \quad AB = z \doteq \mathbf{6.689 \ ft.} \quad \text{(best answer)}.$$

Example 9.14-2c presented these special problems:

1. To solve it by trigonometry one had to know the nature of an isosceles triangle and how to separate it into two right triangles.

2. Linear interpolation between angles 46° 40′ and 46° 50′ had to be used to get cos 46° 46′ $\doteq$ 0.6849.

3. The perimeter 22.54 ft to the nearest 0.01 of a foot and the angle 86° 28′ to the nearest minute are both to four digit accuracy. Obviously, here is a case where standard practice of using five significant digits in computing with the value of cos 46° 46′ *cannot* be followed for the simple reason that Table III gives the trigonometric values only to four significant digits. The best we can do, then, is to use cos 46° 46′ $\doteq$ 0.6849 to four-digit accuracy in the computations.

4. The difficulty of dividing 11.27 by 1.6849 suggests that those who choose to compute with logarithms can save time and energy by working out z in this manner:

If

$$z \doteq \frac{11.27}{1.6849} \doteq \frac{11.27}{1.685},$$

then $\log z \doteq \log 11.27 - \log 1.685,$

$\log z \doteq 1.0519 - 0.2286,$

$\log z \doteq 0.8253,$

and $AB \doteq z \doteq$ **6.689 ft**   (best answer).

EXERCISE 9.D

The basic principles for computing with approximate data must be applied to each problem worked. You can choose whether or not to use logarithms. Their use will, of course, save you both time and effort.

Solve the following right triangles ABC, C is the right angle, and α is the angle of the triangle opposite side a (see Figure 9.D-1).

1. (a) $a \doteq 14.9$, $\alpha \doteq 47°\ 20'$.   (b) $a \doteq 25.0$, $b \doteq 82.4$.

2. (a) $\alpha \doteq 52°\ 14'$, $b \doteq 48.21$.   (b) $\alpha \doteq 72°\ 49'$, $c \doteq 1001$.

3. How high is a tower if from a point on level ground 345 feet from its base the angle of elevation to its top is $36°\ 50'$?

4. Find the angle of elevation of the sun if a woman 5 feet 4 inches tall casts a shadow 16 feet long.

The inclined plane in Figure 9.D-1 makes an angle with the horizontal of $65°\ 13'$. The incline is 1,893 feet long:

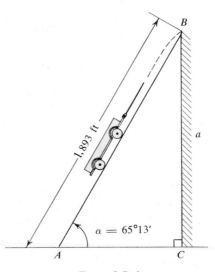

Figure 9.D-1

5. How high is the hill?

6. How far does the cable car move horizontally in making one complete trip either up or down?

From the top of a tower 342 feet high the angle of depression to the nearest part of a boat at its waterline was $28.7°$:

7. How far is the boat from the foot of the tower?

8. Find the air-line distance from the top of the tower to the boat.

9. Find the air-line distance from an airplane, flying 8,520 feet high to a field marker if the angle of depression to the marker is 22° 50′.

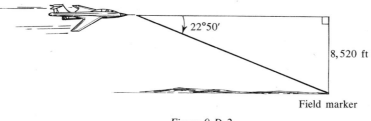

22°50′

8,520 ft

Field marker

Figure 9.D-2

10. Find the climbing angle of a plane if in climbing a straight line of 2,430 feet it rises 227 feet.

11. A ladder should be placed so that the line of the ladder and level ground form an angle of 75° to get greatest safety. How far from a vertical wall should the bottom of a 32-foot ladder be placed to guarantee maximum safety?

12. At an angle of 75° would a 32-foot ladder reach from level ground to the base of a window 22 feet up the vertical wall?

13. Find the base and altitude of an isosceles triangle if one of its equal sides is 34.01 inches and one of its base angles is 22° 06′.

14. A piece of plastic strip 37.29 inches is bent to form an isosceles triangle with its largest angle 93° 21′. Find the length of the sides.

9.15 SOLUTIONS OF OBLIQUE TRIANGLES

In Section 9.14 we found that the six fundamental definitions for circular and/or trigonometric functions are quite adequate to solve for the unknown parts of any right triangle, provided two sides or one side and an acute angle of the right triangle are known.

Since any oblique triangle can be divided into two right triangles, its sides and angles can be determined by the right-triangle method. The right-triangle approach, however, is quite clumsy for many purposes. Therefore, more efficient methods of solving oblique triangles will be presented.

9.15-1 Law of Sines

An angle is either an acute, right, or an obtuse angle. This is demonstrated by drawing three triangles. Figure 9.15-1a contains an acute angle, Figure 9.15-1b a right angle, and Figure 9.15-1c an obtuse angle.

A line segment from *B* perpendicular to *AC* has been drawn in each triangle to form right triangles. Figure 9.15-1b, of course, is already a right triangle and has been studied previously. It has been inserted here merely to indicate the continuity from acute to right to obtuse angles and will not be discussed further in this section.

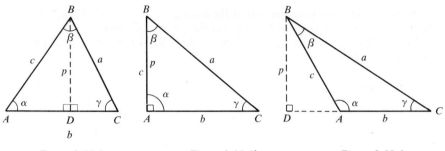

Figure 9.15-1a   Figure 9.15-1b   Figure 9.15-1c

In Figure 9.15-1a:

Right triangle ADB gives $\sin \alpha = \dfrac{p}{c}$ so $p = c \sin \alpha$.

Right triangle CDB gives $\sin \gamma = \dfrac{p}{a}$ so $p = a \sin \gamma$.

By the transitive law, if $a \sin \gamma = p$ and $p = c \sin \alpha$,

then $a \sin \gamma = c \sin \alpha$,

and $\qquad \dfrac{a}{\sin \alpha} = \dfrac{c}{\sin \gamma}.$ (A)

Also in Figure 9.15-1c where α is obtuse we know that the "corresponding acute angle" for α is $(180° - \alpha)$. Because the sine of an angle which is located in the second quadrant (similar to an obtuse angle) is identical to $\sin 180°$ less that angle, then $\sin \alpha = \sin(180° - \alpha)$ and we can write these relations.

For right triangle ADB, $\sin \alpha = \dfrac{p}{c}$ and $p = c \sin \alpha$.

For right triangle CDB, $\sin \gamma = \dfrac{p}{a}$ and $p = a \sin \gamma$.

Again, $\qquad\qquad\qquad \dfrac{a}{\sin \alpha} = \dfrac{c}{\sin \gamma}.$ (A)

By dropping a perpendicular from C on AB in Figure 9.15-1a and following a similar discussion, there results

$\qquad \dfrac{a}{\sin \alpha} = \dfrac{b}{\sin \beta}.$ (B)

Similarly, by dropping a perpendicular from A on BC we get

$\qquad \dfrac{c}{\sin \gamma} = \dfrac{b}{\sin \beta}.$ (C)

When working with the *Law of Sines*, we use that one of the preceding proportions, (*A*), (*B*), or (*C*), which contains the given data and leaves one unknown.
Any one of the preceding proportions is called the Law of Sines, but in its
most complete form the Law of Sines is

$$\frac{a}{\sin\alpha} = \frac{b}{\sin\beta} = \frac{c}{\sin\gamma}. \qquad\qquad \textbf{(Law of Sines)}$$

The **Law of Sines** *states that in any triangle the sides are proportional to the
sines of the opposite angles.*

In solving an oblique triangle, we only need to know three of the six parts,
provided one of the three parts is a side. There are four different ways in which
the required data may be made available:

CASE I: **Two angles and any side.**
CASE II: **Two sides and an angle opposite one of the given sides.**
CASE III: **Two sides and the included angle.**
CASE IV: **Three sides.**

The Law of Sines can be used to complete the solution of an oblique triangle
for Case I and Case II only. As you will learn later, Case III and Case IV will
require the application of the Law of Cosines.

Example 1 of Case I.   Given $\alpha \doteq 78° 42'$, $\beta \doteq 33° 22'$, and $a \doteq 724.3$ feet.
Find γ, b, and c. (Refer to Figure 9.15-1d.)

$$\gamma \doteq 180° - (78° 42' + 33° 22') \doteq 67° 56'.$$

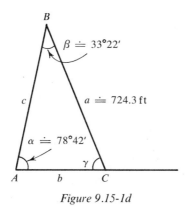

Figure 9.15-1d

The forms of the Law of Sines that apply are

$$\frac{c}{\sin\gamma} = \frac{a}{\sin\alpha} \quad\text{and}\quad \frac{b}{\sin\beta} = \frac{a}{\sin\alpha}.$$

$$c = \frac{a \sin \gamma}{\sin \alpha} \quad \text{and} \quad b = \frac{a \sin \beta}{\sin \alpha}.$$

Using logarithms to simplify the work, the completed solutions are

$\log a \doteq 2.8599$	$\log a \doteq 2.8599$

$$\frac{\log \sin \gamma \doteq 9.9670 - 10}{\log \text{numerator} \doteq 12.8269 - 10}$$

$$\frac{\log \sin \beta \doteq 9.7404 - 10}{\log \text{numerator} \doteq 12.6003 - 10}$$

$$\frac{\log \sin \alpha \doteq 9.9915 - 10}{\log c \doteq 2.8354}$$

$$\frac{\log \sin \alpha \doteq 9.9915 - 10}{\log b \doteq 2.6088}$$

$$c \doteq \mathbf{684.5}$$

$$b \doteq \mathbf{406.3}$$

All data and answers are given to four-digit accuracy.

Example 2 of Case I.   Because of a very strong wind blowing from $N\ 35°\ E$ the pilot of a hurricane hunter plane whose air speed is 350 mph has to head his plane at 320° in order to follow a 305° course.

1. Find the ground speed.
2. Find the velocity of wind.
3. Use Figure 9.15-1e to check the results.

$\alpha \doteq 320° - 305° \doteq 15°.$
$\beta \doteq (360° - 320° + 35°) \doteq 75°.$
$\gamma = 180° - (15° + 75°) \doteq 90°.$

Using the Law of Sines:

$$b = \frac{c \sin \beta}{\sin \gamma} \qquad\qquad a = \frac{c \sin \alpha}{\sin \gamma}$$

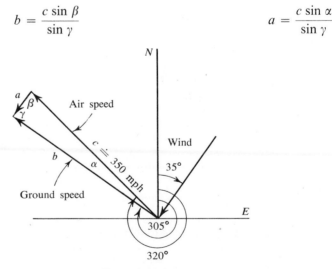

Figure 9.15-1e

$$\log c \doteq 2.5441$$

$$\frac{\log \sin \beta \doteq 9.9849 - 10}{\log \text{numerator} \doteq 12.5290 - 10}$$

$$\frac{\log \sin \gamma \doteq 10.0000 - 10}{\log b \doteq 2.5290}$$

$$b \doteq 338.1$$

or   **b ≐ 340 mph**
(Ground speed to two-digit
accuracy)

$$\log c \doteq 2.5441$$

$$\frac{\log \sin \alpha \doteq 9.4130 - 10}{\log \text{numerator} \doteq 11.9571 - 10}$$

$$\frac{\log \sin \gamma \doteq 10.0000 - 10}{\log a \doteq 1.9571}$$

$$a \doteq 90.6$$

or   **a ≐ 91 mph**
(Wind velocity to two-digit
accuracy)

You have probably noticed that the vectors representing wind, air speed, and ground speed, happened to form a right triangle in Example 2, Case I. Since the *Law of Sines works for any triangle having two given angles and a side*, it works for a right triangle for the same type of data. You understand of course, that if you are certain that the resulting triangle is a right triangle you can, if you choose, always revert to the fundamental trigonometric defini-tions to get the solutions. They usually furnish an easier and quicker way to solve the problem.

Case II of the Law of Sines is called the ambiguous case because the problem may involve two triangles, one triangle, or no triangle at all; when two sides and an angle opposite one of the sides is given.

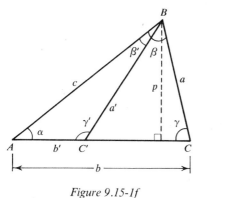

Figure 9.15-1f

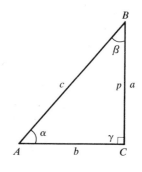

Figure 9.15-1g

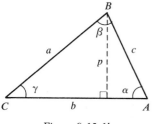

Figure 9.15-1h

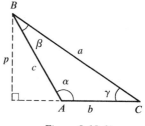

Figure 9.15-1i

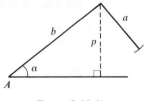

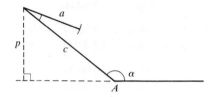

Figure 9.15-1j   Figure 9.15-1k

These six possibilities exist:

Figure 9.15-1f: $p < a < c$,   two triangles are involved.
Figure 9.15-1g: $a = p$,   one triangle is involved.
Figure 9.15-1h: $a \geq c$,   one triangle is involved.
Figure 9.15-1i: $\alpha > 90°$, $a > c$,   one triangle is involved.
Figure 9.15-1j: $a < p$,   no triangle is involved.
Figure 9.15-1k: $\alpha > 90°$, $a < c$,   no triangle is involved.

An example of the most complicated of the six possibilities follows.

    Example of Case II.   Solve for the other parts of the triangle if $a \doteq 78.32$, $c \doteq 87.06$, and $\alpha \doteq 59°\ 34'$.

    As Figure 9.15-1m indicates, $p < a < c$; therefore, two triangles, ABC and $AB'C'$, are to be solved.

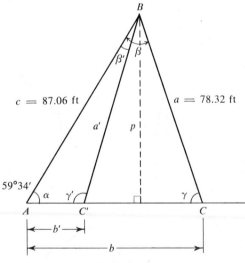

Figure 9.15-1m

Using the Law of Sines on triangle ABC,

$$\sin \gamma = \frac{c \sin \alpha}{a} \qquad\qquad \frac{b}{\sin \beta} = \frac{a}{\sin \alpha}$$

$$\log c \doteq 1.9398$$

$$\frac{\log \sin \alpha \doteq 9.9356 - 10}{\log \text{numerator} \doteq 11.8754 - 10}$$

$$\frac{\log a \doteq 1.8939}{\log \sin \gamma \doteq 9.9815 - 10}$$

$$\gamma \doteq \mathbf{73°\ 23'}$$

$$B \doteq 180° - (\alpha + \gamma)$$

$$\doteq 180° - 132°\ 57'$$

$$\therefore \quad B \doteq \mathbf{47°\ 0.3'}.$$

$$\gamma \doteq 180° - 73°\ 23'$$

$$\gamma' \doteq \mathbf{106°\ 37'}$$

$$\beta' \doteq 180° - (\alpha + \gamma')$$

$$\doteq 180° - 166°\ 11'$$

$$\therefore \quad B' \doteq \mathbf{13°\ 49'}.$$

$$b = \frac{a \sin \beta}{\sin \alpha}$$

$$\log a \doteq 1.8939$$

$$\frac{\log \sin \beta \doteq 9.8668 - 10}{\log \text{numerator} \doteq 11.7607 - 10}$$

$$\frac{\log \sin \alpha \doteq 9.9356 - 10}{\log b \doteq 1.8251}$$

$$\therefore \quad b \doteq \mathbf{66.85}.$$

$$b = \frac{a \sin \beta'}{\sin \alpha}$$

$$\log a \doteq 1.8939$$

$$\frac{\log \sin \beta' \doteq 9.3781 - 10}{\log \text{numerator} \doteq 11.2720 - 10}$$

$$\frac{\log \sin \alpha \doteq 9.9356 - 10}{\log b' \doteq 1.3364}$$

$$\therefore \quad b' \doteq \mathbf{21.70}.$$

9.15-2 Area of Triangles

From geometry we recall that *the area of any triangle equals half the product of its base and altitude*; that is, **Area** $= \frac{1}{2}$ (**base** × **altitude**). We will use this theorem to prove the following theorem:

Theorem: 9.15-2a.   The area of any triangle equals half the product of two sides of the triangle and the sine of the angle included between them.

PROOF: In both Figure 9.15-2(a) and 9.15-2(b) a perpendicular is dropped from B to AC at D. Therefore, the area of triangle ABC is

$$A = \tfrac{1}{2}bp.$$

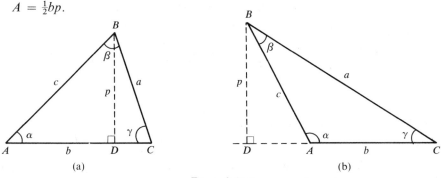

(a)   (b)

Figure 9.15-2

But by trigonometry $p = c \sin \alpha$. Therefore, by substitution

$$A = \tfrac{1}{2}bc \sin \alpha. \qquad\qquad (A)$$

Similarly, by dropping perpendiculars from A on BC and C on AB, we get the formulas

$$A = \tfrac{1}{2}ab \sin \gamma, \qquad\qquad (B)$$

and $\quad A = \tfrac{1}{2}ac \sin \beta. \qquad\qquad (C)$

From the Law of Sines, $\dfrac{a}{\sin \alpha} = \dfrac{b}{\sin \beta} = \dfrac{c}{\sin \gamma}$.

$$a = \frac{b \sin \alpha}{\sin \beta} = \frac{c \sin \alpha}{\sin \gamma}; \qquad\qquad (D)$$

$$b = \frac{a \sin \beta}{\sin \alpha} = \frac{c \sin \beta}{\sin \gamma}; \qquad\qquad (E)$$

and $c = \dfrac{a \sin \gamma}{\sin \alpha} = \dfrac{b \sin \gamma}{\sin \beta}. \qquad\qquad (F)$

Substituting the appropriate values of (E) and (F) in (A). we obtain a formula that will enable us to compute the area of a triangle if we know one side and the three angles. The formula is

$$A = \frac{1}{2}\left(\frac{a \sin \beta}{\sin \alpha}\right)\left(\frac{a \sin \gamma}{\sin \alpha}\right) \sin \alpha,$$

or $A = \dfrac{a^2 \sin \beta \sin \gamma}{2 \sin \alpha}. \qquad\qquad (G)$

Similarly, by substituting appropriate values of (D) and (F) in (B), we get

$$A = \frac{b^2 \sin \alpha \sin \gamma}{2 \sin \beta}. \qquad\qquad (H)$$

Finally, by substituting appropriate values of (D) and (E) in (C), there results

$$A = \frac{c^2 \sin \alpha \sin \beta}{2 \sin \gamma}. \qquad\qquad (I)$$

The best formula for finding the area of a triangle is:

1. (A), (B), or (C) if two sides and an included angle are given,
2. (G), (H), or (I) if one side and three angles are given.

Example: 9.15-2a.   Find the area of a triangle ABC if side $a \doteq 387.6$ feet, side $b \doteq 604.2$ feet, and angle $\gamma \doteq 53° 9'$.

Using $A = \dfrac{ab \sin \gamma}{2}$,

$$\begin{aligned}
\log 387.6 &\doteq 2.5884 \\
\log 604.2 &\doteq 2.7812 \\
\log \sin 53° \, 9' &\doteq 9.9032 - 10 \\
\log \text{numerator} &\doteq \overline{15.2728 - 10} \\
\log 2 &\doteq 0.3010 \\
\log A &\doteq \overline{14.9718 - 10}
\end{aligned}$$

∴ $A \doteq$ **93,720 square feet**   (to four-digit accuracy).

Example: 9.15-2b.   Find the area of a triangle ABC if side a is 125.6 feet, $\gamma \doteq 51° \, 43'$, and $\beta \doteq 62° \, 14'$.

$$\alpha \doteq 180° - (51° \, 43' + 62° \, 14') \doteq 66° \, 03'$$

Using $A = \dfrac{a^2 \sin \beta \sin \gamma}{2 \sin \alpha}$,

$$\begin{aligned}
2 \log 125.6 &\doteq 4.1980 \\
\log \sin 51° \, 43' &\doteq 9.8949 - 10 \\
\log \sin 62° \, 14' &\doteq 9.9469 - 10 \\
\log \text{numerator} &\doteq \overline{24.0398 - 20} \\
\log \sin \alpha = \log \sin 66° \, 03' &\doteq 9.9609 - 10 \\
\log 2A &\doteq \overline{15.0789 - 10} \\
2A &\doteq 119,900
\end{aligned}$$

∴ $A \doteq$ **59,950 square feet**   (to four-digit accuracy).

9.15-3 Law of Cosines

Suppose that the given data for an oblique triangle were either Case III with two sides and the included angle or Case IV with three sides (read Section 9.15-1). The Law of Sines will not apply, but the Law of Cosines, which is about to be developed, will. Thus, with the Law of Sines and the Law of Cosines available to us any triangle, given sufficient data, can be solved.

The **Law of Cosines** *states that in any triangle the square of one side is equal to the sum of the squares of the other two sides less the product of those two sides and the sine of the included angle.*

As indicated by the theorem the Law of Cosines takes one of three possible forms:

  1. $a^2 = b^2 + c^2 - 2bc \cos \alpha$;
  2. $b^2 = a^2 + c^2 - 2ac \cos \beta$;
and 3. $c^2 = a^2 + b^2 - 2ab \cos \gamma$.

To prove that $a^2 = b^2 + c^2 - 2bc \cos \alpha$, drop a perpendicular from B on side AC forming the two right triangles ADB and CDB. Then from either

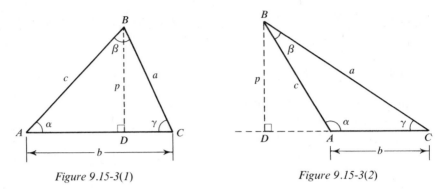

Figure 9.15-3(1)   *Figure 9.15-3(2)*

Figure 9.15-3(1) or Figure 9.15-3(2), where α is acute or obtuse,

$$a^2 = p^2 + (DC)^2.$$ (Pythagorean Theorem)

Figure 9.15-3(1) indicates that $(b - AD) = DC$ and Figure 9.15-3(2) also indicates that $(b + DA)$ whose equivalent is $(b - AD) = DC$. Thus, for either case $(b - AD)$ can be substituted for DC in the equation $a^2 = p^2 + (DC)^2$ giving

$$a^2 = p^2 + (b - AD)^2.$$

Then $a^2 = p^2 + b^2 - 2bAD + (AD)^2,$

$$= b^2 + p^2 + (AD)^2 - 2bAD, \text{ where } p^2 + (AD)^2 = c^2$$

and $AD = c \cos \alpha.$

∴ $a^2 = b^2 + c^2 - 2bc \cos \alpha.$ (Law of Cosines)

In a similar manner a perpendicular dropped from A to BC will give

$$c^2 = a^2 + b^2 - 2ab \cos \gamma.$$ (Law of Cosines)

Likewise, a perpendicular from C on AB will give

$$b^2 = a^2 + c^2 - 2ac \cos \beta.$$ (Law of Cosines)

One of the very interesting things about the Law of Cosines is that it includes the Pythagorean theorem as one of its special cases. This fact is easily shown by taking α = 90°, which guarantees a right angle, and substituting it in

$$a^2 = b^2 + c^2 - 2bc \cos \alpha.$$

We know that cos 90° = 0 and that $2bc(0) = 0$. Therefore, when α = 90° the Law of Cosines becomes

$$a^2 = b^2 + c^2.$$ (Pythagorean Theorem)

Even though the Law of Cosines is one of our most commonly used laws, it does not, because of the additions and subtractions it contains, lend itself well to the solution of triangles by logarithmic computations. This does not mean that logarithms—which apply directly to multiplications, powers, and roots—cannot be used, but if used they have to be used in steps, and this procedure eliminates the advantages that logarithms provide in computations.

Example: 9.15-3a.   The angle between a 52.5-pound force and a 115-pound force is 61° 10′. Find the resultant and its direction.

Use $c^2 = a^2 + b^2 - 2ab \cos \gamma$ and Figure 9.15-3a.

$$c^2 \doteq (52.5)^2 + (115)^2 - 2(52.5)(115) \cos 118° \, 50'$$
$$\doteq (52.5)^2 + (115)^2 + 2(52.5)(115) \cos 61° \, 10'$$
$$\doteq 2{,}756 + 13{,}225 + 12{,}075(0.4823)$$
$$\doteq 2{,}756 + 13{,}225 + 5{,}824$$
$$\doteq 21{,}805,$$
$$c \doteq 147.6.$$
$$\therefore \quad c \doteq \textbf{148 pounds} \qquad \textbf{(resultant} \text{ to three-digit accuracy).}$$

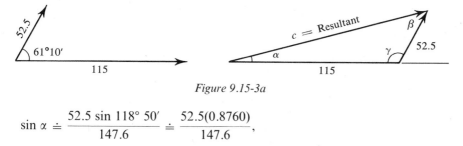

Figure 9.15-3a

$$\sin \alpha \doteq \frac{52.5 \sin 118° \, 50'}{147.6} \doteq \frac{52.5(0.8760)}{147.6},$$

$$\sin \alpha \doteq \frac{45.99}{147.6} \doteq 0.3116.$$

$$\therefore \quad \alpha \doteq \textbf{18° 10′} \qquad \textbf{(direction of resultant} \text{ to three-digit accuracy).}$$

Example: 9.15-3b.   Find the three angles of the triangle shown in Figure 9.15-3b whose sides are respectively 698 feet, 542 feet, and 486 feet.

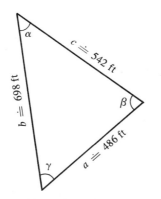

Figure 9.15-3b

Solving for cos α by the Law of Cosines,

$$a^2 = b^2 + c^2 - 2bc \cos \alpha$$

gives $\cos \alpha = \dfrac{b^2 + c^2 - a^2}{2bc}.$

Then $\cos \alpha \doteq \dfrac{(698)^2 + (542)^2 - (486)^2}{2(698)(542)}$

$\doteq 0.7200$

$\alpha \doteq 43° \ 57'.$

∴ $\alpha \doteq$ **44° 00'**   (to nearest 10').

$\cos \beta = \dfrac{a^2 + c^2 - b^2}{2ac}$ $\cos \gamma = \dfrac{a^2 + b^2 - c^2}{2ab},$

$\cos \beta \doteq \dfrac{(486)^2 + (542)^2 - (698)^2}{2(486)(542)}$ $\cos \gamma \doteq \dfrac{(486)^2 + (698)^2 - (542)^2}{2(486)(698)}$

$\doteq 0.0811,$ $\doteq 0.6332,$

$\beta \doteq 85° \ 21'.$ $\gamma \doteq 50° \ 43'.$

β $\doteq$ **85° 20'**   (to nearest 10').   ∴ **γ** $\doteq$ **50° 40'**

All angles have been expressed to three-digit accuracy.
$\alpha + \beta + \gamma \doteq 44° \ 00' + 85° \ 20' + 50° \ 40' \doteq 180°.$ What should the sum of
the interior angles of the triangle be?

Example: 9.15-3c.   A plane is heading due east, as indicated by Figure
9.15-3c, at 430 miles per hour. A wind is blowing in from the northeast at
55 miles per hour. Find the direction of the plane and its ground speed.

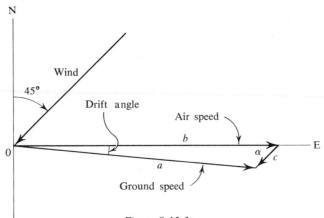

Figure 9.15-3c

Using $a^2 = b^2 + c^2 - 2bc \cos \alpha$, where $\alpha \doteq 45°$, $b \doteq$ air speed, $c \doteq$ wind, and $a \doteq$ ground speed (g.s.), then

$$(\text{g.s.})^2 \doteq (430)^2 + (55)^2 - 2(55)(430) \cos 45°,$$

$$(\text{g.s.})^2 \doteq 184{,}900 + 3{,}025 - 47{,}300(0.7071).$$

$\therefore (\text{g.s.})^2 \doteq 154{,}479.$

ground speed $\doteq 393$ or **390 miles per hour**   (to two-digit accuracy).

To get the direction of the plane, find the drift angle (d.a.) by

$$\sin (\text{d.a.}) \doteq \frac{55 \sin 45°}{393} \doteq \frac{55(0.707)}{393} \doteq 0.0990,$$

$$(\text{d.a.}) \doteq 5° \, 41',$$

drift angle $\doteq 5° \, 40'$ (to two-digit accuracy).

Therefore, **the direction of the plane is** $90° + 5° \, 40'$ or **95° 40′**.

EXERCISE 9.E

The problems in this chapter can be solved either by the Law of Sines or by the Law of Cosines, or both. Each of the four possible cases of presenting data for oblique triangles is present. Logarithms will shorten some of the computations for you. All answers must be written to express no more accuracy than the least accurate data used.

Solve the following triangles and check results:

1. $\alpha = 63°$, $\beta = 41°$, $a = 33$ feet.
2. $\alpha = 56°$, $\gamma = 78°$, $b = 3.7$ feet.
3. $\alpha = 85° \, 10'$, $a = 642$ feet, $b = 382$ feet.
4. $\gamma = 76° \, 20'$, $c = 12.7$ inches, $b = 14.0$ inches.
5. $\gamma = 47° \, 50'$, $a = 924$ inches, $b = 778$ inches.
6. $\beta = 70° \, 30'$, $a = 778$ feet, $c = 248$ feet.
7. $a = 157$ feet, $b = 664$ feet, $c = 314$ feet.
8. $a = 14.4$ inches, $b = 12.9$ inches, $c = 11.4$ inches.
9. $\alpha = 51° \, 37'$ $\gamma = 126° \, 26'$, $a = 3.436$ inches.
10. $\beta = 38° \, 00'$, $\gamma = 106° \, 21'$, $c = 26.35$ inches.

11. One side of a flower bed is 39 feet long. Another side of the triangular bed is 29 feet and the angle opposite it is 43°. Find the remaining angles and side of the triangle.

12. Between A and B there is a lake. Angle BAC measured 47°, angle ACB measured 83°, and the distance between C and B measured 147′. Find the distance from A to B.

13. To find the distance from point A on one side of a river to point C on the opposite side, the line AB was measured along a straight line near the river's edge and found to be 124.6 feet. Angle BAC measured 71° 58′ and angle ABC measured 41° 35′. How long is AC?

14. If the length of one side of a parallelogram is 54.37 inches long and one diagonal of the parallelogram makes angles of 36° 13′ and 48° 17′ with that side, find the length of this diagonal.

15. Solve the triangle ABC given $B = 119°\ 01'$, $b = 1,704$ feet, and $c = 1,987$ feet.

16. Solve the triangle ABC given $a = 5.692$ inches, $b = 14.20$ inches, and $\alpha = 76°\ 58'$.

17. Find the length of the third side of a triangular building that faces 134.21 feet along one street and 128.42 feet along another street. The streets intersect at an angle of $74°\ 28'$.

18. If one side of a triangle is x long, another side is 3.472 times as long, and the angle between the two sides is $32°\ 01'$, find the other two angles and the third side.

19. Airport N is 625.6 miles east of Airport M. An airplane leaves airport M at 2:00 p.m. and flies a course of $34°\ 27'$ at a speed of 342.4 miles per hour. Another plane leaves Airport N and flies a course at a speed of 310.4 miles per hour. What course must the second plane fly to intercept the first plane at 3:00 p.m.?

20. What course would the two planes in Problem 19 have to fly to intercept each other in 90 minutes?

21. Two hikers start from the same point; one walks east 6.4 miles, the other one north $54°\ 40'$ E a distance of 7.6 miles. How far apart are they at the end of the walk?

22. If a hiker walks due east at 3.2 miles per hour and a second hiker, starting at the same point, walks N $54°\ 40'$ E at the rate of 3.8 miles per hour, how far apart will they be after 4 hours?

Find the area of triangle ABC given that

23. $a = 18.37$ feet, $c = 20.43$ feet,   and $\beta = 32°\ 13'$.
24. $\gamma = 104°\ 2'$, $b = 90.04$ inches,   and $a = 74.47$ inches.
25. $\alpha = 81°\ 44'$, $\beta = 56°\ 31'$,   and $b = 617.7$ miles.
26. $c = 297.4$ feet, $\beta = 61°\ 18'$,   and $\alpha = 39°\ 52'$.
27. $\alpha = 60°$, $\beta = 60°$,   and $c = 500$ feet.
28. $\alpha = 30°$, $\beta = 60°$,   and $b = 69$ feet.

29. The angle between the diagonals of a parallelogram is $54°\ 32'$. If the lengths of the diagonals are 61.6 feet and 73.4 feet, what are the lengths of the sides of the parallelogram? What is its area?

30. The three sides of a triangular lot have lengths of 161.4 feet, 191.0 feet, and 207.6 feet. Find its smallest angle. Find the area of the lot.

31. A woman walks 4.72 miles along a road bearing N $6°\ 37'$ E, and then 6.48 miles along a road bearing N $32°\ 14'$ W. How far is she from her starting point and what is the azimuth?

32. To get a certain marker a surveyor follows 647.2 feet along a level line bearing N $87°\ 3'$ E and then 287.0 feet along a line bearing S $20°\ 36'$ W. How far is he from his starting point and what is the azimuth of the resultant?

10

The Complex Number System

If we had had available only a number system of nonnegative integers over the first nine chapters we would have been limited in many ways. We could not have solved an equation as simple as $x + 1 = 0$. Even after the set had been extended to include the set of rational numbers we still could not have solved an equation such as $x^2 - 2 = 0$. Therefore, we were compelled to extend our number system to include the set of real numbers.

The real number system has been adequate to enable us to perform the operations of addition, multiplication, subtraction, division (zero excepted), and extraction of roots of all nonnegative numbers as well as odd roots of nonpositive numbers. As marvelous as this real number system is, it will fail us in many of our future algebraic deliberations. For example, it will fail us in these respects:

1. With only the real numbers available it is impossible to solve an equation such as $x^2 + 1 = 0$. For example, if $x^2 + 1 = 0$, then $x = \sqrt{-1}$ and $x = -\sqrt{-1}$. But a real number of the form $\sqrt{-1}$ does not exist.
2. With only the real number system available, we could not find the roots of a quadratic equation which has a discriminant less than zero (see Section 4.6).

In order to solve many polynomial equations with real coefficients we must extend the real number system R into a new number system. This new number system will be denoted by C and will be called the **complex number system.** As has been our practice in each extension of the number system, this extension will be done in such a manner that the real number system R will be a subset of this new complex number system C.

10.1 SOME ALGEBRA OF ORDERED PAIRS

In order to formulate a definition for complex numbers we need to give some additional attention to ordered pairs (see Definition 3.1-1 and Section 3.2).

If the ordered pair under discussion is (a, b), $a, b \in R$, a will always be considered the first element of the pair and b, which does not necessarily have to be different from a, will be the second element. The set of all ordered pairs of (a, b) forms the Cartesian product $R \times R$; that is,

$$R \times R = \{(a, b) \mid a \in R \quad \text{and} \quad b \in R\}.$$

Let C denote the set of ordered pairs (a, b), (c, d), (e, f), and so on.

Definition: 10.1-1.   *For $a, b, c, d \in R$, any two* **ordered pairs** *(a, b) and (c, d) are* **equal** *if and only if $a = c$ and $b = d$.*

Example: 10.1-1. $(x + 3, 2y - 1) = (0, 3)$ if and only if $x + 3 = 0$ and $2y - 1 = 3$.

Definition: 10.1-2.   *For $a, b, c, d \in R$, the* **sum** *of any two* **ordered pairs** *(a, b) and (c, d) is the ordered pair $(a + c, b + d)$.*

Example: 10.1-2. $(4, 6) + (3, 9) = (4 + 3, 6 + 9) = (7, 15)$.

Definition: 10.1-3.   *For $a, b, c, d \in R$, the* **product** *of any two* **ordered pairs** *(a, b) and (c, d) is the ordered pair $(ac - bd, ad + bc)$.*

Example: 10.1-3. $(4, 6)(3, 9) = (4 \times 3 - 6 \times 9, 4 \times 9 + 6 \times 3) = (-42, 54)$.

Definition 10.1-3 is a good definition and must be accepted even though it may not be at all obvious to you at the moment why $(a, b)(c, d) = (ac - bd, ad + bc)$. Later on this equality can easily be made meaningful to you.

10.2 A COMPLEX NUMBER DEFINED

Definition: 10.2-a.   *A* **complex number** *is an ordered pair of real numbers subject to the following conditions of equality, addition, and multiplication:*

Equality: $(a, b) = (c, d)$ **if and only if** $a = c$ **and** $b = d$.
Addition: $(a, b) + (c, d) = (a + c, b + d)$.
Multiplication: $(a, b)(c, d) = (ac - bd, ad + bc)$.

Notice that the real numbers a, b, c, and d which make up the ordered pairs are playing the same roll in the construction of the complex number system as the integers played in the construction of the set of rational numbers.

Since the purpose of creating a definition for a complex number (Definition 10.2-a) is to provide us with a number system that will enable us to deal with a more extensive group of problems and at the same time provide a number system that will satisfy the field postulates of the real number system, let us observe how our complex number system behaves in regard to some of the field postulates.

Example: 10.2-a.   Prove that the complex numbers (a, b) and (c, d) satisfy the commutative law under addition (see A_2 in Section 2.10).

$$
\begin{aligned}
(a, b) + (c, d) &= (a + c, b + d), & \text{(Definition 10.2-a)} \\
&= (c + a, d + b), & (A_2, \text{Section 2.10}) \\
&= (c, d) + (a, b). & \text{(Definition 10.2-a)} \\
\therefore (a, b) + (c, d) &= (c, d) + (a, b). & (E_3, \text{Section 2.11})
\end{aligned}
$$

Example: 10.2-b.   Show that the complex number $(0, 0)$ is the additive identity for the set C of complex numbers.

$$
\begin{aligned}
(a, b) + (0, 0) &= (a + 0, b + 0), & \text{(Definition 10.2-a)} \\
\therefore (a, b) + (0, 0) &= (a, b). & (A_4, \text{Section 2.10})
\end{aligned}
$$

The complex number $(0, 0)$ is the additive identity for set C, because when it is added to any other complex number (a, b) the result is (a, b).

Example: 10.2-c.   Show that the complex number $(1, 0)$ is the multiplicative identity for the complex number system.

$$
\begin{aligned}
(a, b)(1, 0) &= (a \cdot 1 - b \cdot 0, a \cdot 0 + b \cdot 1). & \text{(Definition 10.2-a)} \\
\therefore (a, b)(1, 0) &= (a, b). & (M_4, \text{Section 2.19}) \\
& & \& \text{ (Theorem 2.12-4)}
\end{aligned}
$$

Because any complex number (a, b) multiplied by $(1, 0)$ gives that number, it follows that the complex number $(1, 0)$ is the multiplicative identity for set C.

Example: 10.2-d.   For $(a, b) \neq (0, 0)$, prove that the multiplicative inverse of (a, b) is $\left(\dfrac{a}{a^2 + b^2}, \dfrac{-b}{a^2 + b^2} \right)$.

$$
\begin{aligned}
(a, b)\left(\frac{a}{a^2 + b^2}, \frac{-b}{a^2 + b^2} \right) &= \left(\frac{a^2}{a^2 + b^2} + \frac{b^2}{a^2 + b^2}, \frac{-ab}{a^2 + b^2} + \frac{ab}{a^2 + b^2} \right) \\
& \hspace{4cm} \text{(Definition 10.2-a)} \\
&= \left(\frac{a^2 + b^2}{a^2 + b^2}, 0 \right).
\end{aligned}
$$

$$
\therefore (a, b)\left(\frac{a}{a^2 + b^2}, \frac{-b}{a^2 + b^2} \right) = (1, 0). \qquad (E_3, \text{Section 2.11})
$$

Since the complex number (a, b) has been multiplied by another complex number and the product is the multiplicative identity $(1, 0)$, then the number $\left(\dfrac{a}{a^2 + b^2}, \dfrac{-b}{a^2 + b^2} \right)$ must be the multiplicative inverse of (a, b) (see M_5 Section 2.10).

Additional proofs to show that the complex number system satisfies all the remaining field postulates can be established. You will be asked to work out some of these proofs in Exercise 10A. In any case, you can be certain that **the complex number system is a field.**

Subtraction of complex numbers is defined in terms of addition of complex numbers, the same as in the case of real numbers (see Definition 2.2-1). For example,

$$(a, b) - (c, d) = (x, y) \quad \text{means} \quad (x, y) + (c, d) = (a, b).$$
Then
$$(x + c, y + d) = (a, b),$$

(Definition 10.2-a)

and
$$x + c = a \quad \text{and} \quad y + d = b. \quad \text{(Definition 10.2-a)}$$
But
$$x = a - c \quad \text{and} \quad y = b - d.$$

(Definition 10.2-a)

$$\therefore (a, b) - (c, d) = (a - c, b - d).$$

Definition: 10.2-b.   *The* **subtraction** *of two* **complex numbers** $(a, b) - (c, d)$ *is the sum of* (a, b) *and the additive inverse of* (c, d). (See A_5 Section 2.10.)

As with the division of real numbers (see Definition 2.5-1), the division of complex numbers is defined in terms of multiplication of complex numbers.

Definition: 10.2-c.   *The* **division** *of two* **complex numbers,** $(a, b) \div (c, d)$, *is the product of* (a, b) *and the multiplicative inverse of* (c, d), *that is,*

$$(a, b) \div (c. d) = (a, b)\left(\frac{c}{c^2 + d^2}, \frac{-d}{c^2 + d^2}\right). \qquad \text{(See Example 10.2-d)}$$

$$= \left(\frac{ac}{c^2 + d^2} + \frac{bd}{c^2 + d^2}, \frac{bc}{c^2 + d^2} - \frac{ad}{c^2 + d^2}\right).$$

(Definition 10.2-a)

$$\therefore (a, b) \div (c, d) = \left(\frac{ac + bd}{c^2 + d^2}, \frac{bc - ad}{c^2 + d^2}\right). \qquad (E_3, \text{ Section 2.11})$$

All combinations of the real numbers a, b, c, or d that would produce zero denominators are, of course, not permitted.

10.2-1 Complex Numbers of the Form $(r, 0)$ where $r \in R$

A set of complex numbers of the form $(r, 0)$, called **the set of real complex numbers,** is a subset of the set C of complex numbers. We will refer to this particular subset of C as set Q. Operating with the elements of set Q, in connection with addition, multiplication, subtraction, and division, we obtain

$$(a, 0) + (b, 0) = (a + 0, b + 0) = (a + b, 0) = a + b. \quad \text{(Definition 10.2-a)}$$

$$(a, 0)(b, 0) = (a \cdot b - 0 \cdot 0, a \cdot 0 + 0 \cdot b) = (ab, 0) = ab.$$

(Definition 10.2-a)

$$(a, 0) - (b, 0) = (a - b, 0) = a - b. \qquad \text{(Definition 10.2-b)}$$

$$(a, 0) \div (b, 0) = (a, 0)\left(\frac{1}{b}, 0\right) = \left(\frac{a}{b}, 0\right) = \frac{a}{b}. \qquad \text{(Definition 10.2-c)}$$

In the preceding operations two important things are to be noticed:

1. The complex number obtained from each of the four operations has exactly the same form as $(r, 0)$.

2. The first member of the complex number obtained from each operation is identical to its corresponding real number. The second member of the resulting complex number is always zero.

Table 10.2-1a

Complex Numbers of Form $(r, 0)$ = Real Numbers of Form r

$$\begin{array}{cc} (A) & (B) \\ (a + b, 0) & = a + b \\ (ab, 0) & = ab \\ (a - b, 0) & = a - b \\ (a \div b, 0) & = a \div b \end{array}$$

Even though we recognize (A), the first of the above sets, as a set of *real complex numbers* and the other set (B) as a set of *real numbers*, the two sets can, for all practical purposes, be considered equal.

One consequence of the fact that $(r, 0) = r$ is that the multiplication of (a, b) by any real number r gives

$$r(a, b) = (r, 0)(a, b) = (ra - 0 \cdot b, rb + 0 \cdot a) = (ra, rb).$$

That is, $r(a, b) = (ra, rb)$.

Between Q, the subset of complex numbers of the form $(r, 0)$ and R, the set of real numbers, there exists a *one-to-one correspondence*. That is,

$(r, 0) \leftrightarrow r$, which means $(r, 0)$ "corresponds" to r and conversely.

This correspondence preserves addition and multiplication as indicated by the following examples.

If $(a, 0) \leftrightarrow a$ and $(b, 0) \leftrightarrow b$, then
$(a, 0) + (b, 0) \leftrightarrow a + b$, and
$(a, 0)(b, 0) \leftrightarrow ab$. $\qquad\qquad\qquad\qquad (a, b \in R)$

Or numerically,

If $(4, 0) \leftrightarrow 4$ and $(7, 0) \leftrightarrow 7$, then
$(4, 0) + (7, 0) \leftrightarrow 4 + 7$, and
$(4, 0)(7, 0) \leftrightarrow 4 \cdot 7$.

In connection with one-to-one correspondence relationships, we often use the Greek word **isomorphism,** which means "the same form."

Definition: 10.2-1a.   *When a one-to-one correspondence exists between two sets, or two algebraic systems, one system is said to be* **isomorphic** *to the other.*

Thus, Q, a subset of the complex number system of the form $(r, 0)$, is isomorphic to R, the set of real numbers. Since Q is a subset of the complex number system C, it follows that

$$R \subset C.$$

In other words, *the real number system is embedded in the complex number system.*

10.2-2 The Complex Number (0, 1)

The ordered pair **(0, 1)**, *a very important complex number, is called the* **imaginary unit** *and is denoted by* **i** (the engineers prefer j).

If $i = (0, 1)$, then

$$i^2 = (0, 1)(0, 1) = (0 \cdot 0 - 1 \cdot 1, 0 \cdot 1 + 1 \cdot 0) = (-1, 0).$$
(See Definition 10.2-a)

Therefore, $$i^2 = (-1, 0) = -1.$$
(See Section 10.2-1)

The imaginary unit may also be expressed as

$$i = \sqrt{-1} \quad \text{or} \quad i = -\sqrt{-1}.$$

The imaginary unit $\sqrt{-1}$ is identical to the unit introduced in Section 4.5. As we remarked at that time, the word "imaginary" used in connection with imaginary numbers is just an unfortunate historical carry-over and has no significance whatsoever. *Imaginary numbers are just as real and significant as any other numbers.* For example, in the geometry of the plane, if we take 1 as the unit and plot the integers along the x axis and take i as the unit and plot i, $2i$, $3i$, and so on, along the axis perpendicular to the x axis, then the proper combination of these two kinds of numbers gives us a number that corresponds to each point in the complex plane.

At this point let us return to the equation $x^2 + 1 = 0$ whose roots were not real numbers. Solving this equation for its roots we get

$$x^2 + 1 = 0,$$
$$x^2 = -1,$$

and $$x = \sqrt{-1} \quad \text{or} \quad x = -\sqrt{-1}.$$

Since we have shown that i may be represented either by $\sqrt{-1}$ or by the complex number $(0, 1)$, it follows that

$x = (0, 1)$ **is a complex root of** $x^2 + 1 = 0$.

Let us check to see if $(0, 1)$ satisfies the given equation. Writing the equation in complex number form we obtain

$$x^2 + 1 = 0,$$
$$x \cdot x = -1,$$

and $x \cdot x = (-1, 0)$.   (See Section 10.2-1)

Substituting $(0, 1)$ for x: $(0, 1)(0, 1) = (-1, 0)$.

Then $(0 \cdot 0 - 1 \cdot 1, 0 \cdot 1 + 1 \cdot 0) = (-1, 0)$,
and $(-1, 0) = (-1, 0)$.

Therefore, the complex number $(0, 1)$ does satisfy the equation $x^2 + 1 = 0$.

It will be left for the reader to show that the complex number $x = (0, -1)$ is another root of the $x^2 + 1 = 0$ equation.

The availability of the imaginary number $(0, 1)$ and the properties of addition and multiplication make it possible for us to write the complex number (a, b), where $a, b \in R$, as

$(a, b) = (a, 0) + (0, b)$,	(Definition 10.1-2)
$(a, b) = (a, 0) + (b, 0)(0, 1)$,	(Substitution)
and $(a, b) = a + bi$.	(See Sections 10.2-1 and 10.2-2)

This conclusion is justified because $(a, 0) = a$; $(b, 0) = b$; and $(0, 1) = i$.

10.3 BINOMIAL FORM OF COMPLEX NUMBERS

It is customary to refer to $a + bi$ $(a, b \in R)$ as the **binomial form** of a complex number. Some authors call $a + bi$ the *rectangular form*; others call it the *normal form*. In $a + bi$ the number **a** is called the **real part** and the number **bi** is called the **imaginary part** of the complex number.

If $b = 0$ in the complex number $a + bi$, the set of complex numbers becomes the set of real numbers. So again we observe that

$$R \subset C.$$

If $a = 0$ and $b \neq 0$ in $a + bi$, we obtain a set of complex numbers of the form bi, which we will denote by P_n. This set is called the set of **pure imaginary numbers** and is also a subset of C. That is,

$$P_n \subset C.$$

Complex numbers defined in terms of ordered pairs (Definition 10.2-a) can now be restated in terms of the *binomial form* as follows:

Definition: 10.3-1.   *For a, b, c, and d real numbers,* **a complex number** *is a number of the form $a + bi$, where i possesses the property $i^2 = -1$ and the following conditions hold:*

Equality: $a + bi = c + di$ **if and only if** $a = c$ **and** $b = d$.

Addition: $(a + bi) + (c + di) = (a + c) + (b + d)i$.
Multiplication: $(a + bi)(c + di) = (ac - bd) + (ad + bc)i$.

The advantage of expressing complex numbers in the binomial form is that we can perform the operations of addition, multiplication, subtraction, and division exactly as we did with real number binomials, with the exception that each i^2 is to be replaced by -1.

In Definition 10.1-3 we stated that the product of any two complex numbers expressed as ordered pairs was

$(a, b)(c, d) = (ac - bd, ad + bc)$.

By using complex numbers in the binomial form we can now show why this definition was so stated.

Example: 10.3-1. Find the product of the two complex numbers $(a + bi)(c + di)$. Then change each complex number from its binomial form to an ordered pair.

Since $(a + bi)(c + di) = ac + adi + cbi + bdi^2$,
then $(a + bi)(c + di) = ac - bd + (ad + bc)i$, a complex number.
As ordered pairs $(a, b)(c, d) = (ac - bd, ad + bc)$, a complex number.

We will need the idea of **conjugate complex numbers** in order to proceed with the next example.

Definition: 10.3-1.   *Two complex numbers of the form a + bi and a − bi are said to be* **conjugate complex numbers.** *Each is the conjugate of the other and their product is always a real number.*

Example: 10.3-2.   Express the quotient of $\dfrac{(1 + i)}{(3 - 2i)}$ as a complex number in binomial form.

$$\frac{(1 + i)}{(3 - 2i)} = \frac{(1 + i)(3 + 2i)}{(3 - 2i)(3 + 2i)} = \frac{3 + 5i - 2}{9 - 4i^2} = \frac{1}{13} + \frac{5i}{13}.$$

Note that $3 - 2i$ and $3 + 2i$ are conjugates and that their product is the real number $9 - 4i^2 = 13$. Note also that this Example 10.3-2 demonstrates the following rule:

To divide one complex number by another, multiply both the denominator and the numerator of the given expression by the conjugate of the denominator, then simplify.

EXERCISE 10.A

Keep in mind these agreements: a, b, c, d, r belong to the set of real numbers. C represents the complex number system. Q is a subset of C of the form $(r, 0)$. P_n is a subset of C of the form bi or of the form $(0, b)$.

1. Under what conditions is (a, b) equal to (c, d)?

2. Find x and y if $(x + 2, y - 3) = (6, 4)$.

3. What is the sum of the complex numbers $(4, 7)$, $(2, -5)$, and $(0, 6)$?

4. Determine the product of $(5, 1)$ and $(0, 3)$.

5. Compute the quotient of $(2, 5) \div (4, 1)$.

6. What is the difference between $(8, 3)$ and $(2, 5)$?

7. Verify the commutative postulate under multiplication for complex numbers.

8. Verify the distributive law for complex numbers.

9. Prove the associative law under multiplication for complex numbers.

10. Prove the associative law under addition for complex numbers.

11. Find the sum of $(4, 9)$ and $(0, 0)$. What special name is given to the second of these complex numbers?

12. Find the product of $(5, -3)$ and $(1, 0)$. What special name is given to the second of these complex numbers?

13. What complex number must be added to $(2, 6)$ to give the identity element?

14. What complex number must be associated with $(1, 5)$ to give the multiplicative identity?

15. Find the quotient of $(7, 3)/(5, -2)$.

16. Is $(r, 0)$ a real complex number? a real number? or a pure imaginary number?

17. Is $(0, r)$ a real complex number? a real number? or a pure imaginary number?

18. If $(5, 0) \leftrightarrow 5$ and $(-2, 0) \leftrightarrow -2$, then to what does $(5, 0) + (-2, 0)$ correspond?

19. If $(-9, 0) \leftrightarrow -9$ and $(k, 0) \leftrightarrow k$, then to what does $(-9, 0)(k, 0)$ correspond?

20. If $i = \sqrt{-1}$, what is the value of i^3?

21. If $i^2 = -1$, find the value of i^5.

Perform the indicated operations.

22. $(5, 3) + (4, -2)$.

23. $(8, 2) - (0, 5)$.

24. $(9, 0) - (0, 2)$.

25. $(-2, -7) + (2, 0)$.

26. $(4, 3)(2, 7)$.

27. $(3, 9)(0, 4)$.

28. $(6, 0) \div (2, 1)$.

29. $(0, 9) \div (4, -2)$.

30–33. Change Problems 22, 24, 26, 28 to binomial form. Perform the indicated operations and compare results.

34–37. Change Problems 23, 25, 27, 29 to binomial form. Perform the indicated operations and compare results.

38. What is the conjugate of the complex number $7 - 2i$? Find the product of $7 - 2i$ and its conjugate. Is the result a real number?

39. State the conjugate of the complex number $4 + 7i$. Find the sum of $4 + 7i$ and its conjugate. Is the result a real number?

40. Find the quotient of $\dfrac{17 - 5i}{5 + 2i}$.

41. Find the quotient of $\dfrac{6 + 9i}{13 - i}$.

42. Show that the conjugate of the conjugate of a complex number is the number itself.

43. Verify the fact that the conjugate of a real number is that real number.

44. Write the reciprocal of $a + bi$. Write another multiplicative inverse of $a + bi$ and prove that the two expressions are equivalent.

45. Write the reciprocal of $i/(1 + i)$. What is the multiplicative inverse of $i/(1 + i)$? Find the product of $i/(1 + i)$ and its multiplicative inverse and express it in complex number form.

Solve for x and check roots:

46. $x^2 + 8 = 0$.
47. $4x^2 + 25 = 0$.

10.4 GEOMETRIC INTERPRETATION OF COMPLEX NUMBERS

A point in a complex plane may be represented in the following two ways:

CASE 1. By an ordered pair of real numbers such as (a, b), equivalent to $a + bi$.

CASE 2. By a directed line $a + bi$ from the origin of the coordinate system to the co-planar point.

From *Case 1* and Figure 10.4-a, it can be observed that *every complex num-*

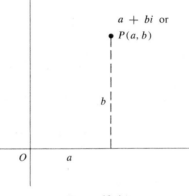

Figure 10.4-a

ber $(a, b) \cong a + bi$ *represents a point in the rectangular coordinate system and each point in the complex plane is represented by a complex number*. Thus, *there is a one-to-one correspondence between the set of complex numbers and the set of points in a plane*.

Case 2 and Figure 10.4-b show that we may also think of the complex number $a + bi$ as a vector. To move directly from O to P is equivalent to moving distance a along, or parallel to, the x axis, and then distance b from the end of a parallel to the y axis. The complex number $a + bi$ is represented by the vector $\overrightarrow{OP}$. *The length of* $\overrightarrow{OP}$ *is*

$$|r| = \sqrt{a^2 + b^2},$$

where r denotes the **modulus** *or* **the absolute value** *of $a + bi$.*

Since each complex number $a + bi$ determines a directed line segment from the origin O to P (see Figure 10.4-b), *there exists a one-to-one correspondence between the complex numbers and their resulting co-planar vectors. Further,*

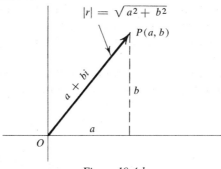

Figure 10.4-b

there exists an isomorphism under addition between the set of complex numbers and the set of vectors which fan out from the origin of the rectangular coordinate system. This isomorphism provides us with the following two procedures:

1. A geometric method of adding complex numbers.
2. An algebraic method of adding vectors.

All numbers obtained from the complex number $a + bi$ when $b = 0$, namely, numbers of the form $a + 0i$, are graphed as points on (or vectors along) the x axis. Consequently, *the x axis is called the* **axis of reals.** All numbers obtained from $a + bi$ when $a = 0$, namely, the numbers of the form

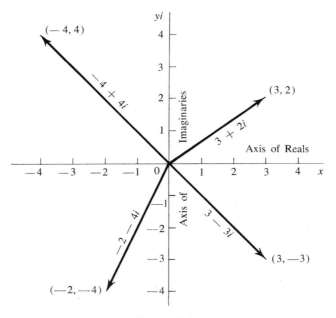

Figure 10.4-c

$0 + bi$, are plotted as points on (or vectors along) the y axis. Thus *the y axis is called the* **axis of imaginaries** *and is designated as* **yi**.

Figure 10.4-c shows complex numbers plotted both as points and as their corresponding vectors.

To demonstrate the geometry of adding the two complex numbers $a + bi$ and $c + di$, as shown in Figure 10.4-d, let $a + bi$ be represented by the vector

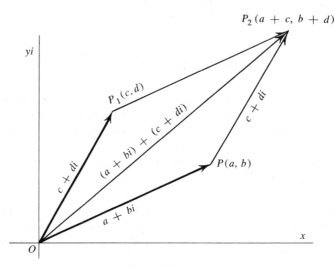

Figure 10.4-d

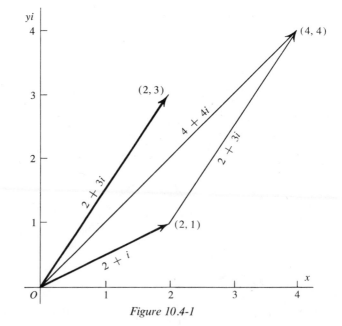

Figure 10.4-1

$\overrightarrow{OP}$ and $c + di$ be represented by the vector $\overrightarrow{OP_1}$. To add these two vectors (see Section 9.12-1 and Figure 9.12-1a on vectors), draw a vector from the terminal point of $\overrightarrow{OP}$ parallel and equal in length to $\overrightarrow{OP_1}$ and label its end point P_2. Draw a vector from the origin to P_2. The vector $\overrightarrow{OP_2}$ represents the sum of

$(a + bi) + (c + di)$.

Example: 10.4-1. By vector addition find the sum of $(2 + 3i)$ and $(2 + i)$.

Draw the vectors $2 + i$ and $2 + 3i$, as in Figure 10.4-1. From the terminal end of $2 + i$ draw a vector equal to and parallel to $2 + 3i$. Then $4 + 4i$ is the resultant vector, and the sum of the two complex numbers is the complex number $4 + 4i$. Algebraically, the sum of

$$(2 + i) + (2 + 3i) = (2 + 2) + (1 + 3)i = 4 + 4i.$$

10.5 POLAR COORDINATES

There are many systems of coordinates. Until now we have been using rectangular coordinates exclusively, but in our study of complex numbers we will find many situations where polar coordinates will serve us better than rectangular coordinates. Each of these coordinate systems has its advantages and its disadvantages in making graphs of functions and in solving equations.

10.5-1 Polar Coordinates of a Point in a Plane

In the polar coordinate system the position of a point P is determined by

1. its distance r from a fixed point O, called *the pole*; and
2. a direction angle θ which relates the line segment $\overrightarrow{OP}$ with the reference line OA.

The **r** in Figure 10.5-1(1) is called the **radius vector** of the point P, and **θ** is

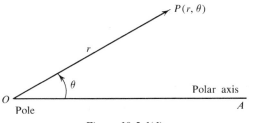

Figure 10.5-1(1)

called the **vectorial angle.** The ordered pair $(\mathbf{r}, \boldsymbol{\theta})$ is the form used to denote **polar coordinates.**

For any given pair of polar coordinates there is a corresponding unique point P. But *it does not follow that for a fixed point P there is always a unique pair of polar coordinates.* There may be many pairs of polar coordinates for the same point.

Example: 10.5-1a.   Use the polar coordinates (5, 60°) to locate point *P*.

Draw a ray *OA* horizontally from the pole *O* to represent the polar axis. Then draw the angle θ with *OA* as its initial side and 60° as its measure. From *O* measure 5 units along the terminal side of angle θ to locate point *P* as shown in Figure 10.5-1a.

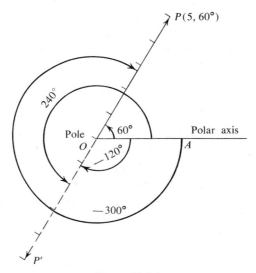

Figure 10.5-1a

The pair of polar coordinates (5, 60°) is, of course, not the only pair of polar coordinates for point *P*. As long as *r* = 5 we can add (or subtract) 2π or 360° and get as many pairs of polar coordinates for *P* as we choose. A few such pairs are (5, 420°), (5, 780°), (5, − 300°), (5, − 660°).

If r falls along the terminal side of the vectorial angle θ, *it is* **positive.** *If r falls along OP′, which is the terminal side of the angle AOP extended, then r is* **negative.** Thus, some additional polar coordinates for *P* when *r* < 0 are (− 5, − 120°), (− 5, 240°), and so on (see Figure 10.5-1a).

For r ∈ *R and n* ∈ *I, if r* > 0, *then a fixed point P on the terminal side of* θ, *r units from the pole O, has polar coordinates of the form* (*r*, θ + 360°*n*). *If r* < 0, *then* θ *must be increased by* 180°.

Example: 10.5-1b.   Write three other pairs of polar coordinates for the point (3, $5\pi/4$).

If, as indicated by Figure 10.5-1b, angle θ is limited to 0 < θ < 2π, three other possible pairs of polar coordinates are (3, − $3\pi/4$), (− 3, $\pi/4$), and (− 3, − $7\pi/4$).

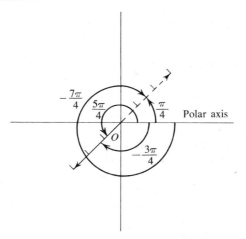

Figure 10.5-1b

10.5-2 Relation of Polar Coordinates to Rectangular Coordinates

If the polar coordinate system is superimposed on the rectangular coordinate system so that

(a) the pole and the origin of the rectangular system coincide, and
(b) the polar axis and the positive x axis coincide,

then as indicated by Figure 10.5-2(1), these relations exist:

1. *Rectangular coordinates in terms of polar coordinates.*

$x = r \cos \theta$ and $y = r \sin \theta$.

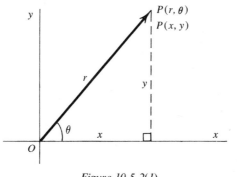

Figure 10.5-2(1)

2. *Polar coordinates in terms of rectangular coordinates.*

$|r| = \sqrt{x^2 + y^2}$.

$$\theta = \arcTan\frac{y}{x}, \quad \text{when } x > 0. \qquad \theta = \arcTan\left(\frac{y}{x} + \pi\right), \quad \text{when } x < 0.$$

The preceding formulas are used to transform polar coordinates to rect-angular coordinates and vice versa.

As previously stated it is at times easier to work with equations expressed in polar coordinates than in rectangular coordinates. Consider for example the polar equation for a circle, $r = 5$. All one has to do to make a graph to represent $r = 5$ is to take a line segment 5 units long as a radius and draw the circumference. The equation in rectangular coordinates, for the polar equation $r = 5$, is $x^2 + y^2 = 25$. But if one does not know immediately that the radius of the circle represented by $x^2 + y^2 = 25$ is 5, and has to discover this fact by the procedure indicated by Example 10.5-2a, the polar method of obtaining the graph would be much easier.

Example: 10.5-2a.   Make a graph of $x^2 + y^2 = 25$. Then transform $x^2 + y^2 = 25$ to polar coordinates and graph it on the same axes.

Substituting $x = r \cos \theta$ and $y = r \sin \theta$ into

$$x^2 + y^2 = 25,$$
$$(r \cos \theta)^2 + (r \sin \theta)^2 = 25,$$
$$r^2 (\cos^2 \theta + \sin^2 \theta) = 25,$$

and
$$r^2 = 25.$$

Therefore, $r = 5$ (as shown in Figure 10.5-2a) is the polar equation.

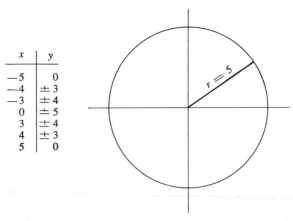

x	y
-5	0
-4	± 3
-3	± 4
0	± 5
3	± 4
4	± 3
5	0

Figure 10.5-2a

Example: 10.5-2b.   Graph the polar equation $r = 2 \sin \theta$. Then transform $r = 2 \sin \theta$ into rectangular coordinates.

In the polar coordinates (r, θ) note that θ, the second element of the ordered pair, is the independent variable and r is the dependent variable. This is exactly

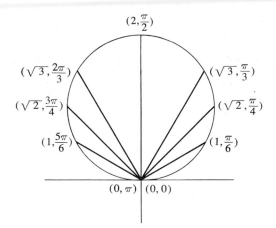

θ	0	$\dfrac{\pi}{6}$	$\dfrac{\pi}{4}$	$\dfrac{\pi}{3}$	$\dfrac{\pi}{2}$	$\dfrac{2\pi}{3}$	$\dfrac{3\pi}{4}$	$\dfrac{5\pi}{6}$	π
r	0	1	$\sqrt{2}$	$\sqrt{3}$	2	$\sqrt{3}$	$\sqrt{2}$	1	0

Figure 10.5-2b

opposite to our usual practice when we work with ordered pairs (x, y) in rectangular coordinates.

Substituting $|r| = \sqrt{x^2 + y^2}$ and $\sin \theta = y/r = y/\sqrt{x^2 + y^2}$ into

$$r = 2 \sin \theta,$$

we get $\sqrt{x^2 + y^2} = 2\dfrac{y}{\sqrt{x^2 + y^2}}.$

Therefore, $x^2 + y^2 = 2y$, as shown in Figure 10.5-2b, is the rectangular form of $r = 2 \sin \theta$.

10.6 POLAR FORM OF A COMPLEX NUMBER

In Section 10.5-2 and Figure 10.5-2(1) we can see that

$x = r \cos \theta \quad$ and $\quad y = r \sin \theta.$

It will be somewhat simpler at this point if we agree that

$a + bi = (x + yi)^n.$

That is, $x + yi$ is an nth root of $a + bi$. Then, substituting the above values of x and y in the complex number $x + yi$, there results

$$x + yi = r \cos \theta + (r \sin \theta)i.$$

Therefore, $x + yi = r(\cos\theta + i\sin\theta)$　　　**(the polar form of a complex number).**

The **r** in the polar form of the complex number **is the modulus** or the absolute value **of the complex number** and is defined to be positive. The angle **θ is** called **the argument** or the amplitude and is usually taken as a positive angle less than 360°. However, θ can be any angle whose initial side is the polar axis and whose terminal side is $\overrightarrow{OP}$. Thus a more general polar form of the complex number is

$$r[\cos(\theta + 2\pi k) + i \sin(\theta + 2\pi k)]$$　　　**(the general polar form of a complex number)**

where $k = 0, 1, 2, 3, \ldots$.

Example: 10.6-1.　　Express the complex number $\left(\dfrac{1}{2} - \dfrac{\sqrt{3}}{2}i\right)$ in polar or trigonometric form (see Figure 10.6-1).

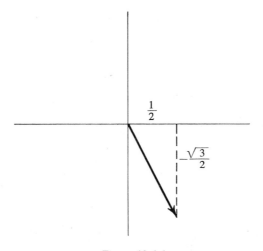

$$\frac{1}{2}$$

$$\frac{\sqrt{3}}{2}$$

Figure 10.6-1

We want to emphasize here that it makes no difference whether the i follows $\sqrt{3}/2$ or precedes it. But to be certain that the i does not get under the radical sign where it does not belong, we will usually put i before the other factor in numerical problems. Then, for

$$\frac{1}{2} - i\frac{\sqrt{3}}{2}, \qquad x = \frac{1}{2}, \qquad y = -\frac{\sqrt{3}}{2}, \qquad \text{and}$$

$$|r| = \sqrt{x^2 + y^2} = \sqrt{\tfrac{1}{4} + \tfrac{3}{4}} = 1.$$

Therefore, $r = \mathbf{1}$.

Since $\left(\dfrac{1}{2} - \dfrac{i\sqrt{3}}{2}\right)$ shows the point represented by the complex number to be in the fourth quadrant, then

$$\tan \theta = \frac{y}{x} = \frac{-\sqrt{3}/2}{1/2} = -\sqrt{3},$$

and θ (in Quadrant IV) = **300°**.

Substituting $r = 1$ and $\theta = 300°$ in the polar form of a complex number,

$$r(\cos \theta + i \sin \theta) = \cos 300° + i \sin 300°.$$

Example: 10.6-2. Express the complex number 10 (cos 135° + i sin 135°) in rectangular form.

In Figure 10.6-2 point P represents the given polar coordinates. Since

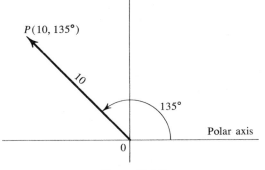

Figure 10.6-2

$r = 10$ and $\theta = 135°$ are given, then

$$x = r \cos \theta = 10 \cos 135° = 10(-\cos 45°) = \frac{-10\sqrt{2}}{2},$$

$$y = r \sin \theta = 10 \sin 135° = 10 \sin 45° = \frac{10\sqrt{2}}{2},$$

and $x + iy = 5(-\sqrt{2} + i\sqrt{2})$.

EXERCISE 10.B

Represent each of the following numbers as a point in the complex plane. Change each complex number to its equivalent polar form.

1. (a) $(1, \sqrt{3})$.   (b) $(4, -1)$.   (c) $(-5, 2)$.   (d) $(-2\sqrt{2}, 4)$.

2. (a) $(1, 0)$. (b) $(\frac{1}{2}, -3)$. (c) $1, \dfrac{\sqrt{3}}{3}$. (d) $(-1, \sqrt{2})$.

3. (a) $1 + 4i$. (b) $2 - i\sqrt{2}$. (c) $-5 + i$. (d) $-3 - i\sqrt{3}$.

4. (a) $-4 + 3i$. (b) $6 - i\sqrt{3}$. (c) $2 + 3i$. (d) $-7 - i\sqrt{2}$.

Represent each of the following numbers as a point in the complex plane. Change each one to its equivalent rectangular form.

5. (a) $(1, 90°)$.   (b) $(-1, 3\pi/4)$.   (c) $(5, -45°)$.   (d) $(-3, 5\pi/4)$.
6. (a) $(2, \pi/2)$.   (b) $(4, -60°)$.   (c) $(3, -3\pi/3)$.   (d) $(-5, -300°)$.
7. (a) $5(\cos 90° + i \sin 90°)$.   (b) $3(\cos 0° + i \sin 0°)$.
   (c) $[\cos(-240°) + i \sin(-240°)]$.   (d) $4[\cos(-135°) + i \sin(-135°)]$.
8. (a) $\cos 45° + i \sin 45°$.   (b) $2[\cos(-180°) + i \sin(-180°)]$.
   (c) $7(\cos 120° + i \sin 120°)$.   (d) $10[\cos(-30°) + i \sin(-30°)]$.

Make a graph of each of the following rectangular equations. Then change each equation to its polar form and check the graph.

9. $y = 3x$.   **10.** $x = 3y$.
11. $2x - 7y = 0$.   **12.** $9y = 6x$.
13. $x^2 + y^2 - 2x = 0$.   **14.** $x^2 + y^2 + 6x = 0$.
15. $x^2 - y^2 = 16$.   **16.** $xy = 7$.

Make a graph of each of the following polar equations. Then change each polar equation to its rectangular form and check the graph.

17. $r = 8$.   **18.** $\theta = 30°$.
19. $r \sin \theta = 3$.   **20.** $r \cos \theta = 5$.

21. $r = 3 \cos \theta$.   **22.** $r = \dfrac{\sin \theta}{2}$.

23. $r = 4 \sin \theta + 3 \cos \theta$. **24.** $r = 5 \cos \theta + 4 \sin \theta$.
25. $r = \sin 2\theta$.   **26.** $r = \cos 2\theta$.
27. $r = 2 \cos \theta - 1$.   **28.** $r = 1 - 2 \sin \theta$.

29. Change $2(\cos 30° + i \sin 30°) + 2(\cos 60° + i \sin 60°)$ to rectangular form and find its sum.

30. Show that the pairs of polar coordinates $(5, 0°)$, $(5, 120°)$, and $(5, 240°)$ are vertices of an equilateral triangle.

10.7 MULTIPLICATION, DIVISION, AND INTEGRAL POWERS OF COMPLEX NUMBERS

The polar (or trigonometric) form of complex numbers is easiest to use in finding products, quotients, powers and roots of complex numbers. The procedures which will be presented are based upon the following theorems.

Theorem: 10.7-1.   The modulus of the product of two complex numbers is the product of the modulus, and the amplitude is the sum of the two given amplitudes.

PROOF: The polar form of the product of any two complex numbers is $[r_1(\cos \theta_1 + i \sin \theta_1)][r_2(\cos \theta_2 + i \sin \theta_2)]$. Its expansion is $r_1 r_2(\cos \theta_1 \cos \theta_2 + i \cos \theta_1 \sin \theta_2 + i \sin \theta_1 \cos \theta_2 - \sin \theta_1 \sin \theta_2)$.

$$\therefore \; r_1 r_2 [\cos(\theta_1 + \theta_2) + i \sin(\theta_1 + \theta_2)].$$

Following the same procedure as used in Theorem 10.7-1, we can show that the product of

$$[r(\cos \theta + i \sin \theta)] \cdot [r(\cos \theta + i \sin \theta)] = r^2[\cos(\theta + \theta) + i \sin(\theta + \theta)],$$
and
$$[r(\cos \theta + i \sin \theta)]^2 = r^2(\cos 2\theta + i \sin 2\theta).$$

Continuing to multiply $r^2(\cos 2\theta + i \sin 2\theta)$ by $r(\cos \theta + i \sin \theta)$, we get

$$[r(\cos \theta + i \sin \theta)]^3 = r^3(\cos 3\theta + i \sin 3\theta).$$
Likewise $[r(\cos \theta + i \sin \theta)]^4 = r^4(\cos 4\theta + i \sin 4\theta)$,

and so on. This furnishes an intuitive approach to the following theorem.

Theorem: 10.7-2. For n any positive integer,

$$[r(\cos \theta + i \sin \theta)]^n = r^n(\cos n\theta + i \sin n\theta). \qquad \textbf{(De Moivre's Theorem)}$$

When the n in De Moivre's theorem is a positive integer, this theorem can be proved by mathematical induction. This will not be done in this text. Actually, the n in the theorem does not have to be limited to integers.

The next theorem is relatively simple and will be left for the reader to prove.

Theorem: 10.7-3. If two complex numbers are equal, their moduli are equal, and their amplitudes are either equal or they differ by integrals of 2π.

One of the most important applications of De Moivre's theorem is in the determining of roots of complex numbers.

Example: 10.7-1. Find the cube roots of the complex number $-4\sqrt{3} + 4i$.

Changing to polar form: $8\left(\dfrac{-\sqrt{3}}{2} + \dfrac{1}{2}i\right) = 8(\cos 150° + i \sin 150°)$. Using

$[r(\cos \theta + i \sin \theta)]^3 = r^3(\cos 3\theta + i \sin 3\theta)$ (De Moivre's theorem) and letting $8(\cos 150° + i \sin 150°) = r^3(\cos 3\theta + i \sin 3\theta)$, then

$r^3 = 8$ and $3\theta = 150° + 360°k$, where $k = 0, 1, 2, \ldots$.
$\therefore r = 2$ and $\theta = 50° + k(120°)$.
Or $r = 2$ and $\theta = 50°, \theta = 170°$, and $\theta = 290°$.

As indicated by Figure 10.7-1, the three cube roots are:

$2(\cos 50° + i \sin 50°)$;
$2(\cos 170° + i \sin 170°)$;
$2(\cos 290° + i \sin 290°)$.

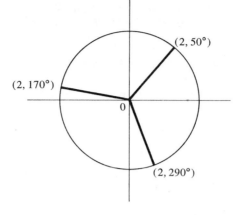

Figure 10.7-1

If k is taken as any other integral value, one of the above three roots will still be obtained. So the three cube roots are unique. This suggests the following theorem, which permits us to find as many roots of a complex number as we choose.

Theorem: 10.7-4. If n is a positive integer, any nonzero complex number has exactly n roots.

The last theorem in connection with complex numbers which will be introduced and proved in this text has to do with the division of complex numbers.

Theorem: 10.7-5. The modulus of the quotient of two complex numbers with a nonzero divisor is the quotient of the moduli, and the amplitude of the quotient is the amplitude of the numerator minus the amplitude of the denominator.

PROOF:

$$\frac{r_1(\cos \theta_1 + i \sin \theta_1)}{r_2(\cos \theta_2 + i \sin \theta_2)}, \quad \text{when multiplied by} \quad \frac{\cos \theta_2 - i \sin \theta_2}{\cos \theta_2 + i \sin \theta_2},$$

is $\dfrac{r_1(\cos \theta_1 \cos \theta_2 - i \cos \theta_1 \sin \theta_2 + i \sin \theta_1 \cos \theta_2 - i^2 \sin \theta_1 \sin \theta_2)}{r_2(\cos^2 \theta_2 - i^2 \sin \theta_2)},$

or $\dfrac{r_1(\cos \theta_1 \cos \theta_2 + \sin \theta_1 \sin \theta_2) + i(\sin \theta_1 \cos \theta_2 - \cos \theta_1 \sin \theta_2)}{r_2(\cos^2 \theta_2 + \sin^2 \theta_2)},$

or $\dfrac{r_1}{r_2}[\cos(\theta_1 - \theta_2) + i \sin(\theta_1 - \theta_2)].$

$$\therefore \frac{r_1(\cos \theta_1 + i \sin \theta_1)}{r_2(\cos \theta_2 + i \sin \theta_2)} = \frac{r_1}{r_2}[\cos(\theta_1 - \theta_2) + i \sin(\theta_1 - \theta_2)].$$

Example: 10.7-2. Find the quotient of $\dfrac{12(\cos 50° + i \sin 50°)}{2(\cos 20° + i \sin 20°)}$.

Using Theorem 10.7-5, $\dfrac{12}{2}[\cos(50° - 20°) + i \sin(50° - 20°)]$.

Polar form, $6(\cos 30° + i \sin 30°)$.

Rectangular form, $6\left[\dfrac{\sqrt{3}}{2} + i\left(\dfrac{1}{2}\right)\right]$,

or $3\sqrt{3} + 3i$.

Example: 10.7-3. Find the product of $2(\cos 20° + i \sin 20°) \cdot 6(\cos 30° + i \sin 30°)$.

Using Theorem 10.7-1: $2 \cdot 6 \ [\cos(20° + 30°) + i \sin(20° + 30°)]$,
or $12(\cos 50° + i \sin 50°)$.

EXERCISE 10.C

Perform the indicated multiplication and division and change the resulting complex numbers to the $x + yi$ form.

1. $[2(\cos 75° + i \sin 75°)][3(\cos 15° + i \sin 15°)]$.
2. $[8(\cos 40° + i \sin 40°)][\cos 25° + i \sin 25°]$.
3. $\left[1\left(\cos \dfrac{\pi}{6} + i \sin \dfrac{\pi}{6}\right)\right]\left[6\left(\cos \dfrac{2\pi}{3} + i \sin \dfrac{2\pi}{3}\right)\right]$.
4. $\left[4\left(\cos \dfrac{\pi}{3} + i \sin \dfrac{\pi}{3}\right)\right]\left[3\left(\cos \dfrac{\pi}{2} + i \sin \dfrac{\pi}{2}\right)\right]$.
5. $6\left(\cos \dfrac{\pi}{2} + i \sin \dfrac{\pi}{2}\right) \div 2\left(\cos \dfrac{\pi}{4} + i \sin \dfrac{\pi}{4}\right)$.
6. $9\left(\cos \dfrac{4\pi}{3} + i \sin \dfrac{4\pi}{3}\right) \div 3\left(\cos \dfrac{\pi}{3} + i \sin \dfrac{\pi}{3}\right)$.
7. $12(\cos 300° + i \sin 300°) \div 4(\cos 60° + i \sin 60°)$.
8. $2(\cos 85° + i \sin 85°) \div (\cos 55° + i \sin 55°)$.
9. Prove that $[3(\cos 15° + i \sin 15°)]^2 = 9(\cos 30° + i \sin 30°)$.
10. Prove that $[2(\cos 15° + i \sin 15°)]^4 = 16(\cos 60° + i \sin 60°)$.

Find the indicated roots of the following complex numbers.

11. The cube roots of $5 + 5\sqrt{3}i$.
12. The fourth roots of $\sqrt{2} - \sqrt{2}i$.
13. The fifth roots of 1.
14. The square roots of i.
15. All fourth roots of $-i$.
16. All cube roots of 27.

Find all roots of the following equations.

17. $x^4 - 16 = 0$.   18. $x^2 + 2 = 0$.
19. $x^3 - 27 = 0$.   20. $x^3 + 27i = 0$.
21. $x^3 - 3 = 2i$.   22. $x^2 = 2 + i$.

23. Prove that the reciprocal of $r(\cos \theta + i \sin \theta) = \dfrac{1}{r}(\cos \theta - i \sin \theta)$.

24. Prove that $\sin \theta = \dfrac{i}{2}\{[\cos(-\theta) + i \sin(-\theta)] - (\cos \theta + i \sin \theta)\}$.

Polynomial Functions of Degree *n*

In Chapter 4, Sections 4.3 and 4.4, we discussed polynomials of first and second degree. We will now extend that study to include polynomials up to degree *n*.

As you proceed through this chapter you will observe that polynomial functions range over the entire complex number system and that they are defined to be algebraic expressions that involve one variable only.

11.1 THE GENERALIZED POLYNOMIAL FUNCTION

Taking $P(x)$ to mean "a polynomial function in the variable x" and a to represent any complex number, the following polynomials are presented for study:

Polynomial Function	Limitation	Kind of Function	Degree
$P(x) = 0$	—	zero	No degree
$P(x) = a_n$	$(a_n \neq 0)$	constant	zero
$P(x) = a_{n-1}x + a_n$	$(a_{n-1} \neq 0)$	linear	first
$P(x) = a_{n-2}x^2 + a_{n-1}x + a_n$	$(a_{n-2} \neq 0)$	quadratic	second
$P(x) = a_{n-3}x^3 + a_{n-2}x^2 + a_{n-1}x + a_n$	$(a_{n-3} \neq 0)$	cubic	third

Continuing, it becomes apparent that the general polynomial function of degree *n* may be defined as follows:

Definition: 11.1-1. *For a any complex number represented by* $a_0, a_1, \ldots,$ a_{n-1}, a_n, *with* $a_0 \neq 0$ *and n a nonnegative integer, the function P in the variable x expressed as*

$$P(x) = a_0 x^n + a_1 x^{n-1} + a_2 x^{n-2} + \cdots + a_{n-3}x^3 + a_{n-2}x^2 + a_{n-1}x + a_n$$

is called a **polynomial function** *of degree n. The domain and range of P(x) is the set of complex numbers.*

You will find that any polynomial that is generated by the preceding definition is a function. Consider the polynomial

	Set *A*	Set *B*
	x	*P(x)*
	0	3
	5	88
	10	273

$$P(x) = 2x^2 + 7x + 3.$$

A few values for x give the ordered pairs

$$[x, P(x)] = (0, 3), (5, 88), \text{ and } (10, 273).$$

You could take as many values for x as you choose and *no two ordered pairs would have the same x value.* This according to Definition 3.5-1 in Chapter 3 guarantees that $2x^2 + 7x + 3$ is a function.

Even though polynomial functions are not numbers, like other functions they do take on many of the characteristics of numbers. For example, if x is 10 in $P(x) = 2x^2 + 7x + 3$, then $P(10)$ gives the number 273. That is, for $x = 10$,

$$P(x) = 2x^2 + 7x + 3 \quad \text{becomes} \quad P(10) = 2(10)^2 + 7(10) + 3(10)^0 = 273.$$

Also, just as numbers have been added, multiplied, subtracted, and divided to give other numbers, so polynomials can be added, multiplied, subtracted, and divided to give other polynomials.

11.2 SOME ARITHMETIC OF POLYNOMIAL FUNCTIONS

Definition: 11.2-1. *Two* **polynomial functions are equal** *if and only if the coefficients of the corresponding powers of the variable are equal.*

Example: 11.2-1. If $P_1(x) = ax^2 + bx + c$ and $P_2x = 3x^2 + 5x + 7$, then by Definition 11.2-1

$$P_1x = P_2x$$

if and only if $a = 3$, $b = 5$, and $c = 7$.

Definition: 11.2-2. *The* **sum of** *the* **polynomials** $a_0x^n + a_1x^{n-1} + \cdots + a_n$ *and* $b_0x^m + b_1x^{m-1} + \cdots + b_m$ *is the polynomial* $(a_0 + b_0)x^n + \cdots + (a_n + b_m)$, *if* $n = m$.

Example: 11.2-2. Find the sum of $18x^3 + 3x^2 - 6$ and $2x^2 - 5x + 4$.

$18x^3 + 3x^2 - 6 + 2x^2 - 5x + 4 \qquad$ is
$(18 + 0)x^3 + (3 + 2)x^2 + (0 - 5)x + (-6 + 4)$.
$\therefore$ the sum is $\mathbf{18x^3 + 5x^2 - 5x - 2}$.

The **difference of two polynomial functions is the inverse of the addition of polynomial functions,** as stated in Definition 11.2-2, and will not be discussed here.

Definition: 11.2-3. *The* **product** *of* $a_0x^n + a_1x^{n-1} + \cdots + a_n$ *and* $b_0x^m + b_1x^{m-1} + \cdots + b_m$ *is the polynomial*

$$a_0b_0x^{n+m} + a_1b_0x^{n+m-1} + \cdots + (a_{n-1}b_m + a_nb_{m-1})x + a_nb_m.$$

Example: 11.2-3. Find the product of $18x^3 + 3x^2 - 6$ and $2x^2 - 5x + 4$.

$(18x^3 + 3x^2 - 6)(2x^2 - 5x + 4)$
$= (18x^3)(2x^2) + (18x^3)(-5x) + (18x^3)(4)$
$\qquad + (3x^2)(2x^2) + (3x^2)(-5x) + (3x^2)(4)$
$\qquad\qquad + (-6)(2x^2) + (-6)(-5x) + (-6)(4)$
$= 36x^5 - (90 + 6)x^4 + (72 - 15)x^3 + (12 - 12)x^2 + 30x - 24.$

$\therefore$ the product is $\mathbf{36x^5 - 84x^4 + 57x^3 + 0 + 30x - 24}$.

In the *division of polynomials* there are several important things that one must know about.

1. The terms of both the dividend and the divisor must be arranged in order of decreasing degree of x.

2. The divisor cannot be zero.

3. When the degree of the remainder is less than the degree of the divisor the division process ends.

4. Each missing term in a dividend must be replaced by a zero coefficient.

Example: 11.2-4.   Divide $36x^5 - 84x^4 + 57x^3 + 0x^2 + 30x - 24$ by $18x^3 + 3x^2 - 6$.

$$
\begin{array}{r}
2x^2 - 5x + 4 \quad Q(x) \\
D(x) \quad 18x^3 + 3x^2 - 6 \overline{\smash{\big)}\,36x^5 - 84x^4 + 57x^3 + 0x^2 + 30x - 24 \quad P(x)} \\
36x^5 + 6x^4 \qquad\qquad -12x^2 \\
\hline
-90x^4 + 57x^3 + 12x^2 + 30x \\
-90x^4 - 15x^3 \qquad\qquad + 30x \\
\hline
72x^3 + 12x^2 \qquad -24 \\
72x^3 + 12x^2 \qquad -24 \\
\hline
0 \quad \mathcal{R}(x)
\end{array}
$$

If we let $P(x)$ represent the dividend polynomial,

$\qquad\qquad$ $D(x)$ the divisor polynomial, $D(x) \neq 0$,

$\qquad\qquad$ $Q(x)$ the quotient polynomial,

$\qquad\qquad$ $\mathcal{R}(x)$ the remainder polynomial,

then we can readily see that the same relation exists in the division of polynomials as exists for numbers. That is,

$$\frac{P(x)}{D(x)} = Q(x) + \frac{\mathcal{R}(x)}{D(x)} \quad \text{just as} \quad \frac{P}{D} = Q + \frac{\mathcal{R}}{D}.$$

Definition: 11.2-4. *If $P(x)$ and $D(x)$ are polynomials with coefficients in the complex number field and $D(x) \neq 0$ is of degree less than or equal to $P(x)$, then the polynomials $Q(x)$ and $\mathcal{R}(x)$ with coefficients in the same field exist and there results the* **division algorithm**

$$P(x) = D(x) \cdot Q(x) + \mathcal{R}(x)$$

with the degree of $\mathcal{R}(x)$ less than the degree of $D(x)$.

Example: 11.2-5. Divide $x^2 + 5x + 6$ by $x + 1$.

$$\frac{P(x)}{D(x)} = \frac{x^2 + 5x + 6}{x + 1} = x + 4 + \frac{2}{x + 1}, \text{ where } Q(x) = x + 4,$$

and $\mathcal{R}(x) = \dfrac{2}{x + 1}$.

Arranging the above data in the form of the *division algorithm*, that is

$$P(x) = D(x) \cdot Q(x) + \mathcal{R}(x),$$

then $x^2 + 5x + 6 = (x + 1)(x + 4) + 2$.

Since the degree of $\mathcal{R}(x)$ is always less than the degree of $D(x)$, and since the degree of $D(x)$ in the preceding example is one, the degree of $\mathcal{R}(x)$ is zero. This means that $\mathcal{R}(x)$ has to be a constant. Is it? *When $\mathcal{R}(x)$ is equal to some constant it is customary to represent it by the symbol $\mathcal{R}$ rather than by $\mathcal{R}(x)$.*

As we will study in greater detail later, *when $\mathcal{R} = 0$, then it is definitely known that $D(x)$ is a factor of the polynomial $P(x)$.*

11.3 REMAINDER AND FACTOR THEOREMS

The **Remainder theorem** will provide a quick and easy way of finding the value of the polynomial function $P(x)$ for each r substituted for x. Further, if the result of the value of the polynomial is zero when r is substituted for x in $P(x)$, then the **Factor theorem** comes into play and we know that $x - r$ is a factor of the polynomial $P(x)$.

Theorem: 11.3-1. (Remainder theorem). If a nonconstant polynomial $P(x)$ is divided by $x - r$, where r is a constant, until a remainder is obtained, then the remainder is $P(r)$.

PROOF:

$$\frac{P(x)}{x - r} = Q(x) + \frac{\mathcal{R}}{x - r}. \qquad\qquad \text{(Given)}$$

$$P(x) = (x - r)Q(x) + \mathcal{R}. \qquad\qquad \text{(Multiply by } x - r)$$

Since the division algorithm $P(x) = D(x)Q(x) + \mathcal{R}(x)$ is true for any value for x, it is true if r is substituted for x. Therefore,

$P(r) = (r - r)Q(r) + \mathcal{R}$.
and $P(r) = (0)Q(r) + \mathcal{R}$.
$\therefore \quad P(r) = \mathcal{R}$.

Example: 11.3-1.   Find the remainder of $P(x) = x^2 + 5x + 6$ divided by $x + 1$ by using the Remainder theorem.

$x + 1 = x - (-1)$ so $r = -1$ in $x - r$. Then substituting -1 for x in $P(x)$,

$P(-1) = (-1)^2 + 5(-1) + 6 = 1 - 5 + 6 = 2$.
$\therefore P(-1) = \mathcal{R} = 2$.

Theorem: 11.3-2. (Factor theorem).   If a constant r gives zero for the polynomial function $P(x)$, then $x - r$ is a factor of $P(x)$, and conversely if $x - r$ is a factor of $P(x)$, then r is a zero value of $P(x)$.

PROOF: If $P(r) = \mathcal{R} = 0$, then by the Remainder theorem

$P(x) = (x - r)Q(x) + \mathcal{R} = (x - r)Q(x)$,
and $x - r$ **is a factor of** $P(x)$.
     If $x - r$ is a factor of $P(x)$,
then $P(x) = (x - r)Q(x)$,
and $P(r) = \mathcal{R} = 0$.

Example: 11.3-2.   Is $x - 4$ a factor of $P(x) = x^3 - 3x^2 - 4x$?
If 4 is substituted for x in $x^3 - 3x^2 - 4x$ and the remainder is 0 (or if the remainder is zero when $x^3 - 3x^2 - 4x$ is divided by $x - 4$), then $x - 4$ is a factor of $x^3 - 3x^2 - 4x$, according to Theorem 11.3-2.

$P(4) = 4^3 - 3(4)^2 - 4(4) = 64 - 48 - 16 = 0$.
$\therefore x - 4$ **is a factor of** $x^3 - 3x^2 - 4x$.

11.4 SYNTHETIC DIVISION

It often is a very tedious task to divide a polynomial $P(x)$ by a nonzero divisor $D(x)$. At times it even becomes difficult to substitute a number for x in $P(x)$ to find the remainder $\mathcal{R}$. Also, many times it is difficult to check to determine if the divisor is a factor of the given polynomial. Fortunately, there is an easy procedure to take care of these difficulties, provided the divisor polynomial is, or can be adjusted to be, a polynomial of first degree with one as the coefficient of the variable. This process is called **synthetic division** or **division by detached coefficients.**

An example will be worked out in complete detail to show how the synthetic division method of performing division of polynomial functions, where $P(x)$ is of degree one or more and $D(x)$ is degree one, is justified.

Example: 11.4-1.   Divide $x^3 - 2x - 65$ by $x - 4$.

STEP I

A polynomial of degree n has $n + 1$ terms. So in working with synthetic division it is most important that you provide $n + 1$ terms for a polynomial of degree n. If any term of the sequence is missing, then a zero coefficient must be inserted. For example, $x^3 - 2x - 65$ should be written as $x^3 + 0x^2 - 2x - 65$. If one fails to insert the terms with zero coefficients then synthetic division fails.

$$
\begin{array}{r}
x^2 + 4x + 14 \quad Q(x) \\
D(x) \quad x - 4 \;\overline{\big)\; x^3 - 0 \; - \; 2x - 65 \quad P(x)} \\
\underline{x^3 - 4x^2} \quad\quad\quad\quad\quad \\
4x^2 - 2x - 65 \\
\underline{4x^2 - 16x} \quad\quad \\
14x - 65 \\
\underline{14x - 56} \\
- 9 \quad (\mathscr{R})
\end{array}
$$

STEP II

1. Step II is Step I with all the x's in $P(x)$ and $D(x)$ omitted.

2. Working with only the coefficients of the terms of the polynomials produces the same quotient coefficients and the same remainder as in Step I.

$$
\begin{array}{r}
1 + 4 + 14 \quad (Q) \\
(D) \quad 1 - 4 \;\overline{\big)\; 1 + 0 \; - \; 2 - 65 \quad (P)} \\
\underline{1 - 4} \longleftarrow \quad\quad \text{Partial} \\
4 - 2 - 65 \quad \text{Products} \\
\underline{4 - 16} \longleftarrow \quad\quad \\
14 - 65 \\
\underline{14 - 56} \\
- 9 \quad (\mathscr{R})
\end{array}
$$

STEP III

1. Since the left terms of the partial products in Step II are duplicates of the numbers directly above them, they can be omitted provided that the left term of the divisor that produced these numbers is also deleted.

2. Note that in Steps II, III, and IV the first coefficient of the quotient is always the first coefficient of the polynomial.

$$
\begin{array}{r}
1 + 4 + 14 \quad (Q) \\
(D) \quad -4 \;\overline{\big)\; 1 + 0 \; - \; 2 - 65 \quad (P)} \\
\underline{- 4} \longleftarrow \quad\quad \text{Partial} \\
4 - 2 - 65 \quad \text{Products} \\
\underline{- 16} \longleftarrow \quad\quad \\
14 - 65 \\
\underline{- 56} \\
- 9 \quad (\mathscr{R})
\end{array}
$$

STEP IV

1. The data in Step III are compressed so that partial products -4, -16, and -56 all fall in the second row in Step IV(A).

$$(A) \qquad (D) \quad -4 \,\big|\, \underline{1 + 0 - 2 - 65} \quad (P)$$
$$\underline{- 4 - 16 - 56}$$
$$\underbrace{1 + 4 + 14}\,\big|\!- 9 \quad (\mathscr{R})$$
$$(Q)$$

2. By changing the signs of the coefficients of the second row in Step IV(A) and adding row 1 and row 2, the first three entries $1 + 4 + 14$ in the third row is the quotient Q and the last entry -9 is the remainder $\mathscr{R}$.

3. Finally, if the sign of the -4 in Step IV(A) is changed to $+4$, the synthetic division carried out, and the first and second rows as they appear in Step IV(B) added, then again the first three entries in the third row are the proper coefficients for the quotient and the fourth entry is the remainder $\mathscr{R} = -9$. A third-degree polynomial divided by a first-degree polynomial gives a polynomial of second degree for a quotient. Therefore, in reinserting the variable x in Q, annex x^2 to the 1, x to the 4, to give $Q(x) = x^2 + 4x + 14$.

$$(B) \qquad (D) \quad 4 \,\big|\, \underline{1 + 0 - 2 - 65} \quad (P)$$
$$\underline{+ 4 + 16 + 56}$$
$$\underbrace{1 + 4 + 14}\,\big|\!- 9 \quad (\mathscr{R})$$
$$(Q)$$

Thus, *to divide a polynomial $P(x)$ of degree greater than zero by $D(x)$ where $D(x)$ is $x - r$ the following steps must be taken in the order given:*

1. Arrange $P(x)$ in descending powers of x.

2. Place a zero coefficient for each missing power of x.

3. Detach the coefficients of $P(x)$ from left to right and write them and their proper signs in a horizontal row.

4. At the left of the coefficients of $P(x)$ write the constant term of the divisor with its sign changed.

5. Always write the coefficient of the first row as the first term in the third row.

6. Multiply the first term of the third row by r and place this product in the second row under the second number in the first row. Add these two numbers and record the sum as the second number in the third row.

7. Multiply the second term of the third row by r and continue the procedure followed in (6) until the remainder $\mathscr{R}$ is obtained.

Example: 11.4-2. Divide $5x^4 + 10x^3 + 6x^2 - 4$ by $x + 2$. Use the synthetic division procedure to obtain $Q(x)$ and $\mathscr{R}$.

$$-2 \overline{)5 + 10 + 6 + 0 - 4}$$
$$\underline{- 10 + 0 - 12 + 24}$$
$$5 + 0 + 6 - 12 \overline{)+ 20} \, .$$

Since $Q = 5 + 0 + 6 - 12$, $Q(x) = 5x^3 + 6x - 12$ and $\mathscr{R} = 20$. Note in Example 11.4-2, and all other examples worked by synthetic division, that $Q(x)$ is always one degree less than $P(x)$.

Example: 11.4-3.   Find $Q(x)$ and $\mathscr{R}$ for

$$2x - 6 \overline{)6x^3 - 8x^2 + 2x - 8.}$$

$D(x)$ must be linear with one for the coefficient of x. Therefore, divide both the dividend and divisor by 2. This will not change the values of the given expression, but will give,

$$x - 3 \overline{)3x^3 - 4x^2 + x - 4.}$$

$$3 \overline{)3 - 4 + 1 - 4}$$
$$\underline{+ 9 + 15 + 48}$$
$$3 + 5 + 16 \overline{)+ 44} \, .$$

Then $Q(x) = 3x^2 + 5x + 16$ and $\mathscr{R} = 44$.

EXERCISE 11.A

1. Find the difference of the polynomial functions $5x^3 - 2x^2 + 6x$ and $x^2 - 3$.

2. Find the sum of the polynomial functions $7x^4 - 2x^2 + 6$ and $x^3 - 5x + 1$.

3. Find the product of the two polynomials in Problem 2.

4. Find the quotient $Q(x)$ and the remainder $\mathscr{R}(x)$ for the polynomials in Problem 1 above.

5. Prove that the product of two polynomials is always a polynomial.

6. Show by at least one counterexample that the quotient of two polynomials is not necessarily a polynomial.

Use synthetic division and the Remainder theorem to find $Q(x)$ and $\mathscr{R}$ for each of the following problems:

7. $x^2 - 7x + 11 \div x - 3$.

8. $2x^2 - 5x - 6 \div x - 5$.

9. $4x^3 - 5x^2 + 7 \div x + 6$.

10. $5x^3 + 2x - 5 \div x + 2$.

11. $6x^4 - 2x^2 + 10 \div 2x - 8$.

12. $10x^5 - 4x^3 + 2x \div 2x - 6$.

13. State the degree of $P(x)$ for Problems 7 through 12.

14. State the degree of $Q(x)$ for Problems 7 through 12.

Use synthetic division in Problems 15 through 20 to show that:

15. $x - 3$ is a factor of $x^4 - 81$.

16. $x - 2$ is a factor of $x^2 - 6x + 8$.

17. $x - a$ is a factor of $x^{15} - a^{15}$.

18. $x + b$ is a factor of $x^{13} + b^{13}$.

19. $x^n + a^n$ is exactly divisible by $x + a$ if n is odd.

20. $x^n - a^n$ is exactly divisible by $x + a$ if n is even.

21. Show that the zero functions of $P(x) = x^3 + 5x^2 + 2x - 8$ are $x = 1$, $x = -2$, and $x = -4$. Write the function in factored form.

22. Show that the zero functions of $P(x) = x^3 + 2x^2 - 35x$ are $x = 0$, $x = 5$, and $x = -7$. What are the three factors of $P(x)$?

23. Show that $x^2 - a^2$ is a factor of $x^{2n} - a^{2n}$ if n is a positive integer.

24. What value of k in $2x^3 - 5x^2 + kx + 2$ will give a remainder of 6 if the function is divided by $x - 2$?

25. If $P(x) = 7x^4 - 6x^2 + 4$, compute $P(-1)$, $P(3)$, and $P(-2)$.

26. If $P(x) = 2x^4 - 5x^3 - x$, compute $P(1)$, $P(-4)$, and $P(5)$.

11.5 POLYNOMIAL FUNCTIONS AND EQUATIONS

The graph of a polynomial function is a smooth continuous curve. In order to know just how the graph of such a function behaves in regard to zeros of the function and how to easily make the graph, we need the support of the following theorems and definitions:

Theorem: 11.5-a. **The Fundamental Theorem of Algebra** states that a complex polynomial function of the form

$$P(x) = a_0 x^n + a_1 x^{n-1} + \cdots + a_{n-1} x + a_n,$$

where $a_0 \neq 0$ and n is an integer greater than zero, has at least one value of x such that $P(x) = 0$.

Because of the complexity of proving the preceding theorem we will assume it to be true and use it to prove a theorem about zeros of a polynomial that is of utmost importance.

Theorem: 11.5-b. For n an integer greater than zero, a polynomial function $P(x)$ of the form

$$P(x) = a_0 x^n + a_1 x^{n-1} + \cdots + a_{n-1} x + a_n \qquad (a_0 \neq 0),$$

has exactly n values of x such that $P(x) = 0$ in the set of complex numbers, provided a multiplicity of k like values is counted k times.

PROOF: By the **Fundamental Theorem of Algebra** $P(x) = 0$ at least when $x = r_1$. Then, by the **Factor theorem** $x - r_1$ is a factor of $P(x)$ and $P(x) = (x - r_1)Q_1(x)$.

But $Q_1(x)$ is a polynomial function which has at least one zero when $x = r_2$. So $x - r_2$ is a factor of $Q_1(x)$. We now have

$$P(x) = (x - r_1)(x - r_2)Q_2(x).$$

Each new quotient is one degree less than the preceding one and the process can be continued n times to give

$$P(x) = (x - r_1)(x - r_2)(x - r_3) \cdots (x - r_n)Q_n(x).$$

Because n factors have been involved, the degree of $Q_n(x)$ is $n - n = 0$ and $Q_n(x)$ is the nonzero complex number a_0.

$$\therefore \ \boldsymbol{P(x) = a_0(x - r_1)(x - r_2)(x - r_3) \cdots (x - r_n),}$$

and, since $x = r_1, r_2, r_3, \ldots, r_n$, $P(x) = 0$ and $P(x)$ has at least n zeros.

Assume that $x = r$ is another zero value. Then none of the factors of $P(x)$ will give a zero. Therefore, **there are exactly n zeros.**

Even though Theorem 11.5-b tells us how many factors and how many corresponding zeros there are, it does not infer that all the factors are distinct. For example, any one of the factors, such as $(x - r_i)^k$ where $i = 1, 2, 3, \ldots, k$, can occur k times. Should this happen $(x - r_i)^k$ is said to be a zero of **multiplicity k.** However, whether or not the factors appear in multiples, the total number of x values such that $P(x) = 0$ remains exactly n in number.

When working with polynomial functions keep this commonly used terminology in mind:

1. **A complex polynomial** function means that its coefficients are complex numbers.

2. **A real polynomial** function means that its coefficients are real numbers.

3. **A rational polynomial** function means that its coefficients are rational numbers.

For the rational polynomial function $P(x) = 3x^5 - 4x^4 + 7x^3 - 2x = 5$, the degree is 5. Likewise, for the rational polynomial function $P(x) = (x - 2)^3(x + 1)^2$ the degree is 5. In this second function it is interesting to note that the zeros of the function can very easily be obtained by substituting 2, 2, 2, -1, and -1 for the x in $P(x)$.

Theorem: 11.5-c. If for a real polynomial function such as $y = P(x)$, a and b are real numbers, and $P(a)$ and $P(b)$ have opposite signs, then $P(x)$ has at least one zero between a and b.

In graphing a polynomial function, $P(a)$ and $P(b)$ in Figure 11.5-c are ordinates; in fact, all values of $P(x)$ are ordinates. Since polynomials are continuous curves and since it is given that $P(a)$ is on one side of the x axis and $P(b)$ is on the other, then a continuous curve from $P(a)$ to $P(b)$ must cross the x axis at least once between a and b. Thus, $P(x) = 0$, at least once between a and b.

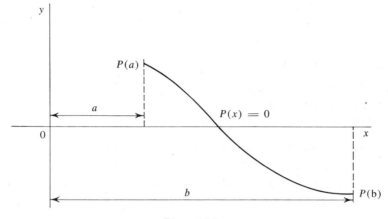

Figure 11.5-c

11.5-1 Upper and Lower Bounds

In searching for the zeros of a real polynomial function the work can usually be shortened by first determining the upper and lower bounds of the zeros (see Definitions 2.15-1 and 2.15-2). These bounds are determined by observing the behavior of the signs in the third line of the synthetic division process.

Definition: 11.5-1a. *If in a synthetic division of $P(x)$ divided by $x - r$, where $r > 0$, all the numbers in the third row are positive, then r is* **an upper bound** *for the positive zeros of $P(x)$.*

Example: 11.5-1a. Find an upper bound for the zeros of $P(x) = x^2 - 3x - 9$. We know that $x = 4$ in (A) is not the upper bound because the ordered pair $[x, P(x)] = (4, -5)$ represents a point that falls below the x axis.

(A)

$$4 \,\overline{\left|\, 1 - 3 - 9 \right.}$$
$$ + 4 + 4$$
$$\overline{\, 1 + 1 \left|- 5 \right.}$$

(B)

$$5 \,\overline{\left|\, 1 - 3 - 9 \right.}$$
$$ + 5 + 10$$
$$\overline{\, 1 + 2 \left|+ 1 \right.}$$

All the members of the third row in (B) are positive. If r were increased beyond 5, all the members in the third row would continue to be positive and the remainder would move farther from zero. Therefore, **5 is an upper bound.**

Definition: 11.5-1b. *If in a synthetic division of $P(x)$ divided by $x - r$, where $r < 0$, all members in the third row alternate in sign, then r is a* **lower bound** *for the negative zeros of $P(x)$.*

Example: 11.5-1b.   Find a lower bound for the zeros of $P(x) = x^2 - 3x - 9$.
In (C), $x = -1$ is not a lower bound because the signs of the members of the third row do not alternate.

(C) $-1 \lfloor 1 - 3 - 9$ (D) $-2 \lfloor 1 - 3 - 9$
$- 1 + 4$ $- 2 + 10$
$\overline{1 - 4\lfloor - 5}$ $\overline{1 - 5\lfloor + 1}$

In (D) the members of the third row alternate in sign. Further, if r is decreased below −2, the signs will remain the same but each member will increase numerically and the remainder will move farther from zero. Therefore, **−2 is a lower bound.**

11.5-2 Zeros of Functions and Roots of Equations

All the preceding definitions and theorems which we have been applying to the zeros of polynomial functions apply equally well to the roots of polynomial equations. So let it be strongly emphasized that

The **zeros** *of a polynomial function are* **identical to** *the* **roots** *of the corresponding polynomial equation.*

Definition: 11.5-2a. *A* **root of a polynomial equation** *is that number that can be substituted for x in P(x) and satisfy the polynomial equation P(x) = 0.*

11.6 GRAPHING POLYNOMIAL FUNCTIONS AND THEIR EQUATIONS

Abel, one of the great mathematicians, proved that it is impossible to solve a polynomial equation of degree five or greater explicitly for x by a finite number of algebraic operations. However, since our principal objective in this chapter is to develop methods that will enable us to solve for both the rational and irrational roots of a polynomial equation of any degree, let us approach the problem by means of graphs.

Example: 11.6-1. Find the roots of the real polynomial equation $x^3 + 2x^2 - x - 2 = 0$. (You should understand, of course, that another way of stating this problem is, "Find the zeros of the polynomial function $x^3 + 2x^2 - x - 2$.")

The work necessary to find a table of values for $P(x)$ when values are assumed for x can be greatly simplified if the necessary synthetic divisions are done mentally and only the third line of each synthetic division is recorded. For example, instead of assuming $x = -3$ and doing this:

$-3 \lfloor 1 + 2 - 1 - 2$
$- 3 + 3 - 6$
$\overline{1 - 1 + 2\lfloor - \mathbf{8}},$

we could mentally multiply the left-hand coefficient in the third row by -3, add it to $+2$ and record the sum -1 as the next entry in the third row. Again, mentally multiply this last entry -1 by -3 and add that 3 to -1 to get the next entry $+2$ in the third row. Finally, multiply the $+2$ by -3 and add it to -2 to get the remainder -8.

The preceding scheme enables us to include in Table 11.6-1 all the data resulting from the selected synthetic divisions. Moreover, it provides enough

Table 11.6-1

	x	Q	$P(x)$
		$x^3 + 2x^2 - x$ -2	
		$1 + 2 - 1$ -2	
Lower Bound⟶	-3	$1 - 1 + 2$	-8
	-2	$1 + 0 - 1$	$+0$
Roots	-1	$1 + 1 - 2$	$+0$
	0	$1 + 2 - 1$	-2
	1	$1 + 3 + 2$	$+0$
Upper Bounds⟶	2	$1 + 4 + 7$	$+12$

ordered pairs $[x, P(x)]$ to make a reasonably accurate graph of the polynomial function $x^3 + 2x^2 - x - 2$.

Table 11.6-1 actually shows the third line results of six different synthetic substitutions. When $x = -3$ the signs of the resulting numbers of Q and $\mathcal{R}$

x	$P(x)$
-3	-8
-2	0
-1.5	$+0.6$
-1	0
0	-2
1	0
2	12

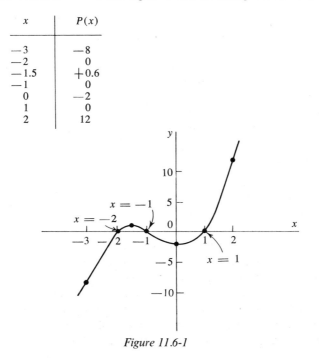

Figure 11.6-1

alternate, indicating a lower bound. When $x = 2$, the signs of each member of Q and $\mathscr{R}$ are positive, indicating an upper bound, but the table shows $x = 1$ to be the **least integral upper bound.**

Also, even before the ordered pairs $[x, P(x)]$ are plotted, it is evident from Table 11.6-1 that three of the assumed values for x gave zeros for the polynomial function. Therefore, these three values, $x = -2$, $x = -1$, and $x = 1$ **are roots** of the polynomial equation $x^3 + 2x^2 - x - 2 = 0$.

The procedure used in plotting a polynomial function such as $P(x) = x^3 + 2x^2 - x - 2$ is to determine enough ordered pairs $[x, P(x)]$ to represent suitable points on the graph and then, knowing that **the graph of a polynomial is a smooth continuous curve,** draw such a curve through the points. This has been done in Figure 11.6-1.

The curve in Figure 11.6-1 shows that *the zeros of $P(x) = x^3 + 2x^2 - x - 2$ are at the points where the graph cuts the x axis.* The abscissas of the points where the graph cuts the x axis are the roots of the equation $x^3 + 2x^2 - x - 2 = 0$.

Example: 11.6-2. By graphic procedures estimate the three roots of the rational polynomial equation $x^3 - 4x^2 - 2x + 8 = 0$. Then determine its smallest positive root accurate to four significant digits.

From Table 11.6-2 the upper and lower bounds tell us that the three real roots are somewhere between $x = -2$ and $x = 5$. More specifically, the roots

Table 11.6-2

		$x^3 - 4x^2 - 2x$	$+8$	
		$1 - 4 - 2$	$+8$	
	x	Q	$P(x)$	
Lower Bound⟶	-2	$1 - 6 + 10$	-12	
	-1	$1 - 5 + 3$	$+5$	
	0	$1 - 4 - 2$	$+8$	
Location	1	$1 - 3 - 5$	$+3$	
of	2	$1 - 2 - 6$	-4	
Roots	3	$1 - 1 - 5$	-7	
	4	$1 + 0 - 2$	$+0$	
Upper Bound⟶	5	$1 + 1 + 3$	$+23$	

are: (a) $x = 4$, because 4 gives a zero of the function; (b) $-2 < x < -1$, because $P(-2)$ is negative and $P(-1)$ is positive; and (c) $1 < x < 2$, because $P(1)$ is positive and $P(2)$ is negative (see Theorem 11.5-c).

The graph of $x^3 - 4x^2 - 2x + 8$, as shown in Figure 11.6-2, enables us to make a slightly better estimate of the two irrational roots. The negative root is $x \doteq -1.5$ and the smallest positive root, which is to be determined accurate to four significant digits, seems to be $x \doteq 1.4$.

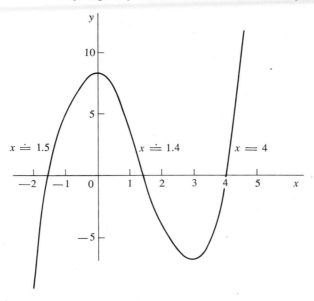

Figure 11.6-2

By synthetic division, $x = 1.4$ substituted into $P(x) = x^3 - 4x^2 - 2x + 8$ gives $P(1.4) = +0.10$. This shows that our estimated value of 1.4 for x is not quite large enough to make $P(x) = 0$.

$$\begin{array}{r|rrrr} 1.4 & 1 & -4 & -2 & +8 \\ & & +1.4 & +3.64 & +7.90 \\ \hline & 1 & -2.6 & +5.64 & +0.10 \end{array} \qquad \begin{array}{r|rrrr} 1.5 & 1 & -4 & -2 & +8 \\ & & +1.5 & -3.75 & -8.63 \\ \hline & 1 & -2.5 & -5.75 & -0.63 \end{array}$$

If x is assumed to be 1.5, then $P(1.5) = -0.63$.

Since 1.4 and 1.5 are real numbers and $P(1.4)$ and $P(1.5)$ have opposite signs, then according to Theorem 11.5-c, there is at least one real root between 1.4 and 1.5.

To determine a more nearly accurate estimate than $x = 1.4$ for the smallest positive root, successive approximation by a linear interpolation method will be used. (Engineers use the linear interpolation method so much that it is often referred to as the engineers' method of approximation.)

As Figure 11.6-2a shows, the procedure is to magnify the horizontal scale of the rectangular coordinate system, making ten divisions between the two consecutive x values to be considered. Then plot the two ordered pairs, connect them with a straight line and read off a new estimate for x. So, plotting the data for x and $P(x)$, we get

Returning to Figure 11.6-2, we can see that the original curve actually concaves down near the point $x = 1.4$. Keeping this fact in mind, we read our next best estimate from the graph in Figure 11.6-2a to be $x \doteq \mathbf{1.41}$.

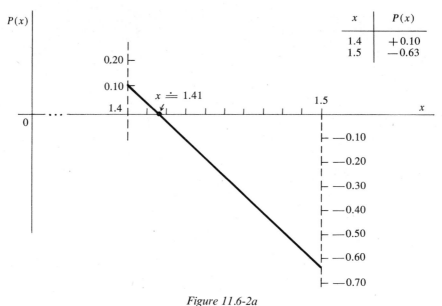

x	$P(x)$
1.4	$+0.10$
1.5	-0.63

Figure 11.6-2a

Next, substitute 1.41 for x in $P(x) = x^3 - 4x^2 - 2x + 8$ to get the remainder $P(1.41) = +0.031$.

$$1.41 \overline{\smash{\big)}\ 1 - 4 \quad\ - 2 \quad\ + 8}$$
$$\ \ + 1.41 - 3.652 - 7.969$$
$$\ \ \overline{1 - 2.59 - 5.652\,|\!+ \mathbf{0.031}}$$

When we move out $x = 1.41$, we have to move up to reach the curve. Thus, $x = 1.41$ is not quite large enough. So we try $x = 1.42$. But the abscissa $x = 1.42$ is too long because now we have to move down -0.043 to reach the curve. If $\mathscr{R}$ for $x = 1.42$ had been positive we, of course, would have had to try $x = 1.43$, and so on, until a negative value for $P(x)$ was obtained.

$$1.42 \overline{\smash{\big)}\ 1 - 4 \quad\ - 2 \quad\ + 8}$$
$$\ \ - 1.42 - 3.664 - 8.043$$
$$\ \ \overline{1 - 2.58 - 5.664\,|\!- 0.043}$$

To find the next best estimate for the irrational root, plot $(1.41, +0.031)$ and $(1.42, -0.043)$ as in Figure 11.6-2b, draw a straight line through the points, and by the *linear interpolation method* read off the value of the point where the straight line crosses the x axis.

Figure 11.6-2b shows the best estimate of x to be 1.414. We know $x \doteq 1.414$ to be **correct** to three significant digits and **accurate** to four significant digits, which is what the problem called for.

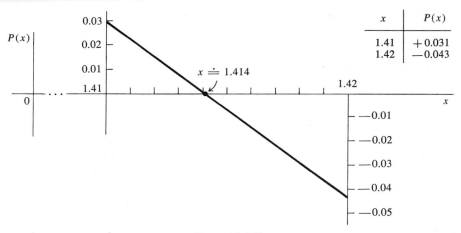

Figure 11.6-2b

Therefore, the *smallest positive root* of the polynomial equation $x^3 - 4x^2 - 2x + 8 = 0$ is $x \doteq \mathbf{1.414.}$

Finding rational or irrational roots of real polynomial equations by the linear interpolation method can be carried to any degree of accuracy desired.

Example: 11.6-3.   Find all the roots of $x^3 - 4x^2 - 2x + 8 = 0$ accurate to four significant digits.

If you will forgive the author for withholding valuable information in Example 11.6-2 in order to first present the linear interpolation method of solving for the roots of any real polynomial equation, he will now suggest an easier way of solving the equation $x^3 - 4x^2 - 2x + 8 = 0$.

In Table 11.6-2 we learned that $x = 4$ gave $P(x) = 0$. So $x = 4$ is a rational root of $x^3 - 4x^2 - 2x + 9 = 0$ and $x - 4$ is a factor of $x^3 - 4x^2 - 2x + 8$. Deleting the factor $x - 4$ from $P(x)$, we get

$$(D)\quad 4\;\overline{)\;1 - 4 - 2 + 8}\quad (P)$$
$$\underline{+ 4 + 0 - 8}$$
$$1 + 0 - 2 \,|\, + 0 \quad (\mathscr{R})$$
$$\underbrace{}_{(Q)}$$

This shows the depressed function to be $Q(x) = x^2 - 2$. It follows that its corresponding equation is $x^2 - 2 = 0$, and its roots are $\sqrt{2}$ and $-\sqrt{2}$.

Therefore, the three real roots of $x^3 - 4x^2 - 2x + 8 = 0$ are

$$x = \mathbf{4}, \quad x \doteq \mathbf{1.414}, \quad \text{and} \quad x \doteq \mathbf{-1.414},$$

that is, one rational root and two irrational roots.

EXERCISE 11.B

1. State the fundamental theorem of algebra in terms of a complex polynomial equation.

2. How many roots does a complex polynomial equation of degree n have? Are its roots necessarily distinct roots? Explain.

3. How many roots does the polynomial $x^5 = 0$ have?

4. How many roots does the polynomial $x^7 = 1$ have?

5. What can one be sure of in a real polynomial function if for two consecutive values a and b, $P(a)$ and $P(b)$ have opposite signs?

6. What do you know about an x value if its use in synthetic division makes all the third-row members positive?

7. What do you know about an x value if its use in synthetic substitution makes the positive and negative signs of the third-row members alternate?

8. If the x values that produce the zeros of a polynomial function were given, how would you determine the roots of the corresponding polynomial equation?

9. Is the lower bound for the roots of a real polynomial equation the greatest lower bound? (See Definitions 2.15-1 and 2.15-2.)

10. Is the upper bound for the roots of a real polynomial equation the least upper bound? (See Definition 2.15-1.)

11.–18. For each of the following rational polynomial functions $P(x)$:

(a) Find an upper bound and a lower bound for the zeros.

(b) Locate the real roots between consecutive integers *for each corresponding polynomial equation.*

(c) Draw the graph.

11. $x^3 + 3x^2 - 6x - 9$.

12. $x^3 - x^2 + 7x + 4$.

13. $4x^3 - 12x^2 + 5x - 3$.

14. $7x^3 + 6x^2 - 8x - 1$.

15. $x^5 - 3x + 4$.

16. $x^5 + 4x^4 - x^2 + 2$.

17. $x^3 + 1$.

18. $x^4 + 3x$.

19.–26. Draw the graphs and find the indicated roots correct to two decimal places for each of these rational polynomial equations. (Correct to two decimal places means accurate to three significant decimal places.)

19. $2x^3 + x^2 + 2x - 3 = 0$.

20. $x^3 - x^2 + x - 8 = 0$.

21. $x^3 - 5x^2 + 10x - 5 = 0$.

22. $x^3 - 3x^2 - 6x + 4 = 0$.

23. $x^4 - 10x + 5 = 0$.

24. $x^4 - x^2 + 6x + 5 = 0$.

25. $x^3 - 2x + 7 = 0$.

26. $x^3 + x^2 - 8 = 0$.

11.7 COMPLEX ROOTS OF POLYNOMIAL EQUATIONS

There is no assurance that the roots of a polynomial equation with real coefficients will be real roots. If the roots are not real they will have to be complex and, as the following theorem states,

complex roots always exist in conjugate pairs (see Definition 10.3-1).

Theorem: 11.7-1. If in a polynomial equation with real coefficients $a + bi$ ($b \neq 0$) is a root of the equation, then its conjugate $a - bi$ is also a root.

PROOF: Since $a + bi$ is a root of $P(x) = 0$, then $P(a + bi) = 0$, and $[x - (a + bi)]$ is a factor of $P(x)$. If it can be shown that $[x - (a - bi)]$ is a factor of $P(x)$, then by the converse of the factor theorem it will follow that

$a - bi$ is a root of $P(x) = 0$.

The product of

$$[x - (a + bi)][x - (a - bi)] = x^2 - 2ax + a^2 + b^2$$
$$= (x - a)^2 + b^2 = D(x).$$

Using the division algorithm (see Definition 11.2-4), we obtain

$$P(x) = [(x - a)^2 + b^2]Q(x) + \mathscr{R}(x).$$

But since $D(x)$ is of degree 2, then $\mathscr{R}(x)$ has to be of lesser degree and can be replaced by the linear expression $cx + d$. Thus,

$$P(x) = [(x - a)^2 + b^2]Q(x) + cx + d. \tag{A}$$

By hypothesis, $a + bi$ is given as a root of $P(x) = 0$. So substitute $a + bi$ for x in (A) to get (B). Then simplify to get (C).

$$P(a + bi) = [(a + bi - a)^2 + b^2]Q(a + bi) + c(a + bi) + d, \tag{B}$$
$$0 = (0) \cdot Q(a + bi) + ca + cbi + d,$$
and $0 = (ca + d) + cbi \quad$ (*a complex number*). $\tag{C}$

A complex number can equal zero if and only if both its real and its imaginary parts equal zero. Thus, since the complex number

$(ca + d) + cbi = 0,$

then it must follow that

$ca + d = 0 \quad$ and $\quad cb = 0.$

If $cb = 0$, then $c = 0$, because by hypothesis $b \neq 0$. If $c = 0$, then both $ca = 0$ and $d = 0$, and $\mathscr{R}(x) = 0$.

So $\mathscr{R}(x) = cx + d = 0.$

Therefore, $x - (a - bi)$ **is a factor of** $P(x)$
and $a - bi$ **is a complex root of** $P(x) = 0$.

11.8 ROOTS OF ODD DEGREE POLYNOMIALS

The following theorem is a consequence of Theorem 11.5-b and the fact that *complex roots of real polynomial equations exist in pairs.*

Theorem: 11.8-1.   A real polynomial equation of odd degree has at least one real root and for n any positive integer it may have $2n - 1$ real roots.

Example 11.8-1.   If one root of the equation $x^3 - 5x^2 + 16x - 30 = 0$ is $1 - 3i$, find the other roots.

Since one root is $1 - 3i$, according to Theorem 11.7-1, another root is $1 + 3i$. The third root is a real root, according to Theorem 11.8-1. By dividing the given equation by the two known roots expressed as factors, the third factor is

$$\frac{x^3 - 5x^2 + 16x - 30}{[x - (1 - 3i)][x - (1 + 3i)]} = \frac{x^3 - 5x^2 + 16x - 30}{x^2 - 2x + 10} = x - 3.$$

Therefore, the **roots are: $x = 3$, $x = 1 + 3i$, $x = 1 - 3i$.**

11.9 RATIONAL ROOTS OF A POLYNOMIAL EQUATION

Up to this point we have learned that the roots of a real polynomial equation may be either real or complex and that the real roots may be found by graphical procedures. We will now prove a theorem that will enable us to find the rational roots of real polynomial equations. Once a rational root is determined algebraically, its corresponding factor will be divided into the function of the polynomial equation, by synthetic division, depressing it one degree. If it is suspected that this depressed equation has another rational root, the process will be repeated. When the depressed equation is of degree 2, the remaining roots will be obtained by the quadratic formula.

Theorem: 11.9-1.   If a polynomial equation

$$P(x) = a_0x^n + a_1x^{n-1} + a_2x^{n-2} + \cdots + a_{n-1}x + a_n = 0$$

with integral coefficients, has a root p/q, where p/q is in its lowest terms, then p is a divisor of a_n and q is a divisor of a_0.

PROOF: Since p/q is given as a root of the equation it may be substituted for x in $P(x) = 0$ to give

$$a_0\left(\frac{p}{q}\right)^n + a_1\left(\frac{p}{q}\right)^{n-1} + a_2\left(\frac{p}{q}\right)^{n-2} + \cdots + a_{n-1}\left(\frac{p}{q}\right) + a_n = 0. \quad (A)$$

Multiplying both sides of the equation by q^n gives

$$a_0p^n + a_1p^{n-1}q + a_2p^{n-2}q^2 + \cdots + a_{n-1}pq^{n-1} + a_nq^n = 0. \quad (B)$$

Subtracting a_nq^n from both sides of the equation and factoring p from each term of the left sides gives

$$p(a_0p^{n-1} + a_1p^{n-2}q + a_2p^{n-3}q^2 + \cdots + a_{n-1}q^{n-1}) = -a_nq^n. \quad (C)$$

Since p/q was defined to be relatively prime, that is, in its lowest terms, it is implied that p and q are integers with no common factors other than 1 and -1. The coefficients were also defined to be integers. Therefore, if p is a factor of the left member in (C), it must also be a factor of $-a_n q^n$. But it is given that p and q have no common factors other than one. Therefore, p cannot be a factor of q or q^n. Consequently,

p is a factor of a_n,

which was to be proved.

If from (B) we subtract $a_0 p^n$ from both sides of the equation and factor q from each term on the left side there results

$$q(a_1 p^{n-1} + a_2 p^{n-2} q + \cdots + a_{n-1} p q^{n-2} + a_n q^{n-1}) = -a_0 p^n. \quad (D)$$

If q is a factor of the left member in (D) it must also be a factor of $-a_0 p^n$. But p and q are given to be relatively prime so q cannot be a factor of p or of p^n. Therefore,

q is a factor of a_0.

and the proof of the theorem is complete.

If in a real polynomial equation a_0 is 1, then $q = 1$ and equation (A) reduces to

$$p^n + a_1 p^{n-1} + a_2 p^{n-2} + \cdots + a_{n-1} p + a_n = 0.$$

Following through steps (B) and (C) of the proof for Theorem 11.9-1 we find that the root p is an exact divisor of a_n as expressed by the following theorem:

Theorem: 11.9-2.   If a polynomial equation

$$P(x) = x^n + a_1 x^{n-1} + a_2 x^{n-2} + \cdots + a_{n-1} x + a_n = 0,$$

$n \in I$ and $n > 0$, and $a_1, a_2, \ldots, a_n \in I$, has a root p, then p must be an integer and an exact divisor of the constant term a_n.

Example: 11.9-1.   Find the roots of the equation $x^3 + 2x^2 - 3x - 10 = 0$:

(a) First find the rational roots, if any.
(b) Then find the remaining roots.

According to Theorem 11.9-1, possible rational roots of the equation are ± 1, ± 2, ± 5, and ± 10. By synthetic division it becomes evident that neither $+1$ or -1 are rational roots. Trying $x = 2$, we get

$$\underline{2\,|\,\begin{array}{l} 1 + 2 - 3 - 10 \\ + 2 + 8 + 10 \end{array}}$$
$$\underbrace{1 + 4 + 5}_{(Q)}\,|\,+\,0 \quad (\mathscr{R})$$

When $P(x)$ is divided by $D(x)$, that is,

$$\frac{P(x)}{D(x)} = \frac{x^3 + 2x^2 - 3x - 10}{x - 2},$$

there results the rational root $x = 2$ and the depressed equation $x^2 + 4x + 5 = 0$.

Since the depressed equation $x^2 + 4x + 5 = 0$ is a quadratic equation, we will use the quadratic formula to find the remaining roots.

$$x = \frac{-b \pm \sqrt{b^2 - 4ac}}{2a} = \frac{-4 \pm \sqrt{16 - 20}}{2} = -2 \pm i.$$

Therefore, the roots of $x^3 + 2x^2 - 3x - 10 = 0$ are

$$x = 2, \quad x = -2 + i, \quad x = -2 - i.$$

Note that *each of the complex roots is the conjugate of the other*. Check to see if each of the derived roots reduces $x^3 + 2x^2 - 3x - 10$ to zero.

Example: 11.9-2. Find the roots of $2x^3 + 5x^2 - 1 = 0$.

Since p may be $+1$ or -1 and q may be $+1$, -1, $+2$ or -2, then the possible rational roots p/q are $+1$, -1, $+\frac{1}{2}$, $-\frac{1}{2}$.

By synthetic division $+1$, -1, and $+\frac{1}{2}$ are not rational roots; so try $x = -\frac{1}{2}$.

$$
\begin{array}{r}
-\tfrac{1}{2}\,\big|\ 2 + 5 + 0 - 1 \\
\ \ \ \ \ \ -1 - 2 + 1 \\
\hline
2 + 4 - 2\,\big|+ \mathbf{0}
\end{array}
$$

Evidently, $x = -\frac{1}{2}$ is a rational root of the equation. The depressed function is

$$\frac{P(x)}{D(x)} = \frac{2x^3 + 5x^2 - 1}{x + \frac{1}{2}} = 2x^2 + 4x - 2.$$

Solving the depressed equation $2x^2 + 4x - 2 = 0$ by the quadratic formula gives

$$x = \frac{-4 \pm \sqrt{16 + 16}}{4} = -1 \pm \sqrt{2}.$$

Therefore, the roots of the equation are

$$x = -\tfrac{1}{2}, \quad x = -1 + \sqrt{2}, \quad \text{and} \quad x = -1 - \sqrt{2}.$$

Multiply together the factors corresponding to the preceding three roots to determine whether or not they give back the original polynomial equation. Also check to see if each root satisfies the given equation.

Example: 11.9-3. Find the roots of $x^5 - x^4 - 2x^3 - 4x^2 - 24x = 0$.

It should be apparent at once that one of the roots is $x = 0$ and that the depressed equation is $x^4 - x^3 - 2x^2 - 4x - 24 = 0$. Since $q = 1$ for this equation, the possible rational roots $p/q = p/1 = p$, are

$$p = \pm 1, \pm 2, \pm 3, \pm 4, \pm 6, \pm 8, \pm 12, \pm 24.$$

Synthetic division shows that $+1$, -1, and $+2$ are not roots of the equation $x^4 - x^3 - 2x^2 - 4x - 24 = 0$, so let us check out -2.

$$
\begin{array}{r|rrrrr}
-2 & 1 & -1 & -2 & -4 & -24 \\
   &   & -2 & +6 & -8 & +24 \\
\hline
   & 1 & -3 & +4 & -12 & +\;\;0 \\
\end{array}
$$

$x = -2$ proves to be a root and the remaining depressed equation is

$$x^3 - 3x^2 + 4x - 12 = 0.$$

Check out $+3$.

$$
\begin{array}{r|rrrr}
+3 & 1 & -3 & +4 & -12 \\
   &   & +3 & 0 & +12 \\
\hline
   & 1 & +0 & +4 & +\;\;0 \\
\end{array}
$$

We find that $x = 3$ is also a root, leaving the depressed quadratic equation $x^2 + 4 = 0$, which is solved by the quadratic formula to give $x = 2i$ and $x = -2i$, a pair of conjugate complex roots. Thus, the roots of

$$x^5 - x^4 - 2x^3 - 4x^2 - 24x = 0$$

are $x = 0$, $x = -2$, $x = 3$, $x = 2i$, and $x = -2i$.

Use these five roots to write an equation. Is the equation identical to the original equation? Then check out each root in succession to see if it reduces the given polynomial to zero.

EXERCISE 11.C

1. Show that it is possible for a rational polynomial equation, that is, one whose co-efficients are rational numbers, to have complex roots.

2. If the roots of a polynomial equation are

$x = 3$, $x = i$,   and $x = -i$,

show that the equation is a rational polynomial equation.

3. If it is certain that the roots of an equation are $x = 1$ and $x = 2 - i$, what is the equation?

4. If $x = 1 - i$ and $x = 2$ are two of the roots of the equation $x^3 - 4x^2 + 6x - 4 = 0$, then what is the third root?

5. List all possible rational roots for the equation $x^3 + 5x^2 - 7x - 2 = 0$.

6. List all possible rational roots for the equation $x^3 + 4x^2 - 5x + 6 = 0$.

7. Find all the rational roots for Problem 5. Are the roots all distinct? Explain.

8. Find all the rational roots for Problem 6. Are the roots distinct?

9. For the equation $4x^4 - 3x^3 + 2x - 5 = 0$:

(a) Find the rational roots, if any.
(b) Find the remaining roots. If they are irrational work them out to three significant-digit accuracy.

10. For the equation $3x^5 - 2x^3 + 4 = 0$:

(a) Find the rational roots, if any.
(b) Find the remaining roots. If they are irrational, find them to three significant-digit accuracy.

11. Search for one negative rational root of the rational polynomial equation $x^3 - 5x^2 + 6x - 2 = 0$. What is your conclusion?

12. Search for one positive rational root of the equation $2x^3 + 3x^2 + x + 6 = 0$. What is your conclusion?

In Problems 13 to 18: first search for the possible rational roots, depress the given equation for each rational root found, and then find all the roots of these equations:

13. $x^4 - 3x^3 + 7x^2 - 15x + 10 = 0$.   **17.** $x^3 - 9x^2 + 19x - 6 = 0$.
14. $x^4 - 3x^3 - 3x^2 + 3x + 2 = 0$.   **18.** $x^3 - 3x^2 - 20x + 32 = 0$.
15. $2x^4 + 5x^3 + 4x^2 + 5x + 2 = 0$.   **19.** $x^3 - 1 = 0$.
16. $2x^4 + 5x^3 + 5x^2 + 20x - 12 = 0$.   **20.** $3x^3 - 81 = 0$.

12

Probability

About the middle of the seventeenth century Chevalier de Méré asked the famous mathematician Blaise Pascal to consider a solution for this gambling problem:

On each play one of the two players of a game scores a point. The chances are equal that either player will score the point. A score of three wins the game, but the game must end when one player has one point and the other two points. Pascal concluded that the stakes should be split 3 to 1 in favor of the player who was ahead. Do you agree?

The **theory of probability** had its beginning with gambling problems like the preceding one. Over the past two centuries this theory and its implications in practical situations have become so important that today we find them being applied not only to gambling problems, but to all kinds of problems in the physical and social sciences and in the everyday activities of industry, business, and government.

Probability theory makes inductive reasoning and the outcomes of experiments more precise. The only thing that this text can do with this broad field of mathematical study is to present the essential mathematical concepts that undergird it.

12.1 PERMUTATIONS

In studying sets throughout Chapter 1 we were not concerned in any way with the possible different arrangements of the elements in a set. However, in using sets in connection with permutations, the emphasis is entirely on the arrangements of the elements. **In permutation, arrangements or order is all-important,** in fact, you do not have a permutation unless there is a different order of the elements of a set. Our immediate concern is to:

1. Find the count of the number of ways the elements in a set can be arranged or ordered.

2. Find methods and formulas to determine the number of ways the elements of a set can be grouped into subsets of the sets.

Before we attempt to order, or to count, the elements of a set, we need to give attention to some basic counting properties. These properties will be introduced by appropriate examples but will not be proved in this text.

12.1-1 The Count of the Number of Elements in a Set

As defined in Section 1.3-3 in Chapter 1, **a cardinal number represents the number of elements in a set.** Since a cardinal number n is associated with each set A, we will use the symbol $n(A)$ to denote the count of the number of elements in the set. That is, count of $n = n(A)$.

The expressions, **cardinal number,** *and the* **count** *will be used interchangeably* throughout the chapter.

Example: 12.1-1a.   If two sets are *disjoint*, show that the sum of the elements in sets A and B is equal to the number of elements in their union.

Let $n(A)$ denote the *count* of the number of elements in set A, and $n(B)$ denote the *count* (or the *cardinal number*) of the elements in set B. Then the cardinal number

$n(A)$ for set $A = \{a_1, a_2, a_3\} = 3$;
$n(B)$ for set $B = \{b_1, b_2, b_3, b_4\} = 4$;

and $n(A) + n(B) = 3 + 4 = 7$;

which is identical to the count of the elements of the union of A and B. This suggests the following property:

Property: 12.1-1a.   *If $A \cap B = \varnothing$, then $n(A \cup B) = n(A) + n(B)$.*

As indicated in Figure 12.1-1b below, two finite sets may not be disjoint. If this happens, how can the count of the sum of the elements be obtained?

Example: 12.1-1b.   Find the count of the elements if set $A = \{1, 2, 3, 4, 7\}$ and set $B = \{2, 5, 6, 7\}$.

In this example $n(A) = 5$ and $n(B) = 4$. But it is quite evident from Figure 12.1-1b that elements 2 and 7, in the intersection of set A and set B, should not be counted twice. Therefore, $n(A \cap B) = 2$ must be subtracted from $n(A) + n(B)$ to give

$n(A) + n(B) - n(A \cap B) = 5 + 4 - 2 = 7$.

The preceding example suggests this property:

Property: 12.1-1b.   *If $A \cap B \neq \varnothing$, then $n(A \cup B) = n(A) + n(B) - n(A \cap B)$.*

Our next problem is to find "the count of the elements" of a **Cartesian product** when the elements of two sets are given.

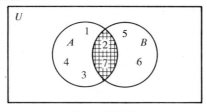

Figure 12.1-1b

Example: 12.1-1c. Find the count of the elements of the product set $(A \times B)$ given the two sets $A = \{1, 2\}$ and $B = \{r, s, t\}$, where r, s, t are real numbers.

From studying the Cartesian product of two finite sets in Chapter 3 (see Definition 3.2-1), we learned that the set of all possible ordered pairs of sets

$$A = \{1, 2\} \quad \text{and} \quad B = \{r, s, t\}$$

is $A \times B = \{(1, r), (1, s), (1, t), (2, r), (2, s), (2, t)\}$.

The first coordinate of each ordered pair of the Cartesian product is either 1 or 2, which makes $n(A) = 2$. For each first ordinate there are three second coordinates, making $n(B) = 3$. Thus, the correct total count of the ordered pairs of $A \times B$ is

$$n(A) \cdot n(B) = 2 \cdot 3 = 6.$$

This example suggests the following property:

Property: 12.1-1c.   *If set A and set B are finite sets, then*

$$n(A \times B) = n(A) \cdot n(B).$$

Property 12.1-1c holds for any number of sets, provided the sets are finite.

Example: 12.1-1d. Suppose that in a local salesroom a certain make of automobile is available in four different colors, three different kinds of hub caps, and two different body styles. How many different choices could one make in buying a car?

According to Property 12.1-1c,

$$n(A \times B \times C) = n(A) \cdot n(B) \cdot n(C)$$

$$\therefore n(A \times B \times C) = 4 \cdot 3 \cdot 2 = 24.$$

There are several ways of visualizing the thought processes involved in problems of this type. A commonly used device is the **tree diagram.** Let us start a tree diagram by first selecting the color C_1. For each C_1 we have three choices of hub caps, H_1, H_2, and H_3; and for each hub cap we have two body styles B_1 and B_2. Continuing in the same manner with colors C_2, C_3, and C_4, the tree diagram will look as shown in Figure 12.1-1c.

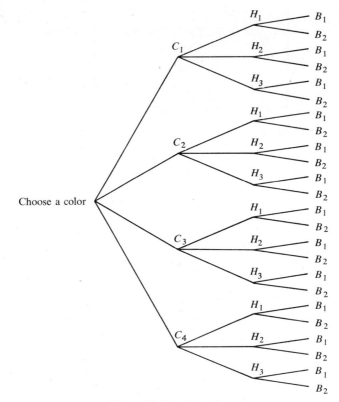

Figure 12.1-1c. Tree Diagram.

In some problems a good way to find the cardinal number of the permutations is to draw a tree diagram and count them. In other cases, simple formulas (which will next be derived) may be used. In many situations the following *fundamental counting principle* is best to use.

Property: 12.1-1d (The Fundamental Counting Principle).   *If one thing can be done in m_1 different ways and if, after it is done in one of these ways, a second thing can be done in m_2 different ways and if, after that is done, a third thing can be done m_3 different ways, and so on, then the total count of the different ways the things can be done is $m_1 \cdot m_2 \cdot m_3 \cdots$,*

12.1-2 Permutation Formulas

A finite set of elements is said to be **linearly ordered** if there is a first element, a second element, and so on. A linear ordering of set $A = \{a_1, a_2, a_3\}$ is

$$
\begin{array}{lll}
a_1a_2a_3 & a_2a_3a_1 & a_3a_2a_1 \\
a_1a_3a_2 & a_2a_1a_3 & a_3a_1a_2
\end{array}
\tag{M}
$$

Definition: 12.1-2a.   *A **permutation** of a finite set is a linear ordering of the elements of the set.*

According to Definition 12.1-2a, each of the linear orders of set A, as shown in (M), is a permutation. According to the fundamental principle of counting (Property 12.1-1d), the total count of permutations of

$\{a_1, a_2, a_3\}$ is $3 \cdot 2 \cdot 1 = 6$.

Because there is a functional relation between the permutation and n and r, we will use the symbol $P(n, r)$ to represent the number of distinct permutations of n different things taken r at a time. (Distinct means that no two things can be alike.)

Theorem: 12.1-2a. The number of distinct permutations of n elements taken r at a time is

$$P(n, r) = n(n - 1)(n - 2) \cdots (n - r + 1) \qquad (r \leq n).$$

PROOF: Since n elements are available, the first place in $P(n, r)$ can be filled n times. There remains $n - 1$ elements to fill the second place, $n - 2$ elements to fill the third place, and finally $n - (r - 1)$ or $n - r + 1$ elements to fill the last or rth place. Thus, by Property 12.1-1d the total count of distinct permutations is given by

$$P(n, r) = n(n - 1)(n - 2) \cdots (n - r + 1), \qquad (r \leq n). \tag{A}$$

By multiplying and dividing the right member of the preceding equation by $(n - r)!$ formula (A) may be written as

$$P(n, r) = \frac{n!}{(n - r)!}. \tag{A_1}$$

(See Chapter 6, Section 6.6-2 for the details on factorials.)

If in Theorem 12.1-2a $r = n$, then $P(n, r)$ becomes $P(n, n)$ and we have the following corollary.

Corollary 12.1-2a. The number of distinct permutations of n elements taken n at a time is

$$P(n, n) = n(n - 1)(n - 2) \cdots (n - r + 1)(n - r) \cdots 3 \cdot 2 \cdot 1, \tag{A_2}$$
or $P(n, n) = n!$

Example: 12.1-2a. How many different numbers can be found for the digits 1, 2, 3, 4, and 5 if no digits are repeated and

(a) $r = 3$?   (b) $r = 4$?   (c) $r = 5$?

(a) Using formula (A): $P(5, 3) = 5 \cdot 4 \cdot 3 = 60$.

Using formula (A_1): $\qquad P(5, 3) = \dfrac{5!}{(5 - 3)!} = \dfrac{5 \cdot 4 \cdot 3 \cdot 2 \cdot 1}{1 \cdot 2} = 60$.

(b) Using formula (A_1): $P(5, 4) = \dfrac{5!}{(5-4)!} = \dfrac{5 \cdot 4 \cdot 3 \cdot 2}{1} = 120.$

(c) Using formula (A_2): $P(5, 5) = 5 \cdot 4 \cdot 3 \cdot 2 \cdot 1 = 120.$

Using formula (A_1): $P(5, 5) = \dfrac{5!}{(5-5)!} = \dfrac{5!}{0!} = \dfrac{5 \cdot 4 \cdot 3 \cdot 2 \cdot 1}{1} = 120.$

Notice that the count of permutations in (b) where 5 digits are permuted 4 at a time is identical to the count of the permutations in (c) where 5 digits are permuted 5 at a time. How can this be possible?

Let us now face the problem: *What if some of the letters in a word are identical?*

Example: 12.1-2b.   How many code words can be obtained from the word "TEETER"?

If the "T's" and the "E's" were distinguishable from each other, the number of permutations would by $(A)_2$ be

$$P(n, n) = P(6,6) = 6 \cdot 5 \cdot 4 \cdot 3 \cdot 2 \cdot 1 = 720.$$

Since the "T's" cannot be distinguishable, one from the other, they can be arranged among themselves 2! times without altering a code word. Likewise, since we cannot distinguish one "E" from another, the "E's" can be arranged among themselves 3! times without altering a code word. Then, if P_d is used to denote the number of distinguishable permutations for the word "TEETER" there results:

$$(2!)(3!)P_d = 6!$$

and $P_d = \dfrac{6!}{(2!)(3!)} = \dfrac{6 \cdot 5 \cdot 4 \cdot 3 \cdot 2 \cdot 1}{(1 \cdot 2)(1 \cdot 2 \cdot 3)} = \mathbf{60}.$

The preceding example suggests this theorem:

Theorem: 12.1-2b.   If P_d is the number of distinct permutations of a set of n things taken n at a time where n_1 things are alike, n_2 things are alike, and so on, then

$$P_d = \dfrac{n!}{n_1!\, n_2! \cdots}.$$

Our next problem has to do with the number of permutations of n elements of a set around a circle. This number of permutations will be different from the number of permutations of n elements arranged in a row because **in arranging objects around a circle there is no unique first position.** The relative position of the elements is not altered by rotating them around the circle.

Example: 12.1-2c.   Find the number of different ways four people can be seated at a round table.

Figure 12.1-2c shows that the relative position of the four people is the same for all four cases. Thus, *the solution of the problem demands that some one person be selected and seated in one of the chairs.* Then there remain 3 people to be arranged in all possible ways in the remaining three chairs.

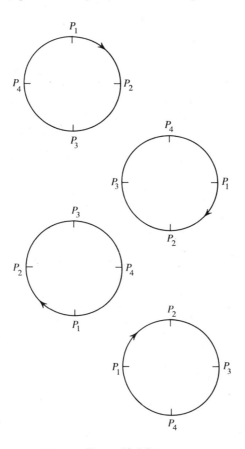

Figure 12.1-2c

In general, *to place n objects around a circle where there is no fixed first position, place the first object arbitrarily, thus leaving n − 1 places to assign the remaining n − 1 objects.* Then (1) · $P(n − 1, n − 1) = (n − 1)!$ is the number of circular (or cyclical) permutations, and the following theorem has been established.

Theorem: 12.1-2c. If $P(n − 1, n − 1)$ represents the total number of cyclic permutations of n things taken n at a time, then

$$P(n − 1, n − 1) = (n − 1)!.$$

EXERCISE 12.A

1. If $A = \{2, 5, 7, 11\}$ and $B = \{13, 17, 19\}$, find $n(A \cup B)$.

2. What is the value of $n(A \cap B)$ for Problem 1?

3. If $A = \{h, i, j, r, t\}$ and $B = \{i, m, r, q\}$ what is the cardinal number of $n(A \cap B)$?

4. Find $n(A \cup B)$ for Problem 3.

5. Given sets $A = \{1, 2, 3\}$ and $B = \{2, 3, 4\}$, find $n(A \times B)$.

6. What is $n(A \times B)$ if $n(A) = 6$ and $n(B) = 10$?

7. Find $n(A \times B \times C)$ for the sets $A = \{m, n\}$, $B = \{1, 2, 3\}$, $C = \{g, h\}$.

8. What is the cardinal number of $n(A \times B \times C)$ for the sets $A = \{1, 2, 3, 4\}$, $B = \{m, n\}$, $C = \{6\}$?

9. Draw a tree diagram for Problem 7.

10. Draw a tree diagram for Problem 8.

11. A man has five pairs of trousers, six different colored shirts, and three pairs of shoes. How many different outfits does he have?

12. A woman has four skirts, six sweaters and seven different pairs of shoes. How many different outfits can she make up?

13. $P(n, r)$ is defined for what values of n? what values of r?

14. Why is it true that $P(n, r)$ is a function of n? a function of r?

15. In how many ways can the letters in the word "argument" be arranged?

16. Find the cardinal number that represents the possible permutations of the letters in the word "amplitude."

17. In how many different ways can six students be arranged in a row?

18. In how many different ways can six students be seated in six chairs at a round table?

19. Twelve people are to be placed around a round table. How many different permutations are possible?

20. How many four-letter code words can be obtained from the word "normalized?"

21. Find the cardinal number for the different permutations of the letters of the word "negotiable," taken all at a time.

22. Find the different permutations of the word "Kissimmi," using all the letters.

23. A family of four enters an airplane which has fifteen available seats. In how many different ways can the family be seated?

24. In how many ways can six people be arranged in a row if two people insist on sitting together?

25. A baseball coach puts his best batter in fourth position and his weakest batter in seventh position. How many ways can he line up this particular 9-man team for batting?

26. From a basketball squad of 12 players only three can play center. How many possible starting line-ups does the coach have?

27. Prove that $P(n, r) = \dfrac{n!}{(n - r)!}$.

28. Prove that $P(n, n - 1) = P(n, n)$.

29. Given that $2P(n, 3) = P(n, 5)$. Find n.

30. Solve $5P(n, 4) = P(n, 5)$ for n.

31. How many two-digit numbers less than 99 can be formed from the digits 2, 5, 6, 7 if repetition of digits is not permitted? if repetition of digits is permitted?

32. If the books in each subject field are to be kept together, in how many ways can five mathematics books, four English books, and three psychology books be arranged on a shelf?

12.2 COMBINATIONS

In contrast to permutations which demand all possible arrangements, **combinations disregard order.** *Whether or not two combinations are the same depends entirely on whether or not the two combinations are made up of the same elements;* the ordering of the elements of a combination is ignored. For example,

$\{a, b, c\}$ and $\{a, c, b\}$ are the same combination,

because they are made up of the same elements. The fact that $\{a, b, c\}$ can be ordered to form six permutations has nothing to do with combinations.

$\{a, b, c\}$ and $\{a, b, d\}$ are two different combinations,

because the element c in $\{a, b, c\}$ has been replaced by the element d in the second set.

From our study of permutations we know that set $A = \{a, b, c, d\}$ has $(4)(3)(2) = 24$ different permutations, provided that any three of the four elements are considered. If, however, the order of elements is disregarded, the only possible combinations of $A = \{a, b, c, d\}$ consisting of subsets of any three elements are

$$\{a, b, c\}, \{a, b, d\}, \{a, c, d\}, \{b, c, d\}. \tag{N}$$

Definition: 12.2-a. *The number of distinct sets of r elements obtained from a set of n elements, with order of elements disregarded, is called a* **combination.**

We will denote the number of combinations that can be formed from n elements taken r at a time in two ways: We will use $C(n, r)$ because of its similarity with $P(n, r)$. We will also use the more modern **base-order form** $\binom{n}{r}$, where n *is the base* of the combinatory number and r *is its order*. There are many other forms in use, such as nCr, $C\binom{n}{r}$, $C_{(n, r)}$ and so on.

Referring back to (N), the four combinations obtained from the set $A = \{a, b, c, d\}$ when three of the four elements were considered at a time, you can readily see that each combination can be arranged in $3!$ permutations. Thus, the number of combinations multiplied by $3!$ is equal to the total number of permutations. That is,

$3! C(4, 3) = P(4, 3)$.

More generally, if *each combination* consisting of r elements can be arranged in $P(r, r) = r!$ ways, then the total number of permutations of n elements taken r at a time is

$P(n, r) = r! C(n, r)$.

Hence, the theorem for combinations is:

Theorem: 12.2-a.   The number of combinations of n elements taken r at a time is

$$C(n, r) = \frac{P(n, r)}{r!} \qquad (0 \le r \le n).$$

Theorem 12.2-a declares that the number of combinations (r-element subsets) of an n-element set A is obtained by counting the total number of permutations of set A taken r at a time and then dividing that count by the distinct permutation of one of the combinations.

Since $\binom{n}{r}$ and $C(n, r)$ are to be used interchangeably so that you can come to feel "at home" with both notations, we can write

$$\binom{n}{r} = C(n, r) = \frac{P(n, r)}{r!} = \frac{(n)(n-1)(n-2)(n-3)\cdots n-r+1}{r!}. \qquad (B)$$

If the numerator and the denominator of (B) are multiplied by $(n - r)!$, the following formula, equivalent to (B), results:

$$C(n, r) = \binom{n}{r} = \frac{P(n, r)}{r!} = \frac{n!}{r!(n-r)!}. \qquad (B_1)$$

It is interesting to note that $n!/r!(n-r)!$ is identical to the number we obtained as the coefficient of the $r + 1$ term when we expanded the binomial formula in Section 6.6-3, Chapter 6.

Example: 12.2-a.   Calculate the number of combinations of 10 objects taken 5 at a time.

Actually, the problem is calling for the number of the 5-element subsets obtained from the 10-object set.

$$\binom{n}{r} = C(n, r) = \frac{P(n, r)}{r!},$$

and $$\binom{10}{5} = C(10, 5) = \frac{P(10, 5)}{5!} = \frac{10 \cdot 9 \cdot 8 \cdot 7 \cdot 6}{1 \cdot 2 \cdot 3 \cdot 4 \cdot 5} = \mathbf{252}.$$

Example: 12.2-b.   How many different amounts of money can be obtained by selecting four coins from a cent, a nickel, a dime, a quarter, and a half-dollar?

This is a combination problem in which you are to find all possible 4-element subsets. It is assumed, of course, that you are not in any way interested in the arrangements of the elements within a subset.

$$\binom{n}{r} = C(n, r) = \frac{P(n, r)}{r!} = \frac{n!}{r!(n-r)!}$$

and $\dbinom{5}{4} = C(5, 4) = \dfrac{P(5, 4)}{4!} = \dfrac{5!}{4!(5 - 4)!} = \dfrac{5 \cdot 4 \cdot 3 \cdot 2 \cdot 1}{1 \cdot 2 \cdot 3 \cdot 4 \cdot 1} = 5.$

Check the result of this problem by actually determining the different amounts of money you can get by using a cent, a nickel, a dime, a quarter and a half-dollar, taking any four at a time.

From the preceding examples one can observe that each time a distinct set of r elements is selected, a distinct set of $n - r$ elements is not chosen. For example, when we select the r-set consisting of a cent, a nickel, a dime and a quarter, there remains a set consisting of the half-dollar. This suggests the following:

Theorem: 12.2-b. If $C(n, r)$, then $C(n, n - r)$, where n and r are nonnegative integers and $n \geq r$.

PROOF: $C(n, r) = \dfrac{n!}{r!(n - r)!}.$ $[(B_1)$ under Section 12.2]

Substituting $n - r$ for r, we get

$$C(n, n - r) = \frac{n!}{(n - r)![n - (n - r)]!} = \frac{n!}{(n - r)!r!}.$$

Therefore, $C(n, r) = C(n, n - r).$ (Transitive postulate)

Using the same argument, it would follow that

$$\binom{n}{r} = \binom{n}{n - r}.$$

Example: 12.2-c.   How many 7-man committees can be chosen from 9 men?

First, we will use $C(n, r)$; then we will use $C(n, n - r)$. Note how much shorter the second form is for this particular problem. *The $C(n, n - r)$ form will always be easier where the number of elements in the r-set is more than half the number of elements in the n-set.* For example,

$$\binom{9}{7} = C(9, 7) = \frac{P(9, 7)}{7!} = \frac{9 \cdot 8 \cdot 7 \cdot 6 \cdot 5 \cdot 4 \cdot 3}{1 \cdot 2 \cdot 3 \cdot 4 \cdot 5 \cdot 6 \cdot 7} = 36;$$

or $\dbinom{9}{9 - 7} = C(9, 2) = \dfrac{P(9, 2)}{2!} = \dfrac{9 \cdot 8}{1 \cdot 2} = 36.$ (This is less work.)

Example: 12.2-d.   How many different hands of five cards can be dealt from a deck of fifty-two cards?

$$\binom{n}{r} = \frac{n!}{r!(n - r)!}.$$

$$\binom{52}{5} = \frac{52!}{5!47!} = \frac{52 \cdot 51 \cdot 50 \cdot 49 \cdot 48}{1 \cdot 2 \cdot 3 \cdot 4 \cdot 5} = 2,598,960.$$

12.2-1 The Special Combination $C(n, 0)$

There is no difficulty in evaluating combinatory numbers of the form $C(n, r)$. and since we know from Definition 6.6-2b, Chapter 6, that

$$0! = 1,$$

we can easily show that

$$C(n, n) = \frac{n!}{n!(n - n)!} = \frac{n!}{n! \cdot 0!} = \frac{n!}{n!} = 1.$$

But what value should be given to $C(n, 0)$? The symbol $C(n, 0)$ infers that there is only one way *not to take* any elements from a set of n elements.

Theorem: 12.2-1. The number of combinations of n elements taken zero at a time is one.

PROOF: Since $\qquad C(n, r) = \dfrac{n!}{r!(n - r)!} \qquad$ [(B_1) under Section 12.2]

and $\qquad\qquad r = 0, \qquad\qquad$ (Given)

then $\qquad C(n, 0) = \dfrac{n!}{0!(n - 0)} = \dfrac{n!}{1(n)!} = 1.$ (Definition 6.6-2b)

Therefore, $C(n, 0) = 1$.

12.2-2 Coefficients of the Binomial Formula in Terms of Combinations

If we refer back to Sections 6.6, 6.6-1, 6.6-2, and 6.6-3 in Chapter 6, we can observe that the expansion of $(a + b)^n$ was the series

$$a^n + \frac{n}{1!}a^{n-1}b + \frac{n(n - 1)}{2!}a^{n-2}b^2 + \cdots + \frac{(n) \cdots (n - r + 1)}{r!}a^{n-r}b^r$$

$$+ \cdots + b^n. \tag{H}$$

We can readily see that

$(a + b)^1 = a + b$, the sum of **one-lettered** products;
$(a + b)^2 = aa + 2ab + bb$, the sum of **two-lettered** products;
$(a + b)^3 = aaa + 3aab + 3abb + bbb$, the sum of **three-lettered** products.

A continuation of this type of expansion suggests the following theorem, which is known as the **binomial theorem.**

Theorem: 12.2-2a. For $n \in N$ and $r \in N_n$, the expansion of $(a + b)^n$ is the sum of all n-lettered products consisting only of a's and b's, with appropriate coefficients. Symbolically,

$$(a + b)^n = \sum_{r=0}^{n} C(n, r)a^{n-r}b^r. \qquad \text{(Binomial theorem)}$$

PROOF: From any one of the n-lettered products in the expansion of $(a + b)^n$ one is free to choose either a or b. If b is chosen from r of the n factors, as in the $(r + 1)$ term shown in (H), then a is automatically the choice from the remaining $n - r$ factors and the resulting product of the a's and b's would be

$$a^{n-r}b^r, \qquad r = \{0, 1, 2, \ldots, n\}.$$

Further, according to Theorem 12.2-b, the r choices of b and, similarly, the $n - r$ choices of a, can be made in $C(n, r)$ ways. Thus, it follows that there are $C(n, r)$ products of $a^{n-r}b^r$ in the binomial expansion of $(a + b)^n$ and that when they are collected they form the expression

$$C(n, r)a^{n-r}b^r, \qquad (C)$$

which is the $(r + 1)$ **general term of the binomial expansion**.

By substituting $r = 0, 1, 2, 3, \ldots, n$ into $C(n, r)a^{n-r}b^r$, we are able to generate

The Expansion of the Binomial Theorem

$$(a + b)^n = C(n, 0)a^n + C(n, 1)a^{n-1}b + C(n, 2)a^{n-2}b^2 + \cdots$$

$$+ C(n, r)a^{n-r}b^r + \cdots + C(n, n - 1)ab^{n-1}$$

$$+ C(n, n)b^n. \qquad (D)$$

Evaluating the combination coefficients in (D), the following expansion is identical to (H) in Section 6.6-3.

$$(a + b)^n = a^n + \frac{n}{1!}a^{n-1}b + \frac{n(n - 2)}{2!}a^{n-2}b^2 + \cdots$$

$$+ \frac{n(n - 1)(n - 2) \cdots n - r + 1}{r!} a^{n-r}b^r + \cdots$$

$$+ nab^{n-1} + b^n. \qquad (H)$$

Also by substituting the *base-order symbols* for the *combination symbols* in (D) we obtain the following very neat ways of writing the binomial expansion:

$$(a + b)^n = \binom{n}{0} a^n + \binom{n}{1} a^{n-1}b + \binom{n}{2}a^{n-2}b^2 + \cdots + \binom{n}{r}a^{n-r}b^r + \cdots$$

$$+ \binom{n}{n - 1}ab^{n-1} + \binom{n}{n}b^n \qquad (E)$$

or $(a + b)^n = \sum\limits_{r=0}^{n} \binom{n}{r} a^{n-r} b^r$.

12.2-3 Total Combinations of a Set of *n* Elements

If we let $a = 1$ and $b = 1$ in the binomial expansion shown in (D), the following very important relation is obtained:

$$(1 + 1)^n = C(n, 0)1^n + C(n, 1)1^n + C(n, 2)1^n + \cdots + C(n, n - 1)1^n$$
$$+ C(n, n)1^n,$$

and $2^n = 1 + C(n, 1) + C(n, 2) + \cdots + C(n, n - 1) + C(n, n).$ (F)

To use the relation (F) as a counting device we will rearrange it in this manner:

$$C(n, 1) + C(n, 2) + \cdots + C(n, n - 1) + C(n, n) = 2^n - 1. \qquad (G)$$

Relationship (G) shows that the total number of subsets of a set of *n* elements taken 1 at a time, 2 at a time, 3 at a time, and so on, up to *n* at a time, is equal to

$$2^n - 1 \qquad\qquad\qquad\qquad\qquad \text{(Counting formula)}$$

Example: 12.2-3a.   Find the different amounts of money that can be obtained from a cent, a nickel, a dime, a quarter, and a half-dollar.

To see how (G) works, use both the expansion and the formula.

$$C(n, 1) + C(n, 2) + C(n, 3) + C(n, 4) + C(n, 5) = 2^n - 1.$$
$$C(5, 1) + C(5, 2) + C(5, 3) + C(5, 4) + C(5, 5) = 2^5 - 1,$$
$$5\ \ +\ \ 10\ \ +\ \ 10\ \ +\ \ 5\ \ +\ \ 1\ \ = 32 - 1,$$
and $31 = 31.$

12.2-4 Mutually Exclusive Events

In counting problems it frequently happens that we are concerned with events where not more than one of the events can happen at a time. *If the occurrence of one event excludes the possibility of occurrence of the others, we say that the events are mutually exclusive.* Mutually exclusive events lead to this very important principle of counting.

Definition: 12.2-4a.   *If sets A and B are disjoint so that set $A \cap B = \emptyset$, then the two sets are said to be* **mutually exclusive.**

If one set of **mutually exclusive events** *occurs in r ways, another set in s ways, another in t ways, and so on, then the events will occur in $r + s + t + \cdots$ ways.*

Example: 12.2-4a.   If two baseball games, three lectures, and a track meet are all scheduled for two o'clock on a Friday afternoon, how many ways does one have to choose his afternoon entertainment?

Since he can go to any one of two baseball games, any one of three lectures, and any one of two track meets, he has

$3 + 2 + 2 = 7$ **possible choices.**

When one choice is definitely made the other six are definitely excluded.

EXERCISE 12.B

1. What is the basic difference between permutations and combinations?

2. When are two combinations distinct?

3. What is the meaning of the symbol $\binom{n}{r}$?

4. Explain why it is true that $\binom{n}{r} = \binom{n}{n-r}$.

5. In how many ways can a committee of three be selected from 15 people?

6. A bag contains 6 different coins. How many different amounts of money can be obtained if three coins are drawn from the bag at a time?

7. Which value of n makes $C(n, 8) = C(n, 4)$?

8. Find the value of n that makes $C(n, 11) = C(n, 7)$.

9. Find the number represented by $\binom{12}{5}$.

10. Determine the number represented by $\binom{9}{9-4}$.

11. Find a set of values for n and r if $C(n, r) = 5$ and $P(n, r) = 120$.

12. If $C(n, r) = 3$ and $P(n, r) = 6$, find a set of values for n and r.

13. If each color is used only once, in how many ways can 6 colors be used to color four different countries on a map?

14. A professor tells his class that he will accept solutions of any 15 problems selected from a 20-problem quiz. In how many ways can 15 problems be selected?

15. Find the total number of distinct lines passing through 6 points in a plane if no 3 of the points lie on the same straight line.

16. Find the total number of distinct lines passing through n distinct points in a plane if no 3 of the points are on the same straight line.

17. In a 10-problem quiz the instructions are to answer any 4 of the first 6 problems and any 2 of the last 4 problems. In how many ways can a student make his selection?

18. In a 10-problem quiz in how many ways could a student select 6 problems if he must select 3 problems from the first 5 problems and 3 problems from the last 5?

19. In the toss of 6 coins in how many ways can the coins show exactly 4 heads? at least 2 heads?

20. In the toss of 8 coins in how many ways can the coins show exactly 6 heads? at least 6 heads?

21. Write a formula that gives the number of subsets of set A of n elements.

22. Write a formula that will give the total possible distinct combinations of one or more elements that can be selected from n elements.

23. In how many ways can a committee of one or more people be selected from 7 people?

24. How many different subsets can be obtained from a set of 7 elements?

25. A committee of 2 boys and 2 girls is to be selected from 9 boys and 12 girls. In how many ways can this committee be selected?

26. In a football squad of 36 men, 4 play quarter back only, 9 play any backfield position other than quarter back, the rest play any line position. How many football teams can be formed?

27. On a Saturday afternoon there are 2 football games being played, three good movies showing, and three bridge parties scheduled. In how many ways could one choose to spend the afternoon if only one choice is to made?

28. In how many ways can a man going on a trip select 3 ties from his 12 ties, 5 shirts from his 8 shirts, and 4 pairs of socks from his 10 pairs of socks?

29. Show that $\binom{n+1}{m+1} = \binom{n}{m} \frac{n+1}{m+1}$.

30. Show that $\binom{n+1}{m} = \binom{n}{m} \frac{n+1}{n-m+1}$.

12.3 ELEMENTARY THEORY OF PROBABILITY

Probability as used in mathematics is a technical word. *Probability is a mathematical procedure that makes it possible to interpret in a numerical way experiments that involve the elements of chance.*

Definition: 12.3. *An **experiment** is an activity that can be repeated a finite number of times under specified conditions.*

Primarily, probability is concerned with experiments whose data do not lead to conclusions that can be stated with a certainty. For example, it may be important to have dependable answers to questions such as these:

1. What is the probability that a man will live to age 70?
2. What is the probability that a woman will die during her 70th year?
3. What is the probability that the rainfall in Washington, D.C. will be more than 15 inches during the month of June?
4. What is the probability that it will snow in Florida in December?

12.3-1 Finite Sample Spaces and Events

In this section an attempt will be made to clarify certain words and phrases that are used in discussing probability theory and the problems of chance.

The phrases **equally likely** and **equally probable** will be considered as undefined terms in the same sense that "point" and "line" are undefined in geometry.

When each member of a set of objects has an *equally likely* chance of being selected, it is called a **random choice** or a **random sample.**

For the time being the word **outcome** will be used to refer to the consequence of an action. Later we will define outcome in relation to a **sample space.**

Let us assume that a coin is tossed. It would seem *equally likely* that the outcome of the toss would be a head or a tail, provided

(a) no bias was introduced in handling the coin, and

(b) the coin was structurally perfect.

Representing heads by *H* and tails by *T*, *the total possible outcomes of tossing a single coin is* represented by the set

$$S = \{H, T\},$$

and is called the **sample space** or **universal set** of the experiment. The **cardinal number** of this particular sample space **is 2.**

If two coins are tossed, one after the other, the total number of possible outcomes for the experiment is shown by the sample space

$$S = \{HH, HT, TH, TT\},$$

and the **cardinal number** of the sample space is **4**.

Suppose in tossing two coins one is only concerned with the outcomes possible when the two coins either fall alike or not alike. The sample space would then be limited in this manner:

$$S_1 = \{\textbf{alike, not alike}\}.$$

As happened with *S*, each outcome of the experiment would correspond exactly to one element of S_1.

Apparently, as shown by *S* and S_1, **an experiment** such as the tossing of two coins may have more than one sample space. It is important that you understand that *it is the kind of outcome called for in a given experiment* that determines the content of the sample space.

Definition: 12.3-1a. *The* **sample space** *S of an experiment is a set of all possible outcomes of the experiment.*

Definition: 12.3-1b. *A* **sample point** *is an element or an outcome in a sample space of an experiment.*

Definition: 12.3-1c. *Each element or sample point of S is called an* **outcome.**

Definition: 12.3-1d. *An* **event** *E is a subset of the sample space S.*

12.3-2 Probability Defined

Examples which will lead to progressively more inclusive definitions of probability will be presented. The final definition will be strictly postulational in nature and will be sufficiently general to include all the definitions that have preceded it.

The notion of probability which we plan to develop is this:

If a thing can successfully happen in *n* ways and fail in *m* ways, then the probability that the event will successfully happen is denoted by *P(E)* and is expressed by the formula

$$P(E) = \frac{n}{n+m}.$$

Example: 12.3-2a. If a structurally perfect die (dice) is tossed in an unbiased manner, find its sample space, the cardinal number of its sample space, the cardinal number of its event, and the probability of the event.

In one toss of the die any one of six possible faces is *equally likely* to turn up. Moreover, if the die is tossed a large number of times, each of the six faces is expected to turn up approximately $\frac{1}{6}$ of the time.

The sample space for this experiment is $S = \{1, 2, 3, 4, 5, 6\}$, where the numerals represent the dots on the faces. The **cardinal number** of S is **6**.

Event E for the experiment may be represented by $E = x$, where the domain of x is the set consisting of the elements of the sample space S. The **cardinal number** of E is **1**.

The two preceding paragraphs establish what our intuition had already suggested; namely, that the probability of the event showing a particular face is

$$P(E) = \frac{1}{6}.$$

This leads to our first definition of probability.

Definition: 12.3-2a. *If n is the cardinal number of a sample space S of an experiment, and if the sample points are equally likely and no bias is involved, then the **probability** of involving any one of the sample points is*

$$P(E) = \frac{1}{n}.$$

In tossing a die suppose we would like to know the probability that one toss would turn up an odd number of dots. In this case the event E would be a subset of the sample space and would contain more than one sample point, that is, $E = \{1, 3, 5\}$ and $n(E) = 3$.

Since for the one toss of the die $n(S) = 6$ and $n(E) = 3$, the probability that one toss will turn up an odd number is

$$P(E) = \frac{n(E)}{n(S)} = \frac{3}{6} = \frac{1}{2}.$$

Thus, our next definition of probability is

Definition: 12.3-2b. *For any discrete, finite, nonempty sample space of an experiment, the **probability** of an event successfully happening is*

$$P(E) = \frac{n(E)}{n(S)}.$$

If it is completely impossible for an event to happen, then E is empty, that is, $E = \varnothing$ and

$$P(E) = \frac{n(E)}{n(S)} \quad \text{becomes} \quad P(\varnothing) = \frac{n(\varnothing)}{n(S)} = 0.$$

If all possible outcomes of the sample spaces are certain to happen, then $E = S$ and

$$P(E) = \frac{n(E)}{n(S)} \quad \text{becomes} \quad P(S) = \frac{n(S)}{n(S)} = 1.$$

From the facts that $P(\varnothing) = 0$ and $P(S) = 1$, it follows that the measure of all probabilities are properly expressed by

$$0 \le P(E) \le 1.$$

One, diminished by the probability that an event can happen, gives the probability that that event will fail. Letting $P(\sim E)$ denote the probability of the failure of an event, we can write

$$1 - P(E) = P(\sim E)$$
or $P(E) + P(\sim E) = 1,$

which implies that *the probability of an event happening plus the probability of that event failing is a certainty*. This makes good mathematical sense.

Definition: 12.3-2c.   *When the elements of the domain of E are sets and the elements of the corresponding range n(E) are real numbers, there exists a function called the* **set function.**

The **domain** of the set function of the sample space $S = \{a, b, c\}$ is all the possible subsets of S. That is,

$$\{\varnothing, \{a\}, \{b\}, \{c\}, \{a, b\}, \{a, c\}, \{b, c\}, \{a, b, c\}\},$$

and the **range** consists of the corresponding cardinal numbers of the subsets as shown in the following table:

E	$\varnothing$	$\{a\}$	$\{b\}$	$\{c\}$	$\{a, b\}$	$\{a, c\}$	$\{b, c\}$	$\{a, b, c\}$
$n(E)$	0	1	1	1	2	2	2	3

Thus, the **range** of the **set function** (see Definition 12.3-2c) is $\{0, 1, 2, 3\}$.

We are now ready to present a *postulational definition for probability.*

Definition: 12.3-2d.   *If S denotes any discrete finite nonempty sample space of an experiment and P is a real valued function with its domain the set of all subsets of S, then P* **is a probability function** *if and only if the following postulates are satisfied*

Postulate 1: $0 \le P(E) \le 1$ $(E \subseteq S)$;
Postulate 2: $P(S) = P(E) + P(\sim E) = 1$;
Postulate 3:   *If* $E_1, E_2, E_3, \ldots \in S$ *and* $E_1, E_2, E_3, \ldots$ *is a finite sequence*

of disjoint subsets of S, then

$$P(E_1 \cup E_2 \cup E_3 \cup \cdots) = P(E_1) + P(E_2) + P(E_3) + \cdots.$$

This postulational probability definition is, of course, the most general and the most dependable of the three definitions developed. In fact, it can be used to develop as special cases the following previously stated definitions:

1. The probability for any one of a set of n mutually exclusive, equally likely, events is $P(E) = 1/n$.
2. The probability for any discrete, finite, nonempty sample spaces is $P(E) = n(E)/(n(S)$.

Example: 12.3-2b. If from a bag that contains 4 red balls, 5 white balls, and 6 blue balls, 6 balls are pulled at one time, find the probability that a pair of balls of each color is obtained.

The cardinal number of the sample space S is obtained by finding the combinations of 15 balls taken 6 at a time.

$$n(S) = \binom{15}{6} = \frac{15 \cdot 14 \cdot 13 \cdot 12 \cdot 11 \cdot 10}{1 \cdot 2 \cdot 3 \cdot 4 \cdot 5 \cdot 6} = 5{,}005 \text{ possibilities.}$$

Two red balls can be drawn from 4 red balls in

$$n(E_1) = \binom{4}{2} = \frac{4 \cdot 3}{1 \cdot 2} = 6 \text{ ways.}$$

Two white balls can be drawn from 5 white balls in

$$n(E_2) = \binom{5}{2} = \frac{5 \cdot 4}{1 \cdot 2} = 10 \text{ ways.}$$

Two blue balls can be drawn from 6 blue balls in

$$n(E_3) = \binom{6}{2} = \frac{6 \cdot 5}{1 \cdot 2} = 15 \text{ ways.}$$

By the fundamental counting property (see Property 12.1-1d),

$$n(E) = n(E_1) \cdot n(E_2) \cdot n(E_3).$$

Therefore, $n(E) = (6)(10)(15) = 900$ ways, and

$$P(E) = \frac{n(E)}{n(S)} = \frac{900}{5{,}005} = \frac{180}{1{,}001}.$$

Example: 12.3-2c. If two dice are tossed, what is the probability that the sum of the dots turned up is 8 or more than 8?

If S_1 represents the set of possible outcomes for one die and S_2 the possible outcomes for the other die, then $n(S_1) = 6$ and $n(S_2) = 6$. The total outcomes for a toss of the two dice is the Cartesian product of S_1 and S_2,

$n(S_1 \times S_2) = n(S_1) \cdot n(S_2) = 6 \times 6 = 36.$ (See Property 12.1-1c)

Our next concern is to find the count of the event

$E = \{(e_1, e_2) \mid e_1 + e_2 \geq 8)\},$

where e_1 is the count of the dots on the first die turned up and e_2 is the count of the dots on the second die turned up. The total possible ordered pairs are

						e_2	
(1, 6)	(2, 6)	(3, 6)	(4, 6)	(5, 6)	(6, 6)	6	
(1, 5)	(2, 5)	(3, 5)	(4, 5)	(5, 5)	(6, 5)	5	
(1, 4)	(2, 4)	(3, 4)	(4, 4)	(5, 4)	(6, 5)	4	
(1, 3)	(2, 3)	(3, 3)	(4, 3)	(5, 3)	(6, 3)	3	
(1, 2)	(2, 2)	(3, 2)	(4, 2)	(5, 2)	(6, 2)	2	
(1, 1)	(2, 1)	(3, 1)	(4, 1)	(5, 1)	(6, 1)	1	
						0	1 2 3 4 5 6 e_1

Figure 12.3-2c

Figure 12.3-2c shows a point for each possible ordered pair. It also shows the 15 points in the upper right-hand corner that represent the outcomes that satisfy the relationship $e_1 + e_2 \geq 8$. Since $n(S) = 36$ and $n(E) = 15$, then

$$P(E) = \frac{n(E)}{n(S)} = \frac{15}{36} = \frac{5}{12}.$$

Example: 12.3-2d.   In selecting a committee of three people from 7 men and 4 women, what is the probability that

(a) the committee will be composed of all men?
(b) the committee will contain 2 men and 1 woman?
(c) the committee will contain 1 man and 2 women?
(d) the committee will be composed of all women?

What is the sum of the probabilities for (a), (b), (c), and (d)?

(a) $n(E_a) = \binom{7}{3} = \dfrac{7 \cdot 6 \cdot 5}{1 \cdot 2 \cdot 3} = 35$ ways to get all men;

$n(S) = \binom{11}{3} = \dfrac{11 \cdot 10 \cdot 9}{1 \cdot 2 \cdot 3} = 165$ possible outcomes;

$p(E_a) = \dfrac{35}{165}.$

(b) $n(E_b) = \binom{7}{2}\binom{4}{1} = \dfrac{7 \cdot 6 \cdot 4}{1 \cdot 2 \cdot 1} = 84$ ways to get 2 men;

$p(E_b) = \dfrac{84}{165}.$

(c) $n(E_c) = \binom{4}{2}\binom{7}{1} = \dfrac{4 \cdot 3 \cdot 7}{1 \cdot 2 \cdot 1} = 42$ ways to get 2 women;

$p(E_c) = \dfrac{42}{165}.$

(d) $n(E_d) = \binom{4}{3} = \dfrac{4 \cdot 3 \cdot 2}{1 \cdot 2 \cdot 3} = 4$ ways to get all women;

$P(E_d) = \dfrac{4}{165}.$

$$P(E_a) + P(E_b) + P(E_c) + P(E_d) = \dfrac{35 + 84 + 42 + 4}{165} = 1.$$

The last statement shows that it is a certainty that all the possible ways of forming a three-person committee from the data given have been considered.

12.3-3 Mathematical Expectation

Definition: 12.3-3a.   *If the probability that an event will occur is P and if it occurs M dollars will be paid to the player, then the **value of the expectation** is PM dollars.*

Example: 12.3-3.   Find the value of a player's expectation if he is to receive $72 provided the sum of the dots turned up by one toss of two dice is a 2 or a 3 or a 12.

The total outcomes for the throw of two dice is $n(S) = 36$.

The possibility of turning up a 2 is $n(E_1) = \dfrac{1}{36}.$

The possibility of turning up a 3 is $n(E_2) = \dfrac{2}{36}.$

The possibility of turning up a 12 is $n(E_3) = \dfrac{1}{36}.$

Then $P(E) = \dfrac{n(E)}{n(S)} = \dfrac{n(E_1) + n(E_2) + n(E_3)}{n(S)} = \dfrac{1 + 2 + 1}{36} = \dfrac{1}{9},$

and the value of the expectation is

$PM = \frac{1}{9}(72) = $ **8 dollars**.

12.3-4 Empirical Probability

In all types of insurance, in medicine, in sociology, in chemistry, physics, in business and industry, and in many practical situations it is not possible to determine the mathematical (**a priori**) probability of the success of an event. In such experiments the best one can do is to observe a very large number of cases and record the **relative frequency** of successes. Probability determined in this manner is called **empirical** probability or **statistical** probability or **a posteriori** probability.

Definition: 12.3-4a. *If m is the total number of observations made under a properly controlled condition and r is the number of times a certain event E occurs, then the ratio r/m is called* **the relative frequency** *of E for the m observations.*

It is reasonable to assume that the greater the number of trials taken, the closer the relative frequency r/m approximates $P(E)$, the probability of success.

Theorem: 12.3-4a. If the total number of trials m is very large, the relative frequency r/m, which records the successful outcomes of event E, differs from the probability $P(E)$ by a minutely small number.

Even though one can never be certain that the relative frequency of a statistical experiment is exactly the mathematical probability $P(E)$, the existing conditions are still sufficiently dependable to justify the following definition:

Definition: 12.3-4b. *If in m trials, where m is extremely large, event E is successful r times, then the* **probability P_e** *of the event being successful is r/m.*

As the following examples will indicate, *empirical probability* applies only when one has dependable knowledge of past events and assumes that approximately the same conditions will continue into the future.

In using Table VII, the 1958 CSO Mortality Table, in the following examples and the exercises, *no distinction will be made between the age of a male and the same age of a female.* However, it has been determined that the results are more accurate if the age of a female is reduced by three years when it is substituted in the age column of the CSO Table.

Example: 12.3-4a. What is the probability that a person age 20 will be alive at age 50?

From the insurance record of 10,000,000 newborn babies, as shown in Table VII on page 411, 9,805,870 are still living at age 10, and 8,762,306 are still living at age 50. Therefore, according to the definite prior experience as recorded in this table, the probability of a person age 10 living to age 50 is

$$P_e = \frac{8,762,306}{9,805,870} = 0.89357.$$

Example: 12.3-4b. If a man at age 70 dies within the next 15 years, his daughter is to receive $20,000. What is the value of her expectation?

From Table VII we learn that at age 70 there are 5,592,012 of 10,000,000 persons still living and at age 85 there are 1,311,348 of the original 10,000,000 living. Then 4,280,664 died during the 15-year period. The probability of the man dying between age 70 and 85 is

$$P_e = \frac{4,280,664}{5,592,012} = 0.765496.$$

The daughter's mathematical expectation is

$$PM = 0.765496(20,000) = \$15,309.92.$$

12.3-5 Odds in Favor of an Event

In regards to a particular event one often hears the question: "*What are the odds in favor of it?*"

Definition: 12.3-5. *The **odds in favor** of event E in the sample space of an experiment are*

$$\frac{P(E)}{P(\sim E)} = \frac{P(E)}{1 - P(E)}, \qquad provided\ P(\sim E) \neq 0.$$

Example: 12.3-5a. If a correctly formed cube has 5 of its faces painted white, the remaining one painted black, what are the odds in favor of tossing a white face? a black face?

$$\text{Odds in favor of } E_w = \frac{P(E)}{P(\sim E)} = \frac{P(E)}{1 - P(E)} = \frac{\frac{5}{6}}{1 - \frac{5}{6}} = \frac{5}{1} \quad \text{or} \quad \textbf{5 to 1.}$$

$$\text{Odds in favor of } E_b = \frac{\frac{1}{6}}{1 - \frac{1}{6}} = \frac{1}{5} \quad \text{or} \quad \textbf{1 to 5.}$$

Odds in favor of E and odds against $(\sim E)$ are the same.

EXERCISE 12.C

1. Express in set form the sample space for the toss of a coin. What is its cardinal number? List the event that a tail turns up. What is the cardinal number of the event?

2. Express in set form the sample space for the toss of a die. What is its cardinal number? List the event that an even number of dots will turn up. What is its cardinal number?

3. List the total possible events in the sample space $\{a, b, c\}$. How many subsets are there?

4. Write out the total possible events in the sample space $\{11, 13, 17\}$. How many events are there?

5. If each event must contain at least three sample points, how many events are there in the sample space $\{2, 4, 6, 8, 10\}$?

6. If each event must contain not more than three sample points, how many events are there in the sample space $\{1, 3, 5, 7, 9\}$?

7. A sample space consists of the digits of the number system. How many events are possible if each event is limited to not more than 2 digits?

8. List the sample space if two odd numbers are chosen at random from the even digits of the number system. How many outcomes are possible?

9. Write out the sample space for the toss of a coin and a die. What is $n(S)$? In how many ways can one of the elements of an event be a head?

10. Three dice are thrown. How many elements are in its sample space? List the event that the sum of the dots turned up do not exceed 8. What is $n(E)$?

11. In one throw of a die what is the probability of turning up a 5? a 5 or a 6?

12. In a toss of two coins what is the probability of getting both heads? both tails? either both heads or both tails?

13. In a toss of four coins what is the probability of failing to get either all heads or all tails?

14. In throwing two regulation dice what is the probability of the sum of the dots adding to 10?

15. A bag contains 6 white balls and 9 black balls. If one ball is taken from the bag in random fashion, what is the probability that the ball will be white? black?

16. In drawing a card from a deck of 52 cards, what is the probability that the card will be a 10?

17. From a class of 15 boys and 25 girls a representative to the social committee is chosen. If the choice is random, what is the probability that the representative is a boy? a girl?

18. From a bag containing the letters for the word *Mississippi* a letter is taken at random. What is the probability that the letter is *i*?

19. From a group of 8 men and 10 women a committee of 7 is to be formed. What is the probability that the committee will contain more than 4 women?

20. In Problem 19 what is the probability that the committee will contain fewer than 4 men?

21. If a number is drawn from the integers 0 to 19 inclusive, what is the probability that it will be an even number? an odd number? What is the sum of these two probabilities?

22. In Problem 21 what is the probability that the number is less than 10? is divisible by 4? is divisible by 20?

23. If from 5 pairs of shoes under the bed a person selects two shoes, what is the probability that the two belong together?

24. In Problem 23, what is the probability that they will be for the same foot?

25. If 3 cards are drawn from a bridge deck of 52 cards, what is the probability that they will all be clubs?

26. In Problem 25 what is the probability that none of them will be clubs?

27. A man is to receive $100 if in pulling a card from a 52-card deck he pulls an Ace. What is his mathematical expectation?

28. What is the value of a person's expectation if in the toss of 3 coins $20 will be paid each time 3 tails turn up?

29. If a man is charged $1.00 for each toss of the coins in Problem 28, in the long run would he be apt to win or lose money? Why?

30. In reference to Problem 27, the charge for pulling a card is $10.00. After many pulls would one be most apt to be a winner or a loser? Why?

31. What is the probability that a 25-year-old girl will live to age 75? What is the probability that she will die during her 75th year?

32. What is the probability that a 5-year-old boy will live to age 90? What is the probability that he will die before age 90?

33. A girl age 6 is to inherit $50,000 if she is living for her 21st birthday. What is the value of this expectation.

34. An invalid child age 4 is to inherit $100,000 if he is still living at the age of 25. What mathematical expectation is involved?

35. If a man is age 68 and his wife is 70, what is the probability that both will be dead before age 80? that both will live to age 90?

36. If a man is age 34 and his wife is 31, what is the probability of both dying within the next 30 years? both living to age 70?

37. A bag contains 9 marbles marked from 1 to 9 inclusively. In drawing one marble from the bag, what are *the odds in favor of* drawing an even-numbered marble? an odd-numbered marble?

38. A bag contains 10 golf balls marked 1 to 10, inclusive. In removing a golf ball from the bag what are the *odds in favor of* getting one marked with a prime number?

39. What are the *odds in favor of* a 6-year-old boy living to age 96?

40. If a coin is tossed 4 times, what are the *odds in favor of* turning up 3 heads.

12.3-6 General Addition Theorem of Probability

Letting E_1 and E_2 represent any two events in a sample space S of an experiment and $n(E_1)$ and $n(E_2)$ the count of the elements in E_1 and E_2, we can restate the Properties 12.1-1a and 12.1-1b as follows:

(A) $n(E_1 \cup E_2) = n(E_1) + n(E_2)$ $(E_1 \cap E_2) = \varnothing$,
(B) $n(E_1 \cup E_2) = n(E_1) + n(E_2) - n(E_1 \cap E_2)$.

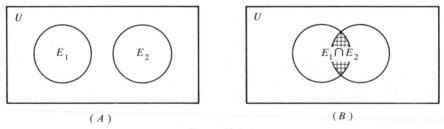

(A) (B)

Figure 12.3-6a

The **Venn diagram** (A) in Figure 12.3-6a shows conclusively that events E_1 and E_2 are mutually exclusive (Section 12.2-4). **Mutually exclusive events are always disjoint sets** and, according to Postulate 3 of Definition 12.3-2d

$$P(E_1 \cup E_2) = P(E_1) + P(E_2)$$

if and only if E_1 and E_2 are mutually exclusive.

But events E_1 and E_2 may not be mutually exclusive, as indicated by the Venn diagram in Figure 12.3-6a (*B*). When this situation occurs, something must be done to keep from counting the elements that are common to E_1 and E_2 twice. Consequently, any time $E_1 \cap E_2 \neq \varnothing$ something must be done to reduce the count of $n(E_1) + n(E_2)$ and to reduce, simultaneously, the probability $P(E_1) + P(E_2)$.

Example: 12.3-6a. If E_1 is the outcome of drawing a Jack from a set of 52 cards and E_2 is the outcome of drawing a Spade, in the draw of one card what is the probability of drawing a Jack or a spade or both?

There are 4 ways out of 52 outcomes to draw a Jack; so the probability of drawing a Jack is $\frac{4}{52}$. There are 13 ways of drawing a Spade; so the probability of drawing a Spade is $\frac{13}{52}$. But there exists one chance out of 52 of drawing the Jack of Spades, and this outcome gives a count both for Jacks and for Spades. This situation definitely points out that $E_1 \cap E_2 \neq \varnothing$. Moreover, it indicates that the probability $n(E_1 \cap E_2)/n(S) = 1/52$ should be subtracted from $P(E_1) + P(E_2)$. If this is done, the resulting probability is

$$P(E_1 \cup E_2) = P(E_1) + P(E_2) - P(E_1 \cap E_2) = \tfrac{4}{52} + \tfrac{13}{52} - \tfrac{1}{52} = \tfrac{16}{52} = \tfrac{4}{13}.$$

Theorem: 12.3-6a. If E_1 and E_2 are any two events in a sample space of an experiment, then

$$P(E_1 \cup E_2) = P(E_1) + P(E_2) - P(E_1 \cap E_2).$$

PROOF: Basically, *probability is the ratio of the number of ways a thing can successfully happen to the number of ways it can happen and fail.* Thus,

$$P(E_1 \cup E_2) = \frac{n(E_1 \cup E_2)}{n(S)} \qquad \text{(Definition 12.3-2c)}$$

$$= \frac{n(E) + n(E) - n(E \cap E)}{n(S)} \qquad \text{(Property 12.1-1b)}$$

$$= \frac{n(E_1)}{n(S)} + \frac{n(E_2)}{n(S)} - \frac{n(E_1 \cap E_2)}{n(S)}. \qquad \begin{array}{l}\text{(Equivalent}\\ \text{fractions)}\end{array}$$

$$\therefore P(E_1 \cup E_2) = P(E_1) + P(E_2) - P(E_1 \cap E_2). \text{ (Definition 12.3-2b)}$$

Example: 12.3-6b. In drawing two cards from a 52-card deck, what is the probability that both of them will be Kings or both of them will be black? The sample space for this experiment is

$$n(S) = \binom{52}{2} = \frac{52 \cdot 51}{1 \cdot 2} = 1{,}326.$$

There are 4 Kings in the deck; so event E_1 has

$$n(E_1) = \binom{4}{2} = \frac{4 \cdot 3}{1 \cdot 2} = 6 \text{ outcomes.}$$

There are 26 black cards in the deck; so event E_2 has

$$n(E_2) = \binom{26}{2} = \frac{26 \cdot 25}{1 \cdot 2} = 325 \text{ outcomes.}$$

There are two black Kings in the deck; so event $(E_1 \cap E_2)$ has

$$n(E_1 \cap E_2) = \binom{2}{2} = \frac{2 \cdot 1}{1 \cdot 2} = 1.$$

Then $P(E_1 \cup E_2) = P(E_1) + P(E_2) - P(E_1 \cap E_2)$

$$= \frac{6}{1,326} + \frac{325}{1,326} - \frac{1}{1,326}.$$

$$\therefore \quad P(E_1 \cup E_2) = \frac{165}{663}.$$

E_1 and E_2 in the preceding example are not mutually exclusive events because the occurrence of one does not completely eliminate the other.

EXERCISE 12.D

1. In drawing a card from a 52-card deck, what is the probability of getting an Ace or a red card? Are these events mutually exclusive?

2. If two cards are drawn from a 52-card deck, what is the probability of getting a five-spot or a black card? Are these events mutually exclusive?

3. What is the probability of getting a 5 in one throw of a pair of dice? What is the value of $(E_1 \cap E_2)$ where $4 + 1$ is E_1 and $3 + 2$ is E_2? What is $P(E_1 \cap E_2)$? Are these events mutually exclusive? Why?

4. In drawing a card from a 52-card deck, what is the probability of getting a Queen or a nonface card? What is $P(E_1 \cap E_2)$? Are these events mutually exclusive? Why?

5. A man enters a department store. The probability that he will buy a pair of shoes is $P(E_1) = 0.80$. The probability that he will buy a pair of socks is $P(E_2) = 0.65$. The probability that he will buy both a pair of shoes and a pair of socks is 0.52. Find the probability that the man will buy a pair of shoes, a pair of socks, or both.

6. There is a 50–50 chance that a woman entering a grocery store will buy bacon or eggs. The probability that she will buy both is 0.25. What is the probability that she will buy bacon, eggs, or both?

7. By Venn diagram show that

$$P(E_1 \cup E_2 \cup E_3) = P(E_1) + P(E_2) + P(E_3) - P(E_1 \cap E_2) - P(E_1 \cap E_3) - P(E_2 \cap E_3)$$

$$+ P(E_1 \cap E_2 \cap E_3).$$

8. Find the value of $P[(E_1 \cup E_2) \cup (E_3 \cup E_4)]$ by repeatedly using Theorem 12.3-5a.

9. A bag contains 4 red, 5 white, and 3 blue balls. If two balls are drawn from it simultaneously, what is the probability that both will be either red or white? that one will be red and the other white?

10. From past experience, a baseball coach predicts that the probability of one of his players knocking a homerun is $\frac{1}{20}$. If he misses the homerun, the probability of his getting a hit is $\frac{7}{20}$. What is his probability of getting either a homerun or a hit?

12.3-7 General Multiplication Theorems of Probability

If the happening of an event does not in any way affect the probability of the occurrence of another event, then the two events are **independent events.**

For example, if the probability of a student winning a tennis tournament is $\frac{3}{5}$ and the probability that he will win a golf tournament is $\frac{4}{5}$, then the probability that he will win both the tennis and the golf tournament is

$$P(E) = P(E_1) \cdot P(E_2) = \tfrac{3}{5} \cdot \tfrac{4}{5} = \tfrac{12}{25}.$$

Definition: 12.3-7a.   *If E_1 and E_2 are events in a sample space of an experiment and if*

$$P(E) = P(E_1 \cap E_2) = P(E_1) \cdot P(E_2).$$

then the events are said to be **independent events.**

As the following theorem indicates, there can be any finite number of events in a given sample space.

Theorem: 12.3-7a.   If $E_1, E_2, E_3, \ldots$ are events in a sample space, and if two or more independent events have probabilities $P(E_1), P(E_2), P(E_3), \ldots$, then the probability that the event will occur is

$$P(E) = P(E_1 \cap E_2 \cap E_3 \cap \cdots) = P(E_1) \cdot P(E_2) \cdot P(E_3) \cdots.$$

PROOF: Event E_1 can occur in $n(E_1)$ ways and occur and fail in $n(S_1)$ ways.
Event E_2 can occur in $n(E_2)$ ways and occur and fail in $n(S_2)$ ways.
Event E_3 can occur in $n(E_3)$ ways and occur and fail in $n(S_3)$ ways.
Then by the fundamental counting property (12.1-1d),

$$n(E) = n(E_1) \cdot n(E_2) \cdot n(E_3) \cdots \quad \text{and} \quad n(S) = n(S_1) \cdot n(S_2) \cdot n(S_3) \cdots.$$

From $P(E) = n(E)/n(S)$ as defined in Example 12.3-2c, it follows that

$$P(E_1 \cap E_2 \cap E_3 \cap \cdots) = \frac{n(E_1)}{n(S_1)} \cdot \frac{n(E_2)}{n(S_2)} \cdot \frac{n(E_3)}{n(S_3)} \cdots = P(E_1) \cdot P(E_2) \cdot P(E_3) \cdots.$$

It often happens that one event depends upon another, as indicated by the following definition:

Definition: 12.3-7b.   *If the occurrence of event E_1 affects the probability of E_2, then event E_2 is said to depend on event E_1, and the probability of E_2 is said to be a* **conditional probability.** *The two events are* **dependent events.**

Example: 12.3-7a. If the probability that a girl will eat her lunch at the Ramada Inn restaurant is $\frac{1}{2}$, the probability that her boy friend will drop in while she is eating is $\frac{1}{4}$, and the probability that the two of them will take in an afternoon movie is $\frac{3}{8}$, then the probability that all these events will take place in the order indicated is

$$P(E) = P(E_1 \cap E_2 \cap E_3) = P(E_1) \cdot P(E_2) \cdot P(E_3) = \tfrac{1}{2} \cdot \tfrac{1}{4} \cdot \tfrac{3}{8} = \tfrac{3}{64}.$$

The symbol commonly used to denote the probability of E_2, where E_2 is dependent on and follows the previous occurrence of E_1, is

$$P(E_2 \mid E_1).$$

This is a very convenient symbol because if E_1 and E_2 happen to be independent, the expression degenerates back to $P(E_2)$.

Definition: 12.3-7c. *For events E_1 and E_2 in a sample space where E_1 has occurred, the* **conditional probability** *is expressed by*

$$P(E_2 \mid E_1) = \frac{P(E_1 \cap E_2)}{P(E_1)} \qquad P(E_1) \neq 0.$$

The equality of this **conditional probability formula** is involved in the theorem that follows.

Theorem: 12.3-7b. If E_1 and E_2 are events in a sample space of an experiment and if $P(E_2 \mid E_1)$ denotes the probability of $P(E_2)$ following the occurrence of E_1, then

$$P(E_1 \cap E_2) = P(E_1) \cdot P(E_2 \mid E_1).$$

PROOF: $P(E_1 \cap E_2) = \dfrac{n(E_1 \cap E_2)}{n(S)}$ (Definition 12.3-2b)

$$= \frac{n(E_1)[n(E_1 \cap E_2)]}{n(E_1)[n(S)]}$$ $[(M)$ and (D) by $n(E_1)]$

$$= \frac{n(E_1)}{n(S)} \cdot \frac{n(E_1 \cap E_2)}{n(E_1)}.$$ (M)

$\therefore$ $P(E_1 \cap E_2) = P(E_1) \cdot P(E_2 \mid E_1).$ (Definitions 12.3-2b and 12.3-7c)

The preceding theorem can, of course, be generalized to cover many dependent events.

EXERCISE 12.E

For each problem to which these ideas apply, try to decide whether the events are independent, dependent, or mutually exclusive.

1. (a) Define a sample space.

(b) What is the sample space if any three cards are to be drawn from a deck of 52 cards?

2. (a) Define a sample point.

(b) If a sample space is {(In, In), (In, Out), (Out, In), and (Out, Out)}, how many sample points does it have?

3. What is the basic idea involved in mathematical (a priori) probability?

4. What must first be done before one can proceed to determine empirical (a posteriori) probability?

5. (a) If two sets are disjoint, are they mutually exclusive? always?

(b) Is the probability of two mutually exclusive events equal to the sum of the probability of each separate event?

6. (a) If two sets are not mutually exclusive, are they disjoint?

(b) Is the probability of two nonmutually exclusive events equal to the sum of the probability of each separate event? Explain.

7. (a) When is a set of events said to be independent?

(b) If the probabilities of three independent events are $\frac{1}{2}$, $\frac{1}{3}$, and $\frac{1}{4}$, what is the probability that the events will take place in the order stated?

8. (a) When is a set of events said to be dependent?

(b) If the probabilities of three dependent events, each depending on the preceding one, are $\frac{3}{4}$, $\frac{2}{3}$, and $\frac{1}{2}$, what is the probability that the events will take place in the order stated?

9. State the basic addition formula for probability.

10. State the basic multiplication formula for probability.

11. If a card is drawn at random from a deck of 52 cards, replaced, and a second card drawn, what is the probability that the same suit was drawn both times?

12. What is the probability in Problem 11 if the first card is not replaced?

13. From a group of 14 men and 16 women, a committee of 5 is chosen.

(a) What is the probability that the committee will consist of exactly three men and two women?

(b) What is the probability that the committee will have at least three men on it?

14. In Problem 13:

(a) What is the probability that at least one woman will be on the committee?

(b) What is the probability that the committee will be all women?

15. If an antiaircraft battery is 20% effective in damaging planes within its range, and a second such battery is 30% effective, what is the probability of damaging a plane that passes within the range of both batteries.

16. A bag contains 6 red and 7 white balls.

(a) If one ball is drawn, find the probability of getting a red or a white ball.

(b) If two balls are drawn, what is the probability of getting two white balls?

17. A bag contains 50 tickets numbered 1, 2, 3, . . . , 50. If two tickets are pulled, what is the probability

(a) that numbers 24 and 25 will be drawn?

(b) that either 24 or 25 will be one of the two tickets?

18. Three cards are drawn from a 52-card deck without replacement. Find the probability that the first two cards are spades and the last one is a club or a diamond.

19. Solve Problem 18 with the change that each card drawn is replaced before the next drawing.

20. The first 11 cards dealt to a bridge player were all hearts. What is the probability that the next two cards will also be hearts?

21. If the probability that Tom will pass in mathematics is 0.80, in physics is 0.70, and in English is 0.90, what is the probability that he will pass mathematics and physics and fail English?

22. In Problem 21 what is the probability that Tom will pass English and fail mathematics and physics?

23. If the letters of the word "trigonometry" are placed in a bag, what is the probability of drawing a *t*, an *r*, or an *o* in a single draw?

24. In Problem 25 what is the probability of pulling a vowel in a single draw?

25. The probability that Mr. Black will be nominated to the office of President of the United States is $\frac{1}{4}$ and if nominated will be elected president is $\frac{5}{7}$. The probability that he will live from election date to the day he takes office is 0.90. What is the probability that Mr. Black will live to be the next president?

26. If in Problem 25 the probability of Mr. Black visiting England during his first year as president is $\frac{1}{7}$, what is the probability that Mr. Black will become President of the United States *and* visit in England?

27. In a 20-question true-false test, what is the probability that without reading the questions a student will get a perfect score?

28. In 10 tosses of a coin what is the probability of getting exactly one head?

29. The probabilities that John and Jean can solve a problem is $\frac{1}{2}$ and $\frac{2}{3}$, respectively. What is the probability that both will solve the problem? that John solves it but Jean fails to solve it?

30. In Problem 29 what is the probability that Jean solves it but John fails to solve it? that neither one solves it?

12.3-8 Repeated Trials Theorem

In studying combinations (see Theorem 12.2-a) we learned that r successes can come from n trials in

$$C(n, r) = \frac{n!}{r!(n - r)!}$$

ways. Each of the $C(n, r)$ ways has the same probability, the ways are mutually exclusive, and all of them are involved in the following theorem:

Theorem: 12.3-8a.   If $P(E)$ is the probability of the success of an event and $P(\sim E)$ is the probability of the event failing in a single instance, and if the probability of the success of the event on repeated trials be independent events, then the probability of exactly r successes in n trials is

$$P(r) = C(n, r)[P(E)]^r[P(\sim E)]^{n-r}. \tag{A}$$

The proof of the preceding theorem can be worked out by following steps similar to those taken in proving Theorem 12.2-2a. This will be left to the student.

Example: 12.3-8a.   If a die is thrown 8 times in succession, what is the probability that it will turn up a 3 exactly 5 of the 8 throws?

Instead of merely substituting the data of this problem in formula (A) and working it out, let us do some reasoning of the type one would have to do if he were proving Theorem 12.3-8a.

The probability of turning up a 3 for each throw is $\frac{1}{6}$ and the probability of not getting a 3 is $\frac{5}{6}$. Thus for a single throw the probability of the event being successful is $(\frac{1}{6})(\frac{5}{6})$. Then the probability of the event being successful 5 out of 8 throws would be $(\frac{1}{6})^5(\frac{5}{6})^3$. But there are $C(8, 5)$ possible mutually exclusive ways that a 3 may turn up in exactly 5 out of 8 throws. Therefore, the probability would be:

$$P(r) = C(8, 5)\left(\frac{1}{6}\right)^5\left(\frac{5}{6}\right)^3$$

$$= \frac{8 \cdot 7 \cdot 6 \cdot 5 \cdot 4}{1 \cdot 2 \cdot 3 \cdot 4 \cdot 5} \cdot \frac{125}{1,679,616} \qquad (B)$$

$$= \frac{7000}{1,679,616}$$

and $P(r) = \dfrac{875}{209,952}.$

It should be noted that equation (B) is exactly the equation that would have been obtained if the data had been substituted directly into formula (A).

Using formula (A) and the fact that $C(n, r) = C(n, n - r)$ from Theorem 12.2-b a probability formula for finding at least r successes out of n trials is developed as follows:

The probability of n trials being successful exactly n times is $[P(E)]^n$. The probability that the event will successfully occur exactly $n - 1$ times is $C(n, n - 1)[P(E)]^{n-1}[P(\sim E)]^1$. The probability that the event will occur exactly $n - 2$ times is $C(n, n - 2)[P(E)]^{n-2}[P(\sim E)]^2$. This continues down to r where the probability is $C(n, n - r)[P(E)]^r[P(\sim E)]^{n-r}$. Since the events are *mutually exclusive* the probability that the event will successfully occur at least r times out of n trials is the sum of the separate probabilities of the $n - r + 1$ terms. Thus,

$$P = C(n, n)[P(E)]^n + C(n, n - 1)[P(E)]^{n-1}[P(\sim E)]^1$$
$$+ C(n, n - 2)[P(E)]^{n-2}[P(\sim E)]^2 + \cdots$$
$$+ C(n, r)[P(E)]^r[P(\sim E)]^{n-r}.$$

Example: 12.3-8b.   If 5 dice are thrown what is the probability that at least 3 of them will turn up a five?

$$P = C(5, 5)\left(\frac{1}{6}\right)^5 + C(5, 4)\left(\frac{1}{6}\right)^4\left(\frac{5}{6}\right)^1 + C(5, 3)\left(\frac{1}{6}\right)^3\left(\frac{5}{6}\right)^2$$

$$= \frac{1}{7,776} + \left(\frac{5 \cdot 4 \cdot 3 \cdot 2}{1 \cdot 2 \cdot 3 \cdot 4}\right)\left(\frac{5}{7,776}\right) + \left(\frac{5 \cdot 4 \cdot 3}{1 \cdot 2 \cdot 3}\right)\left(\frac{25}{7,776}\right).$$

$$\therefore P = \frac{1}{7,776} + \frac{25}{7,776} + \frac{250}{7,776} = \frac{23}{648}.$$

Example: 12.3-8c.   Find the probability of throwing at least one head in three throws of a well-designed coin.

$$P = \left(\frac{1}{2}\right)^3 + C(3, 2)\left(\frac{1}{2}\right)^2\left(\frac{1}{2}\right) + C(3, 1)\left(\frac{1}{2}\right)\left(\frac{1}{2}\right)^2$$

$$= \frac{1}{8} + \frac{3}{8} + \frac{3}{8},$$

and $P = \dfrac{7}{8}$.

EXERCISE 12.F

1. Find the probability of throwing at least 2 eights if 2 dice are thrown 6 times.

2. If a die is thrown 5 times in succession, what is the probability that at least one 4 will turn up?

3. In Problem 2, what is the probability that exactly one 4 will turn up?

4. The batting average of a baseball player is 0.347. What is the probability that he will get exactly three hits in his next seven times at bat?

5. In a ten-question multiple-choice quiz only one answer out of the five given is correct. What is the probability of getting a perfect score by simply guessing?

6. In Problem 5, what is the probability of getting exactly two answers correct by simply guessing?

7. In a 10-question true-false quiz, what is the probability of getting at least 5 correct answers by pure guessing?

8. In Problem 7 what is the probability of getting exactly 7 correct answers?

9. According to past experience, 5 per cent of the students who register for this course will not pass it. In a group of 100 students, what is the probability that exactly 5 students will fail?

10. If 2 per cent of tuberculosis cases are fatal, what is the probability that the next 20 cases discovered will end in full recovery?

11. What is the probability that a baseball player batting 0.322 will get at least two hits in five times at bat?

12. What is the probability that the baseball player in Problem 11 will fail to get a hit?

13. In the toss of a die, what is the probability of turning up a 3-dot face at least once in six trials?

14. In the toss of a die, what is the probability of turning up a 6-dot face not more than twice in six trials.

15. Ten coins are tossed. What is the probability that at least 7 of them will be tails?

16. Ten coins are tossed. What is the probability that not less than 8 of them will be heads?

Tables

Table I *Four-Place Values of Circular Functions*

t, a Real Number; θ, Radian Measure	$\sin t$ or $\sin \theta$	$\csc t$ or $\csc \theta$	$\tan t$ or $\tan \theta$	$\cot t$ or $\cot \theta$	$\sec t$ or $\sec \theta$	$\cos t$ or $\cos \theta$	θ in Degree Measure
0.00	0.0000	No value	0.0000	No value	1.000	1.000	0° 00'
.01	.0100	100.0	.0100	100.0	1.000	1.000	0° 34'
.02	.0200	50.00	.0200	49.99	1.000	0.9998	1° 09'
.03	.0300	33.34	.0300	33.32	1.000	0.9996	1° 43'
.04	.0400	25.01	.0400	24.99	1.001	0.9992	2° 18'
0.05	0.0500	20.01	0.0500	19.98	1.001	0.9988	2° 52'
.06	.0600	16.68	.0601	16.65	1.002	.9982	3° 26'
.07	.0699	14.30	.0701	14.26	1.002	.9976	4° 01'
.08	.0799	12.51	.0802	12.47	1.003	.9968	4° 35'
.09	.0899	11.13	.0902	11.08	1.004	.9960	5° 09'
0.10	0.0998	10.02	0.1003	9.967	1.005	0.9950	5° 44'
.11	.1098	9.109	.1104	9.054	1.006	.9940	6° 18'
.12	.1197	8.353	.1206	8.293	1.007	.9928	6° 53'
.13	.1296	7.714	.1307	7.649	1.009	.9916	7° 27'
.14	.1395	7.166	.1409	7.096	1.010	.9902	8° 01'
0.15	0.1494	6.692	0.1511	6.617	1.011	0.9888	8° 36'
.16	.1593	6.277	.1614	6.197	1.013	.9872	9° 10'
.17	.1692	5.911	.1717	5.826	1.015	.9856	9° 44'
.18	.1790	5.586	.1820	5.495	1.016	.9838	10° 19'
.19	.1889	5.295	.1923	5.200	1.018	.9820	10° 53'
0.20	0.1987	5.033	0.2027	4.933	1.020	0.9801	11° 28'
.21	.2085	4.797	.2131	4.692	1.022	.9780	12° 02'
.22	.2182	4.582	.2236	4.472	1.025	.9759	12° 36'
.23	.2280	4.386	.2341	4.271	1.027	.9737	13° 11'
.24	.2377	4.207	.2447	4.086	1.030	.9713	13° 45'
0.25	0.2474	4.042	0.2553	3.916	1.032	0.9689	14° 19'
.26	.2571	3.890	.2660	3.759	1.035	.9664	14° 54'
.27	.2667	3.749	.2768	3.613	1.038	.9638	15° 28'
.28	.2764	3.619	.2876	3.478	1.041	.9611	16° 03'
.29	.2860	3.497	.2984	3.351	1.044	.9582	16° 37'
0.30	0.2955	3.384	0.3093	3.233	1.047	0.9553	17° 11'
.31	.3051	3.278	.3203	3.122	1.050	.9523	17° 46'
.32	.3146	3.179	.3314	3.018	1.053	.9492	18° 20'
.33	.3240	3.086	.3425	2.920	1.057	.9460	18° 54'
.34	.3335	2.999	.3537	2.827	1.061	.9428	19° 29'
0.35	0.3429	2.916	0.3650	2.740	1.065	0.9394	20° 03'
.36	.3523	2.839	.3764	2.657	1.068	.9359	20° 38'
.37	.3616	2.765	.3879	2.578	1.073	.9323	21° 12'
.38	.3709	2.696	.3994	2.504	1.077	.9287	21° 46'
.39	.3802	2.630	.4111	2.433	1.081	.9249	22° 21'

Table I   *Four-Place Values of Circular Functions*

t, a Real Number; θ, Radian Measure	sin t or sin θ	csc t or csc θ	tan t or tan θ	cot t or cot θ	sec t or sec θ	cos t or cos θ	θ in Degree Measure
0.40	0.3894	2.568	0.4228	2.365	1.086	0.9211	22° 55′
.41	.3986	2.509	.4346	2.301	1.090	.9171	23° 29′
.42	.4078	2.452	.4466	2.239	1.095	.9131	24° 04′
.43	.4169	2.399	.4586	2.180	1.100	.9090	24° 38′
.44	.4259	2.348	.4708	2.124	1.105	.9048	25° 13′
0.45	0.4350	2.299	0.4831	2.070	1.111	0.9004	25° 47′
.46	.4439	2.253	.4954	2.018	1.116	.8961	26° 21′
.47	.4529	2.208	.5080	1.969	1.122	.8916	26° 56′
.48	.4618	2.166	.5206	1.921	1.127	.8870	27° 30′
.49	.4706	2.125	.5334	1.875	1.133	.8823	28° 04′
0.50	0.4794	2.086	0.5463	1.830	1.139	0.8776	28° 39′
.51	.4882	2.048	.5594	1.788	1.146	.8727	29° 13′
.52	.4969	2.013	.5726	1.747	1.152	.8678	29° 48′
.53	.5055	1.978	.5859	1.707	1.159	.8628	30° 22′
.54	.5141	1.945	.5994	1.668	1.166	.8577	30° 56′
0.55	0.5227	1.913	0.6131	1.631	1.173	0.8525	31° 31′
.56	.5312	1.883	.6269	1.595	1.180	.8473	32° 05′
.57	.5396	1.853	.6410	1.560	1.188	.8419	32° 40′
.58	.5480	1.825	.6552	1.526	1.196	.8365	33° 14′
.59	.5564	1.797	.6696	1.494	1.203	.8309	33° 48′
0.60	0.5646	1.771	0.6841	1.462	1.212	0.8253	34° 23′
.61	.5729	1.746	.6989	1.431	1.220	.8196	34° 57′
.62	.5810	1.721	.7139	1.401	1.229	.8139	35° 31′
.63	.5891	1.697	.7291	1.372	1.238	.8080	36° 06′
.64	.5972	1.674	.7445	1.343	1.247	.8021	36° 40′
0.65	0.6052	1.652	0.7602	1.315	1.256	0.7961	37° 15′
.66	.6131	1.631	.7761	1.288	1.266	.7900	37° 49′
.67	.6210	1.610	.7923	1.262	1.276	.7838	38° 23′
.68	.6288	1.590	.8087	1.237	1.286	.7776	38° 58′
.69	.6365	1.571	.8253	1.212	1.297	.7712	39° 32′
0.70	0.6442	1.552	0.8423	1.187	1.307	0.7648	40° 06′
.71	.6518	1.534	.8595	1.163	1.319	.7584	40° 41′
.72	.6594	1.517	.8771	1.140	1.330	.7518	41° 15′
.73	.6669	1.500	.8949	1.117	1.342	.7452	41° 50′
.74	.6743	1.483	.9131	1.095	1.354	.7385	42° 24′
0.75	0.6816	1.467	0.9316	1.073	1.367	0.7317	42° 58′
.76	.6889	1.452	.9505	1.052	1.380	.7248	43° 33′
.77	.6961	1.436	.9697	1.031	1.393	.7179	44° 07′
.78	.7033	1.422	.9893	1.011	1.407	.7109	44° 41′
.79	.7104	1.408	1.009	.9908	1.421	.7038	45° 16′
0.80	0.7174	1.394	1.030	0.9712	1.435	0.6967	45° 50′
.81	.7243	1.381	1.050	.9520	1.450	.6895	46° 25′
.82	.7311	1.368	1.072	.9331	1.466	.6822	46° 59′
.83	.7379	1.355	1.093	.9146	1.482	.6749	47° 33′
.84	.7446	1.343	1.116	.8964	1.498	.6675	48° 08′

Table I *Four-Place Values of Circular Functions*

t, a Real Number; θ, Radian Measure	sin *t* or sin θ	csc *t* or csc θ	tan *t* or tan θ	cot *t* or cot θ	sec *t* or sec θ	cos *t* or cos θ	θ in Degree Measure
0.85	0.7513	1.331	1.138	0.8785	1.515	0.6600	48° 42′
.86	.7578	1.320	1.162	.8609	1.533	.6524	49° 16′
.87	.7643	1.308	1.185	.8437	1.551	.6448	49° 51′
.88	.7707	1.297	1.210	.8267	1.569	.6372	50° 25′
.89	.7771	1.287	1.235	.8100	1.589	.6294	51° 00′
0.90	0.7833	1.277	1.260	0.7936	1.609	0.6216	51° 34′
.91	.7895	1.267	1.286	.7774	1.629	.6137	52° 08′
.92	.7956	1.257	1.313	.7615	1.651	.6058	52° 43′
.93	.8016	1.247	1.341	.7458	1.673	.5978	53° 17′
.94	.8076	1.238	1.369	.7303	1.696	.5898	53° 51′
0.95	0.8134	1.229	1.398	0.7151	1.719	0.5817	54° 26′
.96	.8192	1.221	1.428	.7001	1.744	.5735	55° 00′
.97	.8249	1.212	1.459	.6853	1.769	.5653	55° 35′
.98	.8305	1.204	1.491	.6707	1.795	.5570	56° 09′
.99	.8360	1.196	1.524	.6563	1.823	.5487	56° 43′
1.00	0.8415	1.188	1.557	0.6421	1.851	0.5403	57° 18′
1.01	.8468	1.181	1.592	.6281	1.880	.5319	57° 52′
1.02	.8521	1.174	1.628	.6142	1.911	.5234	58° 27′
1.03	.8573	1.166	1.665	.6005	1.942	.5148	59° 01′
1.04	.8624	1.160	1.704	.5870	1.975	.5062	59° 35′
1.05	0.8674	1.153	1.743	0.5736	2.010	0.4976	60° 10′
1.06	.8724	1.146	1.784	.5604	2.046	.4889	60° 44′
1.07	.8772	1.140	1.827	.5473	2.083	.4801	61° 18′
1.08	.8820	1.134	1.871	.5344	2.122	.4713	61° 53′
1.09	.8866	1.128	1.917	.5216	2.162	.4625	62° 27′
1.10	0.8912	1.122	1.965	0.5090	2.205	0.4536	63° 02′
1.11	.8957	1.116	2.014	.4964	2.249	.4447	63° 36′
1.12	.9001	1.111	2.066	.4840	2.295	.4357	64° 10′
1.13	.9044	1.106	2.120	.4718	2.344	.4267	64° 45′
1.14	.9086	1.101	2.176	.4596	2.395	.4176	65° 19′
1.15	0.9128	1.096	2.234	0.4475	2.448	0.4085	65° 53′
1.16	.9168	1.091	2.296	.4356	2.504	.3993	66° 28′
1.17	.9208	1.086	2.360	.4237	2.563	.3902	67° 02′
1.18	.9246	1.082	2.247	.4120	2.625	.3809	67° 37′
1.19	.9284	1.077	2.498	.4003	2.691	.3717	68° 11′
1.20	0.9320	1.073	2.572	0.3888	2.760	0.3624	68° 45′
1.21	.9356	1.069	2.650	.3773	2.833	.3530	69° 20′
1.22	.9391	1.065	2.733	.3659	2.910	.3436	69° 54′
1.23	.9425	1.061	2.820	.3546	2.992	.3342	70° 28′
1.24	.9458	1.057	2.912	.3434	3.079	.3248	71° 03′
1.25	0.9490	1.054	3.010	0.3323	3.171	0.3153	71° 37′
1.26	.9521	1.050	3.113	.3212	3.270	.3058	72° 12′
1.27	.9551	1.047	3.224	.3102	3.375	.2963	72° 46′
1.28	.9580	1.044	3.341	.2993	3.488	.2867	72° 20′
1.29	.9608	1.041	3.467	.2884	3.609	.2771	73° 55′

Table I *Four-Place Values of Circular Functions*

t, a Real Number; θ, Radian Measure	sin t or sin θ	csc t or csc θ	tan t or tan θ	cot t or cot θ	sec t or sec θ	cos t or cos θ	θ in Degree Measure
1.30	0.9636	1.038	3.602	0.2776	3.738	0.2675	74° 29′
1.31	.9662	1.035	3.747	.2669	3.878	.2579	75° 03′
1.32	.9687	1.032	3.903	.2562	4.029	.2482	75° 38′
1.33	.9711	1.030	4.072	.2456	4.193	.2385	76° 12′
1.34	.9735	1.027	4.256	.2350	4.372	.2288	76° 47′
1.35	0.9757	1.025	4.455	0.2245	4.566	0.2190	77° 21′
1.36	.9779	1.023	4.673	.2140	4.779	.2092	77° 55′
1.37	.9799	1.021	4.913	.2035	5.014	.1994	78° 30′
1.38	.9819	1.018	5.177	.1931	5.273	.1896	79° 04′
1.39	.9837	1.017	5.471	.1828	5.561	.1798	79° 38′
1.40	0.9854	1.015	5.798	0.1725	5.883	0.1700	80° 13′
1.41	.9871	1.013	6.165	.1622	6.246	.1601	80° 47′
1.42	.9887	1.011	6.581	.1519	6.657	.1502	81° 22′
1.43	.9901	1.010	7.055	.1417	7.126	.1403	81° 56′
1.44	.9915	1.009	7.602	.1315	7.667	.1304	82° 30′
1.45	0.9927	1.007	8.238	0.1214	8.299	0.1205	83° 05′
1.46	.9939	1.006	8.989	.1113	9.044	.1106	83° 39′
1.47	.9949	1.005	9.887	.1011	9.938	.1006	84° 13′
1.48	.9959	1.004	10.98	.0910	11.03	.0907	84° 48′
1.49	.9967	1.003	12.35	.0810	12.39	.0807	85° 22′
1.50	0.9975	1.003	14.10	0.0709	14.14	0.0707	85° 57′
1.51	.9982	1.002	16.43	.0609	16.46	.0608	86° 31′
1.52	.9987	1.001	19.67	.0508	19.69	.0508	87° 05′
1.53	.9992	1.001	24.50	.0408	24.52	.0408	87° 40′
1.54	.9995	1.000	32.46	.0308	32.48	.0308	88° 14′
1.55	0.9998	1.000	48.08	0.0208	48.09	0.0208	88° 49′
1.56	.9999	1.000	92.62	.0108	92.63	.0108	89° 23′
1.57	1.000	1.000	1256	.0008	1256	.0008	89° 57′

Table II   *Four-Place Logarithms of Numbers*

Note: Place **0.** before each mantissa.
To interpolate between two mantissas add to the smaller mantissa the proportional part found on the same line. The last digit may be in error by 1.

N	0	1	2	3	4	5	6	7	8	9	1 2 3	4 5 6	7 8 9
1.0	0000	0043	0086	0128	0170	0212	0253	0294	0334	0374	4 8 12	17 21 25	29 33 37
1.1	0414	0453	0492	0531	0569	0607	0645	0682	0719	0755	4 8 11	15 19 23	26 30 34
1.2	0792	0828	0864	0899	0934	0969	1004	1038	1072	1106	3 7 10	14 17 21	24 28 31
1.3	1139	1173	1206	1239	1271	1303	1335	1367	1399	1430	3 6 10	13 16 19	23 26 29
1.4	1461	1492	1523	1553	1584	1614	1644	1673	1703	1732	3 6 9	12 15 18	21 24 27
1.5	1761	1790	1818	1847	1875	1903	1931	1959	1987	2014	3 6 8	11 14 17	20 22 25
1.6	2041	2068	2095	2122	2148	2175	2201	2227	2253	2279	3 5 8	11 13 16	18 21 24
1.7	2304	2330	2355	2380	2405	2430	2455	2480	2504	2529	2 5 7	10 12 15	17 20 22
1.8	2553	2577	2601	2625	2648	2672	2695	2718	2742	2765	2 5 7	9 12 14	16 19 21
1.9	2788	2810	2833	2856	2878	2900	2923	2945	2967	2989	2 4 7	9 11 13	16 18 20
2.0	3010	3032	3054	3075	3096	3118	3139	3160	3181	3201	2 4 6	8 11 13	15 17 19
2.1	3222	3243	3263	3284	3304	3324	3345	3365	3385	3404	2 4 6	8 10 12	14 16 18
2.2	3424	3444	3464	3483	3502	3522	3541	3560	3579	3598	2 4 6	8 10 12	14 15 17
2.3	3617	3636	3655	3674	3692	3711	3729	3747	3766	3784	2 4 6	7 9 11	13 15 17
2.4	3802	3820	3838	3856	3874	3892	3909	3927	3945	3962	2 4 5	7 9 11	12 14 16
2.5	3979	3997	4014	4031	4048	4065	4082	4099	4116	4133	2 3 5	7 9 10	12 14 15
2.6	4150	4166	4183	4200	4216	4232	4249	4265	4281	4298	2 3 5	7 8 10	11 13 15
2.7	4314	4330	4346	4362	4378	4393	4409	4425	4440	4456	2 3 5	6 8 9	11 13 14
2.8	4472	4487	4502	4518	4533	4548	4564	4579	4594	4609	2 3 5	6 8 9	11 12 14
2.9	4624	4639	4654	4669	4683	4698	4713	4728	4742	4757	1 3 4	6 7 9	10 12 13
3.0	4771	4786	4800	4814	4829	4843	4857	4871	4886	4900	1 3 4	6 7 9	10 11 13
3.1	4914	4928	4942	4955	4969	4983	4997	5011	5024	5038	1 3 4	6 7 8	10 11 12
3.2	5051	5065	5079	5092	5105	5119	5132	5145	5159	5172	1 3 4	5 7 8	9 11 12
3.3	5185	5198	5211	5224	5237	5250	5263	5276	5289	5302	1 3 4	5 6 8	9 10 12
3.4	5315	5328	5340	5353	5366	5378	5391	5403	5416	5428	1 3 4	5 6 8	9 10 11
3.5	5441	5453	5465	5478	5490	5502	5514	5527	5539	5551	1 2 4	5 6 7	9 10 11
3.6	5563	5575	5587	5599	5611	5623	5635	5647	5658	5670	1 2 4	5 6 7	8 10 11
3.7	5682	5694	5705	5717	5729	5740	5752	5763	5775	5786	1 2 3	5 6 7	8 9 10
3.8	5798	5809	5821	5832	5843	5855	5866	5877	5888	5899	1 2 3	5 6 7	8 9 10
3.9	5911	5922	5933	5944	5955	5966	5977	5988	5999	6010	1 2 3	4 5 6	8 9 10
4.0	6021	6031	6042	6053	6064	6075	6085	6096	6107	6117	1 2 3	4 5 6	8 9 10
4.1	6128	6138	6149	6160	6170	6180	6191	6201	6212	6222	1 2 3	4 5 6	7 8 9
4.2	6232	6243	6253	6263	6274	6284	6294	6304	6314	6325	1 2 3	4 5 6	7 8 9
4.3	6335	6345	6355	6365	6375	6385	6395	6405	6415	6425	1 2 3	4 5 6	7 8 9
4.4	6435	6444	6454	6464	6474	6484	6493	6503	6513	6522	1 2 3	4 5 6	7 8 9
4.5	6532	6542	6551	6561	6571	6580	6590	6599	6609	6618	1 2 3	4 5 6	7 8 9
4.6	6628	6637	6646	6656	6665	6675	6684	6693	6702	6712	1 2 3	4 5 6	7 7 8
4.7	6721	6730	6739	6749	6758	6767	6776	6785	6794	6803	1 2 3	4 5 5	6 7 8
4.8	6812	6821	6830	6839	6848	6857	6866	6875	6884	6893	1 2 3	4 4 5	6 7 8
4.9	6902	6911	6920	6928	6937	6946	6955	6964	6972	6981	1 2 3	4 4 5	6 7 8
5.0	6990	6998	7007	7016	7024	7033	7042	7050	7059	7067	1 2 3	3 4 5	6 7 8
5.1	7076	7084	7093	7101	7110	7118	7126	7135	7143	7152	1 2 3	3 4 5	6 7 8
5.2	7160	7168	7177	7185	7193	7202	7210	7218	7226	7235	1 2 2	3 4 5	6 7 7
5.3	7243	7251	7259	7267	7275	7284	7292	7300	7308	7316	1 2 2	3 4 5	6 6 7
5.4	7324	7332	7340	7348	7356	7364	7372	7380	7388	7396	1 2 2	3 4 5	6 6 7

The header "Proportional Parts" spans the last three column groups (1 2 3 | 4 5 6 | 7 8 9).

Table II *Four-Place Logarithms of Numbers*

N	0	1	2	3	4	5	6	7	8	9	Proportional Parts								
											1	2	3	4	5	6	7	8	9
5.5	7404	7412	7419	7427	7435	7443	7451	7459	7466	7474	1	2	2	3	4	5	5	6	7
5.6	7482	7490	7497	7505	7513	7520	7528	7536	7543	7551	1	2	2	3	4	5	5	6	7
5.7	7559	7566	7574	7582	7589	7597	7604	7612	7619	7627	1	2	2	3	4	5	5	6	7
5.8	7634	7642	7649	7657	7664	7672	7679	7686	7694	7701	1	1	2	3	4	4	5	6	7
5.9	7709	7716	7723	7731	7738	7745	7752	7760	7767	7774	1	1	2	3	4	4	5	6	7
6.0	7782	7789	7796	7803	7810	7818	7825	7832	7839	7846	1	1	2	3	4	4	5	6	6
6.1	7853	7860	7868	7875	7882	7889	7896	7903	7910	7917	1	1	2	3	4	4	5	6	6
6.2	7924	7931	7938	7945	7952	7959	7966	7973	7980	7987	1	1	2	3	3	4	5	6	6
6.3	7993	8000	8007	8014	8021	8028	8035	8041	8048	8055	1	1	2	3	3	4	5	5	6
6.4	8062	8069	8075	8082	8089	8096	8102	8109	8116	8122	1	1	2	3	3	4	5	5	6
6.5	8129	8136	8142	8149	8156	8162	8169	8176	8182	8189	1	1	2	3	3	4	5	5	6
6.6	8195	8202	8209	8215	8222	8228	8235	8241	8248	8254	1	1	2	3	3	4	5	5	6
6.7	8261	8267	8274	8280	8287	8293	8299	8306	8312	8319	1	1	2	3	3	4	5	5	6
6.8	8325	8331	8338	8344	8351	8357	8363	8370	8376	8382	1	1	2	3	3	4	4	5	6
6.9	8388	8395	8401	8407	8414	8420	8426	8432	8439	8445	1	1	2	2	3	4	4	5	6
7.0	8451	8457	8463	8470	8476	8482	8488	8494	8500	8506	1	1	2	2	3	4	4	5	6
7.1	8513	8519	8525	8531	8537	8543	8549	8555	8561	8567	1	1	2	2	3	4	4	5	5
7.2	8573	8579	8585	8591	8597	8603	8609	8615	8621	8627	1	1	2	2	3	4	4	5	5
7.3	8633	8639	8645	8651	8657	8663	8669	8675	8681	8686	1	1	2	2	3	4	4	5	5
7.4	8692	8698	8704	8710	8716	8722	8727	8733	8739	8745	1	1	2	2	3	4	4	5	5
7.5	8751	8756	8762	8768	8774	8779	8785	8791	8797	8802	1	1	2	2	3	3	4	5	5
7.6	8808	8814	8820	8825	8831	8837	8842	8848	8854	8859	1	1	2	2	3	3	4	5	5
7.7	8865	8871	8876	8882	8887	8893	8899	8904	8910	8915	1	1	2	2	3	3	4	4	5
7.8	8921	8927	8932	8938	8943	8949	8954	8960	8965	8971	1	1	2	2	3	3	4	4	5
7.9	8976	8982	8987	8993	8998	9004	9009	9015	9020	9025	1	1	2	2	3	3	4	4	5
8.0	9031	9036	9042	9047	9053	9058	9063	9069	9074	9079	1	1	2	2	3	3	4	4	5
8.1	9085	9090	9096	9101	9106	9112	9117	9122	9128	9133	1	1	2	2	3	3	4	4	5
8.2	9138	9143	9149	9154	9159	9165	9170	9175	9180	9186	1	1	2	2	3	3	4	4	5
8.3	9191	9196	9201	9206	9212	9217	9222	9227	9232	9238	1	1	2	2	3	3	4	4	5
8.4	9243	9248	9253	9258	9263	9269	9274	9279	9284	9289	1	1	2	2	3	3	4	4	5
8.5	9294	9299	9304	9309	9315	9320	9325	9330	9335	9340	1	1	2	2	3	3	4	4	5
8.6	9345	9350	9355	9360	9365	9370	9375	9380	9385	9390	1	1	2	2	3	3	4	4	5
8.7	9395	9400	9405	9410	9415	9420	9425	9430	9435	9440	0	1	1	2	2	3	3	4	4
8.8	9445	9450	9455	9460	9465	9469	9474	9479	9484	9489	0	1	1	2	2	3	3	4	4
8.9	9494	9499	9504	9509	9513	9518	9523	9528	9533	9538	0	1	1	2	2	3	3	4	4
9.0	9542	9547	9552	9557	9562	9566	9571	9576	9581	9586	0	1	1	2	2	3	3	4	4
9.1	9590	9595	9600	9605	9609	9614	9619	9624	9628	9633	0	1	1	2	2	3	3	4	4
9.2	9638	9643	9647	9652	9657	9661	9666	9671	9675	9680	0	1	1	2	2	3	3	4	4
9.3	9685	9689	9694	9699	9703	9708	9713	9717	9722	9727	0	1	1	2	2	3	3	4	4
9.4	9731	9736	9741	9745	9750	9754	9759	9763	9768	9773	0	1	1	2	2	3	3	4	4
9.5	9777	9782	9786	9791	9795	9800	9805	9809	9814	9818	0	1	1	2	2	3	3	4	4
9.6	9823	9827	9832	9836	9841	9845	9850	9854	9859	9863	0	1	1	2	2	3	3	4	4
9.7	9868	9872	9877	9881	9886	9890	9894	9899	9903	9908	0	1	1	2	2	3	3	4	4
9.8	9912	9917	9921	9926	9930	9934	9939	9943	9948	9952	0	1	1	2	2	3	3	4	4
9.9	9956	9961	9965	9969	9974	9978	9983	9987	9991	9996	0	1	1	2	2	3	3	3	4

Table III *Four-Place Values of Trigonometric Functions*

Angle θ in:		sin θ	csc θ	tan θ	cot θ	sec θ	cos θ		
Degrees	Radians								
0° 00′	0.0000	0.0000	No value	0.0000	No value	1.000	1.0000	1.5708	90° 00′
10	029	029	343.8	029	343.8	000	000	679	50
20	058	058	171.9	058	171.9	000	000	650	40
30	087	087	114.6	087	114.6	000	1.0000	621	30
40	116	116	85.95	116	85.94	000	.9999	592	20
50	145	145	68.76	145	68.75	000	999	563	10
1° 00′	0.0175	0.0175	57.30	0.0175	57.29	1.000	0.9998	1.5533	89° 00′
10	204	204	49.11	204	49.10	000	998	504	50
20	233	233	42.98	233	42.96	000	997	475	40
30	262	262	38.20	262	38.19	000	997	446	30
40	291	291	34.38	291	34.37	000	996	417	20
50	320	320	31.26	320	31.24	001	995	388	10
2° 00′	0.0349	0.0349	28.65	0.0349	28.64	1.001	0.9994	1.5359	88° 00′
10	378	378	26.45	378	26.43	001	993	330	50
20	407	407	24.56	407	24.54	001	992	301	40
30	436	436	22.93	437	22.90	001	990	272	30
40	465	465	21.49	466	21.47	001	989	243	20
50	495	494	20.23	495	20.21	001	988	213	10
3° 00′	0.0524	0.0523	19.11	0.0524	19.08	1.001	0.9986	1.5184	87° 00′
10	553	552	18.10	553	18.07	002	985	155	50
20	582	581	17.20	582	17.17	002	983	126	40
30	611	610	16.38	612	16.35	002	981	097	30
40	640	640	15.64	641	15.60	002	980	068	20
50	669	669	14.96	670	14.92	002	978	039	10
4° 00′	0.0698	0.0698	14.34	0.0699	14.30	1.002	0.9976	1.5010	86° 00′
10	727	727	13.76	729	13.73	003	974	981	50
20	756	765	13.23	758	13.20	003	971	952	40
30	785	785	12.75	787	12.71	003	969	923	30
40	814	814	12.29	816	12.25	003	967	893	20
50	844	843	11.87	846	11.83	004	964	864	10
5° 00′	0.0873	0.0872	11.47	0.0875	11.43	1.004	0.9962	1.4835	85° 00′
10	902	901	11.10	904	11.06	004	959	806	50
20	931	929	10.76	934	10.71	004	957	777	40
30	960	958	10.43	963	10.39	005	954	748	30
40	.0989	.0987	10.13	.0992	10.08	005	951	719	20
50	.1018	.1016	9.839	.1022	9.788	005	948	690	10
6° 00′	0.1047	0.1045	9.567	0.1051	9.514	1.006	0.9945	1.4661	84° 00′
10	076	074	9.309	080	9.255	006	942	632	50
20	105	103	9.065	110	9.010	006	939	603	40
30	134	132	8.834	139	8.777	006	936	573	30
40	164	161	8.614	169	8.556	007	932	544	20
50	193	190	8.405	198	8.345	007	929	515	10
7° 00′	0.1222	0.1219	8.206	0.1228	8.144	1.008	0.9925	1.4486	83° 00′
10	251	248	8.016	257	7.953	008	922	457	50
20	280	276	7.834	287	7.770	008	918	428	40
30	309	305	7.661	317	7.596	009	914	399	30
40	338	334	7.496	346	7.429	009	911	370	20
50	367	363	7.337	376	7.269	009	907	341	10
8° 00′	0.1396	0.1392	7.185	0.1405	7.115	1.010	0.9903	1.4312	82° 00′
		cos θ	sec θ	cot θ	tan θ	csc θ	sin θ	Radians	Degrees
								Angle θ	

Table III Four-Place Values of Trigonometric Functions

Degrees	Radians	sin θ	csc θ	tan θ	cot θ	sec θ	cos θ		
8° 00′	0.1396	0.1392	7.185	0.1405	7.115	1.010	0.9903	1.4312	82° 00′
10	425	421	7.040	435	6.968	010	899	283	50
20	454	449	6.900	465	827	011	894	254	40
30	484	478	765	495	691	011	890	224	30
40	513	507	636	524	561	012	886	195	20
50	542	536	512	554	435	012	881	166	10
9° 00′	0.1571	0.1564	6.392	0.1584	6.314	1.012	0.9877	1.4137	81° 00′
10	600	593	277	614	197	013	872	108	50
20	629	622	166	644	6.084	013	868	079	40
30	658	650	6.059	673	5.976	014	863	050	30
40	687	679	5.955	703	871	014	858	1.4021	20
50	716	708	855	733	769	015	853	1.3992	10
10° 00′	0.1745	0.1736	5.759	0.1763	5.671	1.015	0.9848	1.3963	80° 00′
10	774	765	665	793	576	016	843	934	50
20	804	794	575	823	485	016	838	904	40
30	833	822	487	853	396	017	833	875	30
40	862	851	403	883	309	018	827	846	20
50	891	880	320	914	226	018	822	817	10
11° 00′	0.1920	0.1908	5.241	0.1944	5.145	1.019	0.9816	1.3788	79° 00′
10	949	937	164	.1974	5.066	019	811	759	50
20	.1978	965	089	.2004	4.989	020	805	730	40
30	.2007	.1994	5.016	035	915	020	799	701	30
40	036	.2022	4.945	065	843	021	793	672	20
50	065	051	876	095	773	022	787	643	10
12° 00′	0.2094	0.2079	4.810	0.2126	4.705	1.022	0.9781	1.3614	78° 00′
10	123	108	745	156	638	023	775	584	50
20	153	136	682	186	574	024	769	555	40
30	182	164	620	217	511	024	763	526	30
40	211	193	560	247	449	025	757	497	20
50	240	221	502	278	390	026	750	468	10
13° 00′	0.2269	0.2250	4.445	0.2309	4.331	1.026	0.9744	1.3439	77° 00′
10	298	278	390	339	275	027	737	410	50
20	327	306	336	370	219	028	730	381	40
30	356	334	284	401	165	028	724	352	30
40	385	363	232	432	113	029	717	323	20
50	414	391	182	462	061	030	710	294	10
14° 00′	0.2443	0.2419	4.134	0.2493	4.011	1.031	0.9703	1.3265	76° 00′
10	473	447	086	524	3.962	031	696	235	50
20	502	476	4.039	555	914	032	689	206	40
30	531	504	3.994	586	867	033	681	177	30
40	560	532	950	617	821	034	674	148	20
50	589	560	906	648	776	034	667	119	10
15° 00′	0.2618	0.2588	3.864	0.2679	3.732	1.035	0.9659	1.3090	75° 00′
10	647	616	822	711	689	036	652	061	50
20	676	644	782	742	647	037	644	032	40
30	705	672	742	773	606	038	636	1.3003	30
40	734	700	703	805	566	039	628	1.2974	20
50	763	728	665	836	526	039	621	945	10
16° 00′	0.2793	0.2756	3.628	0.2867	3.487	1.040	0.9613	1.2915	74° 00′
		cos θ	sec θ	cot θ	tan θ	csc θ	sin θ	Radians	Degrees
									Angle θ

Table III *Four-Place Values of Trigonometric Functions*

Angle θ in:		sin θ	csc θ	tan θ	cot θ	sec θ	cos θ		
Degrees	Radians								
16° 00′	0.2793	0.2756	3.628	0.2867	3.487	1.040	0.9613	1.2915	74° 00′
10	822	784	592	899	450	041	605	886	50
20	851	812	556	931	412	042	596	857	40
30	880	840	521	962	376	043	588	828	30
40	909	868	487	.2944	340	044	580	799	20
50	938	896	453	.3026	305	045	572	770	10
17° 00′	0.2967	0.2924	3.420	0.3057	3.271	1.046	0.9563	1.2741	73° 00′
10	.2996	952	388	089	237	047	555	712	50
20	.3025	.2979	357	121	204	048	546	683	40
30	054	.3007	326	153	172	048	537	654	30
40	083	035	295	185	140	049	528	625	20
50	113	062	265	217	108	050	520	595	10
18° 00′	0.3142	0.3090	3.236	0.3249	3.078	1.051	0.9511	1.2566	72° 00′
10	171	118	207	281	047	052	502	537	50
20	200	145	179	314	3.018	053	492	508	40
30	229	173	152	346	2.989	054	483	479	30
40	258	201	124	378	960	056	474	450	20
50	287	228	098	411	932	057	465	421	10
19° 00′	0.3316	0.3256	3.072	0.3443	2.904	1.058	0.9455	1.2392	71° 00′
10	345	283	046	476	877	059	446	363	50
20	374	311	3.021	508	850	060	436	334	40
30	403	338	2.996	541	824	061	426	305	30
40	432	365	971	574	798	062	417	275	20
50	462	393	947	607	773	063	407	246	10
20° 00′	0.3491	0.3420	2.924	0.3640	2.747	1.064	0.9397	1.2217	70° 00′
10	520	448	901	673	723	065	387	188	50
20	549	475	878	706	699	066	377	159	40
30	578	502	855	739	675	068	367	130	30
40	607	529	833	772	651	069	356	101	20
50	636	557	812	805	628	070	346	072	10
21° 00′	0.3665	0.3584	2.790	0.3839	2.605	1.071	0.9336	1.2043	69° 00′
10	694	611	769	872	583	072	325	1.2014	50
20	723	638	749	906	560	074	315	985	40
30	752	665	729	939	539	075	304	956	30
40	782	692	709	.3973	517	076	293	926	20
50	811	719	689	.4006	496	077	283	897	10
22° 00′	0.3840	0.3746	2.669	0.4040	2.475	1.079	0.9272	1.1868	68° 00′
10	869	773	650	074	455	080	261	839	50
20	898	800	632	108	434	081	250	810	40
30	927	827	613	142	414	082	239	781	30
40	956	854	595	176	394	084	228	752	20
50	985	881	577	210	375	085	216	723	10
23° 00′	0.4014	0.3907	2.559	0.4245	2.356	1.086	0.9205	1.1694	67° 00′
10	043	934	542	279	337	088	194	665	50
20	072	961	525	314	318	089	182	636	40
30	102	.3987	508	348	300	090	171	606	30
40	131	.4014	491	383	282	092	159	577	20
50	160	041	475	417	264	093	147	548	10
24° 00′	0.4189	0.4067	2.459	0.4452	2.246	1.095	0.9135	1.1519	66° 00′
		cos θ	sec θ	cot θ	tan θ	csc θ	sin θ	Radians	Degrees
								Angle θ	

Table III *Four-Place Values of Trigonometric Functions*

Angle θ in: Degrees	Radians	sin θ	csc θ	tan θ	cot θ	sec θ	cos θ		
24° 00'	0.4189	0.4067	2.459	0.4452	2.246	1.095	0.9135	1.1519	66° 00'
10	218	094	443	487	229	096	124	490	50
20	247	120	427	522	211	097	112	461	40
30	276	147	411	557	194	099	100	432	30
40	305	173	396	592	177	100	088	403	20
50	334	200	381	628	161	102	075	374	10
25° 00'	0.4363	0.4226	2.366	0.4663	2.145	1.103	0.9063	1.1345	65° 00'
10	392	253	352	699	128	105	051	316	50
20	422	279	337	734	112	106	038	286	40
30	451	305	323	770	097	108	026	257	30
40	480	331	309	806	081	109	013	228	20
50	509	358	295	841	066	111	.9001	199	10
26° 00'	0.4538	0.4384	2.281	0.4877	2.050	1.113	0.8988	1.1170	64° 00'
10	567	410	268	913	035	114	975	141	50
20	596	436	254	950	020	116	962	112	40
30	625	462	241	.4986	2.006	117	949	083	30
40	654	488	228	.5022	1.991	119	936	054	20
50	683	514	215	059	977	121	923	1.1025	10
27° 00'	0.4712	0.4540	2.203	0.5095	1.963	1.122	0.8910	1.0996	63° 00'
10	741	566	190	132	949	124	897	966	50
20	771	592	178	169	935	126	884	937	40
30	800	617	166	206	921	127	870	908	30
40	829	643	154	243	907	129	857	879	20
50	858	669	142	280	894	131	843	850	10
28° 00'	0.4887	0.4695	2.130	0.5317	1.881	1.133	0.8829	1.0821	62° 00'
10	916	720	118	354	868	134	816	792	50
20	945	746	107	392	855	136	802	763	40
30	.4974	772	096	430	842	138	788	734	30
40	.5003	797	085	467	829	140	774	705	20
50	032	823	074	505	816	142	760	676	10
29° 00'	0.5061	0.4848	2.063	0.5543	1.804	1.143	0.8746	1.0647	61° 00'
10	091	874	052	581	792	145	732	617	50
20	120	899	041	619	780	147	718	588	40
30	149	924	031	658	767	149	704	559	30
40	178	950	020	696	756	151	689	530	20
50	207	.4975	010	735	744	153	675	501	10
30° 00'	0.5236	0.5000	2.000	0.5774	1.732	1.155	0.8660	1.0472	60° 00'
10	265	025	1.990	812	720	157	646	443	50
20	294	050	980	851	709	159	631	414	40
30	323	075	970	890	698	161	616	385	30
40	352	100	961	930	686	163	601	356	20
50	381	125	951	.5969	675	165	587	327	10
31° 00'	0.5411	0.5150	1.942	0.6009	1.664	1.167	0.8572	1.0297	59° 00'
10	440	175	932	048	653	169	557	268	50
20	469	200	923	088	643	171	542	239	40
30	498	225	914	128	632	173	526	210	30
40	527	250	905	168	621	175	511	181	20
50	556	275	896	208	611	177	496	152	10
32° 00'	0.5585	0.5299	1.887	0.6249	1.600	1.179	0.8480	1.0123	58° 00'
		cos θ	sec θ	cot θ	tan θ	csc θ	sin θ	Radians	Degrees
								Angle θ	

Table III *Four-Place Values of Trigonometric Functions*

Degrees	Radians	sin θ	csc θ	tan θ	cot θ	sec θ	cos θ		
32° 00'	0.5585	0.5299	1.887	0.6249	1.600	1.179	0.8480	1.0123	58° 00'
10	614	324	878	289	590	181	465	094	50
20	643	348	870	330	580	184	450	065	40
30	672	373	861	371	570	186	434	036	30
40	701	398	853	412	560	188	418	1.0007	20
50	730	422	844	453	550	190	403	.9977	10
33° 00'	0.5760	0.5446	1.836	0.6494	1.540	1.192	0.8387	0.9948	57° 00'
10	789	471	828	536	530	195	371	919	50
20	818	495	820	577	520	197	355	890	40
30	847	519	812	619	511	199	339	861	30
40	876	544	804	661	501	202	323	832	20
50	905	568	796	703	492	204	307	803	10
34° 00'	0.5934	0.5592	1.788	0.6745	1.483	1.206	0.8290	0.9774	56° 00'
10	963	616	781	787	473	209	274	745	50
20	.5992	640	773	830	464	211	258	716	40
30	.6021	664	766	873	455	213	241	687	30
40	050	688	758	916	446	216	225	657	20
50	080	712	751	.6959	437	218	208	628	10
35° 00'	0.6109	0.5736	1.743	0.7002	1.428	1.221	0.8192	0.9599	55° 00'
10	138	760	736	046	419	223	175	570	50
20	167	783	729	089	411	226	158	541	40
30	196	807	722	133	402	228	141	512	30
40	225	831	715	177	393	231	124	483	20
50	254	854	708	221	385	233	107	454	10
36° 00'	0.6283	0.5878	1.701	0.7265	1.376	1.236	0.8090	0.9425	54° 00'
10	312	901	695	310	368	239	073	396	50
20	341	925	688	355	360	241	056	367	40
30	370	948	681	400	351	244	039	338	30
40	400	972	675	445	343	247	021	308	20
50	429	.5995	668	490	335	249	.8004	279	10
37° 00'	0.6458	0.6018	1.662	0.7536	1.327	1.252	0.7986	0.9250	53° 00'
10	487	041	655	581	319	255	696	221	50
20	516	065	649	627	311	258	951	192	40
30	545	088	643	673	303	260	934	163	30
40	574	111	636	720	295	263	916	134	20
50	603	134	630	766	288	266	898	105	10
38° 00'	0.6632	0.6157	1.624	0.7813	1.280	1.269	0.7880	0.9076	52° 00'
10	661	180	618	860	272	272	862	047	50
20	690	202	612	907	265	275	844	.9018	40
30	720	225	606	.7954	257	278	826	.8988	30
40	749	248	601	.8002	250	281	808	959	20
50	778	271	595	050	242	284	790	930	10
39° 00'	0.6807	0.6293	1.589	0.8098	1.235	1.287	0.7771	0.8901	51° 00'
10	836	316	583	146	228	290	753	872	50
20	865	338	578	195	220	293	735	843	40
30	894	361	572	243	213	296	716	814	30
40	923	383	567	292	206	299	698	785	20
50	952	406	561	342	199	302	679	756	10
40° 00'	0.6981	0.6428	1.556	0.8391	1.192	1.305	0.7660	0.8727	50° 00'
		cos θ	sec θ	cot θ	tan θ	csc θ	sin θ	Radians	Degrees
								Angle θ	

Angle θ in:
Degrees Radians

Table III   *Four-Place Values of Trigonometric Functions*

Degrees	Radians	sin θ	csc θ	tan θ	cot θ	sec θ	cos θ		
40° 00′	0.6981	0.6428	1.556	0.8391	1.192	1.305	0.7660	0.8727	50° 00′
10	.7010	450	550	441	185	309	642	698	50
20	039	472	545	491	178	312	623	668	40
30	069	494	540	541	171	315	604	639	30
40	098	517	535	591	164	318	585	610	20
50	127	539	529	642	157	322	566	581	10
41° 00′	0.7156	0.6561	1.524	0.8693	1.150	1.325	0.7547	0.8552	49° 00′
10	185	583	519	744	144	328	528	523	50
20	214	604	514	796	137	332	509	494	40
30	243	626	509	847	130	335	490	465	30
40	272	648	504	899	124	339	470	436	20
50	301	670	499	.8952	117	342	451	407	10
42° 00′	0.7330	0.6691	1.494	0.9004	1.111	1.346	0.7431	0.8378	48° 00′
10	359	713	490	057	104	349	412	348	50
20	389	734	485	110	098	353	392	319	40
30	418	756	480	163	091	356	373	290	30
40	447	777	476	217	085	360	353	261	20
50	476	799	471	271	079	364	333	232	10
43° 00′	0.7505	0.6820	1.466	0.9325	1.072	1.367	0.7314	0.8203	47° 00′
10	534	841	462	380	066	371	294	174	50
20	563	862	457	435	060	375	274	145	40
30	592	884	453	490	054	379	254	116	30
40	621	905	448	545	048	382	234	087	20
50	650	926	444	601	042	386	214	058	10
44° 00′	0.7679	0.6947	1.440	0.9657	1.036	1.390	0.7193	0.8029	46° 00′
10	709	967	435	713	030	394	173	.7999	50
20	738	.6988	431	770	024	398	153	970	40
30	767	.7009	427	827	018	402	133	941	30
40	796	030	423	884	012	406	112	912	20
50	825	050	418	.9942	006	410	092	883	10
45° 00′	0.7854	0.7071	1.414	1.000	1.000	1.414	0.7071	0.7854	45° 00′
		cos θ	sec θ	cot θ	tan θ	csc θ	sin θ	Radians	Degrees
								Angle θ	

Table IV *Four-Place Logarithms of the Trigonometric Functions*

Subtract 10 from each entry in this Table.

Angle θ	L sin θ	L csc θ	L tan θ	L cot θ	L sec θ	L cos θ	
0° 00′	No value	No value	No value	No value	10.0000	10.0000	**90° 00′**
10′	7.4637	12.5363	7.4637	12.5363	.0000	.0000	50′
20′	.7648	.2352	.7648	.2352	.0000	.0000	40′
30′	7.9408	12.0592	7.9409	12.0591	.0000	.0000	30′
40′	8.0658	11.9342	8.0658	11.9342	.0000	.0000	20′
50′	.1627	.8373	.1627	.8373	.0000	10.0000	10′
1° 00′	8.2419	11.7581	8.2419	11.7581	10.0001	9.9999	**89° 00′**
10′	.3088	.6912	.3089	.6911	.0001	.9999	50′
20′	.3668	.6332	.3669	.6331	.0001	.9999	40′
30′	.4179	.5821	.4181	.5819	.0001	.9999	30′
40′	.4637	.5363	.4638	.5362	.0002	.9998	20′
50′	.5050	.4950	.5053	.4947	.0002	.9998	10′
2° 00′	8.5428	11.4572	8.5431	11.4569	10.0003	9.9997	**88° 00′**
10′	5.776	.4224	.5779	.4221	.0003	.9997	50′
20′	.6097	.3903	.6101	.3899	.0004	.9996	40′
30′	.6397	.3603	.6401	.3599	.0004	.9996	30′
40′	.6677	.3323	.6682	.3318	.0005	.9995	20′
50′	.6940	.3060	.6945	.3055	.0005	.9995	10′
3° 00′	8.7188	11.2812	8.7194	11.2806	10.0006	9.9994	**87° 00′**
10′	.7423	.2577	.7429	.2571	.0007	.9993	50′
20′	.7645	.2355	.7652	.2348	.0007	.9993	40′
30′	.7857	.2143	.7865	.2135	.0008	.9992	30′
40′	.8059	.1941	.8067	.1933	.0009	.9991	20′
50′	.8251	.1749	.8261	.1739	.0010	.9990	10′
4° 00′	8.8436	11.1564	8.8446	11.1554	10.0011	9.9989	**86° 00′**
10′	.8613	.1387	.8624	.1376	.0011	.9989	50′
20′	.8783	.1217	.8795	.1205	.0012	.9988	40′
30′	.8946	.1054	.8960	.1040	.0013	.9987	30′
40′	.9104	.0896	.9118	.0882	.0014	.9986	20′
50′	.9256	.0744	.9272	.0728	.0015	.9985	10′
5° 00′	8.9403	11.0597	8.9420	11.0580	10.0017	9.9983	**85° 00′**
10′	.9545	.0455	.9563	.0437	.0018	.9982	50′
20′	.9682	.0318	.9701	.0299	.0019	.9981	40′
30′	.9816	.0184	.9836	.0164	.0020	.9980	30′
40′	8.9945	11.0055	8.9966	11.0034	.0021	.9979	20′
50′	9.0070	10.9930	9.0093	10.9907	.0023	.9977	10′
6° 00′	9.0192	10.9808	9.0216	10.9784	10.0024	9.9976	**84° 00′**
	L cos θ	L sec θ	L cot θ	L tan θ	L csc θ	L sin θ	Angle θ

Table IV   *Four-Place Logarithms of the Trigonometric Functions*

Angle θ	L sin θ	L csc θ	L tan θ	L cot θ	L sec θ	L cos θ	
6° 00′	9.0192	10.9808	9.0216	10.9784	10.0024	9.9976	84° 00′
10′	.0311	.9689	.0336	.9664	.0025	.9975	50′
20′	.0426	.9574	.0453	.9547	.0027	.9973	40′
30′	.0539	.9461	.0567	.9433	.0028	.9972	30′
40′	.0648	.9352	.0678	.9322	.0029	.9971	20′
50′	.0755	.9245	.0786	.9214	.0031	.9969	10′
7° 00′	9.0859	10.9141	9.0891	10.9109	10.0032	9.9968	83° 00′
10′	.0961	.9039	.0995	.9005	.0034	.9966	50′
20′	.1060	.8940	.1096	.8904	.0036	.9964	40′
30′	.1157	.8843	.1194	.8806	.0037	.9963	30′
40′	.1252	.8748	.1291	.8709	.0039	.9961	20′
50′	.1345	.8655	.1385	.8615	.0041	.9959	10′
8° 00′	9.1436	10.8564	9.1478	10.8522	10.0042	9.9958	82° 00′
10′	.1525	.8475	.1569	.8431	.0044	.9956	50′
20′	.1612	.8388	.1658	.8342	.0046	.9954	40′
30′	.1697	.8303	.1745	.8255	.0048	.9952	30′
40′	.1781	.8219	.1831	.8169	.0050	.9950	20′
50′	.1863	.8137	.1915	.8085	.0052	.9948	10′
9° 00′	9.1943	10.8057	9.1997	10.8003	10.0054	9.9946	81° 00′
10′	.2022	.7978	.2078	.7922	.0056	.9944	50′
20′	.2100	.7900	.2158	.7842	.0058	.9942	40′
30′	.2176	.7824	.2236	.7764	.0060	.9940	30′
40′	.2251	.7749	.2313	.7687	.0062	.9938	20′
50′	.2324	.7676	.2389	.7611	.0064	.9936	10′
10° 00′	9.2397	10.7603	9.2463	10.7537	10.0066	9.9934	80° 00′
10′	.2468	.7532	.2536	.7464	.0069	.9931	50′
20′	.2538	.7462	.2609	.7391	.0071	.9929	40′
30′	.2606	.7394	.2680	.7320	.0073	.9927	30′
40′	.2674	.7326	.2750	.7250	.0076	.9924	20′
50′	.2740	.7260	.2819	.7181	.0078	.9922	10′
11° 00′	9.2806	10.7194	9.2887	10.7113	10.0081	9.9919	79° 00′
10′	.2870	.7130	.2953	.7047	.0083	.9917	50′
20′	.2934	.7066	.3020	.6980	.0086	.9914	40′
30′	.2997	.7003	.3085	.6915	.0088	.9912	30′
40′	.3058	.6942	.3149	.6851	.0091	.9909	20′
50′	.3119	.6881	.3212	.6788	.0093	.9907	10′
12° 00′	9.3179	10.6821	9.3275	10.6725	10.0096	9.9904	78° 00′
10′	.3238	.6762	.3336	.6664	.0099	.9901	50′
20′	.3296	.6704	.3397	.6603	.0101	.9899	40′
30′	.3353	.6647	.3458	.6542	.0104	.9896	30′
40′	.3410	.6590	.3517	.6483	.0107	.9893	20′
50′	.3466	.6534	.3576	.6424	.0110	.9890	10′
13° 00′	9.3521	10.6479	9.3634	10.6366	10.0113	9.9887	77° 00′
	L cos θ	L sec θ	L cot θ	L tan θ	L csc θ	L sin θ	Angle θ

Table IV *Four-Place Logarithms of the Trigonometric Functions*

Angle θ	L sin θ	L csc θ	L tan θ	L cot θ	L sec θ	L cos θ	
13° 00′	9.3521	10.6479	9.3634	10.6366	10.0113	9.9887	**77° 00′**
10′	.3575	.6425	.3691	.6309	.0116	.9884	50′
20′	.3629	.6371	.3748	.6252	.0119	.9881	40′
30′	.3682	.6318	.3804	.6196	.0122	.9878	30′
40′	.3734	.6266	.3859	.6141	.0125	.9875	20′
50′	.3786	.6214	.3914	.6086	.0128	.9872	10′
14° 00′	9.3837	10.6163	9.3968	10.6032	10.0131	9.9869	**76° 00′**
10′	.3887	.6113	.4021	.5979	.0134	.9866	50′
20′	.3937	.6063	.4074	.5926	.0137	.9863	40′
30′	.3986	.6014	.4127	.5873	.0141	.9859	30′
40′	.4035	.5965	.4178	.5822	.0144	.9856	20′
50′	.4083	.5917	.4230	.5770	.0147	.9853	10′
15° 00′	9.4130	10.5870	9.4281	10.5719	10.0151	9.9849	**75° 00′**
10′	.4177	.5823	.4331	.5669	.0154	.9846	50′
20′	.4223	.5777	.4381	.5619	.0157	.9843	40′
30′	.4269	.5731	.4430	.5570	.0161	.9839	30′
40′	.4314	.5686	.4479	.5521	.0164	.9836	20′
50′	.4359	.5641	.4527	.5473	.0168	.9832	10′
16° 00′	9.4403	10.5597	9.4575	10.5425	10.0172	9.9828	**74° 00′**
10′	.4447	.5553	.4622	.5378	.0175	.9825	50′
20′	.4491	.5509	.4669	.5331	.0179	.9821	40′
30′	.4533	.5467	.4716	.5284	.0183	.9817	30′
40′	.4576	.5424	.4762	.5238	.0186	.9814	20′
50′	.4618	.5382	.4808	.5192	.0190	.9810	10′
17° 00′	9.4659	10.5341	9.4853	10.5147	10.0194	9.9806	**73° 00′**
10′	.4700	.5300	.4898	.5102	.0198	.9802	50′
20′	.4741	.5259	.4943	.5057	.0202	.9798	40′
30′	.4781	.5219	.4987	.5013	.0206	.9794	30′
40′	.4821	.5179	.5031	.4969	.0210	.9790	20′
50′	.4861	.5139	.5075	.4925	.0214	.9786	10′
18° 00′	9.4900	10.5100	9.5118	10.4882	10.0218	9.9782	**72° 00′**
10′	.4939	.5061	.5161	.4839	.0222	.9778	50′
20′	.4977	.5023	.5203	.4797	.0226	.9774	40′
30′	.5015	.4985	.5245	.4755	.0230	.9770	30′
40′	.5052	.4948	.5287	.4713	.0235	.9765	20′
50′	.5090	.4910	.5329	.4671	.0239	.9761	10′
19° 00′	9.5126	10.4874	9.5370	10.4630	10.0243	9.9757	**71° 00′**
10′	.5163	.4837	.5411	.4589	.0248	.9752	50′
20′	.5199	.4801	.5451	.4549	.0252	.9748	40′
30′	.5235	.4765	.5491	.4509	.0257	.9743	30′
40′	.5270	.4730	.5531	.4469	.0261	.9739	20′
50′	.5306	.4694	.5571	.4429	.0266	.9734	10′
20° 00′	9.5341	10.4659	9.5611	10.4389	10.0270	9.9730	**70° 00′**
	L cos θ	L sec θ	L cot θ	L tan θ	L csc θ	L sin θ	Angle θ

Table IV *Four-Place Logarithms of the Trigonometric Functions*

Angle θ	L sin θ	L csc θ	L tan θ	L cot θ	L sec θ	L cos θ	
20° 00′	9.5341	10.4659	9.5611	10.4389	10.0270	9.9730	70° 00′
10′	.5375	.4625	.5650	.4350	.0275	.9725	50′
20′	.5409	.4591	.5689	.4311	.0279	.9721	40′
30′	.5443	.4557	.5727	.4273	.0284	.9716	30′
40′	.5477	.4523	.5766	.4234	.0289	.9711	20′
50′	.5510	.4490	.5804	.4196	.0294	.9706	10′
21° 00′	9.5543	10.4457	9.5842	10.4158	10.0298	9.9702	69° 00′
10′	.5576	.4424	.5879	.4121	.0303	.9797	50′
20′	.5609	.4391	.5917	.4083	.0308	.9692	40′
30′	.5641	.4359	.5954	.4046	.0313	.9687	30′
40′	.5673	.4327	.5991	.4009	.0318	.9682	20′
50′	.5704	.4296	.6028	.3972	.0323	.9677	10′
22° 00′	9.5736	10.4264	9.6064	10.3936	10.0328	9.9672	68° 00′
10′	.5767	.4233	.6100	.3900	.0333	.9667	50′
20′	.5798	.4202	.6136	.3864	.0339	.9661	40′
30′	.5828	.4172	.6172	.3828	.0344	.9656	30′
40′	.5859	.4141	.6208	.3792	.0349	.9651	20′
50′	.5889	.4111	.6243	.3757	.0354	.9646	10′
23° 00′	9.5919	10.4081	9.6279	10.3721	10.0360	9.9640	67° 00′
10′	.5948	.4052	.6314	.3686	.0365	.9635	50′
20′	.5978	.4022	.6348	.3652	.0371	.9629	40′
30′	.6007	.3993	.6383	.3617	.0376	.9624	30′
40′	.6036	.3964	.6417	.3583	.0382	.9618	20′
50′	.6065	.3935	.6452	.3548	.0387	.9613	10′
24° 00′	9.6093	10.3907	9.6486	10.3514	10.0393	9.9607	66° 00′
10′	.6121	.3879	.6520	.3480	.0398	.9602	50′
20′	.6149	.3851	.6553	.3447	.0404	.9596	40′
30′	.6177	.3823	.6587	.3413	.0410	.9590	30′
40′	.6205	.3795	.6620	.3380	.0416	.9584	20′
50′	.6232	.3768	.6654	.3346	.0421	.9579	10′
25° 00′	9.6259	10.3741	9.6687	10.3313	10.0427	9.9573	65° 00′
10′	.6286	.3714	.6720	.3280	.0433	.9567	50′
20′	.6313	.3687	.6752	.3248	.0439	.9561	40′
30′	.6340	.3660	.6785	.3215	.0445	.9555	30′
40′	.6366	.3634	.6817	.3183	.0451	.9549	20′
50′	.6392	.3608	.6850	.3150	.0457	.9543	10′
26° 00′	9.6418	10.3582	9.6882	10.3118	10.0463	9.9537	64° 00′
10′	.6444	.3556	.6914	.3086	.0470	.9530	50′
20′	.6470	.3530	.6946	.3054	.0476	.9524	40′
30′	.6495	.3505	.6977	.3023	.0482	.9518	30′
40′	.6521	.3479	.7009	.2991	.0488	.9512	20′
50′	.6546	.3454	.7040	.2960	.0495	.9505	10′
27° 00′	9.6570	10.3430	9.7072	10.2928	10.0501	9.9499	63° 00′
	L cos θ	L sec θ	L cot θ	L tan θ	L csc θ	L sin θ	Angle θ

Table IV *Four-Place Logarithms of the Trigonometric Functions*

Angle θ	L sin θ	L csc θ	L tan θ	L cot θ	L sec θ	L cos θ	
27° 00′	9.6570	10.3430	9.7072	10.2928	10.0501	9.9499	**63° 00′**
10′	.6595	.3405	.7103	.2897	.0508	.9492	50′
20′	.6620	.3380	.7134	.2866	.0514	.9486	40′
30′	.6644	.3356	.7165	.2835	.0521	.9479	30′
40′	.6668	.3332	.7196	.2804	.0527	.9473	20′
50′	.6692	.3308	.7226	.2774	.0534	.9466	10′
28° 00′	9.6716	10.3284	9.7257	10.2743	10.0541	9.9459	**62° 00′**
10′	.6740	.3260	.7287	.2713	.0547	.9453	50′
20′	.6763	.3237	.7317	.2683	.0554	.9446	40′
30′	.6787	.3213	.7348	.2652	.0561	.9439	30′
40′	.6810	.3190	.7378	.2622	.0568	.9432	20′
50′	.6833	.3167	.7408	.2592	.0575	.9425	10′
29° 00′	9.6856	10.3144	9.7438	10.2562	10.0582	9.9418	**61° 00′**
10′	.6878	.3122	.7467	.2533	.0589	.9411	50′
20′	.6901	.3099	.7497	.2503	.0596	.9404	40′
30′	.6923	.3077	.7526	.2474	.0603	.9397	30′
40′	.6946	.3054	.7556	.2444	.0610	.9390	20′
50′	.6968	.3032	.7585	.2415	.0617	.9383	10′
30° 00′	9.6990	10.3010	9.7614	10.2386	10.0625	9.9375	**60° 00′**
10′	.7012	.2988	.7644	.2356	.0632	.9368	50′
20′	.7033	.2967	.7673	.2327	.0639	.9361	40′
30′	.7055	.2945	.7701	.2299	.0647	.9353	30′
40′	.7076	.2924	.7730	.2270	.0654	.9346	20′
50′	.7097	.2903	.7759	.2241	.0662	.9338	10′
31° 00′	9.7118	10.2882	9.7788	10.2212	10.0669	9.9331	**59° 00′**
10′	.7139	.2861	.7816	.2184	.0677	.9323	50′
20′	.7160	.2840	.7845	.2155	.0685	.9315	40′
30′	.7181	.2819	.7873	.2127	.0692	.9308	30′
40′	.7201	.2799	.7902	.2098	.0700	.9300	20′
50′	.7222	.2778	.7930	.2070	.0708	.9292	10′
32° 00′	9.7242	10.2758	9.7958	10.2042	10.0716	9.9284	**58° 00′**
10′	.7262	.2738	.7986	.2014	.0724	.9276	50′
20′	.7282	.2718	.8014	.1986	.0732	.9268	40′
30′	.7302	.2698	.8042	.1958	.0740	.9260	30′
40′	.7322	.2678	.8070	.1930	.0748	.9252	20′
50′	.7342	.2658	.8097	.1903	.0756	.9244	10′
33° 00′	9.7361	10.2639	9.8125	10.1875	10.0764	9.9236	**57° 00′**
10′	.7380	.2620	.8153	.1847	.0772	.9228	50′
20′	.7400	.2600	.8180	.1820	.0781	.9219	40′
30′	.7419	.2581	.8208	.1792	.0789	.9211	30′
40′	.7438	.2562	.8235	.1765	.0797	.9203	20′
50′	.7457	.2543	.8263	.1737	.0806	.9194	10′
34° 00′	9.7476	10.2524	9.8290	10.1710	10.0814	9.9186	**56° 00′**
	L cos θ	L sec θ	L cot θ	L tan θ	L csc θ	L sin θ	Angle θ

Table IV   *Four-Place Logarithms of the Trigonometric Functions*

Angle θ	L sin θ	L csc θ	L tan θ	L cot θ	L sec θ	L cos θ	
34° 00′	9.7476	10.2524	9.8290	10.1710	10.0814	9.9186	**56° 00′**
10′	.7494	.2506	.8317	.1683	.0823	.9177	50′
20′	.7513	.2487	.8344	.1656	.0831	.9169	40′
30′	.7531	.2469	.8371	.1629	.0840	.9160	30′
40′	.7550	.2450	.8398	.1602	.0849	.9151	20′
50′	.7568	.2432	.8425	.1575	.0858	.9142	10′
35° 00′	9.7586	10.2414	9.8452	10.1548	10.0866	9.9134	**55° 00′**
10′	.7604	.2396	.8479	.1521	.0875	.9125	50′
20′	.7622	.2378	.8506	.1494	.0884	.9116	40′
30′	.7640	.2360	.8533	.1467	.0893	.9107	30′
40′	.7657	.2343	.8559	.1441	.0902	.9098	20′
50′	.7675	.2325	.8586	.1414	.0911	.9089	10′
36° 00′	9.7692	10.2308	9.8613	10.1387	10.0920	9.9080	**54° 00′**
10′	.7710	.2290	.8639	.1361	.0930	.9070	50′
20′	.7727	.2273	.8666	.1334	.0939	.9061	40′
30′	.7744	.2256	.8692	.1308	.0948	.9052	30′
40′	.7761	.2239	.8718	.1282	.0958	.9042	20′
50′	.7778	.2222	.8745	.1255	.0967	.9033	10′
37° 00′	9.7795	10.2205	9.8771	10.1229	10.0977	9.9023	**53° 00′**
10′	.7811	.2189	.8797	.1203	.0986	.9014	50′
20′	.7828	.2172	.8824	.1176	.0996	.9004	40′
30′	.7844	.2156	.8850	.1150	.1005	.8995	30′
40′	.7861	.2139	.8876	.1124	.1015	.8985	20′
50′	.7877	.2123	.8902	.1098	.1025	.8975	10′
38° 00′	9.7893	10.2107	9.8928	10.1072	10.1035	9.8965	**52° 00′**
10′	.7910	.2090	.8954	.1046	.1045	.8955	50′
20′	.7926	.2074	.8980	.1020	.1055	.8945	40′
30′	.7941	.2059	.9006	.0994	.1065	.8935	30′
40′	.7957	.2043	.9032	.0968	.1075	.8925	20′
50′	.7973	.2027	.9058	.0942	.1085	.8915	10′
39° 00′	9.7989	10.2011	9.9084	10.0916	10.1095	9.8905	**51° 00′**
10′	.8004	.1996	.9110	.0890	.1105	.8895	50′
20′	.8020	.1980	.9135	.0865	.1116	.8884	40′
30′	.8035	.1965	.9161	.0839	.1126	.8874	30′
40′	.8050	.1950	.9187	.0813	.1136	.8864	20′
50′	.8066	.1934	.9212	.0788	.1147	.8853	10′
40° 00′	9.8081	10.1919	9.9238	10.0762	10.1157	9.8843	**50° 00′**
10′	.8096	.1904	.9264	.0736	.1168	.8832	50′
20′	.8111	.1889	.9289	.0711	.1179	.8821	40′
30′	.8125	.1875	.9315	.0685	.1190	.8810	30′
40′	.8140	.1860	.9341	.0659	.1200	.8800	20′
50′	.8155	.1845	.9366	.0634	.1211	.8789	10′
41° 00′	9.8169	10.1831	9.9392	10.0608	10.1222	9.8778	**49° 00′**
	L cos θ	L sec θ	L cot θ	L tan θ	L csc θ	L sin θ	Angle θ

Table IV *Four-Place Logarithms of the Trigonometric Functions*

Angle θ	L sin θ	L csc θ	L tan θ	L cot θ	L sec θ	L cos θ	
41° 00′	9.8169	10.1831	9.9392	10.0608	10.1222	9.8778	**49° 00′**
10′	.8184	.1816	.9417	.0583	.1233	.8767	50′
20′	.8198	.1802	.9443	.0557	.1244	.8756	40′
30′	.8213	.1787	.9468	.0532	.1255	.8745	30′
40′	.8227	.1773	.9494	.0506	.1267	.8733	20′
50′	.8241	.1759	.9519	.0481	.1278	.8722	10′
42° 00′	9.8255	10.1745	9.9544	10.0456	10.1289	9.8711	**48° 00′**
10′	.8269	.1731	.9570	.0430	.1301	.8699	50′
20′	.8283	.1717	.9595	.0405	.1312	.8688	40′
30′	.8297	.1703	.9621	.0379	.1324	.8676	30′
40′	.8311	.1689	.9646	.0354	.1335	.8665	20′
50′	.8324	.1676	.9671	.0329	.1347	.8653	10′
43° 00′	9.8338	10.1662	9.9697	10.0303	10.1359	9.8641	**47° 00′**
10′	.8351	.1649	.9722	.0278	.1371	.8629	50′
20′	.8365	.1635	.9747	.0253	.1382	.8618	40′
30′	.8378	.1622	.9772	.0228	.1394	.8606	30′
40′	.8391	.1609	.9798	.0202	.1406	.8594	20′
50′	.8405	.1595	.9823	.0177	.1418	.8582	10′
44° 00′	9.8418	10.1582	9.9848	10.0152	10.1431	9.8569	**46° 00′**
10′	.8431	.1569	.9874	.0126	.1443	.8557	50′
20′	.8444	.1556	.9899	.0101	.1455	.8545	40′
30′	.8457	.1543	.9924	.0076	.1468	.8532	30′
40′	.8469	.1531	.9949	.0051	.1480	.8520	20′
50′	.8482	.1518	9.9975	.0025	.1493	.8507	10′
45° 00′	9.8495	10.1505	10.0000	10.0000	10.1505	9.8495	**45° 00′**
	L cos θ	L sec θ	L cot θ	L tan θ	L csc θ	L sin θ	Angle θ

Table V *Values of the Exponential Function*

t	e^t	e^{-t}	t	e^t	e^{-t}
0.00	1.0000	1.0000	2.5	12.182	0.0821
0.05	1.0513	0.9512	2.6	13.464	0.0743
0.10	1.1052	0.9048	2.7	14.880	0.0672
0.15	1.1618	0.8607	2.8	16.445	0.0608
0.20	1.2214	0.8187	2.9	18.174	0.0550
0.25	1.2840	0.7788	3.0	20.086	0.0498
0.30	1.3499	0.7408	3.1	22.198	0.0450
0.35	1.4191	0.7047	3.2	24.533	0.0408
0.40	1.4918	0.6703	3.3	27.113	0.0369
0.45	1.5683	0.6376	3.4	29.964	0.0334
0.50	1.6487	0.6065	3.5	33.115	0.0302
0.55	1.7333	0.5769	3.6	36.598	0.0273
0.60	1.8221	0.5488	3.7	40.447	0.0247
0.65	1.9155	0.5220	3.8	44.701	0.0224
0.70	2.0138	0.4966	3.9	49.402	0.0202
0.75	2.1170	0.4724	4.0	54.598	0.0183
0.80	2.2255	0.4493	4.1	60.340	0.0166
0.85	2.3396	0.4274	4.2	66.686	0.0150
0.90	2.4596	0.4066	4.3	73.700	0.0136
0.95	2.5857	0.3867	4.4	81.451	0.0123
1.0	2.7183	0.3679	4.5	90.017	0.0111
1.1	3.0042	0.3329	4.6	99.484	0.0101
1.2	3.3201	0.3012	4.7	109.95	0.0091
1.3	3.6693	0.2725	4.8	121.51	0.0082
1.4	4.0552	0.2466	4.9	134.29	0.0074
1.5	4.4817	0.2231	5.0	148.41	0.0067
1.6	4.9530	0.2019	5.5	244.69	0.0041
1.7	5.4739	0.1827	6.0	403.43	0.0025
1.8	6.0496	0.1653	6.5	665.14	0.0015
1.9	6.6859	0.1496	7.0	1,096.6	0.0009
2.0	7.3891	0.1353	7.5	1,808.0	0.0006
2.1	8.1662	0.1225	8.0	2,981.0	0.0003
2.2	9.0250	0.1108	8.5	4,914.8	0.0002
2.3	9.9742	0.1003	9.0	8,103.1	0.0001
2.4	11.023	0.0907	10.0	22,026	0.00005

Table VI *Natural Logarithms of Numbers from 0 to 250*

N	$\log_e N$	N	$\log_e N$	N	$\log_e N$	N	$\log_e N$	N	$\log_e N$
0	$-\infty$	50	3.91 202	100	4.60 517	150	5.01 064	200	5.29 832
1	0.00 000	51	3.93 183	101	4.61 512	151	5.01 728	201	5.30 330
2	0.69 315	52	3.95 124	102	4.62 497	152	5.02 388	202	5.30 827
3	1.09 861	53	3.97 029	103	4.63 473	153	5.03 044	203	5.31 321
4	1.38 629	54	3.98 898	104	4.64 439	154	5.03 695	204	5.31 812
5	1.60 944	55	4.00 733	105	4.65 393	155	5.04 343	205	5.32 301
6	1.79 176	56	4.02 535	106	4.66 344	156	5.04 986	206	5.32 788
7	1.94 591	57	4.04 305	107	4.67 283	157	5.05 625	207	5.33 272
8	2.07 944	58	4.06 044	108	4.68 213	158	5.06 260	208	5.33 754
9	2.19 722	59	4.07 754	109	4.69 135	159	5.06 890	209	5.34 233
10	2.30 259	60	4.09 434	110	4.70 048	160	5.07 517	210	5.34 711
11	2.39 790	61	4.11 087	111	4.70 953	161	5.08 140	211	5.35 186
12	2.48 491	62	4.12 713	112	4.71 850	162	5.08 760	212	5.35 659
13	2.56 495	63	4.14 313	113	4.72 739	163	5.09 375	213	5.36 129
14	2.63 906	64	4.15 888	114	4.73 620	164	5.09 987	214	5.36 598
15	2.70 805	65	4.17 439	115	4.74 493	165	5.10 595	215	5.37 064
16	2.77 259	66	4.18 965	116	4.75 359	166	5.11 199	216	5.37 528
17	2.83 321	67	4.20 469	117	4.76 217	167	5.11 799	217	5.37 990
18	2.89 037	68	4.21 951	118	4.77 068	168	5.12 396	218	5.38 450
19	2.94 444	69	4.23 411	119	4.77 912	169	5.12 990	219	5.38 907
20	2.99 573	70	4.24 850	120	4.78 749	170	5.13 580	220	5.39 363
21	3.04 452	71	4.26 268	121	4.79 579	171	5.14 166	221	5.39 816
22	3.09 104	72	4.27 667	122	4.80 402	172	5.14 749	222	5.40 268
23	3.13 549	73	4.29 046	123	4.81 218	173	5.15 329	223	5.40 717
24	3.17 805	74	4.30 407	124	4.82 028	174	5.15 906	224	5.41 165
25	3.21 888	75	4.31 749	125	4.82 831	175	5.16 479	225	5.41 610
26	3.25 810	76	4.33 073	126	4.83 628	176	5.17 048	226	5.42 053
27	3.29 584	77	4.34 381	127	4.84 419	177	5.17 615	227	5.42 495
28	3.33 220	78	4.35 671	128	4.85 203	178	5.18 178	228	5.42 935
29	3.36 730	79	4.36 945	129	4.85 981	179	5.18 739	229	5.43 372
30	3.40 120	80	4.38 203	130	4.86 753	180	5.19 296	230	5.43 808
31	3.43 399	81	4.39 445	131	4.87 520	181	5.19 850	231	5.44 242
32	3.46 574	82	4.40 672	132	4.88 280	182	5.20 401	232	5.44 674
33	3.49 651	83	4.41 884	133	4.89 035	183	5.20 949	233	5.45 104
34	3.52 636	84	4.43 082	134	4.89 784	184	5.21 494	234	5.45 532
35	3.55 535	85	4.44 265	135	4.90 527	185	5.22 036	235	5.45 959
36	3.58 352	86	4.45 435	136	4.91 265	186	5.22 575	236	5.46 383
37	3.61 092	87	4.46 591	137	4.91 998	187	5.23 111	237	5.46 806
38	3.63 759	88	4.47 734	138	4.92 725	188	5.23 644	238	5.47 227
39	3.66 356	89	4.48 864	139	4.93 447	189	5.24 175	239	5.47 646
40	3.68 888	90	4.49 981	140	4.94 164	190	5.24 702	240	5.48 064
41	3.71 357	91	4.51 086	141	4.94 876	191	5.25 227	241	5.48 480
42	3.73 767	92	4.52 179	142	4.95 583	192	5.25 750	242	5.48 894
43	3.76 120	93	4.53 260	143	4.96 284	193	5.26 269	243	5.49 306
44	3.78 419	94	4.54 329	144	4.96 981	194	5.26 786	244	5.49 717
45	3.80 666	95	4.55 388	145	4.97 673	195	5.27 300	245	5.50 126
46	3.82 864	96	4.56 435	146	4.98 361	196	5.27 811	246	5.50 533
47	3.85 015	97	4.57 471	147	4.99 043	197	5.28 320	247	5.50 939
48	3.87 120	98	4.58 497	148	4.99 721	198	5.28 827	248	5.51 343
49	3.89 182	99	4.59 512	149	5.00 395	199	5.29 330	249	5.51 745
50	3.91 202	100	4.60 517	150	5.01 064	200	5.29 832	250	5.52 146

Table VII *1958 Commissioners Standard Ordinary Mortality Table*

Age	Number Living	Number Dying	Death Rate per 1,000	Expect-ancy, Years	Age	Number Living	Number Dying	Death Rate per 1,000	Expect-ancy, Years
0	10,000,000	70,800	7.08	68.30	50	8,762,306	72,902	8.32	23.63
1	9.929,200	17,475	1.76	67.78	51	8.689,404	79,160	9.11	22.82
2	9,911,725	15,066	1.52	66.90	52	8,610,244	85,758	9.96	22.03
3	9,896,659	14,449	1.46	66.00	53	8,524,486	92,832	10.89	21.25
4	9,882,210	13,835	1.40	65.10	54	8,431,654	100,337	11.90	20.47
5	9,868,375	13,322	1.35	64.19	55	8,331,317	108,307	13.00	19.11
6	9,855,053	12,812	1.30	63.27	56	8,223,010	116,849	14.21	18.97
7	9,842,241	12,401	1.26	62.35	57	8,406,161	125,970	15.54	18.23
8	9,829,840	12,091	1.23	61.43	58	7,980,191	135,663	17.00	17.51
9	9,817,749	11,879	1.21	60.51	59	7,844,528	145,830	18.59	16.81
10	9,805,870	11,865	1.21	59.58	60	7,698,698	156,592	20.34	16.12
11	9,794,005	12,047	1.23	58.65	61	7,542,106	167,736	22.24	15.44
12	9,781,958	12,325	1.26	57.72	62	7,374,370	179,271	24.31	14.78
13	9,769,633	12,896	1.32	56.80	63	7,195,099	191,174	26.57	14.14
14	9,756,737	13,562	1.39	55.87	64	7,003,925	203,394	29.04	13.51
15	9,743,175	14,225	1.46	54.95	65	6,800,531	215,917	31.75	12.90
16	9,728,950	14,983	1.54	54.03	66	6,584,614	228,749	34.74	12.31
17	9,713,967	15,737	1.62	53.11	67	6,355,865	241,777	38.04	11.73
18	9,698,230	16,390	1.69	52.19	68	6,114,088	254,835	41.68	11.17
19	9,681,840	16,846	1.74	51.28	69	5,859,253	267,241	45.61	10.64
20	9,664,994	17,300	1.79	50.37	70	5,592,012	278,426	49.79	10.12
21	9,647,694	17,655	1.83	49.46	71	5,313,586	287,731	54.15	9.63
22	9,630,039	17,912	1.86	48.55	72	5,025,855	294,766	58.65	9.15
23	9,612,127	18,167	1.89	47.64	73	4,731,089	299,289	63.26	8.69
24	9,593,960	18,324	1.91	46.73	74	4,431,800	301,894	68.12	8.24
25	9,575,636	18,481	1.93	45.82	75	4,129,906	303,011	73.37	7.81
26	9,557,155	18,732	1.96	44.90	76	3,826,895	303,014	79.18	7.39
27	9,538,423	18,981	1.99	43.99	77	3,523,881	301,997	85.70	6.98
28	9,519,442	19,324	2.03	43.08	78	3,221,884	299,829	93.06	6.59
29	9,500,118	19,760	2.08	42.16	79	2,922,055	295,683	101.19	6.21
30	9,480,358	20,193	2.13	41.25	80	2,626,372	288,848	109.98	5.85
31	9,460,165	20,718	2.19	40.34	81	2,337,524	278,983	119.35	5.51
32	9,439,447	21,239	2.25	39.43	82	2,058,541	265,902	129.17	5.19
33	9,418,208	21,850	2.32	38.51	83	1,792,639	249,858	139.38	4.89
34	9,396,358	22,551	2.40	37.60	84	1,542,781	231,433	150.01	4.60
35	9,373,807	23,528	2.51	36.69	85	1,311,348	211,311	161.14	4.32
36	9,350,279	24,685	2.64	35.78	86	1,100,037	190,108	172.82	4.06
37	9,325,594	26,112	2.80	34.88	87	909,929	168,455	185.13	3.80
38	9,299,482	27,991	3.01	33.97	88	741,474	146,997	198.25	3.55
39	9,271,491	30,132	3.25	33.07	89	594,477	126,303	212.46	3.31
40	9,241,359	32,622	3.53	32.18	90	468,174	106,809	228.14	3.06
41	9,208,737	35,362	3.84	31.29	91	361,365	88,813	245.77	2.82
42	9,173,375	38,253	4.17	30.41	92	272,552	72,480	265.93	2.58
43	9,135,122	41,382	4.53	29.54	93	200.072	57,881	289.30	2.33
44	9,093,740	44,741	4.92	28.67	94	142,191	45,026	316.66	2.07
45	9,048,999	48,412	5.35	27.81	95	97,165	34,128	351.24	1.80
46	9,000,587	52,473	5.83	26.95	96	63,037	25,250	400.56	1.51
47	8,948,114	56,910	6.36	26.11	97	37,787	18,456	488.42	1.18
48	8,891,204	61,794	6.95	25.27	98	19,331	12,916	688.15	0.83
49	8,829,410	67,104	7.60	24.45	99	6,415	6,415	1,000.00	0.50

Table VIII *Powers and Roots of Numbers from 1 to 100*

No.	Square	Square Root	Cube	Cube Root	No.	Square	Square Root	Cube	Cube Root
1	1	1.000	1	1.000	51	2,601	7.141	132,651	3.708
2	4	1.414	8	1.260	52	2,704	7.211	140,608	3.733
3	9	1.732	27	1.442	53	2,809	7.280	148,877	3.756
4	16	2.000	64	1.587	54	2,916	7.348	157,464	3.780
5	25	2.236	125	1.710	55	3,025	7.416	166,375	3.803
6	36	2.449	216	1.817	56	3,136	7.483	175,616	3.826
7	49	2.646	343	1.913	57	3,249	7.550	185,193	3.848
8	64	2.828	512	2.000	58	3,364	7.616	195,112	3.871
9	81	3.000	729	2.080	59	3,481	7.681	205,379	3.893
10	100	3.162	1,000	2.154	60	3,600	7.746	216,000	3.915
11	121	3.317	1,331	2.224	61	3,721	7.810	226,981	3.936
12	144	3.464	1,728	2.289	62	3,844	7.874	238,328	3.958
13	169	3.606	2,197	2.351	63	3,969	7.937	250,047	3.979
14	196	3.742	2,744	2.410	64	4,096	8.000	262,144	4.000
15	225	3.873	3,375	2.466	65	4,225	8.062	274,625	4.021
16	256	4.000	4,096	2.520	66	4,356	8.124	287,496	4.041
17	289	4.123	4,913	2.571	67	4,489	8.185	300,763	4.062
18	324	4.243	5,832	2.621	68	4,624	8.246	314,432	4.082
19	361	4.359	6,859	2.668	69	4,761	8.307	328,509	4.102
20	400	4.472	8,000	2.714	70	4,900	8.367	343,000	4.121
21	441	4.583	9,261	2.759	71	5,041	8.426	357,911	4.141
22	484	4.690	10,648	2.802	72	5,184	8.485	373,248	4.160
23	529	4.796	12,167	2.844	73	5,329	8.544	389,017	4.179
24	576	4.899	13,824	2.884	74	5,476	8.602	405,224	4.198
25	625	5.000	15,625	2.924	75	5,625	8.660	421,875	4.217
26	676	5.099	17,576	2.962	76	5,776	8.718	438,976	4.236
27	729	5.196	19,683	3.000	77	5,929	8.775	456,533	4.254
28	784	5.291	21,952	3.037	78	6,084	8.832	474,552	4.273
29	841	5.385	24,389	3.072	79	6,241	8.888	493,039	4.291
30	900	5.477	27,000	3.107	80	6,400	8.944	512,000	4.309
31	961	5.568	29,791	3.141	81	6,561	9.000	531,441	4.327
32	1,024	5.657	32,768	3.175	82	6,724	9.055	551,368	4.344
33	1,089	5.745	35,937	3.208	83	6,889	9.110	571,787	4.362
34	1,156	5.831	39,304	3.240	84	7,056	9.165	592,704	4.380
35	1,225	5.916	42,875	3.271	85	7,225	9.220	614,125	4.397
36	1,296	6.000	46,656	3.302	86	7,396	9.274	636,056	4.414
37	1,369	6.083	50,653	3.332	87	7,569	9.327	658,503	4.431
38	1,444	6.164	54,872	3.362	88	7,744	9.381	681,472	4.448
39	1,521	6.245	59,319	3.391	89	7,921	9.434	704,969	4.465
40	1,600	6.325	64,000	3.420	90	8,100	9.487	729,000	4.481
41	1,661	6.403	68,921	3.448	91	8,281	9.539	753,571	4.498
42	1,764	6.481	74,088	3.476	92	8,464	9.592	778,688	4.514
43	1,849	6.557	79,507	3.503	93	8,649	9.644	804,357	4.531
44	1,936	6.633	85,184	3.530	94	8,836	9.695	830,584	4.547
45	2,025	6.708	91,125	3.557	95	9,025	9.747	857,375	4.563
46	2,116	6.782	97,336	3.583	96	9,216	9.798	884,736	4.579
47	2,209	6.856	103,823	3.609	97	9,409	9.849	912,673	4.595
48	2,304	6.928	110,592	3.634	98	9,604	9.899	941,192	4.610
49	2,401	7.000	117,649	3,659	99	9,801	9.950	970,299	4.626
50	2,500	7.071	125,000	3.648	100	10,000	10.000	1,000,000	4.642

Answers to Odd-numbered Problems

CHAPTER 1

Exercise 1.A (page 6)

1. Some are $\{2, 3\}$; $\varnothing$; $\{\square, \triangle, \bigcirc\}$.
3. (a) $\{1, 2, 3, 4, 5, 6, 7\}$ (b) $\{$Mary, Martha, Melissa$\}$.
    (c) $\{1, 2, 3, 4, 5, 6, 7, 8, 9, 10\}$.
5. $\{2, 4\}$.   **7.** $2^3 = 8$; $\{1, 8, 27\}$; $\{1, 8\}$; $\{1, 27\}$; $\{8, 27\}$; $\{1\}$; $\{8\}$; $\{27\}$; $\varnothing$.
9. a is a member of A; A is a subset of B; empty set; A is equal to B; find the set of all x, such that x is equal to 2.
11. 26.   **13.** Infinite set.   **15.** Any set with five elements; yes.
17. 6.   **19.** Finite; n.

Exercise 1.B (page 13)

1. $\{b, e, f\}$.   **3.** $n(A \cap B) = n(\varnothing) = 0$.
5. Each of them operates on two sets to form a new set.
7. No; $\{$John, Mary, Sue, George, Jane$\}$.
9. $A \cap B = \varnothing$ means that there is no element common to the two sets.
11.

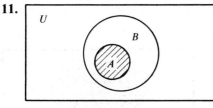

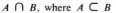

$A \cap B$, where $A \subset B$

13. (a) No; U may have more than A and B as its subsets.
    (b) Yes; using Venn diagrams.

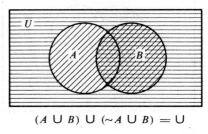

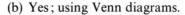

$(A \cup B) \cup (\sim\!A \cup B) = U$

413

15.

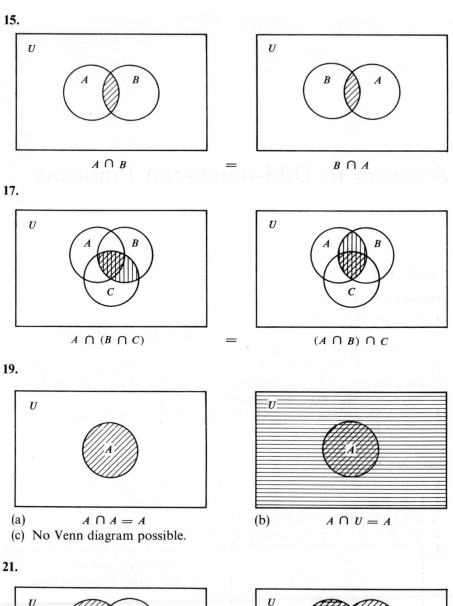

$A \cap B$ = $B \cap A$

17.

$A \cap (B \cap C)$ = $(A \cap B) \cap C$

19.

(a) $A \cap A = A$ (b) $A \cap U = A$
(c) No Venn diagram possible.

21.

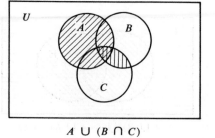

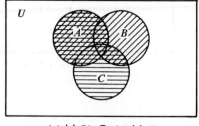

$A \cup (B \cap C)$ = $(A \cup B) \cap (A \cup C)$

23.

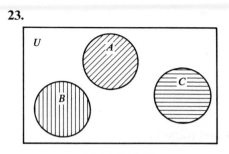

$(A \cup B \cup C)$

25.

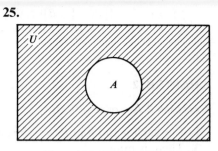

$U - A(A \subset U) = U \cup {\sim}A$

27. (a) $5; 9 + 2 + 5 + 3 + 13 = 32.$
   (b) $13; 8 + 2 + 3 + 5 + 13 = 31.$

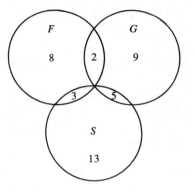

Exercise 1.C   (page 20)

1. $A \cup U = U; A \cap B = (A \cap B) \cap A.$

3. (a) $A \cup ({\sim}A \cap B) = A \cup B$
   $(A \cup {\sim}A) \cap (A \cup B) = A \cup B$
   $U \cap (A \cup B) = A \cup B$
   $\therefore A \cup B = A \cup B.$

   (e) $(A \cap B) \cap (A \cap {\sim}B) = \varnothing$
   $(B \cap A) \cap (A \cap {\sim}B) = \varnothing$
   $[(B \cap A) \cap A] \cap {\sim}B = \varnothing$
   $[B \cap (A \cap A)] \cap {\sim}B = \varnothing$
   $(B \cap A) \cap {\sim}B = \varnothing$
   $(A \cap B) \cap {\sim}B = \varnothing$
   $A \cap (B \cap {\sim}B) = \varnothing$
   $A \cap \varnothing = \varnothing$
   $\therefore \varnothing = \varnothing.$

   (c) $(A \cap {\sim}B) \cup (A \cap B) = A$
   $A \cap ({\sim}B \cup B) = A$
   $A \cap U = A$
   $\therefore A = A.$

   (g) $U = (A \cup B) \cup {\sim}(A \cup B)$
   $U = (A \cup B) \cup ({\sim}A \cap {\sim}B)$
   $U = ({\sim}[{\sim}A] \cup {\sim}[{\sim}B]) \cup$
   $\qquad ({\sim}A \cap {\sim}B)$
   $U = {\sim}({\sim}A \cap {\sim}B) \cup ({\sim}A \cap {\sim}B)$
   $\therefore U = U.$

   (i) $(A \cup U) \cup \varnothing = U$
   $U \cup \varnothing = U$
   $\therefore U = U.$

   (k) $A \cup (A \cup B) \cup [(A \cup B) \cap (C \cup D)] = (A \cup B) \cap (C \cup D)$
   $[(A \cup A) \cup B] \cup [(A \cup B) \cap (C \cup D)] = (A \cup B) \cap (C \cup D)$
   $(A \cup B) \cup [(A \cup B) \cap (C \cup D)] = (A \cup B) \cap (C \cup D)$
   $[(A \cup B) \cup (A \cup B)] \cap (C \cup D) = (A \cup B) \cap (C \cup D)$
   $\therefore (A \cup B) \cap (C \cup D) = (A \cup B) \cap (C \cup D).$

5. $\varnothing = (A \cap B) \cap {\sim}(A \cap B)$
   $\varnothing = (A \cap B) \cap ({\sim}A \cup {\sim}B)$

$$\emptyset = (\sim[\sim A] \cap \sim[\sim B]) \cap (\sim A \cup \sim B)$$
$$\emptyset = \sim(\sim A \cup \sim B) \cap (\sim A \cup \sim B)$$
$$\therefore \emptyset = \emptyset.$$

CHAPTER 2

Exercise 2.A   (pages 30-31)

1. For each a and b in R, $a + b$ is in R and is unique.

3. There is none.

5. $a + (b + c) = (a + b) \pm c.$

7. (a) Closed.   (b) Not closed.   (c) Closed.

9. None of them; yes.   **11.** Yes; no; yes; no.

13. (a) No.   (b) Yes; 1.   **15.** A_5.

17. An infinite number; an infinite number.   **19.** Yes; yes; yes.

21. Yes; $\frac{4}{9}$.

23. A number set that does not have an additive identity does not have an additive inverse in the field postulates. Thus, the set could contain no negative numbers. Nonnegative sets of numbers are *not closed* under subtraction.

25. b or $b = \dfrac{1}{a}$.

27.
$$
\begin{aligned}
(a + b)(c + d) &= (ac + bd) + (ad + bc) & (D)\\
(a + b)(c + d) &= (a + b)c + (a + b)d & (D)\\
&= (ac + bc) + (ad + bd) & (D)\\
&= (ac + bc) + (bd + ad) & (A_2)\\
&= [ac + (bc + bd) + ad] & (A_3)\\
&= [ac + (bd + bc) + ad] & (A_2)\\
&= (ac + bd) + (bc + ad) & (A_3)\\
\therefore (a + b)(c + d) &= (ac + bd) + (ad + bc). & (A_2)
\end{aligned}
$$

29.
$$
\begin{aligned}
[a(b + 1)] + [b + (-a)] &= b(a + 1)\\
[a(b + 1)] + [b + (-a)] &= [ab + a \cdot 1] + [b + (-a)] & (D)\\
&= [ab + a] + [(-a) + b] & (M_4, A_2)\\
&= ab + [a + (-a)] + b & (A_3)\\
&= ab + 0 + b & (A_5)\\
&= ab + b & (A_4)\\
&= ba + b \cdot 1 & (M_2, M_4)\\
\therefore [a(b + 1)] + [b + (-a)] &= b(a + 1). & (D)
\end{aligned}
$$

Exercise 2.B   (page 34)

1. Prove: If $a = b$ and $c = d$, then $a + c = b + d$.

$$
\begin{array}{ll}
a = b & \text{(Hypothesis)}\\
c = d & (H)\\
a + c = a + c & (E_1)\\
\therefore a + c = b + d. & \text{(Substitution, Definition 2.11-1)}
\end{array}
$$

3. Prove: If $ab = ac$ and $a \neq 0$, then $b = c$.

$$\begin{aligned}
ab &= ac && (H) \\
ab + (-ac) &= ac + (-ac) && (E_4) \\
ab + (-ac) &= 0 && (A_5) \\
ab - ac &= 0 && (\text{Definition 2.2-4}) \\
a(b - c) &= 0 && (D) \\
\therefore\ a = 0 \text{ or } b - c &= 0 && (\text{Theorem 2.12-7}) \\
\text{But } a &\neq 0 && (H) \\
\text{So } b - c &= 0 && \\
b - c + c &= 0 + c && (E_4) \\
b &= 0 + c && (A_5) \\
\therefore\ b &= c. && (A_4)
\end{aligned}$$

5. Prove: $-(-a) = a$.

$$\begin{aligned}
-(-a) + (-a) &= 0 && (A_5) \\
[-(-a) + (-a)] + a &= 0 + a && (E_4) \\
[-(-a) + (-a)] + a &= a && (A_4) \\
-(-a) + [(-a) + a] &= a && (A_3) \\
-(-a) + 0 &= a && (A_5) \\
\therefore\ -(-a) &= a. && (A_4)
\end{aligned}$$

7. Prove that $-(ab) = (-a)b$.

$$\begin{aligned}
ba + b(-a) &= b[a + (-a)] && (D) \\
&= b \cdot 0 && (A_5) \\
ba + b(-a) &= 0 && (\text{Theorem 2.12-4}) \\
-(ba) + ba + b(-a) &= -(ba) + 0 && (E_4) \\
0 + b(-a) &= -(ba) + 0 && (A_5) \\
b(-a) &= -(ba) && (A_4) \\
(-a)b &= -(ab) && (M_2) \\
\therefore\ -(ab) &= (-a)b. && (E_2)
\end{aligned}$$

9. Prove: If $a = b$, then $a - c = b - c$.

$$\begin{aligned}
a &= b && (H) \\
a + [(-c) + c] &= b + [b + (-c)] + c && (A_4, A_5) \\
[a + (-c)] + c &= [b + (-c)] + c && (A_3) \\
a + (-c) &= b + (-c) && (\text{Theorem 2.12-1}) \\
\therefore\ a - c &= b - c. && (\text{Definition 2.2-4})
\end{aligned}$$

11. Prove: $d(ab) + a(dc) = ad(b + c)$.

$$\begin{aligned}
d(ab) + a(dc) &= (da)b + (ad)c && (M_3) \\
&= (ad)b + (ad)c && (M_2) \\
&= ad(b + c) && (D) \\
\therefore\ d(ab) + a(dc) &= ad(b + c). && (E_3)
\end{aligned}$$

13. Prove: $(a + b)(a - b) = a^2 - b^2$.

$$\begin{aligned}
(a + b)(a - b) &= (a + b)(a + [-b]) & \text{(Definition 2.2-4)}\\
&= (a + b)a + (a + b)(-b) & (D)\\
&= (a \cdot a + b \cdot a) + (a[-b] + [-b]) & (D)\\
&= (a^2 + ba) + [-ab + (-b^2)] & \text{(Theorem 2.12-5)}\\
&= a^2 + [ba + (-ab)] + (-b^2) & (A_3)\\
&= a^2 + [ab + (-ab)] + (-b)^2 & (M_2)\\
&= a^2 + 0 + (-b)^2 & (A_5)\\
&= a^2 + (-b^2) & (A_4)\\
\therefore (a + b)(a - b) &= a^2 - b^2. & \text{(Definition 2.2-4)}
\end{aligned}$$

15. Prove: If $a = b$, then $-a = -b$.

$$\begin{aligned}
[a + (-a)] = 0 \text{ and } [b + (-b)] &= 0 & (A_5)\\
a + (-a) &= b + (-b) & (E_3)\\
a + (-a) &= a + (-b) & \text{(Definition 2.11-1)}\\
(-a) + [a + (-a)] &= -a + [a + (-b)] & (E_4)\\
(-a) + [a + (-a)] &= [(-a) + a] + (-b) & (A_3)\\
(-a) + 0 &= 0 + (-b) & (A_5)\\
\therefore -a &= -b. & (A_4)
\end{aligned}$$

17. Prove: If $ab = 1$, $a \neq 0$, then $b = 1/a$.

$$\begin{aligned}
\text{Since } a \neq 0, \text{ then } 1/a \text{ exists.} && (M_5)\\
ab = 1 && (H)
\end{aligned}$$

$$(ab)\frac{1}{a} = (1)\frac{1}{a} \qquad\qquad (E_4)$$

$$(ba)\frac{1}{a} = (1)\frac{1}{a} \qquad\qquad (M_2)$$

$$b\left(a \cdot \frac{1}{a}\right) = (1)\frac{1}{a} \qquad\qquad (M_3)$$

$$b(1) = (1)\frac{1}{a} \qquad\qquad (M_5)$$

$$\therefore b = \frac{1}{a}. \qquad\qquad \text{(Theorem 2.12-1a)}$$

19. No, $(a - b) \neq (b - a)$; no, $(a - (b - c)) \neq ((a - b) - c)$.

Exercise 2.C (page 38)

1. (a) $\{-5, 2\}$.   (b) $\{\frac{1}{2}, \frac{2}{3}, \frac{3}{4}\}$.   (c) $\{-\sqrt{2}, 0, |-4|\}$.

3. Prove: If $a > b$, then $a + c > b + c$, c real.

$$\begin{aligned}
a &> b & \text{(Hypothesis)}\\
p &= a - b, \ p \text{ a positive integer} & \text{(Axiom 2.13-1)}\\
a - b &= a - b & (E_1)
\end{aligned}$$

$$p = a + (-b) \qquad \text{(Definition 2.2-4)}$$
$$= [a + (-b)] + 0 \qquad (A_4)$$
$$= [a + (-b)] + [c + (-c)] \qquad (A_5)$$
$$= (a + c) + [(-b) + (-c)] \qquad (A_3)$$
$$= (a + c) + [(-1)b + (-1)c] \qquad \text{(Exercise 2.B-8)}$$
$$= (a + c) + [(-1)(b + c)] \qquad (D)$$
$$p = (a + c) - (b + c) \qquad \text{(Definition 2.2-4)}$$
$$\therefore (a + c) > (b + c). \qquad \text{(Axiom 2.13-1)}$$

5. Prove: If $a \neq b$, then $a < b$ or $b < a$, but not both.

$$a < b \text{ or } a = b \text{ or } b < a \qquad (O_1)$$
$$a \neq b \qquad (H)$$
$$\therefore a < b \text{ or } b < a.$$

Both are not possible because

(1) If $a < b$, then $b > a$.   [Definition 2.14-1(c)]
(2) If $a > b$, then $b < a$.   [Definition 2.14-1(c)]

7. Prove: If $a < 0$ and $b < 0$, then $ab > 0$.

$$a < 0 \qquad (H)$$
$$a + (-a) < 0 + (-a) \qquad (O_3)$$
$$0 < (-a) \qquad (A_5, A_4)$$
$$b < 0 \qquad (H)$$
$$b + (-b) < 0 + (-b) \qquad (O_3)$$
$$0 < (-b) \qquad (A_5, A_4)$$
$$0 \cdot (-b) < (-a)(-b) \qquad (O_4)$$
$$0 < (-a)(-b) \qquad \text{(Theorem 2.12-4)}$$
$$0 < ab \qquad \text{(Theorem 2.12-6)}$$
$$\therefore ab > 0. \qquad \text{[Definition 2.14-1(c)]}$$

9. Prove: The product of two positive numbers, $0 < a$ and $0 < b$, is positive.

$$0 < a \qquad (H)$$
$$0 < b \qquad (H)$$
$$0 \cdot b < a \cdot b \qquad (O_4)$$
$$0 < a \cdot b \qquad \text{(Theorem 2.12-4)}$$
$$\therefore ab \text{ is positive.} \qquad \text{(Definition 2.14-2)}$$

11. Yes.

If $a > 0$, then $a^2 > 0$.

$$a > 0 \qquad (H)$$
$$a \cdot a > 0 \cdot a \qquad (O_4)$$
$$a \cdot a > 0 \qquad \text{(Theorem 2.12-4)}$$
$$\therefore a^2 > 0.$$

13. Prove: If $a \geq b$, then $a^2 + b^2 \geq 2ab$.

$$\text{If } a \geq b, \text{ then } a - b \geq 0 \qquad \text{(Axiom 2.13-1)}$$
$$\text{If } a - b \geq 0, \text{ then } (a - b)(a - b) \geq (a - b) \cdot 0 \qquad (O_4)$$
$$(a - b)a + (a - b)(-b) \geq 0 \qquad (D, \text{ and Theorem 2.12-4})$$
$$a^2 - ba - ab + b^2 \geq 0 \qquad (D, \text{ and Theorem 2.12-6})$$
$$a^2 - ab - ab + b^2 \geq 0 \qquad (M_2)$$
$$a^2 + b^2 - 2ab \geq 0 \qquad (A_1, A_3)$$
$$a^2 + b^2 - 2ab + 2ab \geq 2ab + 0 \qquad (E_4)$$
$$a^2 + b^2 \geq 2ab \qquad (A_5, A_4)$$

∴ If $a \geq b$, then $a^2 + b^2 \geq 2ab$.

15. Prove: If $a > 0$, then $2 < a + a^{-1}$.

$$a > 0 \qquad (H)$$
$$a(a - 2) > 0(a - 2) \qquad (O_4)$$
$$a(a - 2) + 1 > 0 \qquad \text{(Exercise 2B-4)}$$
$$a^2 - 2a + 1 > 0 \qquad (D)$$
$$a^2 - 2a + 2a + 1 > 2a + 0 \qquad (O_3)$$
$$a^2 + 1 > 2a \qquad (A_4, A_5)$$

$$\frac{1}{a}(a^2 + 1) > 2a\left(\frac{1}{a}\right) \qquad (M_5, O_4)$$

$$\frac{1}{a}(a^2 + 1) > 2\left(a \cdot \frac{1}{a}\right) \qquad (M_3)$$

$$\frac{1}{a}(a^2 + 1) > 2 \cdot 1 \qquad (M_5)$$

$$\frac{1}{a}(a^2 + 1) > 2 \qquad (M_4)$$

$$\left(\frac{1}{a}\right)(a^2) + \left(\frac{1}{a}\right)1 > 2 \qquad (D)$$

$$\left(\frac{1}{a}\right)(a \cdot a) + \frac{1}{a} > 2 \qquad (M_4)$$

$$\left(\frac{1}{a} \cdot a\right)a + \frac{1}{a} > 2 \qquad (M_3)$$

$$1 \cdot a + \frac{1}{a} > 2 \qquad (M_5)$$

$$a + \frac{1}{a} > 2 \qquad (M_4)$$

$$a + a^{-1} > 2$$

$$\therefore 2 < a + a^{-1}. \qquad \text{[Definition 2.14-1(c)]}$$

17. $|a| = |(-17)| = +17$; yes, since $a < 0$, then $|a| = -a$.

19. Yes; $\sqrt{9}$; $-\sqrt{10}$.

CHAPTER 3

Exercise 3.A (pages 47–48)

1. $A \times B = \{(1, a), (1, b), (1, c), (2, a), (2, b), (2, c), (3, a), (3, b), (3, c)\}$; 9; 9.

3. $A \times A = \{(5, 5)\}$.   **5.** No; (see Definition 3.1-1).

7. No, an ordered pair must have two entries.

9. An infinite number of ordered pairs is possible; some are $(-2, 0)$, $(-1, 1)$, $(0, 2)$. Since x and y are defined as integers, the graph can only contain discrete points.

11.

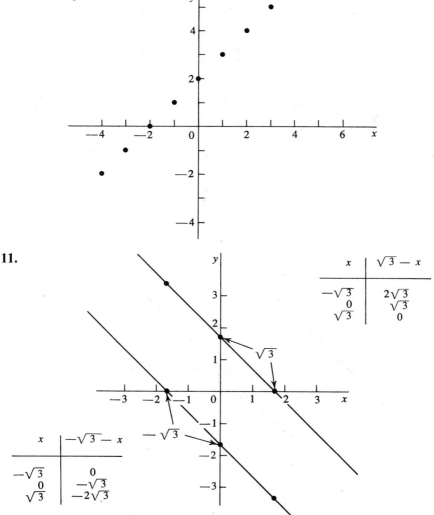

13. Open; neither.

15. No; yes; all real numbers.

17. $+2$.

19. $\{0, 1, 2, 3, 4\}$; $\{-1, 0, 3, 8, 15\}$; yes.

21.

23. $\{(x, y)|x + y = 0\}$.

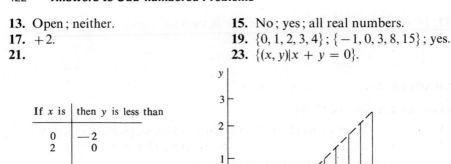

If x is	then y is less than
0	-2
2	0

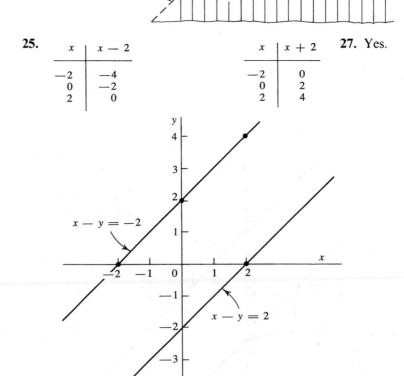

25.

x	$x - 2$
-2	-4
0	-2
2	0

x	$x + 2$
-2	0
0	2
2	4

27. Yes.

Exercise 3.B   (page 54)

1. Yes; yes. Definitions 3.5-1 and 3.4-a.
3. The ordered pairs (3, 4) and (3, 5) have the same first element; yes.
5. Scope = Replacement Set = Domain = $\{-2, -1, 0, 1, 2\}$.   7. 11; 5; 0.
9. $f(x) = 4$ *is* a function according to the vertical line test.

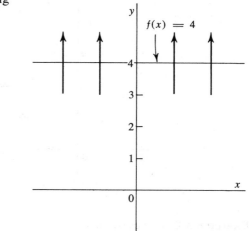

11. Yes; $\{2, 3, 4, 5\}$.
13. Yes; $f = \{[x, f(x)] | f(x) = x + 7\}$ and $f^{-1} = \{[x, f(x)] | x = f(x) + 7\}$.
15. (a) $\{[x, f(x)] | f(x) = x^2\}$, a relation which is a function.
    (b) $\{[x, f(x)] | f(x) = \pm\sqrt{x}\}$, a relation which is not a function.
17. Domain = all real numbers; range = all real numbers.

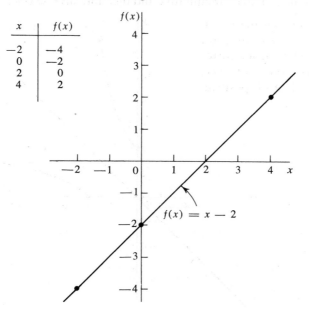

x	$f(x)$
-2	-4
0	-2
2	0
4	2

19. Domain = all real positive numbers; range = all nonnegative integers of the form $3n$, where n is $0, 1, 2, \ldots$.

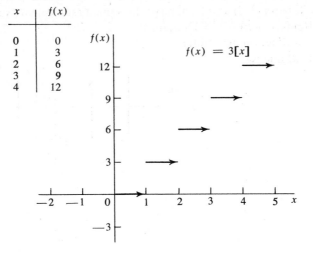

x	$f(x)$
0	0
1	3
2	6
3	9
4	12

$f(x) = 3[x]$

Exercise 3.C (pages 61–62)

1. (a) $(f \circ g)x = f[g(x)] = f(x + 4) = 3(x + 4) - 1 = 3x + 11$.
  (b) $(g \circ f)x = g[f(x)] = g(3x - 1) = (3x - 1) + 4 = 3x + 3$.
  $\therefore$ The functions are *not* commutative.

3. (a) $(f \circ g)x = f[g(x)] = f(x^2 + 4) = \sqrt{(x^2 + 4) - 4} = \sqrt{x^2} = x$.
  $(g \circ f)x = g[f(x)] = g(\sqrt{x - 4}) = (\sqrt{x - 4})^2 + 4 = x - 4 + 4 = x$.
  (b) The functions are commutative and therefore inverse when x is positive.

5. Every point on the graph of the identity function is equidistant from corresponding points on $f(x)$ and $g(x)$ when x is positive.

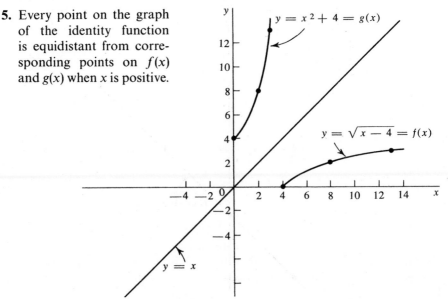

$y = x^2 + 4 = g(x)$

$y = \sqrt{x - 4} = f(x)$

$y = x$

7. $f^{-1} = \left\{ (x, y)y = \dfrac{x - 7}{2} \right\}.$

9. No; f has an inverse function.

11. (a) $(f \circ I_f)x = f[I_f] = f(x) = f.$
(b) $(I_f \circ f)x = I_f[f] = f.$
$\therefore f \circ I_f = I_f \circ f = f.$

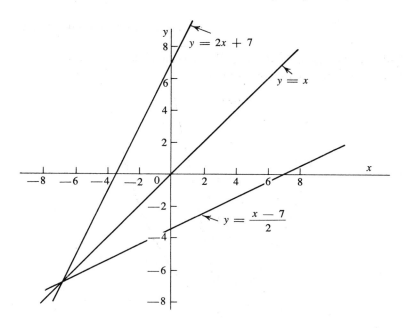

13. Exchanging the domain for the range of the function does not change the values of the function. Therefore, the function is its own inverse.

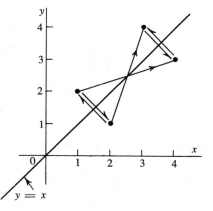

15. No; it fails Property 3 of inverse functions.
17. (a) A vertical line will not pass through more than one point of f.
(b) A horizontal line will not pass through more than one point of f^{-1}.
19. The domain of the inverse is the range of the function.

CHAPTER 4

Exercise 4.A   (pages 71–73)

1. $\{11\}$; all real numbers except 11.   3. $\{x|x = -\frac{8}{5}\}$; $\{-\frac{8}{5}\}$; $-\frac{8}{5}$.

5. $x \neq +4$ for $f(x)$; $x \neq 0$ for $g(x)$; all real numbers except 0 and $+4$; $x = 12$.

7. $x = -2\sqrt{5}$ or $x = 2\sqrt{5}$.   9. $w = 10$; $w = -1$.

11. $F = \dfrac{9c}{5} + 32$.   13. b,c,f,e; (a,d are identical equations).

15. Only two values make it true; all others make it false; $\{0, 9\}$.

17. Yes; the equations are conditional.

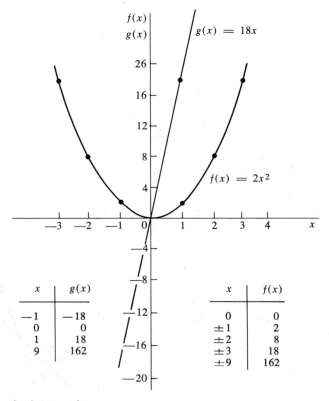

x	g(x)
−1	−18
0	0
1	18
9	162

x	f(x)
0	0
±1	2
±2	8
±3	18
±9	162

19. $\{x|x \leq 2\}$; $\{x|x > 2\}$; yes.

Exercise 4.B   (pages 81–82)

1. Linear; $\left\{x|x = -\dfrac{c}{b}\right\}$.

3. $x = -\frac{4}{3}$ and $y = \frac{5}{2}$; yes; since $ax^2 + bx + c = 0$ can be factored, all specific cases of this form can be factored.

5. $x^2 - 8x + 16 = 0$.

15. (a) $V = kr^2h$.   (b) $k = \dfrac{V}{r^2h}$.   (c) Constant; it is the constant of variation.

17. $k = \dfrac{d}{rt}$; no, because direction is not involved.   **19.** $S \doteq \dfrac{3,920}{3}$ lb.

Exercise 4.E (pages 97–98)

1. $x > 2$.   **3.** $x > -\frac{5}{3}$.   **5.** $x \geq \frac{1}{2}$.   **7.** $x \leq -1$.

9. $\{x | 2 < x < 3\}$.   **11.** $\{y | -4 < y < 6\}$.

13. $x > -\frac{2}{3}$.   **15.** $\{x | -2 < x < \frac{1}{4}\}$.

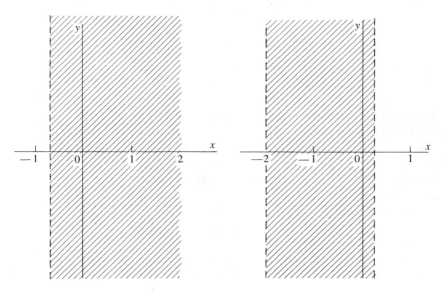

17.

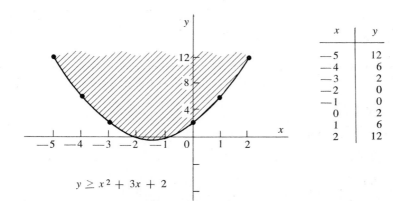

x	y
−5	12
−4	6
−3	2
−2	0
−1	0
0	2
1	6
2	12

$y \geq x^2 + 3x + 2$

19. $\{x|x \geq -2 \text{ and } x \leq 1\}$.

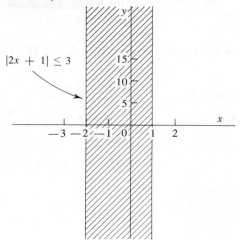

21. There is no solution because x cannot be both less than 8 and more than 8.

23. $a, b \in R, a \neq b$.

Case I: $a > b$ or $a - b > 0$ Case II: $b > a$ or $b - a > 0$

$(a - b)(a - b) > 0(a - b)$ $(b - a)(b - a) > 0(b - a)$

$(a - b)^2 > 0$ $(b - a)^2 > 0$

$a^2 - 2ab + b^2 > 0$ $b^2 - 2ba + a^2 > 0$

$\therefore a^2 + b^2 > 2ab.$ $b^2 + a^2 > 2ba$

                            $\therefore a^2 + b^2 > 2ab.$

25. $k < \frac{1}{8}$.

27. The square of any real number cannot be negative so no graph is possible.

29. $x < -1$ and $0 < x < 1$.

31. $\{x|x \neq 3\}$.

33. $x \geq 1$ or $x \leq -\frac{1}{11}$.

35. $5.9 < x < 6.1$.

37. $1.999 \leq x \leq 2.001$.

39. $x \geq 12.5$ or $x \leq -17.5$.

41. $x \geq \dfrac{4m + 9n}{6(m - 3n)}$ if $m - 3n > 0$, $x \leq \dfrac{4m + 9n}{6(m - 3n)}$ if $m - 3n < 0$.

43.

45.

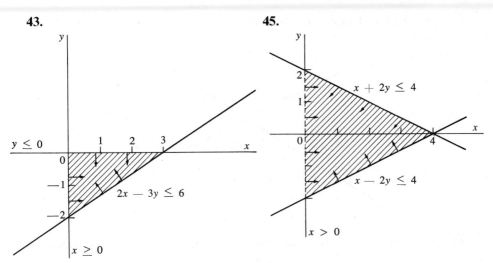

CHAPTER 5

Exercise 5.A   (pages 110–112)

1. $\begin{cases} 9x + y = 13 \\ 4x - 2y = 11. \end{cases}$ **3.** $2x - 3y - 12 = 0.$ **5.** $\frac{2}{3}.$ **7.** $-1.$

9. $y = 3x - 1.$

11. The slopes are $\frac{5}{2}$ and $-\frac{2}{3}$, so the lines intersect.

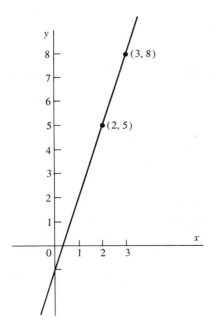

13. The slope $= \frac{2}{3}$ and the y-intercept $= -\frac{4}{3}$; the slope $= -\frac{1}{2}$ and the y-intercept $= 3$.

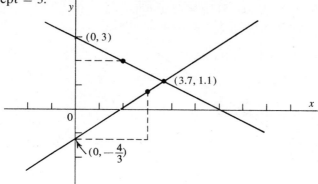

15. The slope $= 2$ and the y-intercept $= -\frac{2}{3}$; the slope $= 2$ and the y-intercept $= -\frac{3}{2}$.

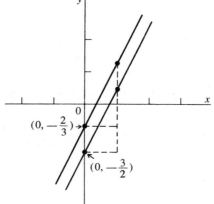

17. The slope $= 0$, and the y-intercept $= \frac{5}{2}$; the slope $= -\frac{4}{7}$ and the y-intercept $= \frac{9}{7}$.

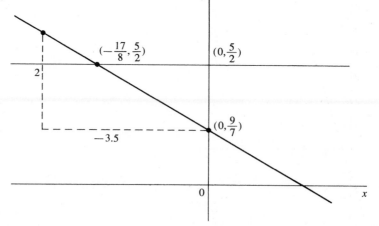

19. $\{(\frac{112}{31}, -\frac{20}{31})\}$. **21.** $\{(0,0)\}$. **23.** $\{\frac{39}{41}, \frac{9}{41}\}$. **25.** $\{(\frac{1}{3}, 0)\}$.
27. The solution set is infinite. **29.** $(0,0)$. **31.** Yes.
33. \$26,666.67 at 4.5% and \$13,333.33 at 6%.
35. 15.7 lb of peanuts and 4.3 lb of cashew nuts.

Exercise 5.B (pages 120–121)

1. $x = \frac{5}{36}$; $y = -\frac{19}{18}$; $z = -\frac{53}{36}$. **3.** $x = -\frac{3}{26}$; $y = -\frac{19}{13}$; $z = \frac{31}{26}$.

5. $x = \dfrac{9 - 8k}{7}$; $y = \dfrac{-4 - 5k}{7}$; $z = k$. **7.** 34. **9.** $a_{22}a_{33} - a_{31}a_{23}$.

11. 0. **13.** -69. **15.** $-15xy$. **17.** $x = \frac{55}{31}$; $y = \frac{18}{31}$; $z = -\frac{11}{31}$.
19. $x = 0$; $y = 0$; $z = 0$, a trivial **21.** $x = \frac{89}{21}$; $y = -\frac{29}{21}$; $z = -\frac{87}{42}$.
   solution.

CHAPTER 6

Exercise 6.A (pages 125–126)

1. $s(n) = \{5, 7, 9, 11, \ldots, (2n + 3), \ldots\}$. **3.** $s(n) = -\frac{5}{3}, -\frac{5}{8}, -\frac{1}{3}, -\frac{5}{24}, -\frac{1}{7}, \ldots$

5. $s(n) = 0, \frac{1}{2}, -\frac{2}{3}, \frac{3}{4}, -\frac{4}{5}, \ldots$ **7.** $s_r = -16, -9, 10, 47, 108, \ldots$

9. n^2; $\displaystyle\sum_{i=1}^{n} i^2$. **11.** $n + 1$; $\displaystyle\sum_{i=-3}^{n} i + 1$.

13. $(-1)^n n$; $\displaystyle\sum_{i=3}^{n} (-1)^n i$. **15.** $3 + \dfrac{1}{n}$; $\displaystyle\sum_{i=1}^{5} 3 + \dfrac{1}{i}$.

17. See Definitions 6.1-1 and 6.1-2. **19.** $0 + 3 + 8 + 15 + 24 + 35 + 48$
   $+ 63$.

21. $17 + 31 + 49 + 71 + 97$. **23.** $-1 + \frac{1}{8} - \frac{1}{27} + \frac{1}{64} - \frac{1}{125}$.

25. Undefined, $+1 - \frac{1}{8} + \frac{1}{81}$. **27.** $1 + 2 + 3 + 4 + \cdots + n + \cdots$.

29. $15 + 24 + 35 + \cdots + j(j + 2) + \cdots$.

31. $\displaystyle\sum_{i=3}^{\infty} i(i + 1)$.

Exercise 6.B (pages 131–133)

1. See Definitions 6.3-a, 6.3-1b, and 6.3-b. **3.** $L = a + (n - 1)d$.
5. $L_{15} = 99$; $S_{15} = 750$. **7.** $L_8 = 512$; $S_8 = 1,020$.
9. (a) No; the next term may be other than 9. (b) No; prime numbers.
11. $\frac{43}{4}, \frac{78}{4}, \frac{113}{4}$. **13.** 27 or -27. **15.** $S_n = 77$.
17. 66. **19.** 39. **21.** 121. **23.** $\frac{156}{625}$. **25.** $\frac{244}{729}$.
27. $\frac{9}{3} + \frac{11}{3} + \frac{13}{3} + \frac{15}{3} + \frac{17}{3} + \frac{19}{3} + \frac{23}{3} + \frac{25}{3}$. **29.** $128 + 32 + 8 + 2 + \frac{1}{2}$.

31. $d = \frac{12}{5}$; $L_7 = \frac{28}{5}$. **33.** $S_n = \dfrac{k}{2}[0 + 2k - 2]$; $\therefore S_n = k^2 - k$.

35. 512,000 bacteria.   **37.** 18.5% interest rate.

Exercise 6.C (pages 134–135)

1. Yes; 2; no; $|r|$ not less than 1.   **3.** $|r| < 1$.   **5.** $\frac{16}{3}$.   **7.** $\frac{27}{2}$.

9. $\frac{2\sqrt{10}}{\sqrt{2}-1}$.   **11.** $\frac{3}{2}$.   **13.** $\frac{3}{11}$.   **15.** $\frac{715}{333}$.

17. $\frac{63,492}{111,111}$.   **19.** 240 ft.

Exercise 6.D (pages 138–139)

1. $7 \cdot 6 \cdot 5 \cdot 4 \cdot 3 \cdot 2 \cdot 1 = 5{,}040$.   **3.** $9 \cdot 8 \cdot 7 \cdot 6 \cdot 5 \cdot 4 \cdot 3 \cdot 2 \cdot 1 = 362{,}880$.

5. $5 \cdot 4 \cdot 3 \cdot 2 \cdot 1 \cdot 7 \cdot 6 \cdot 5 \cdot 4 \cdot 3 \cdot 2 \cdot 1 = 604{,}800$.   **7.** $\dfrac{5!}{5!} = 1$.

9. $\dfrac{n(n-1)!}{(n-1)!} = n$.   **11.** $\dfrac{(n+3)(n+2)!}{(n+1)(n+2)!} = \dfrac{n+3}{n+1}$.   **13.** $\dfrac{23!}{18!}$.

15. $x^7 + 7x^6y + 21x^5y^2 + 35x^4y^3 + 35x^3y^4 + 21x^2y^5 + 7xy^6 + y^7$.

17. $128w^7 - 1{,}344w^6 + 6{,}048w^5 - 15{,}120w^4 + 22{,}680w^3 - 20{,}412w^2$
$+ 10{,}206w - 2{,}187$.

19. $s^{10} - 5s^8t + 10s^6t^2 - 10s^4t^3 + 5s^2t^4 - t^5$.

21. $512a^9 - 6{,}912a^8b + 41{,}472a^7b^2 - 145{,}152a^6b^3 + 326{,}592a^5b^4$
$- 489{,}888a^4b^5 + 489{,}888a^3b^6 - 314{,}928a^2b^7 + 118{,}098ab^8 - 19{,}683b^9$.

23. $1 + 0.3 + 0.036 + 0.00216 + 0.0000648 + 0.0000007776 \doteq 1.33822558$.

25. $1 - 0.3 + 15(0.05)^2 - 20(0.05)^3 + 15(0.05)^4 - 6(0.05)^5 + (0.05)^6$
$\doteq 1.34009564$.

27. $-42{,}997{,}760x^{11}y^9$.   **29.** $\dfrac{1}{x^2} + \dfrac{4}{x^3} + \dfrac{12}{x^4} + \dfrac{32}{x^5} + \cdots$.

31. $3 + \dfrac{1}{10} - \dfrac{1}{600} + \dfrac{27}{48\,600} + \cdots$.   **33.** \$1,418.52.

CHAPTER 7

Exercise 7.A (pages 149–150)

1. All real numbers; $\{y|\ -1 \le y \le 1\}$.   **3.** $r = 1$.

5. Arc length and the rectangular coordinates of a point as it moves around the circumference of a unit circle.

7. $\dfrac{2\pi}{3}$.

9. Yes; no; no; each P represents integral multiples of 2π added to a given arc length t.

11. (a) Yes; $\cos t = \pm \sqrt{1 - \sin^2 t}$.   (b) $\cot t = \pm \dfrac{\sqrt{1 - \sin^2 t}}{\sin t}$.

13. $1; -1$; none; none.   **15.** 1 to 0; yes; no.

17. Period; its graph repeats itself in successive intervals of 2π.

19. 0; no; n must be an integer.   **21.** 1.   **23.** See Section 7.6.

25. Third; first.   **27.** $t = \pi; t = \dfrac{3\pi}{2}$.

Exercise 7.B   (pages 157–158)

1. I, IV; II, III.   **3.** $\left(\dfrac{\pi}{2}, 0\right); \left(\dfrac{3\pi}{2}, 0\right)$.

5. (a) Since $t = 0$, $\sin\left(0 + \dfrac{\pi}{2}\right) = \cos 0$; $\sin\left(\dfrac{\pi}{2}\right) = \cos 0$; $1 = 1$.

   (b) $t = \dfrac{\pi}{2}$, yes.   (c) $t = \pi$, yes.

   (d) $t = \dfrac{3\pi}{2}$, yes.   (e) all t, yes.

7. III, IV; I, II.

9. (a) $4; \pi$.   (b) $(0, 4); (\pi, 4); \left(\dfrac{\pi}{2}, -4\right)$.

   (c) $\left(\dfrac{\pi}{4}, 0\right); \left(\dfrac{3\pi}{4}, 0\right)$.   (d) See Figure 7.11-2.

11. (a) $\cos\left(\dfrac{\pi}{2} + 2\pi(2)\right) = \cos\dfrac{\pi}{2}$ **13.** $\left(\dfrac{1}{\sqrt{2}}, -\dfrac{1}{\sqrt{2}}\right)$.

   $\cos\left(\dfrac{\pi}{2} + 4\pi\right) = \cos\dfrac{\pi}{2}$ **15.** $5; \dfrac{2\pi}{3}; \dfrac{\pi}{3}$; to the right because the phase shift is positive.

   $\therefore \cos\dfrac{\pi}{2} = \cos\dfrac{\pi}{2}$.

   (b) $\cos\left(\dfrac{\pi}{2} + 2\pi(10)\right) = \cos\dfrac{\pi}{2}$

   $\cos\left(\dfrac{\pi}{2} + 20\pi\right) = \cos\dfrac{\pi}{2}$

   $\therefore \cos\dfrac{\pi}{2} = \cos\dfrac{\pi}{2}$.

   (c) No.   (d) 0.

17. $x = 5\cos(3t - \pi)$.

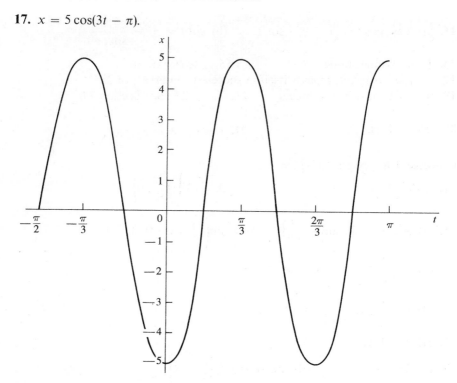

19. Graph falls to left of origin; 3, yes.

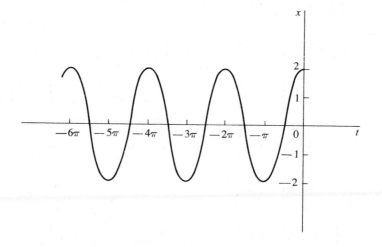

21. Every point on the graph of $x = 2\cos(-4t) + 4$ is mapped 4 higher than the corresponding point on the graph of $x = 2\cos(-4t)$; up.

23. (a) See Definitions 7.9-1 and 7.10-1.   (b) 3; π; $\pi/4$; $+0.5$.

25. Ordinates; on vertical axis or parallel to it.

Exercise 7.C (pages 174–177)

1.

t	$\sin t$	$\cos t$	$\tan t$	$\cot t$	$\sec t$	$\csc t$
$4\left(\dfrac{\pi}{3}\right)$	$-\dfrac{\sqrt{3}}{2}$	$-\dfrac{1}{2}$	$\sqrt{3}$	$\dfrac{1}{\sqrt{3}}$	-2	$-\dfrac{2}{\sqrt{3}}$
$5\left(\dfrac{\pi}{4}\right)$	$-\dfrac{1}{\sqrt{2}}$	$-\dfrac{1}{\sqrt{2}}$	1	1	$-\sqrt{2}$	$-\sqrt{2}$
$7\left(\dfrac{\pi}{6}\right)$	$-\dfrac{1}{2}$	$-\dfrac{\sqrt{3}}{2}$	$\dfrac{1}{\sqrt{3}}$	$\sqrt{3}$	$-\dfrac{2}{\sqrt{3}}$	-2

3.

(a) (b) (c)

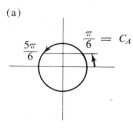 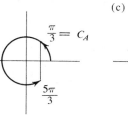 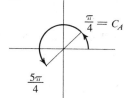

(d) (e) (f)

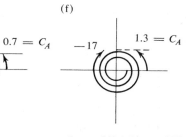

$$5n \doteq 5(3.14) \doteq 15.70$$
$$-17 + 15.70 \doteq 1.30$$
$$\therefore \ C_A \doteq 1.3$$

5. (a); (c); (d); (g); and (i).

7. (a) III, IV. (b) II. (c) I. (d) III. (e) I. (f) none.

9. An infinite number; (1, 0).

11. $x = -\frac{5}{13}$; $\sin t = \frac{12}{13}$; $\cos t = -\frac{5}{13}$; $\tan t = -\frac{12}{5}$; $\cot t = -\frac{5}{12}$; $\sec t = -\frac{13}{5}$; $\csc t = \frac{13}{12}$.

13. $\cos t = \dfrac{\sqrt{3}}{2}$; $\tan t = -\dfrac{1}{\sqrt{3}}$; $\cot t = -\sqrt{3}$; $\sec t = \dfrac{2}{\sqrt{3}}$; $\csc t = -2$.

15. $\sin t \doteq 0.4 - 0.01067 + 0.000085 - 0.0000003 + \cdots \doteq 0.3894.$

17. $\sin^2\left(\dfrac{\pi}{4}\right) + \cos^2\left(\dfrac{\pi}{4}\right) = 1.$

$$\left(\dfrac{1}{\sqrt{2}}\right)^2 + \left(\dfrac{1}{\sqrt{2}}\right)^2 = 1$$

$$\tfrac{1}{2} + \tfrac{1}{2} = 1$$

$$\therefore\ 1 = 1.$$

19. (a) False.
(b) False.
(c) False.
(d) False.
(e) False.
(f) False.

21. $\dfrac{\sqrt{3}}{2}.$

23. This is an extension of Tables 7.13-a and 7.13b and is left for the student.

25. (a) $-1 \le y \le 1.$ (b) $y \ge 1$ and $y \le -1.$ (c) $(\pi/2, 1).\ (3\pi/2, -1).$

27. (a) All real numbers except odd multiples of $\pi/2$.
(b) All real numbers except even multiples of $\pi/2$.
(c) $(\pi/4, 1);\ (3\pi/4, -1).$

Exercise 7.D (pages 181–183)

1. $\cot t = \cos t \csc t.$

$$= \cos t \left(\dfrac{1}{\sin t}\right)$$

$$= \dfrac{\cos t}{\sin t}$$

$$\therefore \cot t = \cot t.$$

3. $\dfrac{\cos t}{1 - \sin t} = \dfrac{1 + \sin t}{\cos t}.$

$$= \dfrac{(1 + \sin t)\ (1 - \sin t)}{(\cos t)\ (1 - \sin t)}$$

$$= \dfrac{1 - \sin^2 t}{\cos t(1 - \sin t)}$$

$$= \dfrac{\cos^2 t}{\cos t(1 - \sin t)}$$

$$\therefore\ \dfrac{\cos t}{1 - \sin t} = \dfrac{\cos t}{1 - \sin t}.$$

5. $\dfrac{\cos t}{\sec t} = 1 - \dfrac{\sin t}{\csc t}.$

$$\cos t\left(\dfrac{1}{\sec t}\right) = 1 - \sin t\left(\dfrac{1}{\csc t}\right)$$

$$\cos t \cos t = 1 - \sin^2 t$$

$$\therefore\ \cos^2 t = \cos^2 t.$$

7. $(1 - \sin^2 t)(1 + \tan^2 t) = 1.$

$$\cos^2 t\left(1 + \dfrac{\sin^2 t}{\cos^2 t}\right) = 1$$

$$\cos^2 t + \cos^2 t\left(\dfrac{\sin^2 t}{\cos^2 t}\right) = 1$$

$$\therefore\ \cos^2 t + \sin^2 t = 1$$

$$\text{or } 1 = 1.$$

9. $\tan^2 t - \sin^2 t = \tan^2 t \sin^2 t.$

$$\frac{\sin^2 t}{\cos^2 t} - \sin^2 t = \frac{\sin^2 t}{\cos^2 t} \sin^2 t$$

$$\frac{\sin^2 t - \sin^2 t \cos^2 t}{\cos^2 t} = \frac{\sin^4 t}{\cos^2 t}$$

$$\frac{\sin^2 t(1 - \cos^2 t)}{\cos^2 t} = \frac{\sin^4 t}{\cos^2 t}$$

$$\frac{\sin^2 t \sin^2 t}{\cos^2 t} = \frac{\sin^4 t}{\cos^2 t}$$

$$\therefore \frac{\sin^4 t}{\cos^2 t} = \frac{\sin^4 t}{\cos^2 t}.$$

11. $(1 - \cos t)(1 + \cos t) = 1 - \cos^2 t = \sin^2 t.$

13. $\dfrac{1 + \cot^2 t}{\sec t} = \dfrac{\csc^2 t}{\sec t} = \csc t \cot t.$

15. $\dfrac{\cos t}{\sin t} - \dfrac{\csc t}{\cos t} = \dfrac{\cos t}{\sin t} - \dfrac{\dfrac{1}{\sin t}}{\cos t}.$

$$= \frac{\cos t}{\sin t} - \frac{1}{\sin t \cos t}$$

$$= \frac{\cos^2 t}{\sin t \cos t} - \frac{1}{\sin t \cos t}$$

$$= \frac{-1 + \cos^2 t}{\sin t \cos t}$$

$$= \frac{-\sin^2 t}{\sin t \cos t}$$

$$= -\frac{\sin t}{\cos t}$$

$$= -\tan(t)$$

$$\therefore \frac{\cos t}{\sin t} - \frac{\csc t}{\cos t} = \tan(-t).$$

17. $\dfrac{\cot t + 1}{\cot t - 1} = \dfrac{1 + \tan t}{1 - \tan t}.$

$$\frac{\dfrac{\cos t}{\sin t} + \dfrac{\sin t}{\sin t}}{\dfrac{\cos t}{\sin t} - \dfrac{\sin t}{\sin t}} = \frac{\dfrac{\cos t}{\cos t} + \dfrac{\sin t}{\cos t}}{\dfrac{\cos t}{\cos t} - \dfrac{\sin t}{\cos t}}$$

$$\frac{\dfrac{\cos t + \sin t}{\sin t}}{\dfrac{\cos t - \sin t}{\sin t}} = \frac{\dfrac{\cos t + \sin t}{\cos t}}{\dfrac{\cos t - \sin t}{\cos t}}$$

$$\therefore \frac{\cos t + \sin t}{\cos t - \sin t} = \frac{\cos t + \sin t}{\cos t - \sin t}.$$

19.
$$(\tan t + \cot t)(\sin t + \cos t) = \csc t + \sec t$$

$$\tan t \sin t + \tan t \cos t + \cot t \sin t + \cot t \cos t = \csc t + \sec t$$

$$\tan t \sin t + \left(\frac{\sin t}{\cos t}\cos t\right) + \left(\frac{\cos t}{\sin t}\sin t\right) + \cot t \cos t = \csc t + \sec t$$

$$\tan t \sin t + \sin t + \cos t + \cot t \cos t = \csc t + \sec t$$

$$\frac{\sin^2 t}{\cos t} + \sin t + \cos t + \frac{\cos^2 t}{\sin t} = \csc t + \sec t$$

$$\frac{1 - \cos^2 t}{\cos t} + \sin t + \cos t + \frac{1 - \sin^2 t}{\sin t} = \csc t + \sec t$$

$$\sec t - \cos t + \sin t + \cos t + \csc t - \sin t = \csc t + \sec t$$

$$\sec t + \csc t = \csc t + \sec t$$

$$\therefore \csc t + \sec t = \csc t + \sec t.$$

21. $\sin t \cos t \cot t + \sin t \cos t \tan t = 1.$

$$\sin t \cos t \frac{\cos t}{\sin t} + \sin t \cos t \frac{\sin t}{\cos t} = 1$$

$$\therefore \cos^2 t + \sin^2 t = 1.$$

$$1 = 1$$

23. $\dfrac{\csc t + \cot t}{\tan t + \sin t} = \cot t \csc t.$

$$\frac{\dfrac{1}{\sin t} + \dfrac{\cos t}{\sin t}}{\dfrac{\sin t}{\cos t} + \dfrac{\sin t \cos t}{\cos t}} = \left(\frac{\cos t}{\sin t}\right)\left(\frac{1}{\sin t}\right)$$

$$\frac{\dfrac{1 + \cos t}{\sin t}}{\dfrac{\sin t + \sin t \cos t}{\cos t}} = \frac{\cos t}{\sin^2 t}$$

$$\frac{\dfrac{1 + \cos t}{\sin t}}{\dfrac{\sin t(1 + \cos t)}{\cos t}} = \frac{\cos t}{\sin^2 t}$$

$$\frac{(1 + \cos t)(\cos t)}{(\sin^2 t)(1 + \cos t)} = \frac{\cos t}{\sin^2 t}$$

$$\therefore \frac{\cos t}{\sin^2 t} = \frac{\cos t}{\sin^2 t}.$$

25. $\sin t \tan t = \sec t - \cos t.$

$$\sin t \frac{\sin t}{\cos t} = \sec t - \cos t$$

$$\frac{\sin^2 t}{\cos t} = \sec t - \cos t$$

$$\frac{1 - \cos^2 t}{\cos t} = \sec t - \cos t.$$

$$\therefore \sec t - \cos t = \sec t - \cos t.$$

27. $\sin t + \cos t = \dfrac{\sin t}{1 - \cot t} + \dfrac{\cos t}{1 - \tan t}.$

$$= \frac{\sin t}{\dfrac{\sin t}{\sin t} - \dfrac{\cos t}{\sin t}} + \frac{\cos t}{\dfrac{\cos t}{\cos t} - \dfrac{\sin t}{\cos t}}$$

$$= \frac{\dfrac{\sin t}{\sin t - \cos t}}{\sin t} + \frac{\dfrac{\cos t}{\cos t - \sin t}}{\sin t}$$

$$= \frac{\sin^2 t}{\sin t - \cos t} + \frac{\cos^2 t}{\cos t - \sin t}$$

$$= \frac{\sin^2 t - \cos^2 t}{\sin t - \cos t}$$

$$= \frac{(\sin t - \cos t)(\sin t + \cos t)}{\sin t - \cos t}$$

$$\therefore \sin t + \cos t = \sin t + \cos t.$$

29. $(1 - \cos t)(2 - 2 \sin t) = (1 - \sin t - \cos t)^2.$
$$\therefore 2 - 2 \cos t - 2 \sin t + 2 \cos t \sin t = 2 - 2 \cos t - 2 \sin t + 2 \cos t \sin t.$$

Exercise 7.E   (pages 188–189)

1. $t = \dfrac{\pi}{3}; \dfrac{2\pi}{3}.$ **3.** $t = \dfrac{5\pi}{6}; \dfrac{11\pi}{6}.$ **5.** $t = 1.37; 4.52.$ **7.** $t \doteq 0; 0.72; 5.56.$

9. $t \doteq 0.93; 1.97.$ **11.** $t \doteq \dfrac{\pi}{4}; \dfrac{5\pi}{4}; 1.10; 4.25.$ **13.** $t = \dfrac{\pi}{2}; \dfrac{3\pi}{2}; \dfrac{3\pi}{4}; \dfrac{7\pi}{4}.$

15. $t \doteq \dfrac{\pi}{2}; \dfrac{3\pi}{2}; 0.46; 3.61.$ **17.** $t = \dfrac{\pi}{3}; \dfrac{2\pi}{3}; \dfrac{4\pi}{3}; \dfrac{5\pi}{3}; \dfrac{\pi}{6}; \dfrac{5\pi}{6}; \dfrac{7\pi}{6}; \dfrac{11\pi}{6}.$

19. $t \doteq 2.55; 5.70.$ **21.** $t = \dfrac{\pi}{2}, \dfrac{3\pi}{2}.$ **23.** $t = \dfrac{\pi}{3}; \dfrac{5\pi}{6}; \dfrac{\pi}{4}; \dfrac{5\pi}{4}.$

25. No solution.

Exercise 7.F   (pages 204–206)

1.
$$\frac{\sin(s + t)}{\cos s \cos t} = \tan s + \tan t.$$

$$\frac{\sin s \cos t + \cos s \sin t}{\cos s \cos t} = \tan s + \tan t$$

$$\frac{\sin s \cos t}{\cos s \cos t} + \frac{\cos s \sin t}{\cos s \cos t} = \tan s + \tan t$$

$$\frac{\sin s}{\cos s} + \frac{\sin t}{\cos t} = \tan s + \tan t$$

$$\therefore \ \tan s + \tan t = \tan s + \tan t.$$

3.
$$\sin\!\left(t + \frac{\pi}{3}\right) - \cos\!\left(t + \frac{\pi}{6}\right) = \sin t.$$

$$\left(\sin t \cos \frac{\pi}{3} + \cos t \sin \frac{\pi}{3}\right) - \left(\cos t \cos \frac{\pi}{6} - \sin t \sin \frac{\pi}{6}\right) = \sin t$$

$$\left[\sin t\!\left(\frac{1}{2}\right) + \cos t\!\left(\frac{\sqrt{3}}{2}\right)\right] - \left[\cos t\!\left(\frac{\sqrt{3}}{2}\right) - \sin t\!\left(\frac{1}{2}\right)\right] = \sin t$$

$$\frac{1}{2}\sin t + \frac{\sqrt{3}\cos t}{2} - \frac{\sqrt{3}\cos t}{2} + \frac{1}{2}\sin t = \sin t$$

$$\therefore \ \sin t = \sin t.$$

5.
$$\sin\!\left(t - \frac{2\pi}{3}\right) = \frac{-(\sqrt{3}\cos t + \sin t)}{2}.$$

$$\sin t \cos \frac{2\pi}{3} - \cos t \sin \frac{2\pi}{3} = \frac{-(\sqrt{3}\cos t + \sin t)}{2}$$

$$\sin t\left(-\frac{1}{2}\right) - \cos t\left(\frac{\sqrt{3}}{2}\right) = \frac{-(\sqrt{3}\cos t + \sin t)}{2}$$

$$\frac{-\sin t}{2} - \frac{\sqrt{3}\cos t}{2} = \frac{-(\sqrt{3}\cos t + \sin t)}{2}$$

$$\frac{-\sqrt{3}\cos t - \sin t}{2} =. \frac{-(\sqrt{3}\cos t + \sin t)}{2}$$

$$\therefore \frac{-(\sqrt{3}\cos t + \sin t)}{2} = \frac{-(\sqrt{3}\cos t + \sin t)}{2}.$$

7. $\cos 2t + 1 = 2\sin t(\csc t - \sin t).$

$$2\cos^2 t - 1 + 1 = 2\sin t(\csc t - \sin t)$$

$$2\cos^2 t = 2\sin t(\csc t - \sin t)$$

$$2(1 - \sin^2 t) = 2(\sin t \csc t - \sin^2 t)$$

$$\therefore (1 - \sin^2 t) = (1 - \sin^2 t).$$

9. $$\sin 2t = \frac{2\cot t}{1 + \cot^2 t}.$$

$$2\sin t \cos t = \frac{2\cot t}{\csc^2 t} = \frac{2\cos t}{\sin t}\sin^2 t$$

$$\therefore 2\sin t \cos t = 2\cos t \sin t.$$

11. $\tan(-s) - \tan(\pi - s) = \tan 2\pi.$

$$-\tan s - \frac{(\tan \pi - \tan s)}{1 + \tan \pi \tan s} = 0$$

$$-\tan s - \frac{0 - \tan s}{1 + (0)(\tan s)} = 0$$

$$-\tan s - (-\tan s) = 0$$

$$\therefore 0 = 0.$$

13. $\cos 2s = \cos^4 s - \sin^4 s.$

$$\cos^2 s - \sin^2 s = (\cos^2 s - \sin^2 s)(\cos^2 s + \sin^2 s)$$

$$\therefore \cos^2 s - \sin^2 s = \cos^2 s - \sin^2 s.$$

15. $\sin 3t = \sin 2t \cos t + \cos 2t \sin t.$

$$\sin(2t + t) = \sin 2t \cos t + \cos 2t \sin t$$

$$\therefore \sin(2t + t) = \sin(2t + t).$$

17.
$$4 \sin^3 s + \sin 3s = 3 \sin s.$$
$$4 \sin^3 s + \sin(2s + s) = 3 \sin s$$
$$4 \sin^3 s + \sin 2s \cos s + \cos 2s \sin s = 3 \sin s$$
$$4 \sin^3 s + (2 \sin s \cos s)(\cos s) + (1 - 2 \sin^2 s)(\sin s) = 3 \sin s$$
$$4 \sin^3 s + (2 \sin s \cos^2 s) + (\sin s - 2 \sin^3 s) = 3 \sin s$$
$$4 \sin^3 s + 2 \sin s(1 - \sin^2 s) + (\sin s - 2 \sin^3 s) = 3 \sin s$$
$$4 \sin^3 s + (2 \sin s - 2 \sin^3 s) + (\sin s - 2 \sin^3 s) = 3 \sin s$$
$$4 \sin^3 s + 2 \sin s - 2 \sin^3 s + \sin s - 2 \sin^3 s = 3 \sin s$$
$$\therefore\ 3 \sin s = 3 \sin s.$$

19.
$$\sin 4s = 4 \sin s \cos s \cos 2s.$$
Since $\sin 4s = \sin 2(2s) = 2 \sin 2s \cos 2s$, then
$$2 \sin 2s \cos 2s = 4 \sin s \cos s \cos 2s$$
$$2(2 \sin s \cos s) \cos 2s = 4 \sin s \cos s \cos 2s$$
$$\therefore\ 4 \sin s \cos s \cos 2s = 4 \sin s \cos s \cos 2s.$$

21.
$$\cos\left(\frac{\pi}{4} + s\right) = \frac{\sqrt{2}(\cos s - \sin s)}{2}.$$

$$\cos\frac{\pi}{4}\cos s - \sin\frac{\pi}{4}\sin s = \frac{\sqrt{2}(\cos s - \sin s)}{2}$$

$$\left(\frac{1}{\sqrt{2}}\right)\cos s - \left(\frac{1}{\sqrt{2}}\right)\sin s = \frac{\sqrt{2}(\cos s - \sin s)}{2}$$

$$\frac{1}{\sqrt{2}}(\cos s - \sin s) = \frac{\sqrt{2}(\cos s - \sin s)}{2}$$

$$\frac{\sqrt{2}}{2}(\cos s - \sin s) = \frac{\sqrt{2}(\cos s - \sin s)}{2}$$

$$\therefore\ \frac{\sqrt{2}(\cos s - \sin s)}{2} = \frac{\sqrt{2}(\cos s - \sin s)}{2}$$

23.
$$\tan\left(\frac{\pi}{3} - t\right) = \frac{\sqrt{3}\tan t}{\sqrt{3}\tan t + 1}.$$

$$\frac{\tan\dfrac{\pi}{3} - \tan t}{1 + \tan\dfrac{\pi}{3}\tan t} = \frac{\sqrt{3}\tan t}{\sqrt{3}\tan t + 1}$$

$$\frac{\sqrt{3} - \tan t}{1 + \sqrt{3}\tan t} = \frac{\sqrt{3}\tan t}{\sqrt{3}\tan t + 1}$$

25. $\frac{56}{65}$.

27. $-\frac{16}{63}$.

29. $\frac{24}{7}$.

31. $\frac{1}{5}$.

33. $\dfrac{\sin 6t}{2} + \dfrac{\sin 2t}{2}$.

35. $\cos 10t + \cos 4t$.

37. $2\sin\dfrac{\pi}{6}\cos\dfrac{\pi}{12}$.

$$\therefore \frac{\sqrt{3}-\tan t}{\sqrt{3}\tan t + 1} = \frac{\sqrt{3}-\tan t}{\sqrt{3}\tan t + 1}$$

39. $2\cos\dfrac{5\pi}{12}\sin\dfrac{\pi}{12}$

41. $\dfrac{\tan(s-t)}{\tan(s+t)} = \dfrac{\sin 2s - \sin 2t}{\sin 2s + \sin 2t}$

$$= \frac{2\cos(s+t)\sin(s-t)}{2\sin(s+t)\cos(s-t)} = \cot(s+t)\tan(s-t) = \frac{\tan(s-t)}{\tan(s+t)}$$

$$\therefore \frac{\tan(s-t)}{\tan(s+t)} = \frac{\tan(s-t)}{\tan(s+t)}.$$

43. $\dfrac{\sin 6t - \sin 2t}{-(\cos 6t - \cos 2t)} = \dfrac{(-1)(-1)2\cos 4t \sin 2t}{2\sin 4t \sin 2t} = \cot 4t.$

$$\therefore \frac{\sin 6t - \sin 2t}{\cos 2t - \cos 6t} = \cot 4t.$$

45. $2\sin s \sin 3s = \cos 2s - \cos 4s.$

$$= -2\sin\left(\frac{2s+4s}{2}\right)\sin\left(\frac{2s-4s}{2}\right)$$

$$= -2\sin(3s)\sin(-s)$$

$$= 2\sin 3s \sin s$$

$$\therefore 2\sin s \sin 3s = 2\sin s \sin 3s.$$

47.

$$\frac{\sin^2 3t}{\sin t} = \sin t + [\sin 3t + \sin 5t].$$

$$\frac{[\sin(2t+t)]^2}{\sin t} = \sin t + [2\sin 4t \cos t]$$

$$\frac{[\sin 2t \cos t + \cos 2t \sin t]^2}{\sin t} = \sin t + [2\sin 4t \cos t]$$

$$\frac{[(2\sin t \cos^2 t) + (2\cos^2 t - 1)(\sin t)]^2}{\sin t} = \sin t + [2\sin 4t \cos t]$$

$$\frac{16\sin^2 t \cos^4 t - 8\cos^2 t \sin^2 t + \sin^2 t}{\sin t} = \sin t + [2\sin 4t \cos t]$$

$$\frac{\sin^2 t(16\cos^4 t - 8\cos^2 t + 1)}{\sin t} = \sin t + 2\sin 2(2t)\cos t$$

$$\sin t(16\cos^4 t - 8\cos^2 t + 1) = \sin t + 2(2\sin 2t \cos 2t)\cos t$$
$$= \sin t + 4(2\sin t \cos^2 t)\cos 2t$$
$$= \sin t + 8\sin t \cos^2 t(2\cos^2 t - 1)$$
$$= \sin t + 16\sin t \cos^4 t$$
$$- 8\sin t \cos^2 t$$
$$= \sin t(1 + 16\cos^4 t - 8\cos^2 t)$$
$$\therefore \ \sin t(16\cos^4 t - 8\cos^2 t + 1) = \sin t(16\cos^4 t - 8\cos^2 t + 1).$$

49. $t = \dfrac{\pi}{2}; \dfrac{3\pi}{2}; \dfrac{\pi}{6}; \dfrac{5\pi}{6}; \dfrac{11\pi}{6}.$

Exercise 7.G (pages 218–219)

1. $\dfrac{\pi}{2}.$ **3.** $\dfrac{\pi}{6}.$ **5.** $\dfrac{\pi}{2}.$ **7.** $-\dfrac{\pi}{6}.$ **9.** $\dfrac{\pi}{2}.$

11. $\dfrac{3\pi}{4} + 2\pi n; \dfrac{7\pi}{4} + 2\pi n.$ **13.** $-\dfrac{1}{\sqrt{3}}.$ **15.** $\dfrac{1}{\sqrt{2}}.$

17. $\dfrac{\sqrt{3}}{2}.$ **19.** $\dfrac{4}{5}.$ **21.** $\dfrac{5}{13}.$ **23.** $\dfrac{\pi}{6}.$

25. $\dfrac{\pi}{2}.$ **27.** 1.45. **29.** $-\dfrac{\pi}{4}.$ **31.** $\dfrac{\pi}{2}.$

33. $\text{arcSin } w + \text{arcCos } w = \dfrac{\pi}{2}.$

Let $W = \text{arcSin } w + \text{arcCos } w$

$W = w_1 + w_2.$

If $w_1 = \text{arcSin } w$, $\text{Sin } w_1 = w$, $\text{Cos } w_1 = \sqrt{1 - w^2}.$
If $w_2 = \text{arcCos } w$, $\text{Cos } w_1 = w$, $\text{Sin } w_2 = \sqrt{1 - w^2}.$

$\text{Sin } W = \text{Sin}(w_1 + w_2) = \text{Sin } w_1 \text{ Cos } w_2 + \text{Cos } w_1 \text{ Sin } w_2$
$$= (w)(w) + (\sqrt{1 - w^2})(\sqrt{1 - w^2})$$
$$= w^2 + (1 - w^2),$$

$\text{Sin } W = 1.$

$\therefore \ W = \dfrac{\pi}{2}.$

35. $\text{arcSin } \dfrac{v}{\sqrt{1 + v^2}} - \text{arcTan } v = 0.$

Let $W = w_1 - w_2$; $w_1 = \arcSin \dfrac{v}{\sqrt{1 + v^2}}$ and $w_2 = \arcTan v$.

$\Sin w_1 = \dfrac{v}{\sqrt{1 + v^2}}$ and $\Cos w_1 = \dfrac{1}{\sqrt{1 + v^2}}$; $\Sin w_2 = \dfrac{v}{\sqrt{1 + v^2}}$ and

$\Cos w_2 = \dfrac{1}{\sqrt{1 + v^2}}$.

$\Sin W = \Sin(w_1 - w_2) = \Sin w_1 \Cos w_2 - \Cos w_1 \Sin w_2 = \Sin 0$

$$= \frac{v}{\sqrt{1 + v^2}} \cdot \frac{1}{\sqrt{1 + v^2}} - \frac{1}{\sqrt{1 + v^2}} \cdot \frac{v}{\sqrt{1 + v^2}} = 0$$

$$\therefore 0 = 0.$$

37. $\dfrac{\pi}{4}$.

39.   **41.**

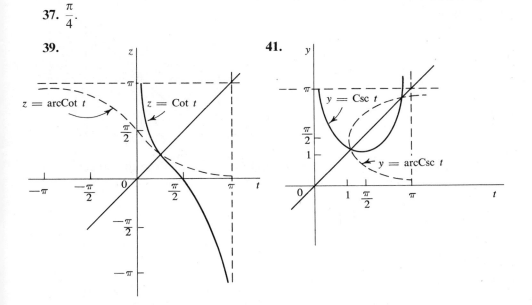

CHAPTER 8

Exercise 8.A (pages 226–227)

1. 3.   **3.** $-\dfrac{1}{243}$.   **5.** $\dfrac{1}{64}$.   **7.** 9.

9. $\sqrt{\dfrac{43}{11}}$.   **11.** $\dfrac{1}{64a^5}$.   **13.** 1.   **15.** $x^9 y^9$.

17. $\sqrt[3]{b^2}$.   **19.** $32\sqrt[5]{w^3}$.   **21.** $\sqrt[3]{49x^4 y^2}$.   **23.** $c^{1/5}$.

25. $(3x - 4y)^{1/2}$.   **27.** $\left(\dfrac{e^{2x} + e^{-2x}}{2}\right)^{1/2}$.   **29.** $x + y$.

31. $\dfrac{1-2x}{2}$.   **33.** 81.   **35.** 16.   **37.** $\dfrac{1}{64}$.

Exercise 8.B (pages 233–234)

1. The function degenerates into a straight line; neither, it is constant.
3. $y = -(b^x)$; as x increases, y decreases and vice versa.
5. $x = b^y$ or $\log_b x = y$ (all positive real numbers).
7. Section 8.4 will help with graphs and answers.
9. None; it doesn't.
11. No; 1; if $b = 1$, the function will degenerate into a straight line.
13. (a) $x = [f(x)]^2$.   (b) $f(x) = x$.   (c) $x = b^y$.   (d) $y = x^2 + 5$ or
    $x = \sqrt{y - 5}$.
15. It acts as a reflector of a function into its inverse.

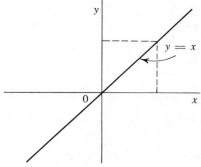

17. The domain of $f(x)$ equals the range of $f^{-1}(x)\,(= R)$ and the range of $f(x)$ equals the domain of $f^{-1}(x)\,(= R)$.

$$f[f^{-1}(x)] = f^{-1}[f(x)] = I$$
$$(x + 2) - 2 = (x - 2) + 2 = x$$
$$\therefore x = x = x.$$

19.

x	y
0	1
1	1.54
2	3.76
3	10.20
4	27.80

$$y = \dfrac{e^x + e^{-x}}{2}$$

21. (a) $t = 11.9$ yr.   (b) Challenge problem for student.

Exercise 8.C (pages 242–243)
1. $\log_b x = y$.   **3.** b is the base; y is a logarithm.
5. 1; 1 to any power is equal to itself. **7.** $y = 5$.
9. $y \doteq -0.9542$ or $y \doteq 9.0458 - 10$.
11. $\log_b(x)^y = \log_b(x \cdot x \cdot x \cdot x, \dots$ to y factors of x).
                  $= \log_b x + \log_b x + \log_b x + \cdots +$ to y terms of $\log_b x$
       $\therefore \log_b(x)^y = y \log_b x$.

13. $\log_{100} 10 = \frac{1}{2}$.
15. (a) $673 = 6.73 \times 10^2$.   (b) $87{,}640 = 8.7640 \times 10^4$.
    (c) $0.0047 = 4.7 \times 10^{-3}$.   (d) $0.0000972 = 9.72 \times 10^{-5}$.
17. 2; power to which 10 must be raised to give the number.
19. (a) 1.6794.   (b) $\bar{2}.6803$.   (c) 4.9203.   (d) $\bar{1}.3932$.
21. (a) 8.634×10^1.   (b) 86.34×10^0.   (c) $8{,}634 \times 10^{-2}$.
    (d) $86{,}340 \times 10^{-3}$.   (e) 863.4×10^{-1}.
23. 1,260.   **25.** 0.4694.   **27.** 1,160.   **29.** 10.89.
31. 41.53.   **33.** 6.562.   **35.** 25.95.   **37.** $r \doteq 2.450$ in.
39. 7699 cu ft.

CHAPTER 9

Exercise 9.A (pages 256–258)
1. (a) 1 ton; 22.   (b) 0.01 ft; 600.   (c) 1 inch; 163.   (d) 100 miles; 35.
    (e) 1^0; 5.   (f) $\frac{1}{8}$ inch; 44.   (g) 1 oz; 100.   (h) 1 ft; 1,634.
    (i) 0.01 sec; 3926.
3. (a) 28.7 and 30.   (b) 10.8 and 10.   (c) 36,300 and 40,000.
    (d) 47,400 and 50,000.   (e) 78,100 and 80,000.   (f) 2.55 and 3.
5. 338.
7. (a) 0.0015.   (b) 0.1.   (c) 0.014.   (d) 0.00347.   (e) 0.0001180.
    (f) 0.0004496.
9. (0.1267) 0.1 cubic inch "best" answer.
11.

(a)   (b)   (c)

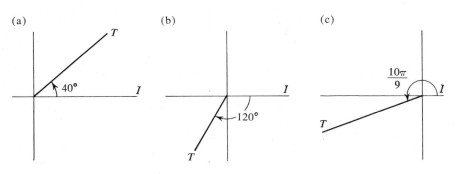

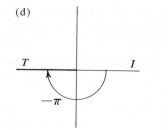

(d)

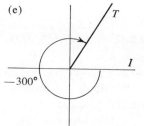

(e)

13. 1.

15. (a) 270°.   (b) (−1.14) − 1°.   (c) 572.9°.   (d) 57.3°.   (e) (171.8) 172°.
(f) 57.53°.   (g) −135°.   (h) 20°.   (i) 54.7°.   (j) (206.3) 210°.
(k) −60°.   (l) (−17.2) − 20°.

17. (a) $\frac{1}{3}$.   (b) (0.029166)0.02912.   (c) 0.3311.   (d) $-\frac{1}{6}$.
(e) −(0.10047) − 0.1005. (f) −0.1949.   (g) −0.597.   (h) 0.
(i) (0.07555)0.0756.   (j) $\frac{1}{18}$.   (k) $\frac{5}{3}$.   (l) $-\frac{1}{36}$.

19. 115.5°.

21. (a) 90° and $\dfrac{\pi}{2}$.   (b) 60° and $\dfrac{\pi}{3}$.   (c) 34° 30′ and 0.6022.

(d) 100° 33′ and 1.755.

23. (2.52) 2.5 ft.   **25.** 27.64 radians.

27. $\csc\dfrac{\pi}{10} \doteq \csc(0.3142) \doteq 3.236$; $\csc\dfrac{\pi}{10} = \csc 18° \doteq 3.236$.

29. If $\sec\theta \doteq 1.547$, then $\theta \doteq 49° \, 44′$;
$\theta \doteq 49° \, 44′$ is equivalent to $t \doteq 0.8687$; $\sec(0.8687) \doteq 1.547$.

Exercise 9.B (pages 273–275)

1. (a)

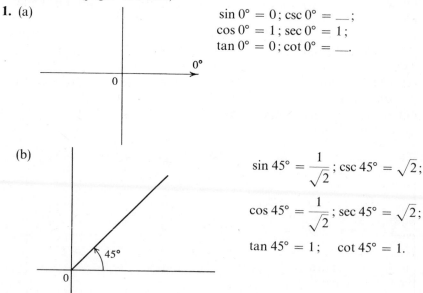

$\sin 0° = 0$; $\csc 0° = $ ___ ;
$\cos 0° = 1$; $\sec 0° = 1$;
$\tan 0° = 0$; $\cot 0° = $ ___.

(b)

$\sin 45° = \dfrac{1}{\sqrt{2}}$; $\csc 45° = \sqrt{2}$;

$\cos 45° = \dfrac{1}{\sqrt{2}}$; $\sec 45° = \sqrt{2}$;

$\tan 45° = 1$; $\cot 45° = 1$.

(c)

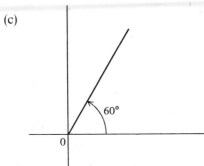

$$\sin 60° = \frac{\sqrt{3}}{2}; \csc 60° = \frac{2}{\sqrt{3}};$$

$$\cos 60° = \frac{1}{2}; \quad \sec 60° = 2;$$

$$\tan 60° = \sqrt{3}; \cot 60° = \frac{1}{\sqrt{3}}.$$

3. (a) 1. Domain of sine = set of all angles;
   2. domain of tangent = set of all angles except odd multiples of 90°;
   3. domain of secant = set of all angles except odd multiples of 90°.
   (b) 1. Range of sine = $\{R \mid -1 \leq R \leq 1, R$ a real number$\}$;
   2. range of tangent = set of all real numbers;
   3. range of secant = $\{R \mid R \leq -1$ or $R \geq 1\}$.
5. The corresponding trigonometric values differ in signs only.
7. A trigonometric value of any corresponding acute angle can be found in Table III.
9. (a) 68°.   (b) 40°.   (c) 50°.   (d) 18°.   (e) 20°.   (f) 74°.
   (g) 30°.   (h) 20°.
11. 68° is corresponding acute angle in Quadrant I.
   $\sin 428° \doteq 0.9272$; $\csc 428° \doteq 1.079$;
   $\cos 428° \doteq 0.3746$; $\sec 428° \doteq 2.669$;
   $\tan 428° \doteq 2.475$; $\cot 428° \doteq 0.4040$.

13. (a) $\cos 51°$.   (b) $\tan 8°$.   (c) $\csc(76° - \alpha)$.   (d) $\sec(40 + \alpha)$.
   (e) $\sin(66° - \alpha - \beta)$.   (f) $\cot \beta$.

15. $\sin \beta = \dfrac{b}{c}$; $\csc \beta = \dfrac{c}{b}$;

   $\cos \beta = \dfrac{a}{c}$; $\sec \beta = \dfrac{c}{a}$.

   $\tan \beta = \dfrac{b}{a}$; $\cot \beta = \dfrac{a}{b}$.

17. (a) $\csc \theta$.   (b) $\cot \theta$.   (c) $\cos \theta$.
19. $\cos \alpha = \frac{24}{25}$; $\tan \alpha = -\frac{7}{24}$; $\cot \alpha = -\frac{24}{7}$; $\sec \alpha = \frac{25}{24}$; $\csc \alpha = -\frac{25}{7}$.
21. $\sin t_2 = \frac{5}{13}$; $\csc t_2 = \frac{13}{5}$;
   $\cos t_2 = -\frac{12}{13}$; $\sec t_2 = -\frac{13}{12}$;
   $\tan t_2 = -\frac{5}{12}$; $\cot t_2 = -\frac{12}{5}$.
23. $\sin \theta = \pm\frac{15}{17}$; $\tan \theta = \pm\frac{15}{8}$; $\cot \theta = \pm\frac{8}{15}$;
   $\sec \theta = \frac{17}{8}$; $\csc \theta = \pm\frac{17}{15}$.
25. $-\frac{24}{25}$.

27. (a) 0.9419.   (b) $\theta \doteq 207° \, 33'$ and $332° \, 27'$.

29. 0.

Exercise 9.C (pages 287–288)

1. A vector has direction and magnitude.

3. $\overrightarrow{AB}$ must be parallel to $\overrightarrow{CD}$ and have the same magnitude and direction.

5. No.   **7.** See example 9.12-1a.   **9.** An infinite number.

11. Find the sum of the horizontal components of the three vectors.

13. A vector.

15. By Section 9.12-1, Letting Rv = resultant vector

$(\vec{v}_1 + \vec{v}_2) = R\vec{v}_{12}$; Sum of $R\vec{v}_{12} + \vec{v}_3 = R\vec{v}_{123}$.
Sum of $(\vec{v}_2 + \vec{v}_3) = R\vec{v}_{23}$; Sum of $R\vec{v}_{23} + \vec{v}_1 = R\vec{v}_{123}$.
$\therefore$ By transitive law $(\vec{v}_1 + \vec{v}_2) + \vec{v}_3 = \vec{v}_1 + (\vec{v}_2 + \vec{v}_3)$.

17. (v_x, v_y) is an ordered pair in a rectangular coordinate system while $[v_x, v_y]$ is a vector.

19. $[4, 60°] = [2, 2\sqrt{3}]$.   **21.** (137.98)138.0 lb; (105.84)105.8 lb.

23. $\theta \doteq (4° \, 43') \, 4° \, 40'$; azimuth, $85° \, 17' \doteq 85° \, 20'$; ground speed $\doteq$ (344.1) 344 mph.

Exercise 9.D (pages 292–293)

1. (a) $c \doteq 20.3$; $b \doteq 13.8$; $\beta \doteq 42° \, 40'$.
  (b) $c \doteq 86.1$; $\alpha \doteq 17° \, 10'$; $\beta \doteq 76° \, 50'$.

3. 258 ft.   **5.** 1,719 ft.   **7.** 625 ft.   **9.** (21,956) 22,000 ft.

11. (8.28) 8.3 ft.   **13.** Altitude 12.79 inches; base 63.02 inches.

Exercise 9.E (pages 305–306)

1. $\gamma \doteq 76°$; $b \doteq (24.39)$ 24 ft; $c \doteq (35.93)$ 36 ft.

3. $\beta \doteq (36° \, 22')$ $36° \, 20'$; $\gamma \doteq (58° \, 28')$ $58° \, 30'$; $c \doteq (549.2)$ 549 ft.

5. $c \doteq (702.8)$ 703 inches; $\alpha \doteq (77° \, 11')$ $77° \, 10'$; $\beta \doteq (54° \, 59')$ $55° \, 0'$.

7. $\cos \alpha \doteq 1.2347$, no triangle exists.

9. $\beta \doteq 1° \, 57'$; $b \doteq (0.14899)$ 0.1490 in.; $c \doteq (0.35272)$ 0.3527 in.

11. $\gamma \doteq (66° \, 32')$ $67°$; $\alpha \doteq 70°$; $a \doteq (39.9)$ 40 ft.

13. $\gamma \doteq 66° \, 27' \, AC \doteq 90.21$ ft.

15. $\sin \gamma \doteq 1.0197$ so no triangle exists.   **17.** $c \doteq (155.797)$ 155.80 ft.

19. The shortest distance from N to the line of flight of the plane leaving M is 353.9 mph. Therefore, the plane leaving N cannot intercept the other plane at any point in one hour.

21. 4.4 miles.   **23.** $A \doteq (100.036)$ 100.0 sq. ft.   **25.** 150,700 sq miles.

27. $A \doteq (54,125)$ 50,000 sq ft.   **29.** (31.383) 31.4 ft; (60.06) 60.1 ft;
  $A \doteq (1,841.13)$ 1,840 sq ft.

31. (10.58) 10.6 ft from starting point; azimuth, N16° 1'W.

CHAPTER 10

Exercise 10.A (pages 314–316)

1. If $a = c$ and $b = d$. **3.** $(6, 8)$. **5.** $(\frac{13}{17}, \frac{18}{17})$.

7. $(a, b)(c, d) = (c, d)(a, b)$.
$$= (ca - db, cb + da)$$
$$= (ca - db, da + cb)$$
$$= (ac - bd, ad + bc)$$
$\therefore (a, b)(c, d) = (a, b)(c, d)$.

9. $(a, b)[(c, d)(e, f)] = (a, b)[ce - df, cf + de]$.
$$= [a(ce - df) - b(cf + de)], [a(cf + de) + b(ce - df)]$$
$$= [(ace - adf - bcf - bde), (acf + ade + bce - bdf)]$$
$$= [(ace - bde - adf - bcf), (acf - bdf + ade + bce)]$$
$$= [(ac - bd)e - (ad + bc)f], [(ac - bd)f + (ad + bc)e]$$
$$= [(ac - bd), (ad + bc)](e, f)$$
$\therefore (a, b)[(c, d)(e, f)] = [(a, b)(c, d)](e, f)$.

11. $(4, 9)$; additive identity. **13.** $(-2, -6)$. **15.** $(1, 1)$.

17. No; no; yes. **19.** $-9k$. **21.** $\sqrt{-1}$ or i.

23. $(8, -3)$. **25.** $(0, -7)$. **27.** $(0 - 36, 12 + 0) = (-36, 12)$.

29. $(-\frac{9}{10}, \frac{9}{5})$. **31.** $9 - 2i$. **33.** $\frac{12}{5} - \frac{6}{5}i$.

35. $-7i$. **37.** $-\frac{9}{10} + \frac{9}{5}i$.

39. $4 - 7i$; $(4 + 7i) + (4 - 7i) = 8$; yes. **41.** $\frac{69}{170} + \frac{123}{170}i$.

43. Real number $= a + 0i = a$; **45.** $\dfrac{1 + i}{i}$; $1 - i$; $(1, 0)$.
conjugate $= a - 0i = a$.
$\therefore a = a$.

47. $\pm \frac{5}{2}i$.

Exercise 10.B (pages 325–326)

1. (a) $(2, 60°)$. (b) $(\sqrt{17}, 345° 58')$. (c) $(\sqrt{29}, 158° 12')$.
(d) $(\sqrt{24}, 125° 16')$.

3. (a) $(\sqrt{17}, 75° 58')$. (b) $(\sqrt{6}, 324° 44')$. (c) $(\sqrt{26}, 168° 41')$.
(d) $(2\sqrt{3}, 210°)$.

5. (a) $(0, 1)$. (b) $\left(\dfrac{1}{\sqrt{2}} - \dfrac{1}{\sqrt{2}}\right)$. (c) $\left(\dfrac{5\sqrt{2}}{2}, -\dfrac{5\sqrt{2}}{2}\right)$.

(d) $\left(\dfrac{3\sqrt{2}}{2}, \dfrac{3\sqrt{2}}{2}\right)$.

7. (a) $(0, 5)$. (b) $(3, 0)$. (c) $\left(-\dfrac{1}{2}, \dfrac{\sqrt{3}}{2}\right)$. (d) $(-2\sqrt{2}, -2\sqrt{2})$.

9. $y = 3x$; $\tan \theta = 3$.

11. $2x - 7y = 0$; $y = \frac{2}{7}x$; $\tan \theta = \frac{2}{7}$.

13. $x^2 + y^2 - 2x = 0$;
$r^2 - 2r \cos \theta = 0$

θ	$\cos \theta$	r
0	1	0 or 2
$\frac{\pi}{6}$	$\frac{\sqrt{3}}{2}$	0 or $\sqrt{3}$
$\frac{\pi}{3}$	$\frac{1}{2}$	0 or 1
$\frac{\pi}{2}$	0	0 or 0

15. $x^2 - y^2 = 16$;
$r^2 \cos 2\theta = 16$.

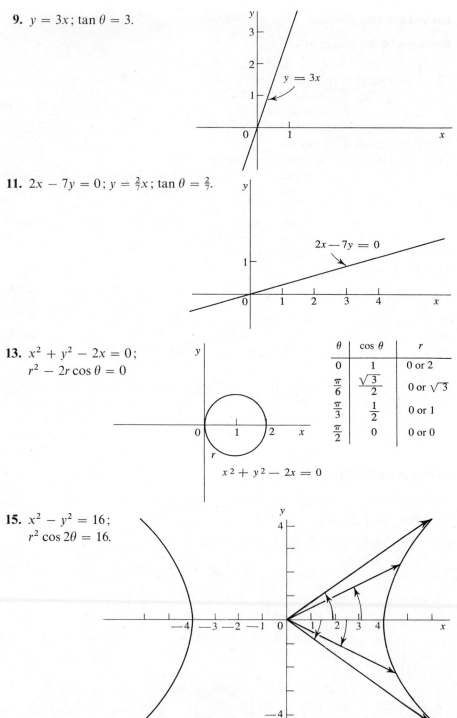

17. $r = 8$; $x^2 + y^2 = 64$.

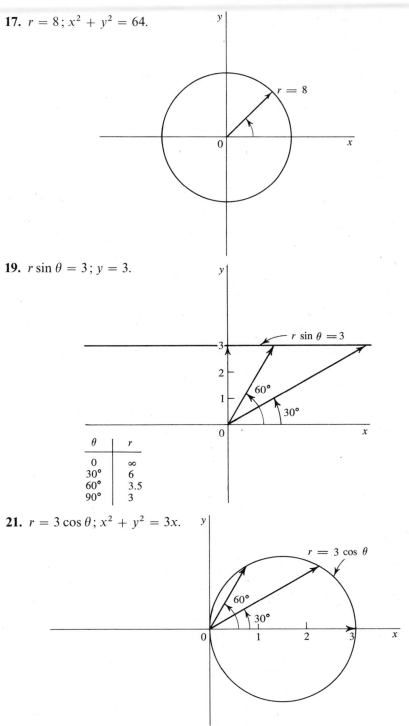

19. $r \sin \theta = 3$; $y = 3$.

θ	r
0	∞
30°	6
60°	3.5
90°	3

21. $r = 3 \cos \theta$; $x^2 + y^2 = 3x$.

Graphs for Problems 23, 25, and 27 left for the student.

23. $r = 4 \sin \theta + 3 \cos \theta$; $x^2 - 3x + y^2 - 4y = 0$.

25. $r = \sin 2\theta$; $(x^2 + y^2)^{3/2} = 2xy$.

27. $r = 2 \cos \theta - 1$; $x^2 + y^2 = 2x - \sqrt{x^2 + y^2}$.   **29.** $1 + \sqrt{3} + i(1 + \sqrt{3})$

Exercise 10.C (pages 329–330)

1. $6(\cos 90° + i \sin 90°)$; $6i$.   **3.** $6\left(\cos \dfrac{5\pi}{6} + i \sin \dfrac{5\pi}{6}\right)$; $-3\sqrt{3} + 3i$.

5. $3\left(\cos \dfrac{\pi}{4} + i \sin \dfrac{\pi}{4}\right)$; $\dfrac{3\sqrt{2}}{2} + \dfrac{3\sqrt{2}}{2}i$.

7. $3(\cos 240° + 9 \sin 240°)$; $-\dfrac{3}{2} - \dfrac{3\sqrt{3}}{2}i$.

9. $[3(\cos 15° + i \sin 15°)]^2 = 3^2[\cos 2(15°) + i \sin 2(15°)]$
$$= 9(\cos 30° + i \sin 30°).$$

11. $r = \sqrt[3]{10}$; $\theta \doteq 20° + k(120°)$, $k = 0, 1, 2$; $\sqrt[3]{10}(\cos 20° + i \sin 20°)$; $\sqrt[3]{10}(\cos 140° + i \sin 140°)$; $\sqrt[3]{10}(\cos 260° + i \sin 260°)$.

13. $r = 1$; $\theta \doteq 0° + 72°k$, where $k = 0, 1, 2, 3, 4$; $(\cos 0° + i \sin 0°)$; $(\cos 72° + i \sin 72°)$; $(\cos 144° + i \sin 144°)$; $(\cos 216° + i \sin 216°)$; $(\cos 288° + i \sin 288°)$.

15. $r = \sqrt[4]{-1}$; $\theta \doteq 22° \, 30' + 90°k$, where $k = 0, 1, 2, 3$; $\sqrt[4]{-1}(\cos 22° \, 30' + i \sin 22° \, 30')$; $\sqrt[4]{-1}(\cos 112° \, 30' + i \sin 112° \, 30')$; $\sqrt[4]{-1}(\cos 202° \, 30' + i \sin 202° \, 30')$; $\sqrt[4]{-1}(\cos 292° \, 30' + i \sin 292° \, 30')$.

17. 2; -2; $2i$; $-2i$.   **19.** $x = 3$; $x = \dfrac{-3 \pm 3\sqrt{-3}}{2}$.

21. $x = (3 + 2i)^{1/3}$; $x = \dfrac{-(3 + 2i)^{1/3}(1 \pm 3i)}{2}$.

23. Reciprocal of $r(\cos \theta + i \sin \theta)$ is $\dfrac{1}{r(\cos \theta + i \sin \theta)}$.

Let $1 = 1(\cos 0° + i \sin 0°)$.

Then $\dfrac{1}{r(\cos 0° + i \sin 0°)} = \dfrac{1(\cos 0° + i \sin 0°)}{r(\cos \theta + i \sin \theta)}$

$$= \dfrac{1}{r}(\cos 0° - \theta) + i(\sin 0° - \theta)$$

$$= \dfrac{1}{r}(\cos \theta - i \sin \theta).$$

CHAPTER 11

Exercise 11.A (pages 338–339)

1. $5x^3 - 3x^2 + 6x + 3.$

3. $7x^7 - 37x^5 + 7x^4 + 16x^3 - 2x^2 - 30x + 6.$

5. See Definition 11.2-3.

7. $Q(x) = x - 4;\ \mathscr{R}(x) = -1.$

9. $Q(x) = 4x^2 - 29x + 174;\ \mathscr{R}(x) = -1{,}037.$

11. $Q(x) = 3x^3 + 12x^2 + 47x + 188;\ \mathscr{R}(x) = 757.$

13. (7) 2; (8) 2; (9) 3; (10) 3; (11) 4; (12) 5.

15. $\mathscr{R} = 0.$

17. $\mathscr{R} = 0.$

19. Since n is odd, $x^n + a^n$ has an even number of terms. Therefore,

$$\underline{-a} \mid 1 + 0 + 0 + 0 + 0 + 0 + \cdots + \quad 0 \quad + a^n$$

$$\frac{-a + a^2 - a^3 + a^4 - a^5 + \cdots + a^{n-1} - a^n}{1 - a + a^2 - a^3 + a^4 - a^5 + \cdots + a^{n-1} \mid 0}.$$

21.
$$
\begin{array}{r}
\underline{1}\mid 1 + 5 + 2 - 8 \\
+1 + 6 - 8 \\
\underline{-2}\mid 1 + 6 + 8 \mid\ 0 = \mathscr{R} \\
-2 - 8 \\
\underline{-4}\mid 1 + 4 \mid\ 0 = \mathscr{R} \\
-4 \\
1 \mid\ 0 = \mathscr{R} \qquad \therefore\ P(x) = (x - 1)(x + 2)(x + 4).
\end{array}
$$

23. Let $x^2 - a^2 = 0$, then $x^2 = a^2$.
   If $x^2 = a^2$, then $(x^2)^n - (a^2)^n = (a^2)^n - (a^2)^n = 0$.
   $\therefore\ x^2 - a^2$ is a factor of $(x^2)^n - (a^2)^n$.

25. (a) $P(-1) = 5.$ (b) $P(3) = 517.$ (c) $P(-2) = 92.$

Exercise 11.B (page 348)

1. See Theorem 11.5-a.   3. 5.

5. The function has a zero value between a and b.

7. It is a lower bound.   9. No.

11.

$$x^3 \quad +3x^2 \quad -6x \quad -9$$
$$1 \quad +3 \quad -6 \quad -9$$

	x		Q		$P(x)$
Lower bound → −5	1	−2	+4	−29
Root —— −4	1	−1	−2	−1
−3	1	+0	−6	+9
Root —— −2	1	+1	−8	+7
−1	1	+2	−8	−1
0	1	+3	−6	−9
1	1	+4	−2	−11
Root —— 2	1	+5	+4	−1
Upper bound —— 3	1	+9	+21	+54

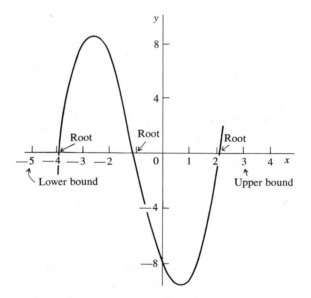

(a) Upper bound $x = 3$; lower bound $x = -5$.

(b) Real roots, $2 < x < 3$; $-2 < x < -1$; $-4 < x < -3$.

13.

$$4x^3 - 12x^2 + 5x \quad -3$$
$$4 \quad -12 \quad +5 \quad -3$$

	x		Q		$P(x)$
Lower bound → 0	4	−12	+5	−3
1	4	−8	−3	−6
Root —— 2	4	−4	−3	−9
Upper bound → 3	4	+0	+5	+12

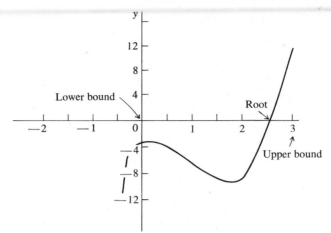

(a) Upper bound $x = 3$; lower bound $x = 0$.
(b) Real roots, $2 < x < 3$.

15.

		x^5			$-3x$	$+4$
	1	$+0$	$+0$	$+0$	-3	$+4$

	x		Q			$P(x)$
Root $\overset{-2}{\underset{-1}{\rightarrow}}$	1	-2	$+4$	-8	$+11$	-18
	1	-1	$+1$	-1	-2	$+6$
0	1	$+0$	$+0$	$+0$	-3	$+4$
1	1	$+1$	$+1$	$+1$	-2	$+2$
2	1	$+2$	$+4$	$+8$	$+13$	$+30$

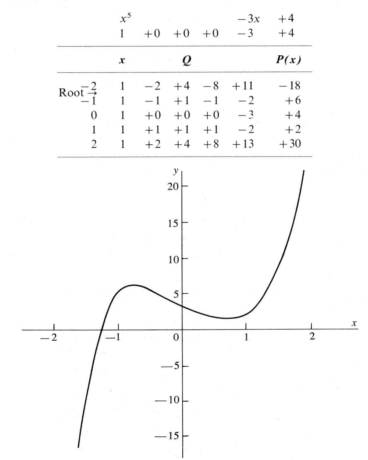

(a) Upper bound 2; lower bound −2.

(b) Real roots, −2 < x < −1.

17.

	x^3			+1
	1	+0	+0	+1

	x	Q		$P(x)$
Root → −1	1	−1	+1	+0
0	1	+0	+0	+1
1	1	+1	+1	+2

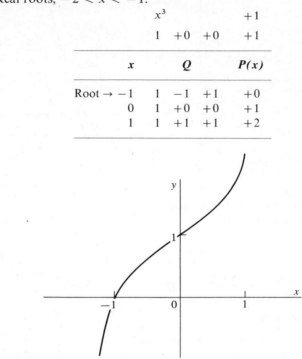

(a) Upper bound $x = 0$; lower bound $x = -1$.

(b) Real root, $x = -1$.

19. $2x^3 + x^2 + 2x - 3 \doteq 0.$

	$2x^3 + x^2 + 2x$			−3
	2	+1	+2	−3

x	Q			$P(x)$
−1	2	−1	+3	−6
Root → 0	2	+1	+2	−3
1	2	+3	+5	+2

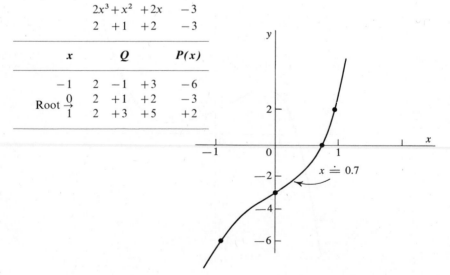

$x \doteq 0.7$

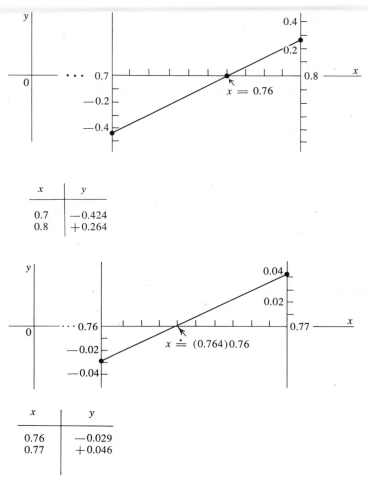

x	y
0.7	−0.424
0.8	+0.264

x	y
0.76	−0.029
0.77	+0.046

For problems 21, 23, and 25 make graphs similar to those shown in Problem 19.
21. $x \doteq (0.7249)\,0.72.$ **23.** $x \doteq (0.507)\,0.51\,;\; x \doteq (1.953)\,1.95.$
25. $x \doteq (-2.258) - 2.26,$ to two correct decimal places.

Exercise 11.C   (pages 353–354)

1. $x^3 - 2x^2 - 3x - 10;\; x = 2,\; x = -2 + i;\; x = -2 - i.$
3. $(x - 1)[x - (2 - i)][x - (2 + i)] = (x^2 - 4x + 5)(x - 1)$
  $= x^3 - 5x^2 + 9x - 5.$
5. $\pm 1;\; \pm 2.$ **7.** Possible rational roots are $\pm 1,\; \pm 2,$
                      but there are *no rational roots.*
9. (a) Rational root $= -1.$ (b) Irrational root $\doteq (1.168)\,1.17.$
11. There is no negative root because $x = 0$ is a lower bound.
13. $x = 1$ is a root and depressed equation is $x^3 - 2x^2 + 5x - 10 = 0;$
   $x = 2$ is a root and depressed equation is $x^2 + 5 = 0.$ Roots of $x^2 + 5 = 0$
   are $x = \sqrt{5}i$ and $x = -i\sqrt{5}.$ Therefore roots are $1;\; 2;\; i\sqrt{5}$ and $-i\sqrt{5}.$

15. Upper bound is $x = 0$ so no positive rational roots. Possible negative roots are -2; -1; $-\frac{1}{2}$. $x = -2$ is a root with depressed equation $2x^3 + x^2 + 2x +1 = 0$; $x = -\frac{1}{2}$ is a root with depressed equation $2x^2 + 2 = 0$. Roots of $x^2 + 1 = 0$ are $x = i$ and $x = -i$. Therefore, roots are -2, $-\frac{1}{2}$, i, and $-i$.

17. $x = 0$ is lower bound so no negative roots. Possible rational roots are $+1$, $+2$, $+3$, $+6$. $x = 6$ is a root. Depressed equation is $x^2 - 3x + 1 = 0$ and $x = \dfrac{3 \pm i\sqrt{5}}{2}$. Therefore roots are 6; $\dfrac{3}{2} + \dfrac{i\sqrt{5}}{2}$; $\dfrac{3}{2} - \dfrac{i\sqrt{5}}{2}$.

19. Possible rational roots are ± 1. $x = 1$ is root. Depressed equation is $x^2 + x + 1 = 0$ and $x = \dfrac{-1 \pm i\sqrt{3}}{2}$. Therefore roots are 1; $-\dfrac{1}{2} + \dfrac{i\sqrt{3}}{2}$; $-\dfrac{1}{2} - \dfrac{i\sqrt{3}}{2}$.

Exercise 12.A (page 362)

1. 7.   **3.** 2.   **5.** 9.   **7.** 12.

9.

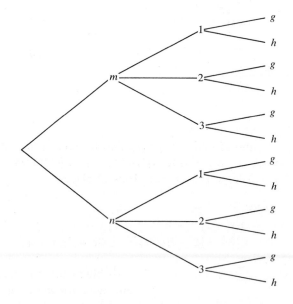

11. 90.
13. All positive integral values; all positive integral values where $r \leq n$.
15. 40,320.   **17.** 720.   **19.** 39,916,800.
21. 3,628,800.   **23.** 32,760.   **25.** 5,040.

27. $P(n, r) = \dfrac{(n)(n-1)(n-2)\cdots(n-r+1)(n-r)(n-r-1)\cdots 4\cdot 3\cdot 2\cdot 1}{(n-r)!}$

$$= \frac{n!}{(n-r)!}.$$

29. 5.   **31.** 12; 16.

Exercise 12.B (pages 369–370)

1. In permutations, order is of prime importance. Combinations disregard order.

3. $\dbinom{n}{r}$ means the number of combinations of n objects taken r at a time, order disregarded.

5. 455.   **7.** 12   **9.** 792.   **11.** $n = 5; r = 4$.
13. 15.   **15.** 15.   **17.** 90.   **19.** 15; 57.
21. 2^n.   **23.** 127.   **25.** 2,376.   **27.** 8.

29. $\dbinom{n+1}{m+1} = C(n+1, m+1) = \dfrac{P(n+1, m+1)}{(m+1)!}$.

$$= \frac{(n+1)(n)(n-1)\cdots n-m+2}{(m+1)(m)!} = \frac{(n+1)}{(m+1)}\binom{n}{m}.$$

Exercise 12.C (pages 378–380)

1. $S = \{H, T\}; n(S) = 2; E = \{T\}; n(E) = 1$.
3. $\{a\}, \{b\}, \{c\}, \{a, b\}, \{a, c\}, \{b, c\}, \{a, b, c\}, \varnothing; 8$.
5. 16   **7.** 100.
9. $\{(H, 1), (H, 2), (H, 3), (H, 4), (H, 5), (H, 6), (T, 1), (T, 2), (T, 3), (T, 4), (T, 5),$
$(T, 6)\}; n(S) = 12; n(E) = 6$.
11. $\frac{1}{6}; \frac{1}{3}$.   **13.** $\frac{7}{8}$.   **15.** $\frac{2}{5}; \frac{3}{5}$.   **17.** $\frac{3}{8}; \frac{5}{8}$.
19. 0.28.   **21.** $\frac{1}{2}; \frac{1}{2}; 1$.   **23.** $\frac{1}{9}$.   **25.** $\frac{11}{850}$.
27. $7.69.
29. Win. He pays $1.00 per toss while his value expectation is $2.50 per toss.
31. 0.4313; 0.0734.   **33.** $48,947.95.
35. 0.3025 and 0.006410.   **37.** 5 to 4.   **39.** 63,037 to 9,792,016.

Exercise 12.D (pages 382–383)

1. $\frac{7}{13}$; no.   **3.** $\frac{1}{9}$; $E_1 \cap E_2 = \varnothing$; $P(E_1 \cap E_2) = 0$; yes; because $E_1 \cap E_2 \neq \varnothing$.

5. $P(A \cup B) = 0.93$.

7.

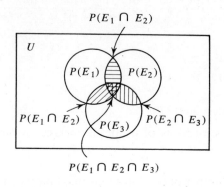

$$P(E_1 \cap E_2 \cap E_3)$$

9. $\frac{8}{33}; \frac{10}{33}.$

Exercise 12.E (pages 384–386)

1. (a) See Definition 12.3-1a.   (b) It is a set of all ordered triple of cards.

3. If a thing can happen in n ways and fail in m ways, then the probability that the event will happen is

$$P(E) = \frac{n}{n + m}.$$

5. (a) Yes, yes.   (b) Yes.   **7.** (a) See Section 12.3-7   (b) $\frac{1}{24}$.

9. See Theorem 12.3-6a.   **11.** $\frac{1}{4}$.   **13.** (a) $= \frac{80}{261}$. (b) $= \frac{113}{261}$.

15. 0.44.   **17.** $a = \dfrac{1}{2,450}; b = \dfrac{66}{625}$.   **19.** $\frac{1}{32}$.

21. $\frac{7}{125}$.   **23.** $\frac{1}{2}$.   **25.** $\frac{9}{56}$.

27. $\dfrac{1}{1,048,576}.$ **29.** $\frac{1}{3}; \frac{1}{6}$.

Exercise 12.F (page 388)

1. $\dfrac{41,259}{419,904}.$ **3.** $\dfrac{3,125}{7,776}.$ **5.** 0.000000102 or $\dfrac{1}{9,765,625}.$

7. $\frac{319}{512}.$ **9.** $1.4 \times 10^{-25}.$ **11.** 0.516.

13. $\dfrac{31,031}{46,656}.$ **15.** $\frac{11}{.64}.$

Index

Abscissa, 40
Absolute error, 250
Absolute value(s), 36, 316
  of circular functions, 164
  of inequalities, 36, 92
  graphs of, 46, 53
Accuracy of an approximate number, 253
  degree of, 254
  by relative error, 253
  by significant digits, 253
Acute angle trigonometry, 265–267
Addition, of approximate numbers, 251
  of complex numbers, 308, 314
  of ordered pairs, 308
  of polynomials, 332
  property of, 29
  theorem of probability, 380
  of vectors, 277–278
    by parallelogram, 277
    by triangle, 277
Addition postulate(s), 35
  of a field, 28, 29
Additive inverse, 22
  of an ordered pair, 310
  of a real number, 22, 28, 29
  uniqueness of, 32
Admissible value(s), 42, 65
Air speed vector, 285
Algebra, fundamental theorem of, 339
  of numbers, 6
  of ordered pairs, 308
  of sets, 14
Algebraic functions, 220
Algebraic nature of vectors, 282
Algorithm, division, 334
Ambiguous Case, law of sines, 297
Amplitude, 147
  of a complex number, 324
  of $y = a \sin bt$, 152
Analytic trigonometry, 244
Antilogarithm, 234
Angle(s), 244
  acute, 265

of any size, 262
azimuth, 283
bearing, 283
complementary, 268
corresponding acute, 262
cosecant of, 259, 260
cosine of an, 259
cotangent of an, 259, 260
coterminal, 245
degree measure of an, 245
of depression, 289
drift, 287
of elevation, 288
initial side of an, 244
measurement of an, 244
negative, 245
positive, 245, 262
quadrantal, 262
radian measure of, 245
reference, 262
secant of, 259, 260
sine of, 259
in standard position, 245
tangent of, 259
terminal side of, 244
trigonometry, 244
vectorial, 319
vertex of an, 244
A posteriori probability, 377
A priori probability, 377
Approximate Numbers, 249–256
  accuracy of, 253
  addition of, 251
  division of, 255
  multiplication of, 254
  square roots of, 255
  subtraction of, 251
  in trigonometry, 256
Arc, corresponding, 169, 170
  coterminal, 169
  length, 141, 142, 246, 248
  unit of, measurement of, 246
Area of a triangle, 299

Argument of a complex number, 324
Arithmetic of polynomial functions, 332
Arithmetic sequence, 123, 126
Arithmetic series, 126
    common difference of an, 126
    mean of an, 128
    means of an, 127
    nth term of an, 126
    sum of an, 126, 127
Associative, law, 16
    postulates, 17, 28
Axes, Cartesian coordinate system, 39
Axioms, 35
Axis of, imaginaries, 318
    reals, 317
    symmetry, 210
Azimuth angle, 283

Base of a logarithm, 234
Base-order form, combinations, 363
Bearing angles, 283
Binary operations, 7, 8
Binomial, expansion, 137
    form of complex number, 313
    formula, 137
    general term of, 137, 138, 367
    in terms of combinations, 366–367
    series, 135
    theorem, 136, 366
Bound, greatest lower, 37
    least upper, 37, 344
    lower, 37, 341
    upper, 37, 341
Bracket, function, 53
    vectors, 281
Buying by installment, 128

Cancellation law, of addition, 32
    of multiplication, 32
Cardinal number, 4, 356, 371
Cartesian coordinate system, 39
Cartesian product, 40, 41, 43, 68, 356
Characteristic of a logarithm, 238
Choice, random, 370
Circle, elements around a, 360, 361
    unit, 140
    winding around a, 142
Circular function(s), 140, 141
    absolute values of, 164
    of any real number, 168, 189
    definitions of, 145
    graphs of, 155, 166–168
    inverse of, 207
    of $\pi/6$, $\pi/4$, and $\pi/3$, 159–166
    restrictions on, 209
    signs for, 159
    table of, 390
Circular permutations, 360–361
Closed set, 15
Closure, 14, 15
Closure postulates, 17, 22, 28
Coefficient(s), detached, 335
    of a polynomial, 332, 333, 348, 350
    of terms in a binomial expansion, 366–367
Cofactor of a determinant, 115
    even position, 115
    odd position, 115

Cofunctions, 268
    relations, 269
Combination(s), 363
    base-order form, 363
    for a set of n elements, 368
    formulas, 364–366
    n things, r at a time, 364–366
    n things, o at a time, 366
    use in binomial expansion, 366–367
Combined variation, 89
Common difference in series, 126
Common logarithms, 237
    table of, 394
Common ratio, in series, 130
Commutative law, 15
Commutative postulates, 17, 28
Complement, of a set, 7
    relative, 10
Complementary angles, 268
Complementation postulates, 17
Complete ordered field, 37
Completeness property, 37
Complex numbers, 79, 307, 308, 313
    addition of, 308
    amplitude of, 324
    argument of, 324
    binomial form of, 313
    conjugate, 314
    division of, 310, 329
    equality of, 308, 313, 327
    field of, 310
    geometric interpretation of, 316–318
    imaginary part of, 313
        unit of, 312
    integral powers of, 326
    multiplication of, 308, 327
    normal form of, 313
    ordered pairs as, 308
    polar form of, 323, 324
    real, 313
    real part of, 313
    rectangular form of, 313
    roots of, 80, 312, 348
    subtraction of, 310
    trigonometric form of, 323, 324
Complex polynomial functions, 340
Components of a vector, 278, 281
Composite functions, 54, 55
Composition of ordinates, 156
Compound amount formula, 232
Conclusion of a theorem, 32
Conditional equations, 65
Conditional inequality, 46, 92
Conditional probability, 384
Conditional statements, 65
Conjugate, complex numbers, 314
    pairs, 314, 348
Consistency postulate, 18
Constant, 43
    of variation, 88
Continuous curve, 339
Continuous interest, 233
Continuum, 27, 37
Coordinate system, Cartesian, 39
    one dimensional, 23, 39
    polar, 319
    rectangular, 39
    two dimensional, 39

Correspondence, one to many, 43
one to one, 4, 49
rule of, 44
Corresponding acute angle, 262
Corresponding arc, 169, 170
Correct digits, 346
Cosecant function, 145, 259, 260, 267
domain of, 261
graph of, 167
of negative number, 169
range of, 261
Cosine(s) function, 145, 259, 266
of difference of two numbers, 188, 192
domain of, 146, 209, 261
graph of, 155, 156, 167
of half a number, 197
hyperbolic, 232
inverse function of, 209, 211, 212
law of, 301–305
of a negative number, 148
of $\pi/2$ less a number, 193
of sum of two numbers, 194
of twice a number, 196
range of, 146, 209, 261
series, 173
zeros of, 146, 157, 166, 167
Cotangent function, 145, 259–260, 267
domain of, 261
of difference of two numbers, 196
graph of, 168
of a negative number, 169, 194
of $\pi/2$ less a number, 194
range of, 261
of sum of two numbers, 195
zeros of, 166, 167
Coterminal angle, 245
Coterminal arc, 169
Coterminal number, 169
Count, of elements in a set, 356
of significant digits, 253
of units of measure, 252
true, 254
Counterexample, 23
Counting, fundamental principle of, 358
numbers, 356
properties, 356–357
Course of plane, 285
Cramer's rule, 109
Critical points, 143
Curves, continuous, 339
sinusoidal, 146

Data, approximate, 249
Decimal fractions, nonrepeating, 26
repeating, 26, 134
terminating, 26
Decreasing monotone function, 149, 222
Degree, of accuracy, 254
of an equation, 63, 70, 331
as measure of an angle, 245
of a polynomial, 331
De Moivre's theorem, 327
De Morgan's theorems, 18
Dependent events, 383
Dependent systems of equations, 103
Dependent variable, 45
Depressed function, 347

Depression, angle of, 289
Detached coefficients, 335
Determinant(s), 108–109, 114–118
cofactor of an element of, 115
elements of, 108, 115
formulas, 109, 117
minor of an element of, 114
principal diagonal, 108, 114
of second order, 108, 110
secondary diagonal, 108, 114
solving equations by, 108, 114
of third order, 114
with zeros, 110, 118
Diagram, tree, 358
Venn, 7, 8–13, 357, 380
Difference, formulas, 192
of two approximate numbers, 251, 252
of two functions, 199
of two numbers, 23, 190
of two polynomials, 332
of two vectors, 282
Digits, significant, 252
correct, 346
Direct variation, 88
Directed distances, 275
Direction angle of a vector, 275
Discrete points, 52
Discrete set, 1, 23
Discriminant of quadratic equation, 80
properties, of, 80
Disjoint, sets, 5, 8, 64, 356, 380
Displacement, 155
Distance, arc, 142
formula for, 189, 190
Distributive laws, 16, 17
Distributive postulates, 18, 29
Division, 24
algorithm, 334
of approximate numbers, 255
of complex numbers, 310, 329
by detached coefficients, 335
of polynomials, 333
synthetic, 335–338
by zero, 24, 42
Domain(s), of arcCosine function, 209
of arcSine function, 209
of arcTangent function, 209
of cosecant function, 209
of cosine function, 146, 261
of cotangent function, 261
of exponential function, 227
of a function, 45
of logarithmic function, 228
of polynomial function, 332
of a relation, 45
restriction of, 209
of secant function, 261
of sine function, 146, 261
table of, 261
of tangent function, 261
of a variable, 45
Double the number formula, for cosine
function, 196
for sine function, 196
for tangent function, 196
Drift angle, 287
Duality, 18

e, as base of natural logarithms, 231
  as the limit of a series, 231
  as a transcendental number, 230
Element(s), around a circle, 360
  of a determinant, 108, 115
  in a set, 1, 2, 356
  uniqueness of, 2, 5
Elevation, angle of, 289
Empirical probability, 377
Empty set, 3
Equality, 4, 5
  addition law for, 29
  of complex numbers, 308, 313, 327
  multiplication law for, 29
  of ordered pairs, 308
  of polynomials, 332
  postulates, 29
  properties of, 29
  of sets, 5
  of vectors, 276, 282
Equation(s), 63
  complex roots of, 80, 348
  conditional, 65
  degree of, 63, 70, 331
  equivalent, 68
  equivalent systems of, 106, 112
  exponential, 220
  first degree, one variable, 70
  first degree, two variables, 70
  homogeneous linear, 119
  identical, 65
  irrational, 81
  linear, one variable, 70, 84, 99
    three variables, 112, 118
    two variables, 70, 84, 99, 102, 103, 108
  null, 65
  polar, 321
  polynomial, 84
  quadratic, one variable, 73, 84
  radical, 83, 84
  rational roots of, 80, 350–353
  roots of, 64, 76, 80, 342, 350
  simultaneous, 99
  solution set of, 64
  systems of linear, 99, 103, 112, 118, 119
  trigonometric, 183
Equivalence relations, 45, 46
Equivalent equation, 68
Equivalent form, 209
Equivalent method, 106, 112
Equivalent sets, 4
Equivalent systems, 104
Equivalent vectors, 275, 282
Error, absolute, 250
  per cent, 254
  relative, 253
Even function, 149
Even natural number, 3
Even position, 115
Event(s), 371
  dependent, 383
  elements in an, 371
  independent, 383
  mutually exclusive, 368, 380
  odds in favor of an, 378
  probability of an, 372–373
Exact numbers, 250

Expansion, of a binomial, 137, 367
  of a determinant, 108, 115–117
Expectation, mathematical, 376
  value of, 376
Experiment, 370
Explicit function, 99
Exponent(s), 222
  fractional, 224
  integral, 224
  laws of, 222–223
  as logarithms, 234
  negative, 224
  zero, 223
Exponential equations, 220
Exponential function, 221
  graph of, 221, 227
  inverse, 227
  table of values of, 409
Extraneous roots, 69, 85
Extraneous solutions, 69

Factor, 68
  theorem, 335
  zero as a, 33
Factorial numbers, 136
Factoring, 69
False set, 64
Field, 27, 28
  completely ordered, 37
  number, 27, 28
  ordered, 35
Field postulates, 28
  for complex numbers, 28, 309–310
  for ordered pairs, 28, 309–310
  for rational numbers, 28
  for real numbers, 28
Finite cardinal number, 4
Finite sample space, 370–371
Finite sequence function, 126
Finite set, 4, 6
First degree equation(s), in one variable, 70
  in two variables, 70
  slope intercept form of, 100
  standard form for, 102
Fixed vectors, 281
Formula(s), binomial, 137
  circular function, 199–201
  cofunction, 269
  combination, 364–366
  compound amount, 232
  determinant, 109, 117
  difference of two numbers, 199
  distance, 190, 199
  half a number, 200
  installment, 129
  law of cosines, 301, 302
  law of sines, 295
  *n*th term, 126, 130
  permutation, 359–361
  polar, 321–322
  probability, 372, 376, 380, 381, 383, 384,
    386, 387
  product of two functions, 200
  quadratic, 74
  slope, 100
  special reduction formulas, 200
  sum of series, 127, 130
  sum of two functions, 200–201

Formula(s)(*Cont.*)
sum of two numbers, 199
trigonometric, 199-201
Fraction, nonrepeating decimal, 26
repeating decimal, 26, 134
terminating decimal, 26
Fractional exponents, 224
Free vectors, 281
Function(s), 48
absolute value, 46, 53
algebraic, 220
bracket, 53
circular, 140, 141, 145
composite, 54, 55
constant, 331
cosecant, 145, 259–260, 267
cosine, 145, 259, 266
cotangent, 145, 259, 260, 267
cubic, 331
decreasing monotone, 149, 222
depressed, 347
domain of a, 45
even, 149
explicit, 99
exponential, 221, 222
finite sequence, 123
graphs of, 44, 49, 51, 52, 53, 56, 58, 59, 61,
67, 71, 76, 77, 78, 150, 155, 166–168,
221, 229
hyperbolic, 232
identity, 56, 57, 210
implicit, 100
increasing monotone, 149, 222
infinite sequence, 123
inverse, 49, 57, 207
of circular, 207
of composite, 55, 60
of cosine, 209, 211–212
of exponential, 227
of logarithmic, 230
of sine, 209, 211–212
of tangent, 209, 214–215
linear, 70
logarithmic, 228
notation, 48
odd, 148
of negative numbers, 148
period of a, 146
periodic, 147
polynomial, 331, 339
probability, 373
quadratic, 73
range of, 45
reciprocal, 166, 268
reversible, 58
secant, 145, 259, 260, 267
sequence, 123
set, 373
sine, 145, 259, 266
tangent, 145, 259, 266
transcendental, 220
trigonometric, 258–260, 265–267
dependent nature of, 270
zero value of a, 70, 76, 335, 342
Fundamental concepts of inequalities, 35, 46,
92–95
Fundamental counting principle, 358
Fundamental identities, 177–178

Fundamental theorem of algebra, 339

General quadratic, equation, 73, 84
function, 73
General term of binomial expansion, 137,
138, 367
Geometric interpretation of a complex
number, 316–318
Geometric sequences, 123, 130
Geometric series, 129–131
common ratio of a, 130
finite, 130
infinite, 133
mean of a, 131
means of a, 131
*n*th term of a, 130
sum of an infinite, 134
sum of *n* terms of a, 130
Graph(s), absolute value function, 46, 53
bracker function, 53
Cartesian product, 41
circular functions, 166–168
cosecant function, 167
cosine function, 155, 161
cotangent function, 168
exponential function, 221
first degree equations, 70, 93, 104
functions, 44, 49, 51, 52, 56, 67, 76, 77, 78
inequalities, two variable, 46, 95, 96
inverse, functions, 58, 59, 60
of cosine, 211, 212
of exponential, 230
of logarithmic, 230
of sine, 210–212
of tangent, 213–215
linear functions, 51, 104
logarithmic function, 229, 230
parabola, 76, 77, 78
polynomial functions, 342–347
quadratic function, 51
relations, 44
secant function, 167
sine function, 167, 211–212
systems of linear equations, 104–106
tangent function, 168, 209, 214–215
Graphical method of solving equations, 76,
104–106, 343–347
Greatest lower bound, 37
Ground speed vector, 285

Half a number formula(s), 200
for cosine functions, 197
for sine functions, 197
for tangent functions, 197
Harmonic motion, 155
Heading, 287
Homogeneous systems of equations, 119
Hyperbolic cosine, 232
Hyperbolic sine, 232
Hyperbolic tangent, 232
Hypothesis of a theorem, 32

Idempotent postulates, 17
Identical equations, 65
Identities, algebraic, 65
fundamental, 177–178
proof of, 177, 189–199
summary of, 199–200
trigonometric, 177, 189–199

Identity element, 28, 280, 309
  for addition of complex numbers, 309
  for addition of real numbers, 28
  for addition of vectors, 280
  for multiplication of complex numbers, 309
  for multiplication of real numbers, 28
  uniqueness of, 32
Identity function, 56, 57, 210
Identity postulates, 17, 28
Imaginary axis, 318
Imaginary number, 79
Imaginary part of complex number, 313
Imaginary pure, 79, 313
Imaginary unit, 79, 312
Implicit functions, 100
Improper subset, 3
Inclusion principle, 3, 27
Inconsistent system of equations, 103
Increasing monotone function, 149, 222
Independent events, 380
Independent system of equations, 103
Independent variable, 45
Inequalities, 35, 92
  absolute, 92
  algebraic solution, 93
  conditional, 46, 92
  graphs of, 46, 95, 96
  opposite sense, 92
  properties of, 92, 93
  relations, 35
  same sense, 92
Infinite geometric series, 133
Infinite sequence function, 123
Infinite set, 4, 5
Installment buying, 128
  formula for, 129
Integer(s), negative, 22
  nonnegative, 23
  positive, 1
  set of, 23
  zero, 22
Integral exponents, 224
Integral numbers, 23
Integral power of complex numbers, 326
Intercept-slope formula, 100
Interest, continuous, 233
  rate, 128
Interpolation, linear, 185, 239, 273
Intersection, of sets, 8, 9
  operator, 8
Initial point of vector, 275
  side, 244
Inverse(s), additive, 22, 29
  of circular functions, 207
  of composite functions, 55, 60
  of cosine function, 209, 211–212
  of exponent function, 227, 230
  function, 49, 57, 60, 207
    properties of, 60
  graphs of, 59, 61, 211–215
  of logarithmic function, 230
  multiplicative, 29
    domain, 209
    equivalent form, 209
    range, 209
  postulates, 29
  relations, 60, 208
    principal values of, 208

of sine function, 209–210
of tangent function, 209, 214–215
variation, 188
Irrational equations, 84
Irrational exponents, 221
Irrational numbers, 25, 26
Irrational roots, 80, 344–347
Isomorphism, 311, 312

Joint variation, 89

k roots alike, 341

Law(s), associative, 16
  cancellation, 32
  commutative, 15
  of cosines, 301–305
  De Moivre's, 327
  De Morgan's, 18
  distributive, 16, 17, 18, 29
  of exponents, 222–223
  of logarithm, 234–236
  of natural growth, 237
  Newton's, 89
  reflexive, 29
  of sines, 293–299
    ambiguous case, 297
  symmetric, 29
  transitive, 29
Least upper bound, 37
Length, of arc, 142, 246, 248
  unit of, 23
"Less than" relation, 35
Limit, of a series, 133, 173, 231, 233
  of sum of an infinite series, 134, 231
Line segment, directed, 275
  length of a, 190
  slope of a, 100
Linear equations, 70, 84, 99
  homogeneous, 119
  standard form of, 102
  in three variables, 112–120
  in two variables, 102–110
Linear functions, 70
  inequalities, 93
  interpolation, 185, 239, 273
  polynomial, 331
Linearly ordered set, 388
Logarithm(s), 234–242
  anti, 234
  common, 235, 237
  change of base of, 235
  characteristics of, 238
  as exponents, 234
  functions of, 228
  graphs of, 229, 230
  laws of, 234–236
  mantissas of, 238
  natural, 235
  in standard form, 238
  table of, 392
Lower bound, 37, 341
  least, 37

Magnitude of a vector, 275
Mantissa of a logarithm, 238
Mapping, 48
Mathematical expectation, 376

Mathematical system, 21
Maximum point on a graph, 77, 143
Mean(s), arithmetic, 127, 128
    geometric, 131
Measurement, of an angle, 244
    of an arc, 246
    precision of, 250
    unit of, 40, 250
Minimum point on a graph, 77, 143
Minor of an element, 114
Modulus of a complex number, 316,
    324
    of a vector, 282
Monotone, decreasing function, 149,
    222
    increasing function, 149, 222
Multiplication, associative law of, 28
    of approximate numbers, 254
    cancellation law of, 32
    commutative law of, 28
    of complex numbers, 308, 314, 327
    of polynomials, 333
    property, 20
    theorems in probability, 383
    of a vector by a scalar, 279
Multiplicative identity, 28
Multiplicative inverse, 29, 32
Multiplicative postulate, 35
Multiplicity of roots, 341
Mutually exclusive events, 368, 380
    sum of, 368

n factorial, 136
n roots of a complex number, 328
nth term of series, 126, 130
Natural logarithms, 235
Natural number(s), 1, 21
    even, 3
    odd, 3
    ordered set of, 1
Negative angle, 245
Negative exponents, 224
Negative integers, 22
Negative numbers, 36, 148
Newton's law, 89
Nonnegative integers, 23
Nonrepeating decimal fractions, 26
Nonsolution set, 64
Nontrivial solution, 120
Notation, for function, 48
    scientific, 238
    sigma, 124
Null equation, 65
Null set, 3, 5
Null vector, 276
Number(s), algebra of, 6
    approximate, 249–256
    cardinal, 4, 356, 371
    complex, 79, 307, 308, 310, 313, 314
    cosecant of a, 145
    cosine of a, 145
    cotangent of a, 145
    coterminal, 169
    counting, 1
    difference of two, 23, 190
    e, 230
    of elements in a set, 356
    even natural, 3

exact, 250
    factorial, 136
    field, 27, 28
    finite cardinal, 4
    i, 79
    imaginary, pure, 79, 313
    integral, 23
    irrational, 25, 26
    natural, 1, 21
    negative, 23
    negative real, 36
        circular functions of, 148
        trigonometric functions of, 265
    odd natural, 3
    order of, 1
    phase, 154
    pi, 141
    positive, 36
    positive real, 36
    quadrantal, 143
    rational, 24, 25
    real, 26
    relatively prime, 25
    rounded, 251
    scale, 23
    scientific notation of, 238
    secant of a, 145
    sine of a, 145
    tangent of a, 145
    transcendental, 230
    whole, 23
    zero, 22

Oblique triangles, solutions, 293–305
Odd function, 148
    natural numbers, 3
    position, 14
Odds in favor, probability, 378
One-to-many correspondence, 43
One-to-one correspondences, 4, 43
Open sentence(s), 42, 63, 92
    conditional, 65
    equivalent, 68
    identical, 65
    solution set of, 64
Operation(s), applied to three sets, 12
    under addition, 28
    binary, 7, 8
    complement, 7
    intersection, 8
    under multiplication, 28
    unary, 7
    union, 10, 11
Opposite sense, 92
Order, of natural numbers, 1
    of permutations, 355
    properties, 35
Ordered field, 35
    complete, 37
    rational numbers as, 37
    real numbers as, 37
Ordered pair(s), 40
    additive inverse of, 310
    algebra of, 308
    associative laws for, 309–310
    in Cartesian products, 41, 308
    commutative laws for, 309–310
    as complex number, 803

Ordered pair(s) (*Cont.*)
  coordinates of, 40
  difference of, 308
  distributive laws for, 309–310
  division of, 310
  equality of, 308
  graphs of, 41, 44, 46
  identity elements for, 309–310
  multiplication of, 308
  set of, 41, 308
  subtraction of, 310
  sum of, 308
  as vector, 281
Ordered triple, 113
Ordinate(s), 40
  composition of, 155
Origin, on a number line, 23
  rectangular coordinate systems, 40
Orthogonal projections, 278
Outcome(s), of a random sample, 371
  of an experiment, 371

Pairs, conjugate, 348
  ordered, 40
Parabola, 76
  graph of, 76–78
Parallelogram law for addition of vectors, 277
Pascal's triangle, 135
Per cent error, 254
Period of a function, 146
  of $y = a \sin bt$, 152
Periodic functions, 147
Permutation(s), 355, 358
  arrangement of, 355
  circular, 360–361
  fundamental principle of, 358
  formulas, 358
  n things, n at a time, 359
  n things, r at a time, 359
  with some elements alike, 360
Phase, number, 154
  shift, 153, 154
Pi, 141
Plane, course of, 287
Point(s), coordinates of, 40
  critical, 143
  discrete, 44
  initial, 275
  maximum, 77, 143
  minimum 77, 143
  in a plane, 40, 42, 46
  projection of a, 266
  sample, 371
  terminal, 275
Polar axis, 319
Polar coordinates of a point, 319
Polar equations, 321, 322
Polar form of complex number, 323
Pole, 319
Polynomial equation, 84
  coefficient of, 348, 350
  complex roots of, 348
  rational roots of, 351
  roots of, 342
  roots of odd degree, 349
Polynomial function(s), 331, 339
  approximating zero values of, 342–347

arithmetic of, 332
coefficients of, 332, 333
constant, 331
cubic, 331
degree of, 331
difference of two, 332
division of, 333
equality of, 332
graph of, 343–347
linear, 331
product of, 333
quadratic, 331
rational, 341
real, 341
sum of, 332
zeros of a, 335, 342
Positive real numbers, 36
Positive angle, 245, 262
Positive integers, 1
Postulate(s), field, 28
  of closure, 22
  equality, 29
  meaning of, 14
  of an ordered field, 35
  of set theory, 17, 18
Power set, 4
Precision of a measurement, 250
Principal, diagonal, 108, 114
  nth root, 85
  values of inverse relations, 208
Principle, of counting, 1
  of duality, 18
  of inclusion, 3, 27
  of substitution, 29
Probability, theory, 355, 370–388
  addition theorem, 380
  a posteriori, 377
  a priori, 377
  conditional, 384
  definitions of, 372, 373
  empirical, 377
  of failure, 373
  function, 372, 373
  multiplication theorems, 383
  of mutually exclusive events, 380
  statistical, 377
  of success, 373
Product set (see Cartesian product)
Product(s), Cartesian, 41, 68
  of approximate data, 254
  of complex numbers, 308, 327
  of conjugates of complex numbers, 314
  of ordered pairs, 308
  of polynomials, 333
  of roots of a quadratic equation, 82
  of two-function formulas, 198
  of vector and a scalar, 279
Projection, of a point, 266
  orthogonal, 278
Proof of a theorem, 19, 31, 32
Proofs of theorem(s), 18
  circular functions, 188–199
  factor, 335
  inequalities, 35
  numbers, 31–33
  probability, addition, 381
    conditional, 384
    multiplication, 383

Proofs of theorem(s), probability (*Cont.*)
  repeated trials, 386
  remainder, 334
  set, 18
Proper subset, 3
Proportion, 88
Property(ies), of addition, 29
  of completeness, 37
  of counting, 356–357
  of equality, 29
  of inequalities, 92–93
  of inverse circular functions, 207
  of inverse functions, 60
  of logarithms, 228
  of multiplications, 29
  of order, 35
  of the quadratic discriminant, 80
  of slope, 101
  of subtraction, 22
  of vectors, 280
Pure imaginary number, 79, 313
Pythagorean theorem, 145, 161, 190, 302

Quadrant, 40
Quadrantal angle, 262
Quadrantal number, 143
Quadratic equation, 73, 84
  standard form of, 75
Quadratic discriminant, 80
Quadratic formula, 74
Quadratic roots, complex, 80
  equal, 80
  irrational, 80
  rational, 80
  unequal, 80
Quadratic function(s), 73
  graph of, 51, 76, 77, 78
  maximum point of, 77
  minimum point of, 77
Quotient, of order pairs, 310
  of two complex numbers, 310
  of two polynomials, 333

$R \times R$, 42, 43, 68
Radian measure of an angle, 245
Radical equations, 83, 84
  of second order, 85
Radius vector, 319
Random choice, 370
Random sample, 370
Range(s), 45
  of arcCosine function, 209
  of an arcSine function, 209
  of an arcTangent function, 209
  of a cosecant function, 261
  of a cosine function, 261
  of a cotangent function, 261
  of an exponential function, 227
  of a function, 45
  of a logarithmic function, 228
  of a polynomial function, 322
  of a relation, 45
  of a secant function, 261
  of a set function, 373
  of a sine function, 261
  table of, 261
  fo a tangent function, 261
Rate, interest, 128

Ratio, 88
  common, 130
  trigonometric, 259
Rational number(s), 24, 25
  set of, 24
Rational polynomial function, 340
Rational roots, 80, 343, 350–353
Real complex numbers, 310
Real number(s), 26
  absolute value of a, 36
  completeness property of, 37
  equality postulates of, 29
  field postulates of, 28
  negative, 36
  order postulates of, 35
  positive, 36
  set of, 26
Real polynomial functions, 340
Reals, axis of, 317
Reciprocal, 29
  functions, 166, 268
  relations, 269
Rectangular coordinate system, 39
Reduction formulas, 200
Reference angle, 262
Reference line of a vector, 281
Reflexive law, 29
Relation(s), 35, 43
  domain of, 45
  equivalence, 45, 46
  inverse, 60, 208
  polar vs rectangular, 321
  range of, 45
  reciprocal, 269
  reflexive, 46
  symmetric, 46
  transitive, 46
Relative complement, 10
Relative error, 253
Relative frequency of event, 377
Relatively prime numbers, 25
Remainder, 335
  theorem, 334
Repeating decimal fraction, 26, 134
  trial theorem, 386
Replacement set, 42
Restriction of domain, 209
Resultant, 277
Reversible function, 58
Revolution, 245
Right triangles, 288
  solution of, 288
Root(s), 64
  bound of, 34
  complex, 348
  of complex numbers, 80, 312
  equal, 80
  of an equation, 64, 76, 342
  extraneous, 69, 85
  irrational, 80, 344–347
  multiplicity of, 340
  of odd degree equation, 349
  of polynomial equations, 342, 348–353
  principal, 85
  product of, 82
  of quadratic equation, 75, 80
  rational, 80, 343, 350–352
  sum of, 82

Roster method for sets, 2
Rounding numbers, 251
Rule, method for sets, 2
  Cramer's, 109
  of correspondence, 44

Sample, point, 371
  random, 370
Sample space, 371
  elements in, 371
  event in, 371
  outcomes in a, 371
  sample points in, 371
Scalar, product of a vector and a, 277
  quantity, 276
Scale, number, 23
Scientific notation, 238
Scope, 42
Secant function, 145, 259, 260, 267
  domain of, 261
  graph of, 167
  of a negative number, 169
  range of, 261
Second degree equation(s), 73, 84
  discriminant of, 80
  by formula, 74
  by graphs, 76–78, 96
  in one variable, 73
  solution by factoring, 74
Second degree inequalities, 95
Second order, determinants, 108, 110
  radical equations, 85
Secondary diagonal, 108, 114
Selector of set, 64, 65
Sense, same, 92
  opposite, 92, 276
Sentences, open, 42, 63, 92
Sequence, 122
  arithmetic, 123, 126
  function, 123
  geometric, 123, 130
  finite, 123
  infinite, 123
  infinite geometric, 133
Series, 124
  arithmetic, 126
  binomial, 135
  cosine, 173
  for e, 231
  geometric, 130
  limit of a, 133, 173, 231, 233
  infinite geometric, 133
  sigma notations for, 124
  sine, 173
Set(s), 1–19
  algebra of, 14
  builder notation, 44
  Cartesian product of, 41
  closed, 15
  complement of a, 7
  completely ordered, 37
  of complex numbers, 307, 313
  concept of, 1
  count of elements in a, 356
  description of a, 2
  discrete, 1, 23
  disjoint, 5, 8, 64, 356, 380
  element of a, 1, 2

elements in a, 1
empty, 3, 5
equality of, 5
equivalent, 4
false, 64
finite, 4, 6
function, 373
  domain of, 373
  range of, 373
of imaginary numbers, 312, 313
inclusion, 3, 27
infinite, 4, 5
of integers, 23
intersection of, 9
of irrational numbers 25, 26
linearly ordered, 358
of natural numbers 1, 21
of nonnegative numbers, 23
nonsolution, 64
null, 3, 5
operations on, 6
of positive numbers, 1
power, 4
of rational numbers, 24, 25
of real numbers, 26
replacement, 42
by roster method, 2
by rule method, 2
selector, 64, 65
solution, 42, 64, 92
truth, 64
union of, 11
universal, 2, 3, 371
well-defined, 2, 4
of whole numbers, 23
Set theory postulates, 17
Shift, phase, 153, 154
Sigma notation, 124
Significant digits, 252
  count of, 253
Simple harmonic motion, 155
Simultaneous equations, 99
  consistent and dependent, 103
  consistent and independent, 103
  homogeneous, 119
  inconsistent, 103
  solution of, 103
Sine(s), function, 145, 259, 266
  amplitude of, 152
  of difference of two numbers, 195
  displacement of, 155
  domain of, 146, 209, 261
  graph of, 150, 167
  of half a number, 197
  hyperbolic, 232
  inverse of, 209, 211–212
  law of, 293–299
  of a negative number, 148
  period of, 147, 167
  of $\pi/2$ minus a number, 194
  range of, 146, 209, 261
  series, 173
  of sum of two numbers, 195
  of twice a number, 196
  wave, 146
  zeros of, 166, 167
Sinusoid, 146
Slope, 100

Slope (*Cont.*)
  formula, 100
  intercept form, 100
  properties of, 101
Solution(s), 64
  by Cramer's rule, 109
  of equations, 64
  by equivalent equations, 106
  extraneous, 69
  by determinants, 108
  by graphs, 104
  of inequalities, 92
  nontrivial, 120
  of oblique triangle, 293–305
  of right triangles, 288
  set, 42, 64, 92
  simultaneous, 103
  trivial, 120
Special reduction formulas, 200
Square roots of approximate numbers, 255
Standard form, for linear equation, 102
  for logarithms, 238
  for quadratic equation, 75
Standard position of angle, 75, 245
Statistical probability, 377
Straight line(s), equations, 100
  parallel to x axis, 102
  parallel to y axis, 102
  slope of, 100–102
Subset(s), 2, 3
  improper, 3
  of $R \times R$, 42, 43, 68
  proper, 3
Substitution principle, 29
Subtraction, 22
  of approximate numbers, 251
  of complex numbers, 310
  of ordered pairs, 308
  of vectors, 278, 279
Sum, of approximate data, 251
  of arithmetic series, 127
  of cardinal numbers, 356
  of complex numbers, 332
  of geometric series, 130, 134
  of ordered pairs, 308
  of polynomials, 332
  of roots of quadratic equations, 82
  of two functions formulas, 198, 199
  of two numbers formulas, 194, 195
  of vector, 277, 282
Summation notation, 124
Symmetry, 59, 148, 164
  axis of, 210
Symmetric law, 29
  relation, 46
Synthetic division, 335–338
System(s), of complex numbers, 307
  of equivalent equations, 106, 112
  of homogeneous linear equations, 119
  of linear equations, 99, 103, 112, 118, 119
  mathematical, 21
  of natural numbers, 21
  of rational numbers, 24
  of real numbers, 26
  of rectangular coordinates, 39

Table(s), complex vs real numbers, 321

degree of accuracy, 254
domains and ranges of
  circular and trigonometric functions, 261
  inverse circular function, 209
  restricted circular functions, 209
exponential functions, 409
  vs logarithms, 237
mortality, 411
natural logarithms, 410
powers and roots, 412
precision of numbers, 251
real numbers vs radians, 392–393
significant digits, 252, 254
signs for circular functions, 159
sine and cosine values, 146
trigonometric functions, 396–401
  logarithms of, 402–408
  values of 0°, 30°, 45°, 60°, 90°, 261
  values of $\pi/6$, $\pi/4$, $\pi/3$, 165
Tangent functions, 145, 259, 266
  of difference of two numbers, 196
  domain of, 209, 261
  graph of, 168
  of half a number, 197
  hyperbolic, 232
  inverse of, 209, 214–215
  of negative number, 169, 193
  of $\pi/2$ less a number, 194
  of sum of two numbers, 195
  range of, 209, 261
  zeros of, 261
Terminal point of a vector, 275
  side, 244
Terminating decimal fraction, 26
Theorem(s), binomial, 136, 366
  conclusion of, 32
  De Moivre's, 327
  De Morgan's, 18
  dual, 18
  factor, 335
  fundamental, of algebra, 339
  hypothesis of, 32
  probability theorems, 377, 381, 383, 384, 386
  proofs of, 18, 31, 32, 35, 188–199, 334, 335
  Pythagorean, 141, 161, 190, 302
  remainder, 334
  repeated trials, 386
Theory of probability, 370–388
  of sets, 1
Third order determinants, 114, 116
Three equations, three variables, 112, 114
Transcendental function, 220
Transcendental number, 230
Transitive law, 29
Transitive postulates, 18, 35
Transitive relation, 46
Tree diagram, 358
Triangle law for adding vectors, 277
Triangle(s), area of, 299
  oblique, 293–305
  Pascal's, 135
  right, 288
Trichotomy postulate, 35
Trigonometric equation(s), 183
  formulas, 199–201
Trigonometric functions, 258–260, 266–267
  of an acute angle, 265–267

Trigonometric functions (*Cont.*)
  of any angle, 262
  of any number, 168
  graphs of, 150, 155, 167, 168
  identity, 177
  logarithms of, 394–395
Trigonometry, analytic, 244
  angle, 244
  approximate data used in, 256
Triple(s), 112
  ordered, 113
Trivial solution, 120
True count, 254
Truth set, 64
Two-dimensional vectors, 281
Two linear equations, two variables, 103
  three variables, 118

Unary operator, 7
Union of sets, 10, 11
Uniqueness, of additive inverse, 32
  of element, 25
  of identity element, 32
  of multiplicative inverse, 33
Unit, arc, 246
  of angular measure, 246
  circle, 140
    winding around, 142
  imaginary, 79, 312
  of length, 23
  of measurement, 40, 250
Universal set, 2, 3, 371
Upper bound, 37, 341
  least, 37
  for zeros of a polynomial function, 341

Value(s), absolute, 36, 164, 316
  admissible, 42, 65
  dependent, 45
  independent, 45
  mathematical expectation, 376
  principal, 208
  scope, 42
  zero, 70, 76, 166
Variable, 42
  admissible values of, 42
  domain of a, 45
  range of a, 45
  scope of a, 146
Variation, 88
  combined, 89
  constant of, 88
  direct, 88
  formulas, 88, 89
  inverse, 88
  joint, 89
Vector(s), 275–287
  addition of, 277–278
  air speed, 285
  algebraic nature of, 282
  components of a, 278, 281
  difference of, 279

direction angle of, 275
equivalent, 276, 282
fixed, 281
free, 281
ground speed, 285
initial point of a, 275
magnitude of a, 275
null, 276
opposite sense, 275
ordered pairs as, 281
orthogonal, 278
parallelogram law for addition, 277
product with scalar, 279
properties of, 280
quantities, 275
quantity, 275
radius, 319
rectangular components of, 281
reference line for a, 281
resultant of, 277
same sense, 276
subtraction of, 278, 279
sum of, 277, 282
terminal point of a, 275
triangular law for addition, 277
two-dimensional, 281
wind, 285
x component of, 281
y component of, 281
zero, 276, 283
Vectorial angle, 319
Venn diagram, 7, 8–13, 357, 380
Vertex, 77, 244

Wave, sine, 146
Well-defined set, 2, 4
Whole number, 23
Wind vector, 285

x axis, 40
x component, 281
x coordinate, 40
x intercept, 70

y axis, 40
y component, 281
y coordinate, 40

Zero(s), 22
  as an exponent, 223
  as a factor, 33
  as identity element, 28
  determinants, 110, 118
  division by, 24, 42
  of an equation, 70
  factorial, 137
  of a function, 70, 76, 335, 342
  magnitude, 225
  of trigonometric functions, 146, 151, 157, 166, 167
  vector, 276, 283

Gager, William Atkins
Contemporary College Algebra
And Trigonometry

DATE DUE

FEB 20 74			
DEC 3 7			
GAYLORD			PRINTED IN U.S.A.

List of Symbols [continued]

Symbol	Meaning	Page
$\sin^{-1} y$	equivalent to arcsin y	208
arcSin t	inverse of sin t, $t \in R$	209
arcCos t	inverse of cos t, $t \in R$	209
arcTan t	inverse of tan t, $t \in R$	209
Sin t	restricted sine function	209
Cos t	restricted cosine function	209
Tan t	restricted tangent function	209
e^x	exponential function	221
$\sqrt[n]{b^m}$	positive nth root of b^m	225
$\log_b x = y$	equivalent to $x = b^y$	228
$\log_e x$	logarithmic function	228
e	2.718218285...	230
sinh t	hyperbolic sine of t	232
cosh t	hyperbolic cosine of t	232
tanh t	hyperbolic tangent of t	232
antilog$_b$ $y = x$	equivalent to $\log_b x = y$	234
$\overline{3.4698}$	only characteristic 3 is negative	240
θ	Greek letter theta	245
α	Greek letter alpha	245
β	Greek letter beta	245
γ	Greek letter gamma	245
ϕ	Greek letter phi	262
$\overrightarrow{AB}$	vector AB	276
$\overrightarrow{BA}$	vector BA	276
$\lvert n\rvert \cdot \lvert \mathbf{a}\rvert$	scalar times a vector	280
$[\ \ ]$	vector brackets	281
$\sqrt{v_x^2 + v_y^2}$	modulus of vector $\lvert\mathbf{v}\rvert$	282
$[0, 0]$	vector $\overrightarrow{AA}$	283
C	the complex number system	307
(a, b)	a complex number	308
Q	complex numbers of form $(r, 0)$	310
$(r, 0) \leftrightarrow r$	$(r, 0)$ corresponds to r	311
$(0, 1)$	imaginary unit i	312